Instructor's Solutions Manual
for Keller and Warrack's

Statistics
for Management and Economics
Sixth Edition

Gerald Keller
Wilfrid Laurier University

THOMSON

BROOKS/COLE

Australia • Canada • Mexico • Singapore • Spain • United Kingdom • United States

Printed in the United States of America
1 2 3 4 5 6 7 06 05 04 03 02

0-534-39193-1

For more information about our products, contact us at:
Thomson Learning Academic Resource Center
1-800-423-0563

For permission to use material from this text, contact us by:
Phone: 1-800-730-2214
Fax: 1-800-731-2215
Web: www.thomsonrights.com

Asia
Thomson Learning
5 Shenton Way #01-01
UIC Building
Singapore 068808

Australia
Nelson Thomson Learning
102 Dodds Street
South Street
South Melbourne, Victoria 3205
Australia

Canada
Nelson Thomson Learning
1120 Birchmount Road
Toronto, Ontario M1K 5G4
Canada

Europe/Middle East/South Africa
Thomson Learning
High Holborn House
50-51 Bedford Row
London WC1R 4LR
United Kingdom

Latin America
Thomson Learning
Seneca, 53
Colonia Polanco
11560 Mexico D.F.
Mexico

Spain
Paraninfo Thomson Learning
Calle/Magallanes, 25
28015 Madrid, Spain

TABLE OF CONTENTS

How We Produced the Solutions

How We Produced the Solutions

Chapter 2

Excel was employed to draw the histograms, bar charts, pie charts, line charts, and scatter diagrams.

Chapter 4

Excel was used to draw box plots and compute the descriptive statistics for exercises with data sets.

Chapters 6 through 9

Probabilities were computed manually. Probability trees were used where possible.

Chapters 10 through 20

Calculations for exercises that provided statistics either in the exercise itself or in Appendix A were completed manually. Confidence interval estimates used critical values obtained from the tables in Appendix B. In some cases we were required to use approximations. As a consequence some confidence interval estimates will differ slightly from those produced by computer. In tests of hypothesis where the sampling distribution is normal, p-values were computed manually using Table 3. Excel was employed to calculate the p-value for all other tests.

Appendix A in the student edition of this book does not contain statistics for the chapter review exercises in Chapters 12 and 13 and the exercises in the two review chapters (14 and 24). (We wanted to provide students with an opportunity to practice their technique-identification skills.) Excel produced these solutions. Appendix A of the Annotated Instructor's Edition lists the statistics for the chapter review exercises in Chapters 12 and 13.

Chapters 13, 14, and 24

We employed the F-test of two variances at the 5% significance level to decide which one of the equal-variances or unequal-variances t-test and estimator of the difference between two means to use to solve the problem. Additionally, for exercises that compare two populations and are accompanied by data files, our answers were derived by defining the sample from population 1 as the data stored in the first column (often column A in Excel and column 1 in Minitab). The data stored in the second column represent the sample from population 2. Paired differences were defined as the difference between the variable in the first column minus the variable in the second column.

Chapters 17 and 24

In the exercises whose datasets contained interval data we used a nonparametric technique after examining the relevant histograms and subjectively judging the variable to be "extremely nonnormal."

Chapters 19 and 20

Excel produced all the solutions to these exercises.

Chapter 21

Most solutions were produced manually. Excel solved the more time-consuming exercises.

Chapter 22

All control charts were produced by Excel.

Chapter 23

Solutions to these exercises were completed manually.

All answers have been-double-checked for accuracy. However, we cannot be absolutely certain that there are no errors. When and if we discover mistakes we will post corrected answers on our web page. (See page 16 in the textbook for the address.) If you find any errors, please email the author (address on web page). We will be happy to acknowledge you with the discovery.

Chapter 1

1.2 Descriptive statistics summarizes a set of data. Inferential statistics makes inferences about populations from samples.

1.3.a The political choices of the 25,000 registered voters

b. The political choices of the 200 voters interviewed

c Statistic

1.4a The complete production run

b 1000 chips

c Proportion of the production run that is defective

d Proportion of sample chips that are defective (7.5%)

e Parameter

f Statistic

g Because the sample proportion is less than 10%, we can conclude that the claim is true.

1.5 Survey graduates of your major as well as others and ask each person to report his or her highest starting salary offer. Use statistical techniques to compare results.

1.6a Flip the coin 100 times and count the number of heads and tails

b Outcomes of flips

c Outcomes of the 100 flips

d Proportion of heads

e Proportion of heads in the 100 flips

1.8a The population consists of the fuel mileage of all the taxis in the fleet.

b The owner would like to know the mean mileage.

c The sample consists of the 50 observations.

d The statistic the owner would use is the mean of the 50 observations.

e The statistic would be used to estimate the parameter from which the owner can calculate total costs. We computed the sample mean to be 19.8 mpg.

Chapter 2

2.1 Nominal: Occupation, undergraduate major. Ordinal: Rating of university professor, Taste test ratings. Interval: age, income

2.2 a Interval
b Interval
c Nominal
d Ordinal

2.3 a Interval
b Nominal
c Ordinal
d Interval
e Interval

2.4 a Nominal
b Interval
c Nominal
d Interval
e Ordinal

2.5 a Interval
b Interval
c Nominal
d Interval
e Nominal83

2.6 a Interval
b Interval
c Nominal
d Ordinal
e Interval

2.7 a Interval

b Nominal

c. Nominal

d Interval

e Ordinal

2.8 a Interval

b Ordinal

c Nominal

d Ordinal

2.9 a Interval

b Nominal

c Nominal

2.10 a Ordinal

b Ordinal

c Ordinal

2.11 9 or 10

2.12 10 or 11

2.13 a 7 to 9

b Interval width $\approx \dfrac{188-37}{8} = 18.9$ (rounded to 20); upper limits: 40, 60, 80, 100, 120, 140, 160 180,

200

2.14 a 7 to 9

b Interval width $\approx \dfrac{6.1-5.2}{7} = .13$ (rounded to .15); upper limits: 5.25, 5.40, 5.55, 5.70, 5.85, 6.00, 6.15

2.15a

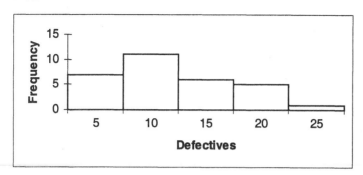

b

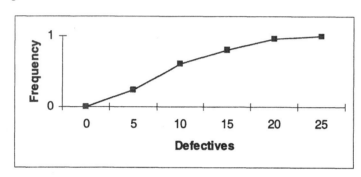

c The histogram is unimodal and somewhat positively skewed.

2.16 a

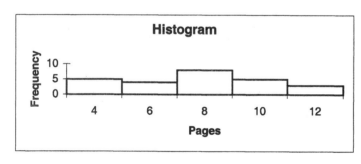

b

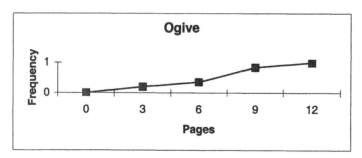

2.17 a

Stem & Leaf Display			
Stems	**Leaves**		
2	->566889		
3	->01233345566778899		
4	->00111166689		
5	->00123		
6	->1		

b

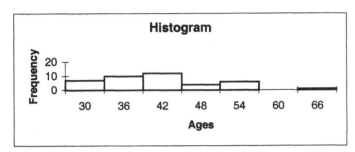

c

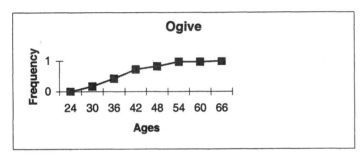

2.18

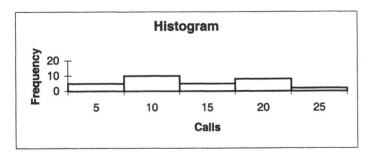

2.19 a

Stem & Leaf Display		
Stems	Leaves	
30	->0112222222356667777788	
31	->001113568	
32	->024777	
33	->0047	
34	->024455	
35	->7	
36	->7	
37	->9	

b

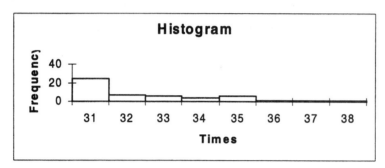

2.20 a

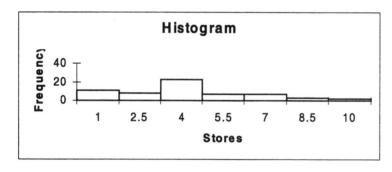

b

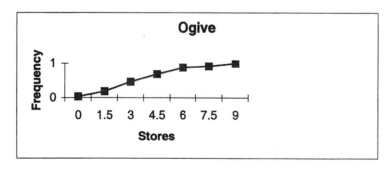

2.21

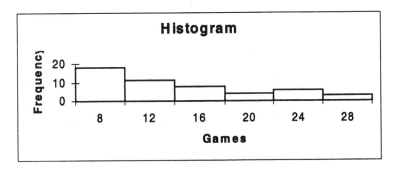

2.22 a

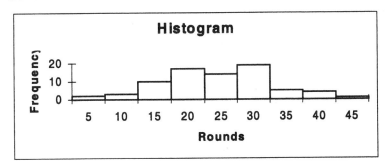

b

Stem & Leaf Display				
Stems	Leaves			
0	->359			
1	->00233344455566778888888899			
2	->0000122333444445555666678888889999			
3	->00000112556668			
4	->2			

c

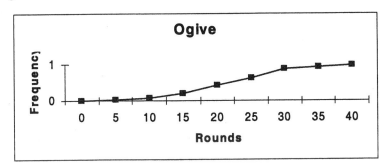

7

2.23

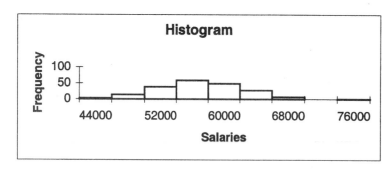

2.24 a The number of bins should be 7, 8, or 9. We chose 7.

b

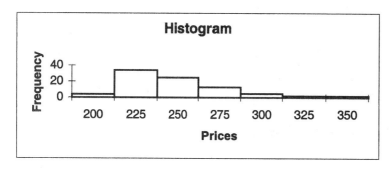

c The histogram is positively skewed, unimodal, and not bell-shaped.

d We learn that most prices lie between 200 and 275 thousand dollars with a small number of houses selling for more than $275,000.

2.25

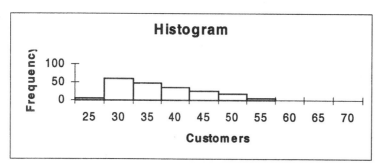

2.26 a The histogram should contain 9 or 10 bins. We chose 10.

b

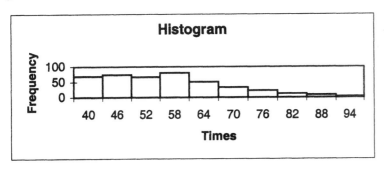

c The histogram is positively skewed.

d There is more than one modal class.

e The histogram is not bell-shaped.

2.27 a The histogram should contain 9 or 10 bins

b

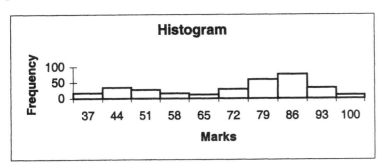

c The histogram is negatively skewed.

d There are two modal classes.

e The histogram is not bell-shaped.

2.28

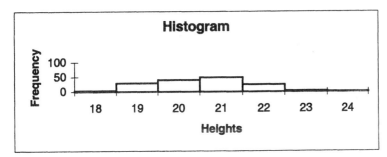

The histogram is unimodal, bell-shaped and roughly symmetric. Most of the heights lie between 18 and 23 inches.

2.29 a

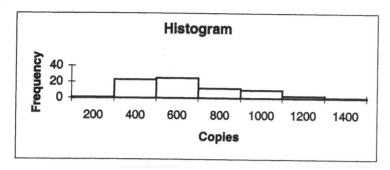

b The histogram is unimodal and positively skewed.

c On most days the number of copies made is between 200 and 1000. On a small percentage of days more than 1000 copies are made.

2.30

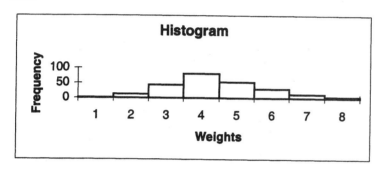

The histogram is unimodal, symmetric and bell-shaped. Most tomatoes weigh between 2 and 7 ounces with a small fraction weighing less than 2 ounces or more than 7 ounces.

2.31 a

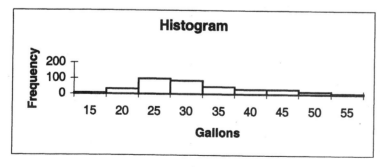

b The histogram is positively skewed and unimodal.

c Most households use between 20 and 45 gallons per day. The center of the distributions appears to be around 25 to 30 gallons.

2.32

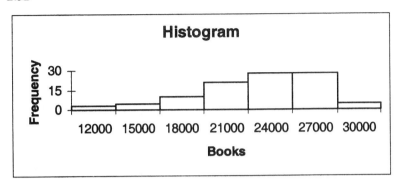

The histogram of the number of books shipped daily is negatively skewed, It appears that there is a maximum number that the company can ship.

2.33 a

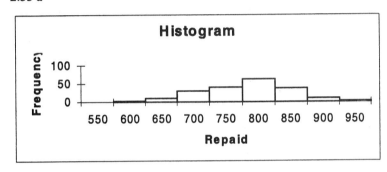

b

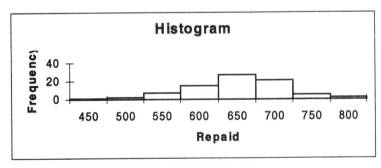

c The scorecards appear to be relatively poor predictors.

2.34 a

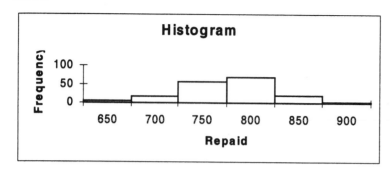

b

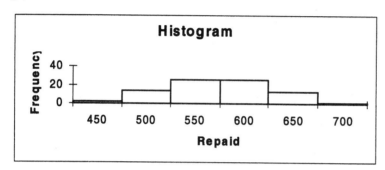

d This scorecard is a much better predictor.

2.35 a

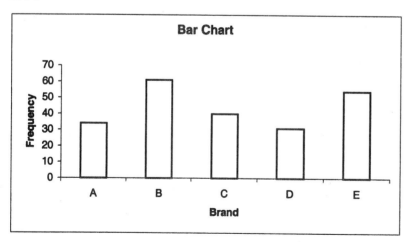

b

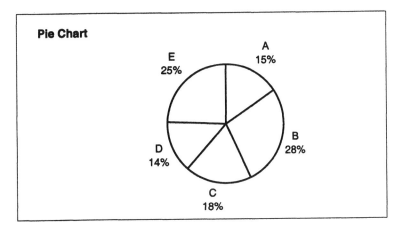

c Brands B and E are most popular, but no one brand dominates the market.

2.36 a

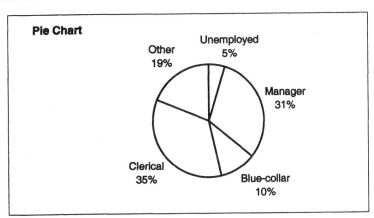

2.37

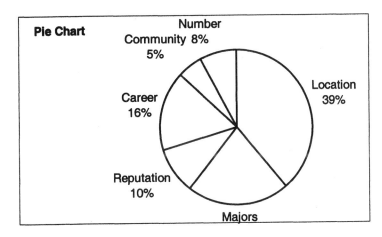

2.38

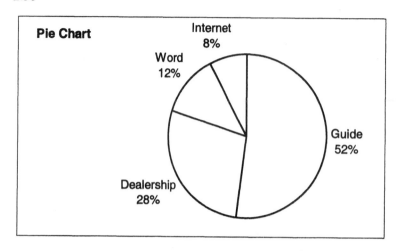

2.39

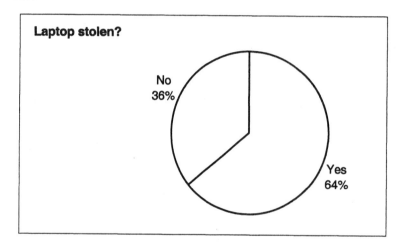

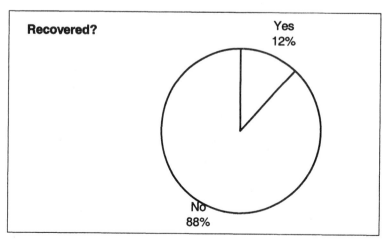

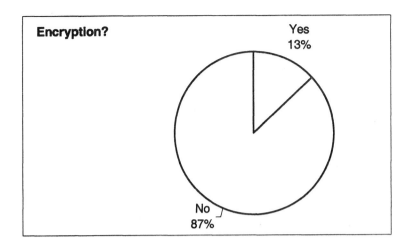

2.40

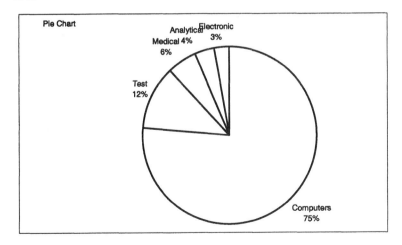

2.41

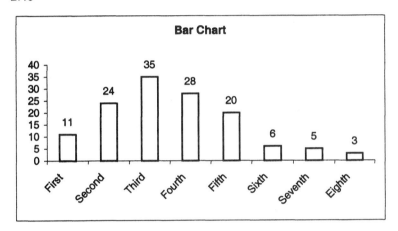

2.42a A bar chart is suitable for these results. A pie chart is incorrect.

b

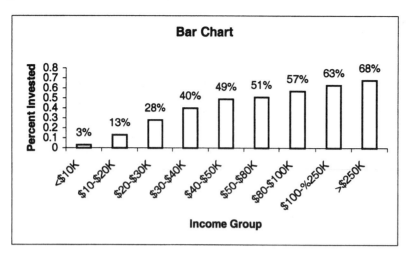

2.43a

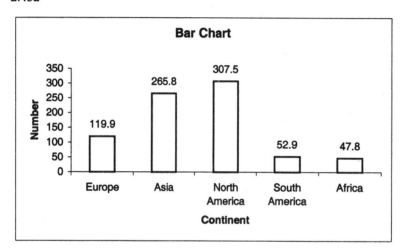

b

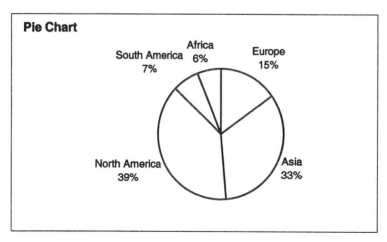

16

2.44

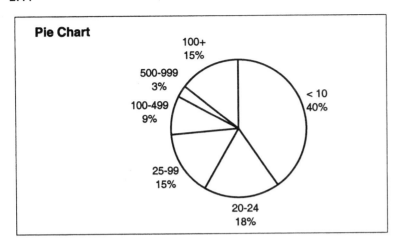

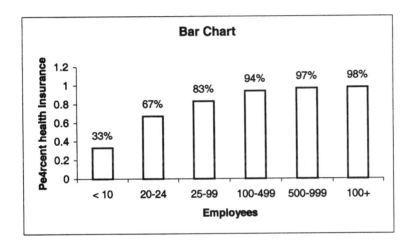

2.45

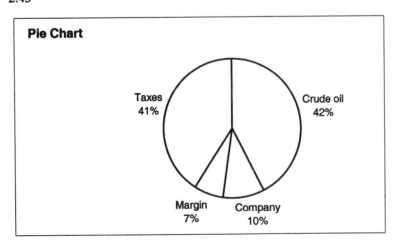

2.46

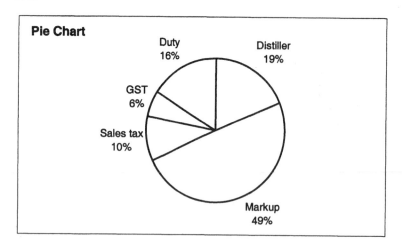

2.47a

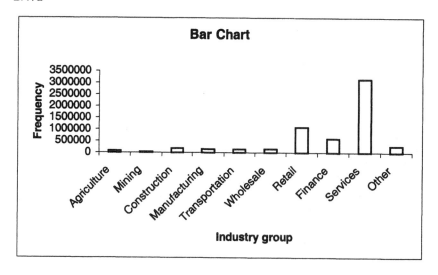

b

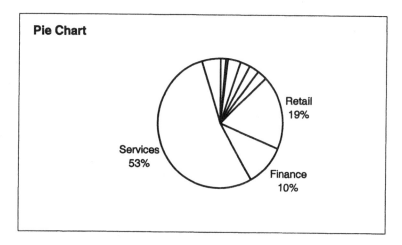

c Both charts indicate that the service and retail industry dominate.

18

2.48

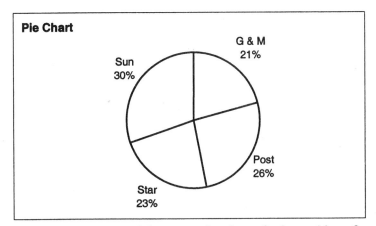

The four newspapers each have a market share of subway riders of approximately 25%.

2.49a

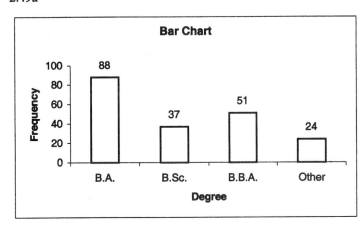

b

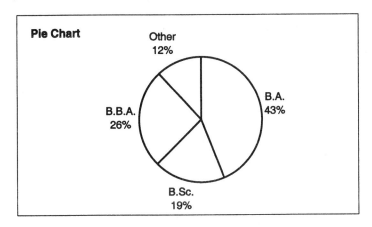

c Most applicants have the B.A. degree, about one-quarter have a B.B.A. and one-fifth have a B.Sc.

2.50

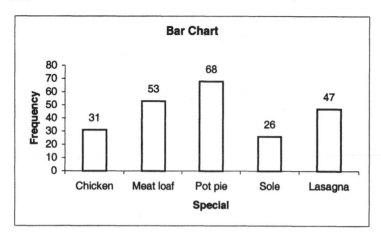

The two most popular specials are turkey pot pie and meat loaf.

2.51

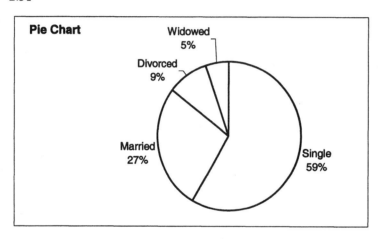

59% of students are single, 27% are married, 9% are divorced, and the rest are widowed.

2.52 a

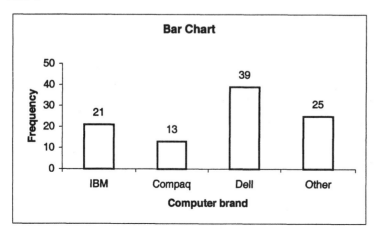

b

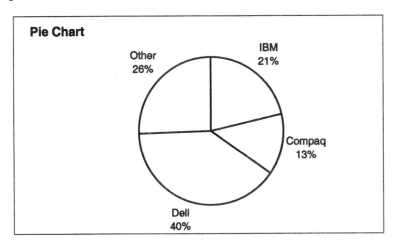

c Dell is most popular with 40% proportion, followed by other, 26%, IBM, 21% and Compaq, 13%.

2.53 a

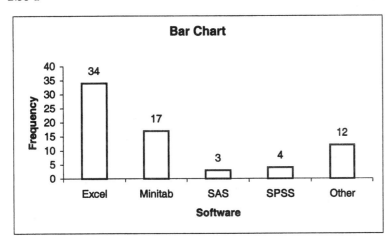

b

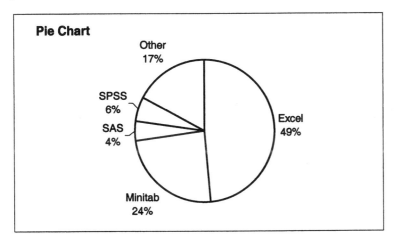

c Excel is the choice of about half the sample, one-quarter have opted for Minitab, and a small fraction chose SAS and SPSS.

2.54

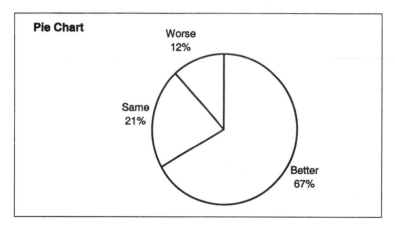

 67% said the economy would get better, 21% said the same, and the rest stated that the economy would worsen.

2.55

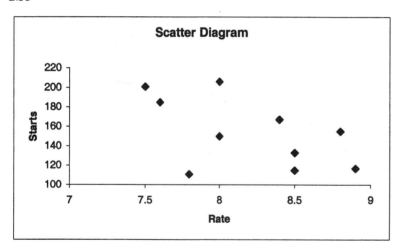

There is a moderately strong negative linear relationship.

2.56 Males

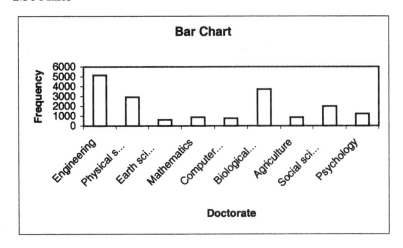

Females

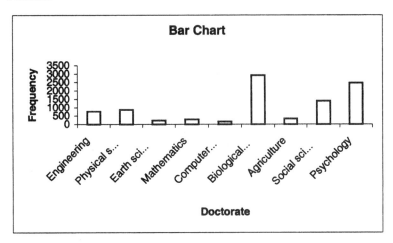

The two bar charts are somewhat similar.

2.57

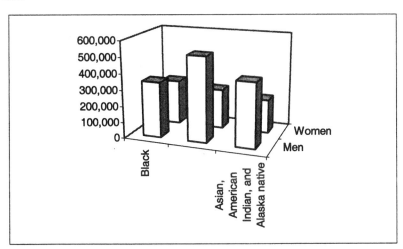

The variables race and gender are only slightly related.

2.58

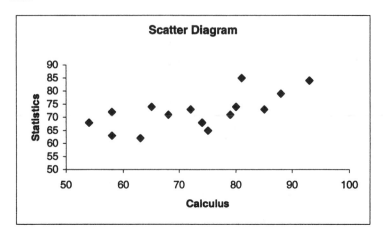

There is a moderately strong positive relationship between calculus and statistics marks.

2.59

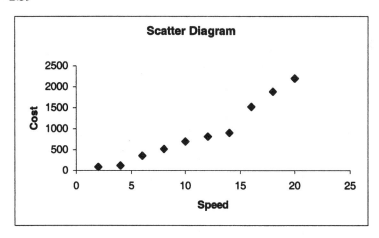

There is a strong positive linear relationship (although there appears to be a quadratic relationship).

2.60

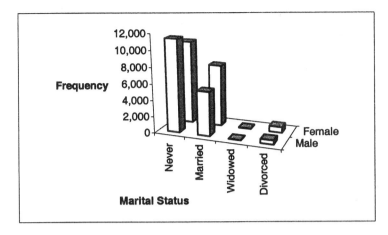

Gender and marital status are unrelated.

2.61a

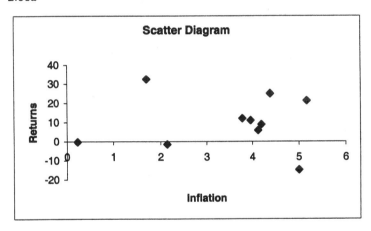

b There is no sign of a linear relationship between inflation (the independent variable) and returns (the dependent variable). Common stocks do not provide a hedge against inflation.

2.62 a

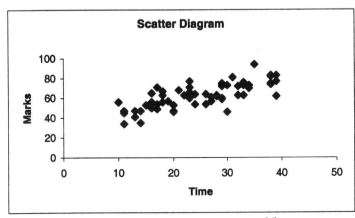

b There is a strong positive linear relationship between time spent studying and marks.

2.63

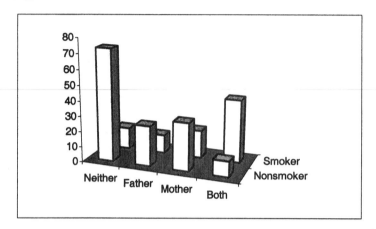

The two nominal variables are strongly correlated.

2.64a

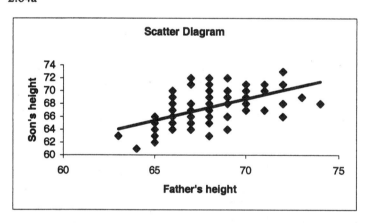

b The direction is positive.

c There does appear to be a linear relationship.

2.65

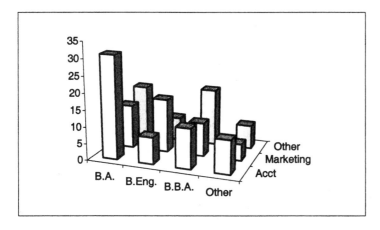

The two nominal variables are related.

2.66a

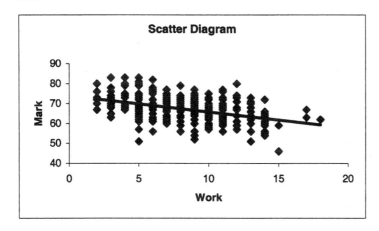

b There is apparently a weak negative linear relationship.

2.67a

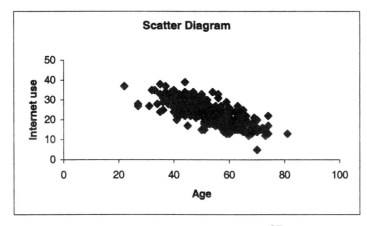

b There is a strong negative linear relationship. The older one is the less the use of the Internet.

2.68

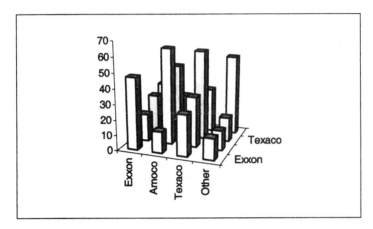

There is a relationship between the last two purchases. There is some brand loyalty.

2.69a

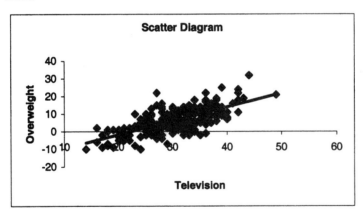

b The direction is positive

c There appears to be a strong linear relationship between the two variables.

2.70a

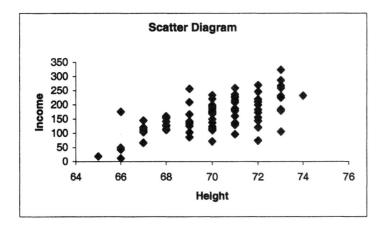

b There is a moderately strong linear relationship between the two variables. Taller MBA graduates earn more on average than shorter ones.

2.71

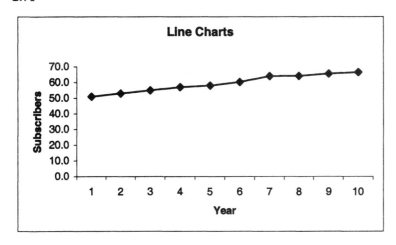

2.72

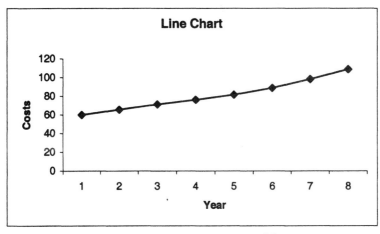

2.73a

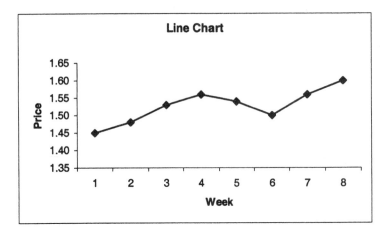

b There has been an increase in price over the 8 week period.

2.74

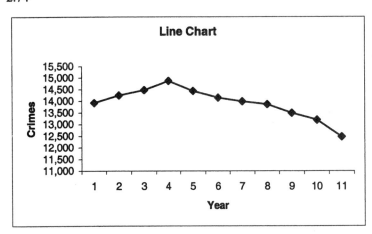

After rising for 3 years, the number of crimes has steadily decreased.

2.75

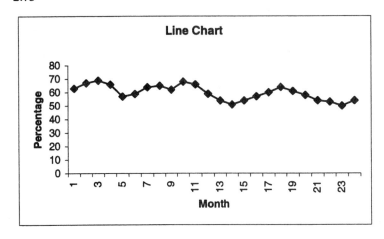

There is some month-to-month fluctuation, but the percentage was only slightly lower after 24 months.

2.76

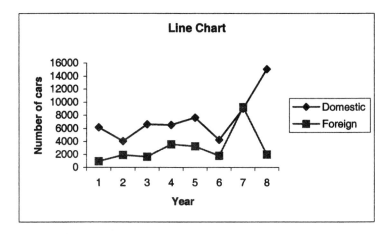

The number of recalls of domestic cars was increasing whereas the number of recalls of foreign cars remains flat.

2.77a

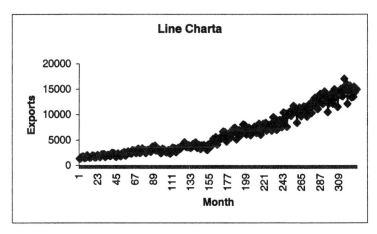

b

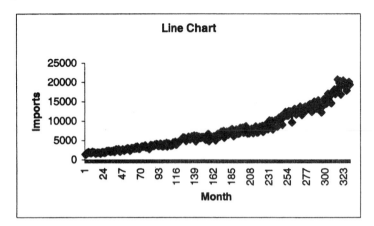

c

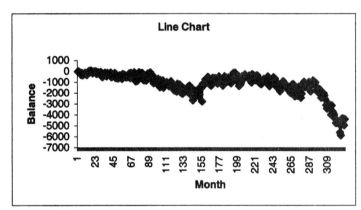

d Trade between the two countries has increased exponentially. However, imports from Canada have increased at a faster rate than exports to Canada.

2.78a

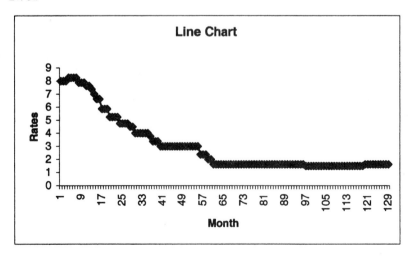

32

b There was a large decrease over the first half of the period, but has leveled since.

2.79

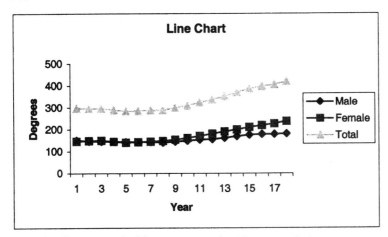

There has been a gradual increase over the 18-year period.

2.80a

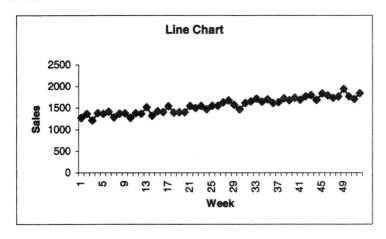

b There has been a gradual weekly increase in sales.

33

2.81

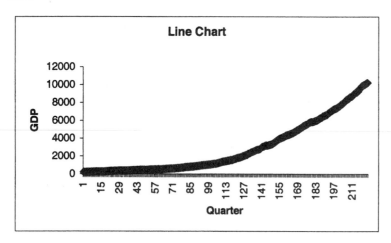

The quarterly figures have grown exponentially.

2.82

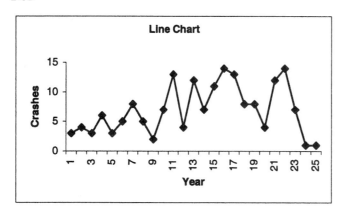

After an erratic increase over the first 20 years the number has fallen in the past 4 years.

2.83

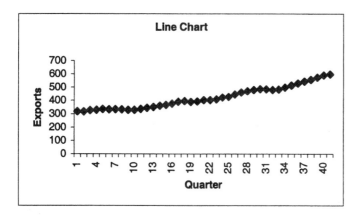

There have been steady increases

2.84

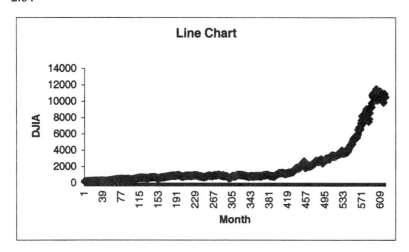

The trend until month 408 was slow but steady. Since then the index has grown exponentially.

2.85

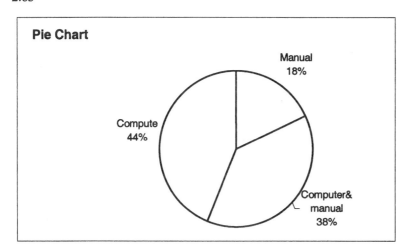

The most popular approach is to use the computer exclusively, closely followed by a combination of manual calculations and computer solutions. Would be statistics textbook authors are recommended to write books that combine both approaches.

2.86

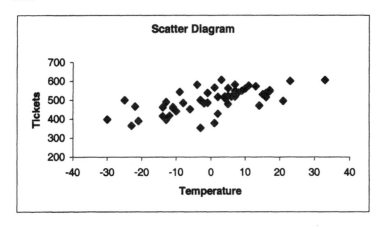

There is a moderately strong positive linear relationship between temperature and the number of tickets.

2.87

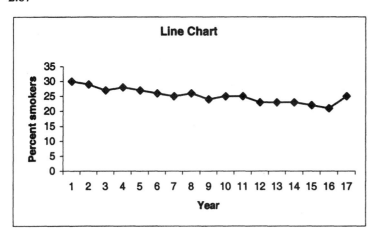

There has been a gradual decline.

2.88

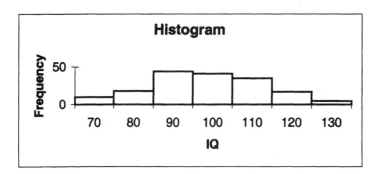

Most of the IQs are distributed between 70 and 120. The center of the distribution is about 90.

2.89

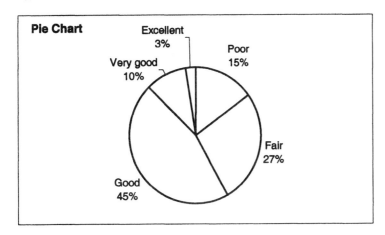

Most of the responses rate the food as good or fair.

2.90

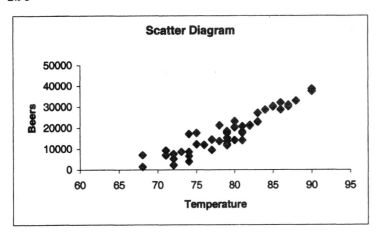

There is a strong positive linear relationship between temperature and the number of beers sold.

2.91

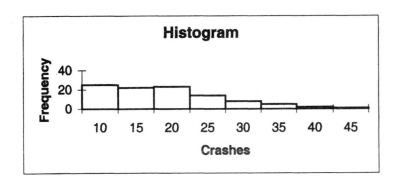

Most computer users have less 25 crashes per 12 week period.

Most computer users have less 25 crashes per 12 week period.

2.92

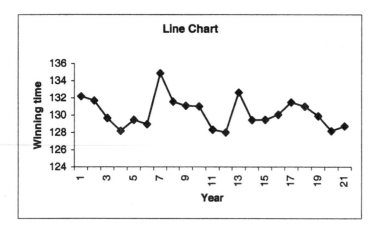

Although there are year-to-year fluctuations the winning time appears to be constant.

2.93

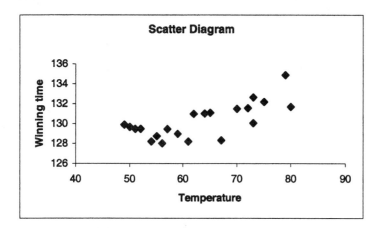

There is a strong positive linear relationship between temperature and winning times. This explains the fluctuations in the line chart in Exercise 2.92.

2.94

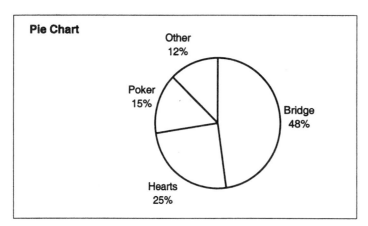

Most students play bridge.

2.95

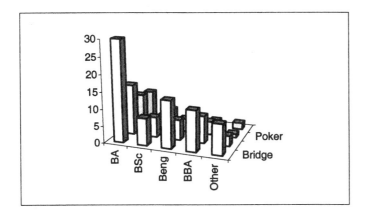

The two nominal variables are weakly related.

2.96

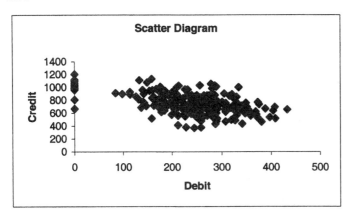

There is a moderately strong negative linear relationship.

2.97

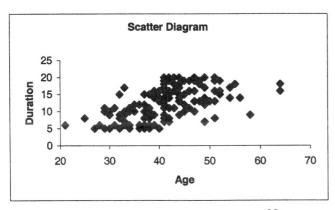

There is a weak positive linear relationship between age and duration of symptoms.

2.98

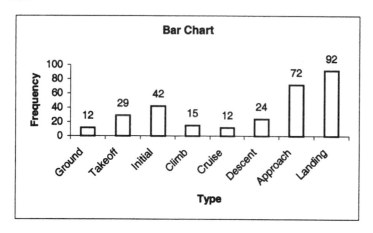

Approach and landing appear to be the most common.

2.99a

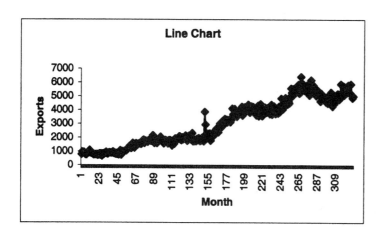

b

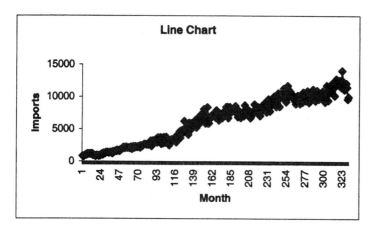

c

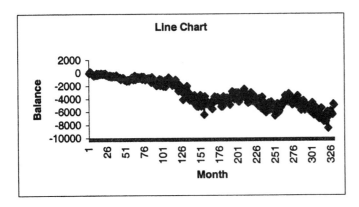

d Imports to Japan and exports from Japan have grown over the past 28 years. However, imports have grown much more quickly.

2.100

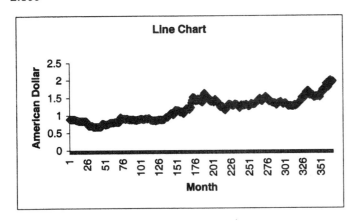

The value of the American dollar has risen over the years.

2.101

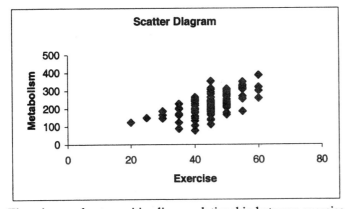

There is a moderate positive linear relationship between exercise and metabolism.

2.102

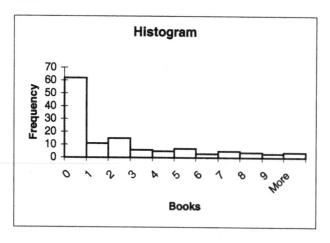

Most students borrowed no books.

2.103

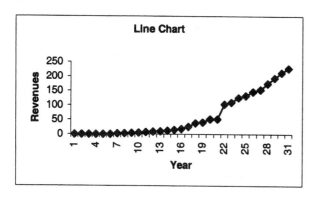

Growth in revenues has increased exponentially.

2.104

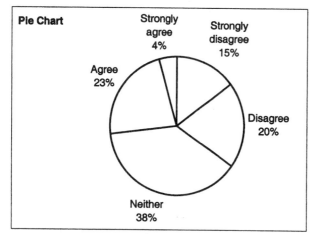

Most students would not agree.

2.105a

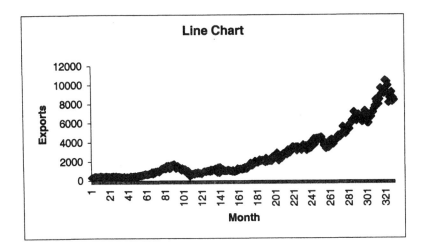

b

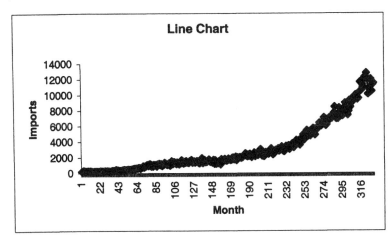

c

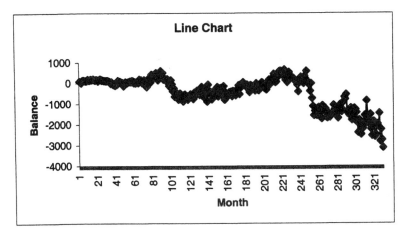

d Trade has been increasing but imports have increased faster than exports to Mexico.

2.106

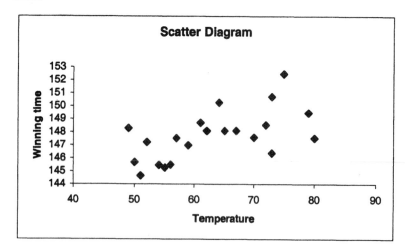

There is a moderately strong positive linear relationship between temperature and winning time.

2.107

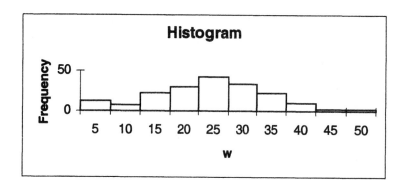

Many people gain between 10 and 35 pounds.

2.108a

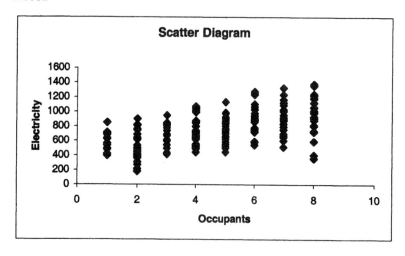

b There is moderately strong positive linear relationship between the number of occupants and electricity use.

2.109

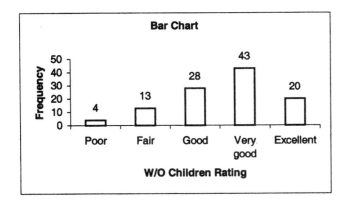

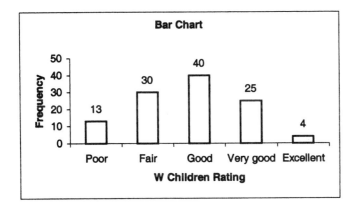

The without children ratings tend to be higher.

2.110

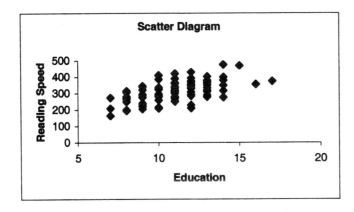

There is a moderately strong linear relationship between years of education and reading speed.

2.111

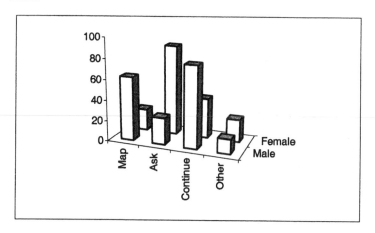

There are large differences between male and female responses.

2.112

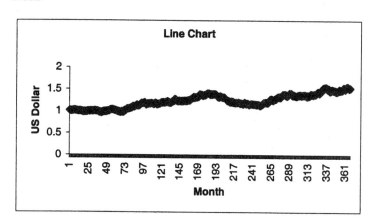

The US dollar has steadily increased in value compared to the Canadian dollar.

2.113

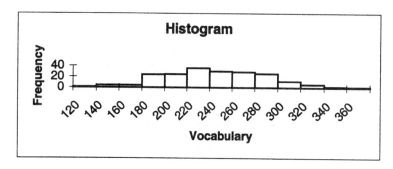

Most vocabularies lie between 160 and 280 words.

2.114

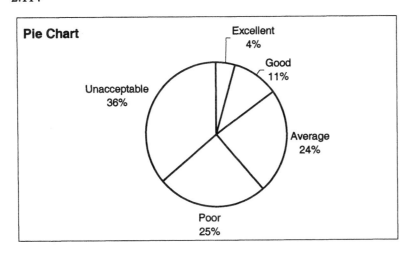

The overall impression is poor.

2.115

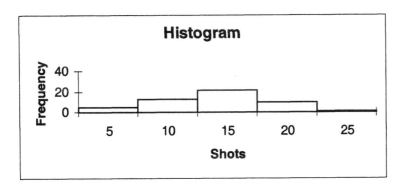

The number of shots is quite variable.

2.116

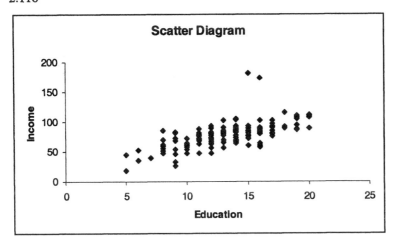

47

There is a moderately strong positive linear relationship between education and income.

2.117

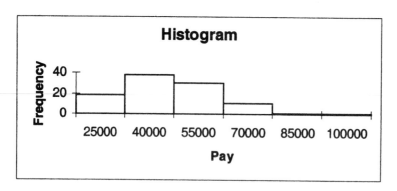

Most directors earned between $25,000 and $55,000.

2.118

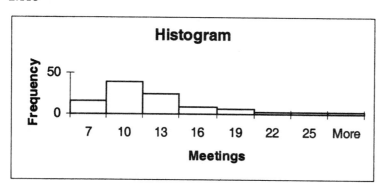

Most directors attended less than 13 meetings.

2.119

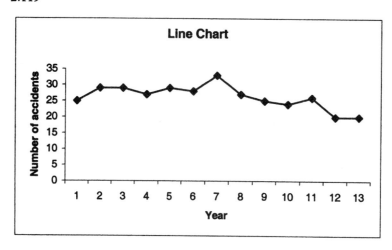

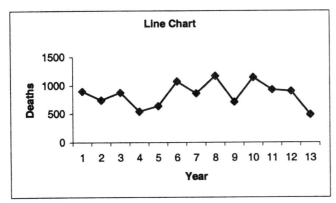

The number of accidents and the number of deaths have remained stable.

2.120

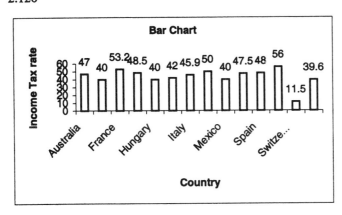

All countries, except Switzerland set their highest income tax rate at about 40% or higher.

2.121

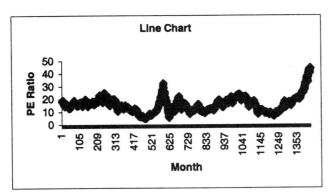

The average PE ratio appears to lie between 10 and 20 except for two periods, just before the 1929 stock market crash and in the 1990's.

Chapter 3

3.1

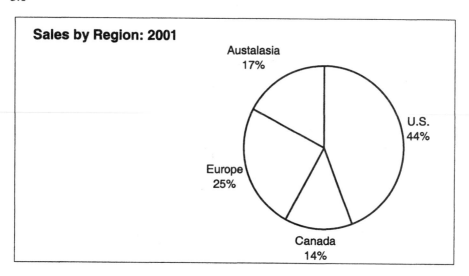

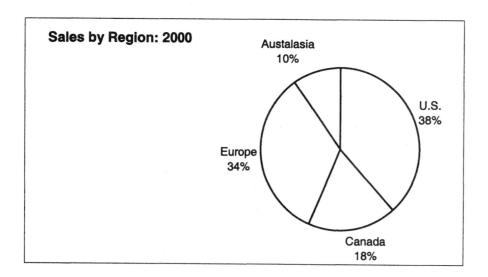

Sales to all regions have increased in 2001 over the 2000 levels. But the pie charts reveal significant differences in the percentage of total sales to each region. The percentage of sales to Australasia has increased by 70%, while the percentages of sales to each of Canada and Europe have fallen by almost 25%.

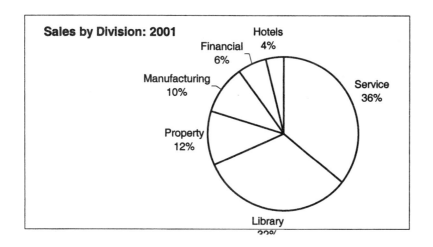

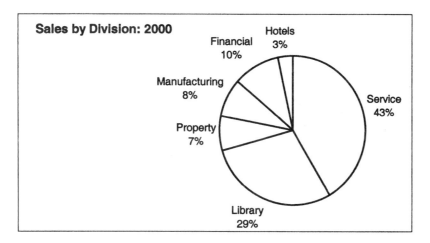

Sales to all divisions (except Financial Systems) have increased in 2001 over the 2000 levels. But the pie charts reveal significant differences in the percentage of total sales by each division. The percentage of total sales by the Construction and Property Management division has increased by more than 50%, while the percentage of sales by the Financial Systems division has fallen by 40%.

3.2 Grade D, at best. Because the chart is cluttered and not organized for clarity, the reader cannot quickly grasp the information being conveyed. The pictures of the workers add nothing of value.

3.3 While it is interesting to observe the historical relationship between the Canadian and American dollars, the chart could convey more meaningful information if it included, along the time line, a brief description of significant political and economic events that may have contributed to the dollar fluctuations. For example, the Canadian dollar tends to fall during periods of declining resource prices, and during periods of increasing separatist sentiment in Quebec.

51

3.4 Interest rates were increased throughout 1994, following a sharp increase in GDP growth at the end of 1993. The inflation rate remained fairly stable throughout 1994, providing at least some justification for the increase in interest rates.

3.5 The chart receives a grade of D, at best. From the chart, we observe that hardcover best sellers in 1994 were least popular in July and August, after which time their popularity continued to rise until Christmas week, when their popularity reached a peak. This information (even if it is of interest) can be conveyed just as well without a graph.

3.6 This graph should receive at least a grade of B. This graph allows the reader to easily compare the trends in the employment growth rates for the four different education groups. During the early 1990's, growth in employment increased significantly for the most educated group, but declined sharply for the least educated group.

3.7 The following graph should probably receive a grade of B.

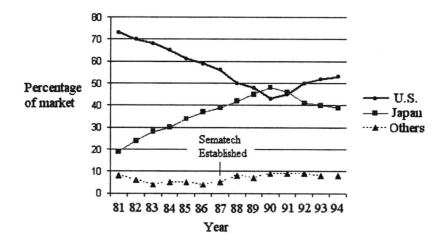

3.8

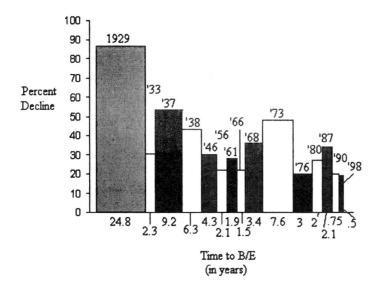

3.9a

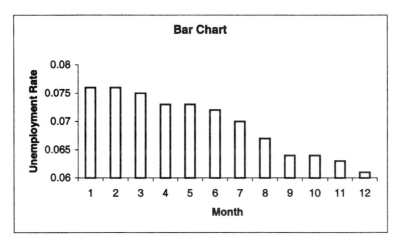

b

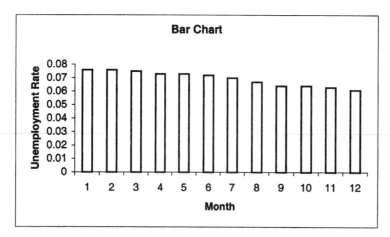

c The first chart makes it appear that there has been a large decrease in the unemployment rate. In the second chart the unemployment rate appears to be virtually constant.

d The second chart is more accurate.

3.10 To make the comparison clear we cg=hanged the units of income to tens of thousands.

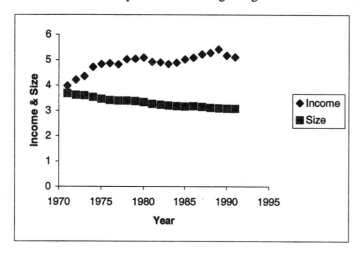

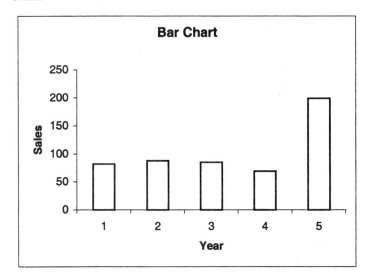

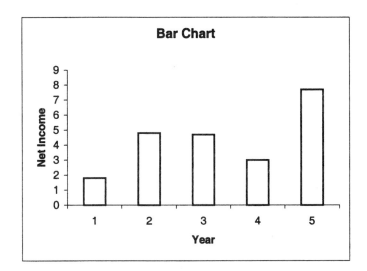

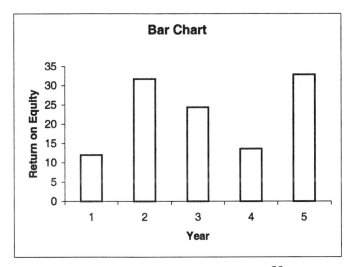

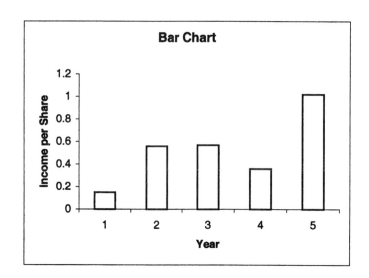

b

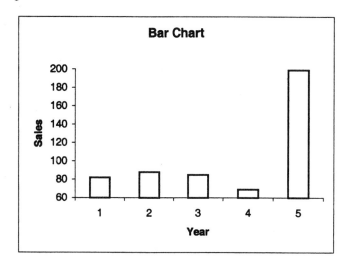

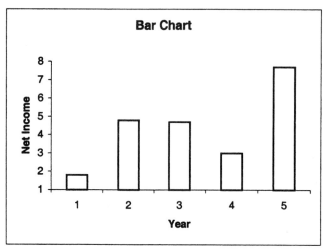

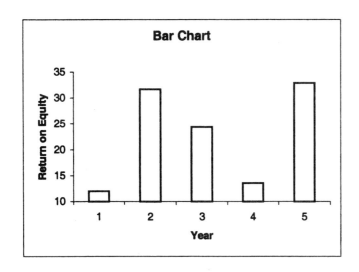

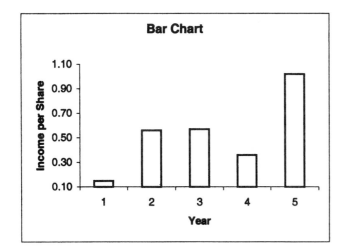

Another way to distort the graphs is to omit the data for years 1990 and 1992.

3.12a

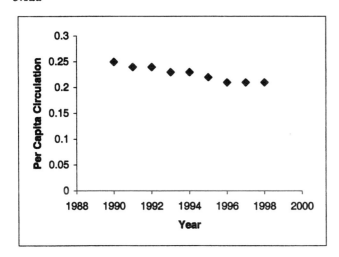

b

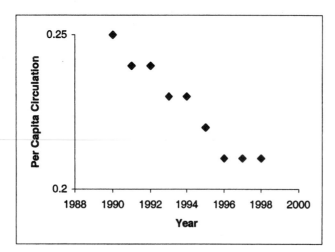

Chapter 4

4.1 a $\bar{x} = \dfrac{\sum x_i}{n} = \dfrac{52+25+15+0+104+44+60+30+33+81+40+5}{12} = \dfrac{489}{12} = 40.75$

Ordered data: 0, 5, 15, 25, 30, 33, 40, 44, 52, 60, 81, 104; Median = (33 + 40)/2 = 36.5

Mode = all

4.2 a $\bar{x} = \dfrac{\sum x_i}{n} = \dfrac{5+7+0+3+15+6+5+9+3+8+10+5+2+0+12}{15} = \dfrac{90}{15} = 6.0$

Ordered data: 0, 0, 2, 3, 3, 5, 5, 5, 6, 7, 8, 9, 10, 12, 15; Median = 5

Mode = 5

b The mean number of sick days is 6, the median is 5, and the most frequent number of sick days is 5.

4.3 a $\bar{x} = \dfrac{\sum x_i}{n} = \dfrac{5.5+7.2+1.6+22.0+8.7+2.8+5.3+3.4+12.5+18.6+8.3+6.6}{12} = \dfrac{102.5}{12} = 8.54$

Ordered data: 1.6, 2.8, 3.4, 5.3, 5.5, 6.6, 7.2, 8.3, 8.7, 12.5, 18.6, 22.0; Median = 6.9

Mode = all

b The mean number of miles jogged is 8.54. Half the sample jogged more than 6.9 miles and half jogged less.

4.4 a $\bar{x} = \dfrac{\sum x_i}{n} = \dfrac{33+29+45+60+42+19+52+38+36}{9} = \dfrac{354}{9} = 39.3$

Ordered data: 19, 29, 33, 36, 38, 42, 45, 52, 60; Median = 38

Mode: all

b The mean amount of time is 39.3 minutes. Half the group took less than 38 minutes.

4.5 a $\bar{x} = \dfrac{\sum x_i}{n} = \dfrac{14+8+3+2+6+4+9+13+10+12+7+4+9+13+15+8+11+12+4+0}{20}$

$\quad = \dfrac{164}{20} = 8.2$

Ordered data: 0, 2, 3, 4, 4, 4, 6, 7, 8, 8, 9, 9, 10, 11, 12, 12, 13, 13, 14, 15; Median = 8.5

Mode = 4

b The mean number of days to submit grades is 8.2, the median is 8.5, and the mode is 4.

4.6 $R_g = \sqrt[3]{(1+R_1)(1+R_2)(1+R_3)} - 1 = \sqrt[3]{(1+.25)(1-.10)(1+.50)} - 1 = .19$

$4.7\ R_g = \sqrt[4]{(1+R_1)(1+R_2)(1+R_3)(1+R_4)} - 1 = \sqrt[4]{(1+.50)(1+.30)(1-.50)(1-.25)} - 1 = -.075$

$4.8\ a\ \bar{x} = \dfrac{\sum x_i}{n} = \dfrac{.10+.22+.06-.05+.20}{5} = \dfrac{.53}{5} = .106$

Ordered data: -.05, .06, .10, .20, .22; Median = .10

$b\ R_g = \sqrt[5]{(1+R_1)(1+R_2)(1+R_3)(1+R_4)(1+R_5)} - 1 = \sqrt[5]{(1+.10)(1+.22)(1+.06)(1-.05)(1+.20)} - 1 =$

.102

c The geometric mean

$4.9\ a\ \bar{x} = \dfrac{\sum x_i}{n} = \dfrac{-.15-.20+.15-.08+.50}{5} = \dfrac{.22}{5} = .044$

Ordered data: -.20, -.15, -.08, .15, .50; Median = -.08

$b\ R_g = \sqrt[5]{(1+R_1)(1+R_2)(1+R_3)(1+R_4)(1+R_5)} - 1 = \sqrt[5]{(1-.15)(1-.20)(1+.15)(1-.08)(1+.50)} - 1 =$

.015

c The geometric mean

$4.10\ a$ Year 1 rate of return $= \dfrac{1200-1000}{1000} = .20$

Year 2 rate of return $= \dfrac{1200-1200}{1200} = 0$

Year 3 rate of return $= \dfrac{1500-1200}{1200} = .25$

Year 4 rate of return $= \dfrac{2000-1500}{1500} = .33$

$b\ \bar{x} = \dfrac{\sum x_i}{n} = \dfrac{.20+0+.25+.33}{4} = \dfrac{.78}{4} = .195$

Ordered data: 0, .20, .25, .33; Median = .225

$c\ R_g = \sqrt[4]{(1+R_1)(1+R_2)(1+R_3)(1+R_4)} - 1 = \sqrt[4]{(1+.20)(1+0)(1+.25)(1+.33)} - 1 = .188$

d The geometric mean is because $1000(1.188)^4 = 2000$

$4.11\ a$ Year 1 rate of return $= \dfrac{14-10}{10} = .40$

Year 2 rate of return $= \dfrac{15-14}{14} = .071$

Year 3 rate of return $= \dfrac{22-15}{15} = .467$

Year 4 rate of return $= \dfrac{30-22}{22} = .364$

Year 5 rate of return $= \dfrac{25-30}{30} = -.167$

b $\bar{x} = \dfrac{\sum x_i}{n} = \dfrac{.40+.071+.467+.364-.167}{5} = \dfrac{1.135}{5} = .227$

Ordered data: -.167, .071, .364, .40, .467; Median = .364

c $R_g = \sqrt[5]{(1+R_1)(1+R_2)(1+R_3)(1+R_4)(1+R_5)} - 1 =$

$\sqrt[5]{(1+.40)(1+.071)(1+.467)(1+.364)(1-.167)} - 1$

$$= .201$$

d $10(1.201)^5 = 25$

4.12 a $\bar{x} = 24{,}329$; median $= 24{,}461$

b The mean starting salary is \$24,329. Half the sample earned less than \$24,461.

4.13 a $\bar{x} = 11.19$; median $= 11$

b The mean number of days is 11.19 and half the sample took less than 11 days and half took more than 11 days to pay.

4.14a $\bar{x} = 152.02$; median $= 158$

b The mean expenditure is \$152.02 and half the sample spent less than \$158

14.15a $\bar{x} = 3793.75$; median $= 2527.50$

b $\bar{x} = 2800.01$; median $= 2432.00$

b The mean distance for business travelers is much larger than that of pleasure travelers. However, the medians are similar.

4.16a $\bar{x} = 30.53$; median $= 31$

b The mean training time is 30.53. Half the sample trained for less than 31 hours.

4.17a $\bar{x} = 32.91$; median $= 32$; mode $= 32$

b The mean speed is 32.91 mph. Half the sample traveled slower than 32 mph and half traveled faster. The mode is 32.

4.18 $\bar{x} = 472.35$; median = 472.5

b The mean expenditure is \$472.35. Half the sample spent less than \$472.50

4.19 $\bar{x} = \dfrac{\sum x_i}{n} = \dfrac{9+3+7+4+1+7+5+4}{8} = \dfrac{40}{8} = 5$

$s^2 = \dfrac{\sum(x_i - \bar{x})^2}{n-1} = \dfrac{[(9-5)^2 + (3-5)^2 + ... + (4-5)^2]}{8-1} = \dfrac{46}{7} = 6.57$

4.20 $\bar{x} = \dfrac{\sum x_i}{n} = \dfrac{4+5+3+6+5+6+5+6}{8} = \dfrac{40}{8} = 5$

$s^2 = \dfrac{\sum(x_i - \bar{x})^2}{n-1} = \dfrac{[(4-5)^2 + (5-5)^2 + ... + (6-5)^2]}{8-1} = \dfrac{8}{7} = 1.14$

4.21 $\bar{x} = \dfrac{\sum x_i}{n} = \dfrac{12+6+22+31+23+13+15+17+21}{9} = \dfrac{160}{9} = 17.78$

$s^2 = \dfrac{\sum(x_i - \bar{x})^2}{n-1} = \dfrac{[(12-17.78)^2 + (6-17.78)^2 + ... + (21-17.78)^2]}{9-1} = \dfrac{433.56}{8} = 54.19$

$s = \sqrt{s^2} = \sqrt{54.19} = 7.36$

4.22 $\bar{x} = \dfrac{\sum x_i}{n} = \dfrac{0+(-5)+(-3)+6+4+(-4)+1+(-5)+0+3}{10} = \dfrac{-3}{10} = -.3$

$s^2 = \dfrac{\sum(x_i - \bar{x})^2}{n-1} = \dfrac{[(0-(-.3))^2 + ((-5)-(-.3))^2 + ... + (3-(-.3))^2]}{10-1} = \dfrac{136.1}{9} = 15.12$

$s = \sqrt{s^2} = \sqrt{15.12} = 3.89$

4.23 The data in (b) appear to be most similar to one another.

4.24 a: $s^2 = 51.5$

b: $s^2 = 6.5$

c: $s^2 = 174.5$

4.25 Variance cannot be negative because it is the sum of *squared* differences.

4.26 6, 6, 6, 6, 6

4.27 a about 68%

b about 95%

c About 99.7%

4.28 a From the empirical rule we know that approximately 68% of the observations fall between 46 and 54. Thus 16% are less than 46 (the other 16% are above 54).

b Approximately 95% of the observations are between 42 and 58. Thus, only 2.5% are above 58 and all the rest, 97.5% are below 58.

c See (a) above; 16% are above 54.

4.29 a at least 75%

b at least 88.9%

4.30 a Nothing

b At least 75% lie between 60 and 180.

c At least 88.9% lie between 30 and 210.

4.31 Range = 25.85, $s^2 = 29.46$, and s = 5.43; there is considerable variation between prices; at least 75% of the prices .

4.32 $s^2 = 40.73$ mph^2 , and s = 6.38 mph; at least 75% of the speeds lie within 12.76 mph of the mean;

at least 88.9% of the speeds lie within 16.29 mph of the mean

4.33 a

Punter	Variance	Standard deviation
1	40.22	6.34
2	14.81	3.85
3	3.63	1.91

b Punter 3 is the most consistent.

4.34 $s^2 = .0858$ cm^2 , and s = .2929cm; at least 75% of the lengths lie within .5858 of the mean; at least 88.9% of the rods will lie within .8787 cm of the mean.

4.35 $\bar{x} = 175.73$; $s = 62.1$; At least 75% of the withdrawals lie between \$51.53 and \$299.93; at least 88.9% of the withdrawals lie between 0 and \$362.03.

4.36a $s = 15.01$

b In approximately 68% of the days the number of arrivals falls between 83 (rounded from 83.04) and 113; on approximately 95% of the hours the number of arrivals fall between 68 and 128; on approximately 99.7% of the hours the number of arrivals fall between 53 and 143.

4.37 First quartile: $L_{25} = (15+1)\dfrac{25}{100} = (16)(.25) = 4$; the fourth number is 3.

Second quartile: $L_{50} = (15+1)\dfrac{50}{100} = (16)(.5) = 8$; the eighth number is 5.

Third quartile: $L_{75} = (15+1)\dfrac{75}{100} = (16)(.75) = 12$; the twelfth number is 7.

4.38 30th percentile: $L_{30} = (10+1)\dfrac{30}{100} = (11)(.30) = 3.3$; the 30th percentile is 22.3.

80th percentile: $L_{80} = (10+1)\dfrac{80}{100} = (11)(.80) = 8.8$; the 80th percentile 30.8.

4.39 20th percentile: $L_{20} = (10+1)\dfrac{20}{100} = (11)(.20) = 2.2$; the 20th percentile is $43 + .2(51-43) = 44.6$.

40th percentile: $L_{40} = (10+1)\dfrac{40}{100} = (11)(.40) = 4.4$; the 40th percentile $52 + .4(60-52) = 55.2$.

4.40 First quartile: $L_{25} = (13+1)\dfrac{25}{100} = (14)(.25) = 3.5$; the first quartile 13.05.

Second quartile: $L_{50} = (13+1)\dfrac{50}{100} = (14)(.5) = 7$; the second quartile is 14.7.

Third quartile: $L_{75} = (13+1)\dfrac{75}{100} = (14)(.75) = 10.5$; the third quartile is 15.6.

4.41 Third decile: $L_{305} = (15+1)\dfrac{30}{100} = (16)(.30) = 4.8$; the third decile is 6.6.

Sixth decile: $L_{60} = (15+1)\dfrac{60}{100} = (16)(.60) = 9.6$; the sixth decile is 17.6.

4.42 Interquartile range $= 15.6 - 13.05 = 2.55$

4.43 Interquartile range = 7 – 3 = 4

4.44 First quartile = 5.75, third quartile = 15; interquartile range = 15 – 5.75 = 9.25

4.45

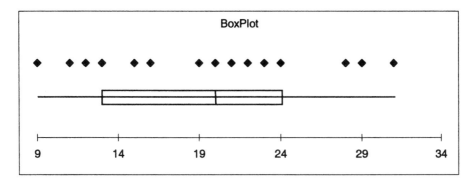

4.46

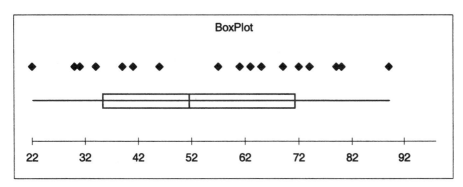

4.47a First quartile = 2, second quartile = 4, and third quartile = 8.

b Most executives spend little time reading resumes. Keep it short.

4.48 Dogs

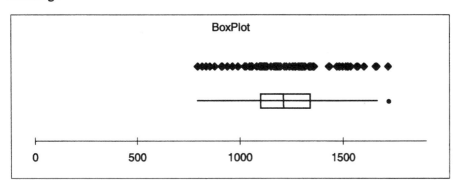

Cats

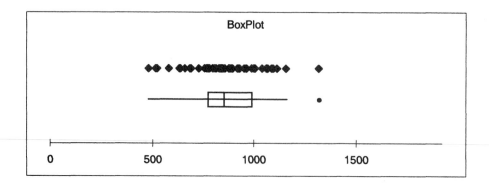

Dogs cost more money than cats. Both sets of expenses are positively skewed.

4.49 First quartile = 50, second quartile = 125, and third quartile = 260. The amounts are positively skewed.

4.50 BA

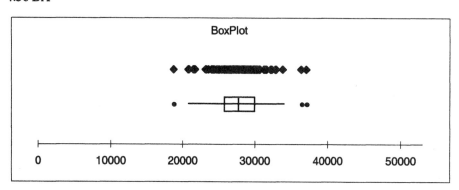

BSc

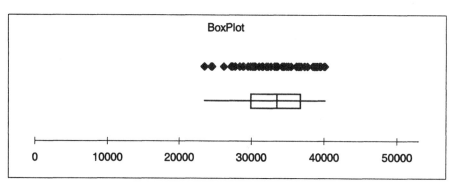

BBA

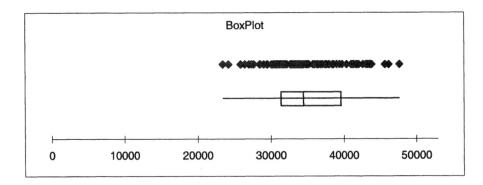

Other

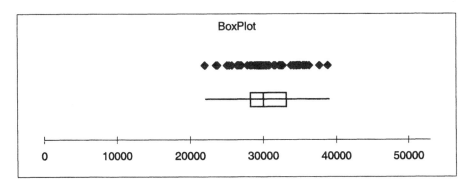

The starting salaries of BA and other are the lowest and least variable. Starting salaries for BBA and BSc are higher.

4.51 a

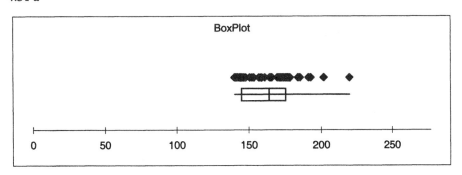

b The quartiles are 145.11, 164.17, and 175.18

c There are no outliers.

d The data are positively skewed. One-quarter of the times are below 145.11 and one-quarter are above 175.18.

4.52a Private course:

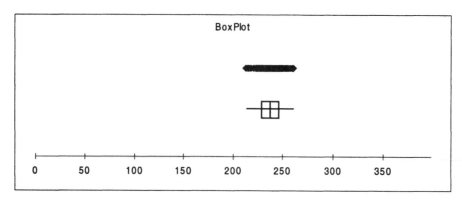

Public course:

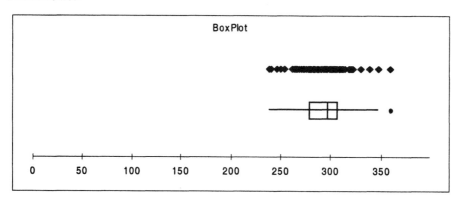

b The amount of time taken to complete rounds on the public course are larger and more variable than those played on private courses.

4.53 a The quartiles are 26, 28.5, and 32
b the times are positively skewed.

4.54 The quartiles are 697.19, 804.90, and 909.38. One-quarter of mortgage payments are less than $607.19 and one quarter exceed $909.38.

4.55

x_i	y_i	$(x_i - \bar{x})(y_i - \bar{y})$
3	8	-4.375
5	4	-0.375
2	9	-9.625
9	2	-14.875
6	4	-1.875
3	7	-2.625
9	3	-10.625
1	7	-5.625
$\bar{x} = 4.75$	$\bar{y} = 5.5$	-50.000

$$\text{cov(x,y)} = \frac{-50.000}{7} = -7.1429$$

$$r = \frac{\text{cov}(x, y)}{s_x s_y} = \frac{-7.14}{(3.0589)(2.5635)} = -.9109$$

4.56

x_i	y_i	$(x_i - \bar{x})(y_i - \bar{y})$
45	77	182.03
22	31	354.53
16	28	584.63
50	49	-179.67
44	63	26.73
31	84	-73.47
48	40	-282.17
27	92	-225.07
30	72	-47.97
28	67	-40.87
$\bar{x} = 34.1$	$\bar{y} = 60.3$	298.7

$$\text{cov(x,y)} = \frac{298.7}{9} = 33.19$$

$$r = \frac{\text{cov}(x, y)}{s_x s_y} = \frac{33.19}{(11.79)(22.30)} = .1262$$

4.57

x_i	y_i	$(x_i - \bar{x})(y_i - \bar{y})$
153	1,526	30,842.26
202	1,849	2,455.56
199	1,906	1,740.66
315	2,460	44,823.66
148	1,602	27,771.66
194	1,731	6,566.16
250	2,208	6,656.16
167	2,041	-2,521.64
305	2,595	51,746.16
258	2,008	599.06
$\bar{x} = 219.1$	$\bar{y} = 1,992.6$	170,679.40

a $\text{cov(x,y)} = \dfrac{170,679.40}{9} = 18,964.38$

b $r = \dfrac{\text{cov}(x, y)}{s_x s_y} = \dfrac{18,964.38}{(60.1008)(349.1521)} = .9037$

c There is a strong positive linear relationship.

4.58

x_i	y_i	$(x_i - \bar{x})(y_i - \bar{y})$
23	9.6	69.51
46	11.3	3.94
60	12.8	6.46
54	9.8	-6.64
28	8.9	73.29
33	12.5	-7.69
25	12.0	1.96
31	11.4	13.56
36	12.6	-7.92
88	13.7	59.99
90	14.4	90.48
99	15.9	183.28
$\bar{x} = 51.08$	$\bar{y} = 12.08$	480.23

a $cov(x,y) = \dfrac{480.23}{11} = 43.66$

b $r = \dfrac{cov(x, y)}{s_x s_y} = \dfrac{43.66}{(27.38)(2.05)} = .7788$

c There is a moderately strong positive linear relationship.

4.59 There is a negative linear relationship. The strength is unknown.

4.60 $r = \dfrac{cov(x, y)}{s_x s_y} = \dfrac{-150}{(16)(12)} = -.7813$

There is a moderately strong negative linear relationship.

4.61

	IQ Twin 1	IQ Twin 2
IQ Twin 1	1	
IQ Twin 2	0.6850	1

r = .6850; there is a moderately strong positive linear relationship.

4.62 a

	Cigarettes	Days
Cigarettes	107.81	
Days	20.46	19.72

cov(x,y) = 20.46(231/230) = 20.55

b

	Cigarettes	Days
Cigarettes	1	
Days	0.4437	1

r = .4437

c The coefficient of correlation tells us that there is a weak positive linear relationship between smoking and the duration of colds.

4.63a

	Marks	Time
Marks	1	
Time	0.7475	1

r = .7475

b There is a strong positive linear relationship between study time as marks.

4.64 a

	Age	Internet
Age	1	
Internet	-0.7501	1

r = -.7501

b There is a strong negative linear relationship between age and Internet use.

4.65

	Score	Time
Score	1	
Time	0.6868	1

r = .6868; there is a moderately strong positive linear relationship. The poorer the golfer (high scorer) the larger the amount of time he or she takes to complete a round.

4.66

	Height	Income
Height	1	
Income	0.6460	1

r = .6460. There is a moderately strong positive linear relationship.

4.67a

	Selling Expenses	Total Sales
Selling Expenses	3.86	
Total Sales	26.53	280.02

cov(x,y) = 26.53(18/17) = 28.09

	Selling Expenses	Total Sales
Selling Expenses	1	
Total Sales	0.8068	1

r = .8068

b

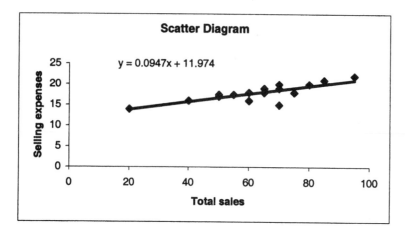

$\hat{y}$ = 11.974 + .0947x; Fixed costs = \$11,974, variable costs = \$0.0947

4.68

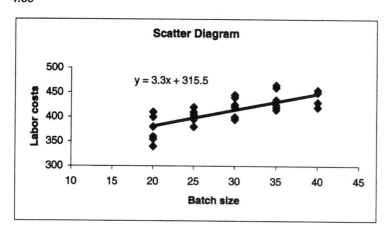

$\hat{y}$ = 315.5 + 3.3x; Fixed costs = \$315.50, variable costs = \$3.30

4.69

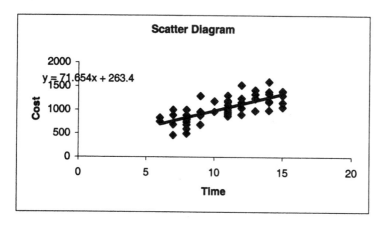

$\hat{y} = 263.4 + 71.65x$; Fixed costs = \$263.40, variable costs = \$71.65

4.70

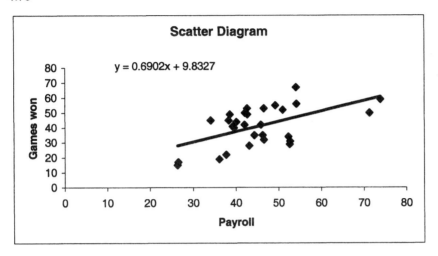

$\hat{y} = 9.8327 + .6902x$; Cost to win one more game = 1million/.6902 = \$1,448,855

4.71

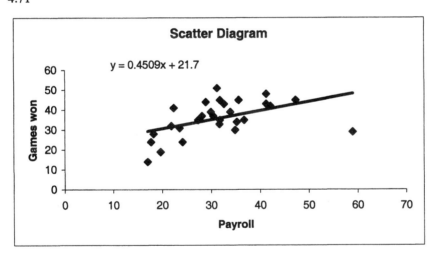

$\hat{y} = 21.7 + .4509x$; Cost to win one more game = 1million/..4509 = \$2,217,787

4.72 $\bar{x} = 7.08$, s = 2.93

4.73 $\bar{x} = 38.85$, s = 8.54

4.74

Stores	
Mean	3.75
Standard Error	0.29
Median	4
Mode	4
Standard Deviation	2.23
Sample Variance	4.97
Kurtosis	-0.23
Skewness	0.51
Range	9
Minimum	0
Maximum	9
Sum	225
Count	60

$\bar{x} = 3.75$, median = 4, s = 2.23

4.75 $\bar{x} = 55,311$, s = 5271

4.76a s = 12.93

b At least 75% of the times lie within 25.86 minutes of the mean; at least 88.9% of the times lie within 38.79 minutes of the mean.

c It is more precise.

4.77 $\bar{x} = 69.34$, median = 76, s = 17.93

4.78 $\bar{x} = 3.90$, median = 3.81, s = 1.32

4.79

Bone Loss	
Mean	35.01
Standard Error	0.69
Median	36
Mode	38
Standard Deviation	7.68
Sample Variance	59.04
Kurtosis	0.08
Skewness	-0.19
Range	38
Minimum	15
Maximum	53
Sum	4376
Count	125

a $\bar{x} = 35.0$, median = 36

b s = 7.68

c Half of the bone density losses lie below 36. At least 75% of the numbers lie between 19.64 and 50.36, at least 88.9% of the numbers lie between 11.96 and 58.04.

4.80

Coffees	
Mean	29913
Standard Error	1722
Median	30660
Mode	#N/A
Standard Deviation	12174
Sample Variance	148213791
Kurtosis	0.12
Skewness	0.22
Range	59082
Minimum	3647
Maximum	62729
Sum	1495639
Count	50

a $\bar{x}$ = 29,913, median = 30,660

b s^2 = 148,213,791; s = 12,174

c

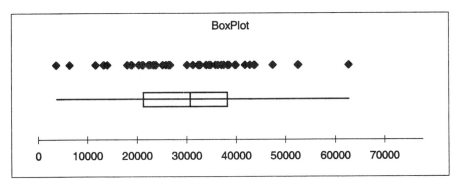

d The number of coffees sold varies considerably.

4.81

	Bone Loss	Age
Bone Loss	1	
Age	0.5742	1

r = .5742; there is a moderately strong linear relations ship between age and bone density loss.

4.82a

	Temperature	Coffees
Temperature	260	
Coffees	-144003	145249515

cov(x,y) = -144,003(50/49) = -146,942

	Temperature	Coffees
Temperature	1	
Coffees	-0.7409	1

r = -.7409

b $\hat{y} = 49,337 - 554x$

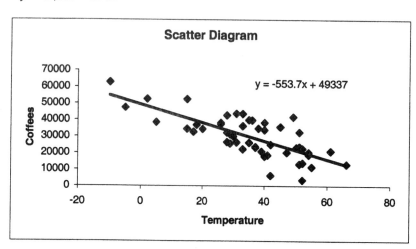

c There is a moderately strong negative linear relationship. For each additional degree of temperature the number of coffees sold decreases on average by 554 cups.

d In this exercise we determined that the number of cups of coffee sold is related to temperature, which may explain the variability in coffee sales. .

4.83a mean, median, and standard deviation

b

Total Score	
Mean	93.90
Standard Error	0.77
Median	94
Mode	94
Standard Deviation	7.72
Sample Variance	59.55
Kurtosis	0.20
Skewness	0.24
Range	39
Minimum	76
Maximum	115
Sum	9390
Count	100

$\bar{x} = 93.9$, s = 7.717

c We hope Chris is better at statistics than he is golf.

4.84

Internet	
Mean	26.32
Standard Error	0.60
Median	26
Mode	21
Standard Deviation	9.41
Sample Variance	88.57
Kurtosis	-0.071
Skewness	0.15
Range	52
Minimum	2
Maximum	54
Sum	6579
Count	250

a $\bar{x} = 26.32$ and median = 26

b $s^2 = 88.57$, s = 9.41

c

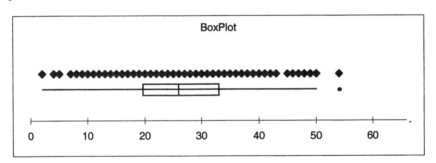

d The times are positively skewed. Half the times are above 26 hours.

4.85

	Total Score	Putts
Total Score	1	
Putts	0.8956	1

There is a strong positive linear relationship between total score and number of putts.

4.86a

	Education	Internet
Education	3.67	
Internet	11.55	88.22

cov(x,y) = 11.55(250/249) = 11.60

77

	Education	Internet
Education	1	
Internet	0.6418	1

b

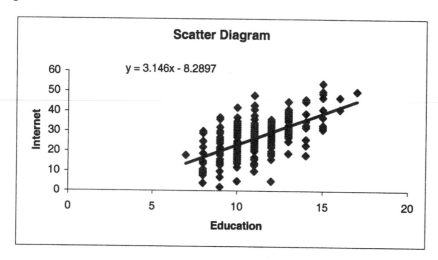

c There is a moderately strong positive linear relationship between Internet use and education. For each additional year of education Internet use increases on average by 3.15 hours per month.

d This exercise helps explain the variation in Internet use.

4.87

Corn	
Mean	150.77
Standard Error	1.61
Median	150.5
Mode	154
Standard Deviation	19.76
Sample Variance	390.38
Kurtosis	-0.13
Skewness	0.08
Range	107
Minimum	101
Maximum	208
Sum	22616
Count	150

$\bar{x} = 150.77$, median = 150.5, and s = 19.76. The average crop yield is 150.77 and there is a great deal of variation from one plot to another.

4.88a

	Corn	Rainfall
Corn	387.78	
Rainfall	1118.57	8738.66

cov(x,y) = 1118.575(150/149) = 1126.07

	Corn	Rainfall
Corn	1	
Rainfall	0.6076	1

b

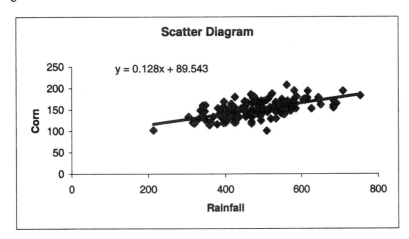

c There is a moderately strong positive linear relationship between yield and rainfall. For each additional inch of rainfall yield increases on average by .13 bushels.

d In this exercise we determined that yield is related to rainfall, which helps explain the variability in corn yield.

4.89a

	Corn	Fertilizer
Corn	387.78	
Fertilizer	333.39	1849.79

cov(x,y) = 333.39(150/149) = 335.62

	Corn	Fertilizer
Corn	1	
Fertilizer	0.3936	1

r = .3936

b

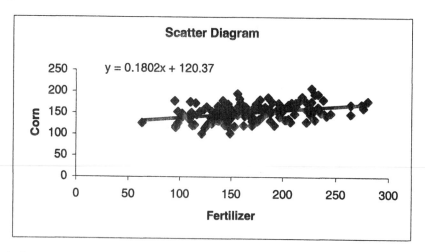

b $\hat{y} = 120.37 + .18$ Fertilizer

c There is a relatively weak positive linear relationship.

d Some of the variation in crop yields is explained by the variation in fertilizer.

4.90a, b, and c

Vocabulary	
Mean	226.49
Standard Error	3.11
Median	223
Mode	215
Standard Deviation	43.99
Sample Variance	1934.8
Kurtosis	-0.27
Skewness	0.089
Range	240
Minimum	114
Maximum	354
Sum	45297
Count	200
Largest(50)	259
Smallest(50)	193

a The mean vocabulary is 226.49 words. The median is 223, which tells us that half the children had vocabularies greater than 223 words and half had less.

b The variance is 1934.8 and the standard deviation is 43.99. Both indicate a great deal of variation between children.

c The quartiles are 193, 223, and 259.

4.91a

	Temperature	Winning times
Temperature	1	
Winning time:	0.7242	1

b There is a moderately strong positive linear relationship between the winning times of men and temperatures.

c They appear to provide the same type of information.

4.92a

	Temperature	Winning times
Temperature	1	
Winning times	0.5984	1

b There is a moderately strong positive linear relationship between the winning times of women and temperatures.

c They appear to provide the same type of information.

4.93

	Education	Income
Education	1	
Income	0.6593	1

r = .6593

	Coefficients
Intercept	23.63
Education	4.14

$\hat{y} = 23.63 + 4.14x$

4.94a

Debts	
Mean	12067
Standard Error	179.9
Median	12047
Mode	11621
Standard Deviation	2632
Sample Variance	6929745
Kurtosis	-0.41
Skewness	-0.21
Range	12499
Minimum	4626
Maximum	17125
Sum	2582254
Count	214

b The mean debt is $12,067. Half the sample incurred debts below $12,047 and half incurred debts above. The mode is $11,621.

Case 4.1a

Ages

	Means	Medians	Standard deviations
BMW	45.3	45	4.4
Cadillac	61.0	61	3.7
Lexus	50.4	50	6.1
Lincoln	59.7	60	4.7
Mercedes Benz	52.3	52	7.7

Incomes

	Means	Medians	Standard deviations
BMW	140,544	139,908	33,864
Cadillac	107,832	106,997	15,398
Lexus	154,404	155,846	30,525
Lincoln	111,199	110,488	21,173
Mercedes Benz	184,215	186,070	47,554

Education

	Means	Medians	Standard deviations
BMW	15.8	16	1.9
Cadillac	12.8	13	1.6
Lexus	15.8	16	2.5
Lincoln	13.1	13	1.6
Mercedes Benz	17.3	17	1.8

b

Ages

BMW

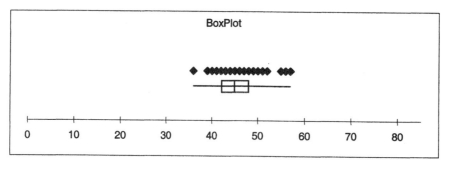

Cadillac

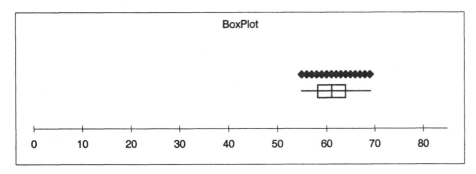

Lexus

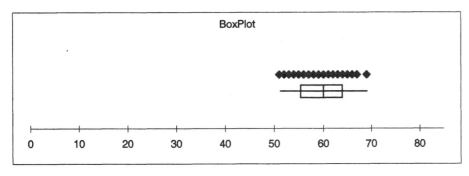

Lincoln

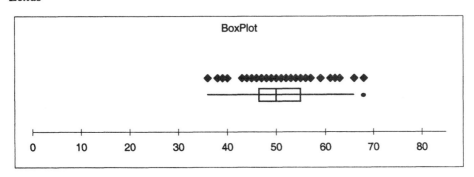

Mercedes

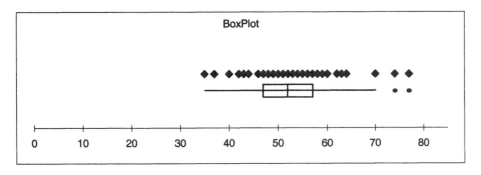

Income

BMW

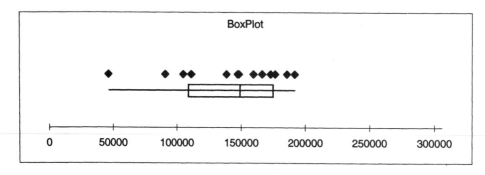

Cadillac

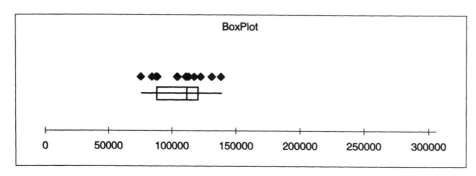

Lexus

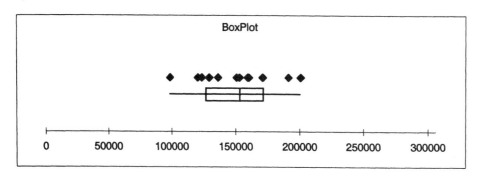

Lincoln

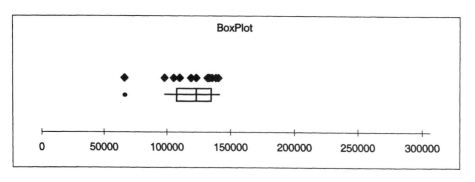

Mercedes

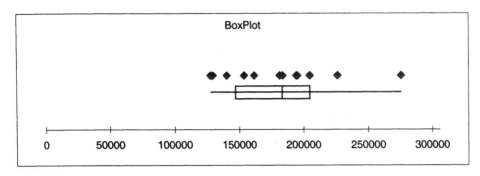

Education

BMW

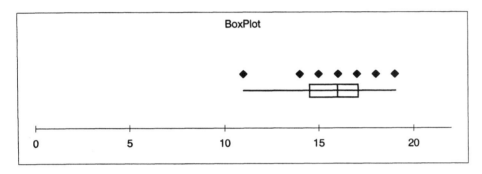

Cadillac

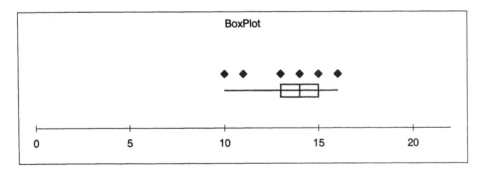

Lexus

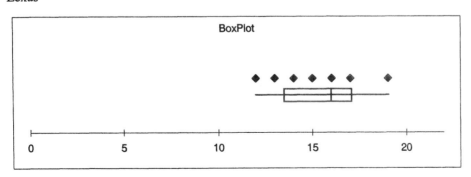

Lincoln

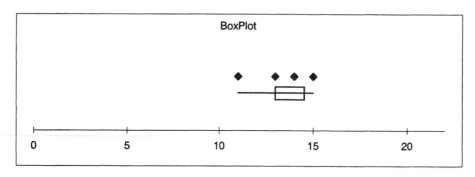

Mercedes

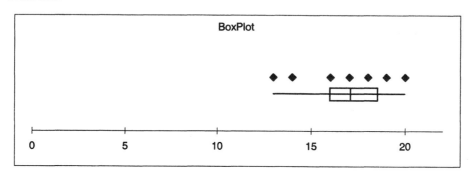

The statistics and box plots paint a clear picture. Cadillac owners are older, earn less income, and have less education than the owners of the other luxury cars.

Chapter 5

5.1 In an observational study, there is no attempt to control factors that might influence the variable of interest. In an experimental study, a factor (such as regular use of a fitness center) is controlled by randomly selecting who is exposed to that factor, thereby reducing the influence of other factors on the variable of interest.

5.2a The study is observational. The statistics practitioner did not randomly assign stores to buy cans or bottles.

b Randomly assign some stores to receive only cans and others to receive only bottles.

5.3 Randomly sample smokers and nonsmokers and compute the proportion of each group that has lung cancer.

b The study is observational. Experimental data would require the statistics practitioner to randomly assign some people to smoke and others not to smoke.

5.4a A survey can be conducted by means of a personal interview, a telephone interview, or a self-administered questionnaire.

b A personal interview has a high response rate relative to other survey methods, but is expensive because of the need to hire well-trained interviewers and possibly pay travel-related costs if the survey is conducted over a large geographical area. A personal interview also will likely result in fewer incorrect responses that arise when respondents misunderstand some questions. A telephone interview is less expensive, but will likely result in a lower response rate. A self-administered questionnaire is least expensive, but suffers from lower response rates and accuracy than interviews.

5.5 Five important points to consider when designing a questionnaire are as follows:

(1) The questionnaire should be short.

(2) Questions should be short, clearly worded, and unambiguous.

(3) Consider using dichotomous or multiple-choice questions, but take care that respondents needn't make unspecified assumptions before answering the questions.

(4) Avoid using leading questions.

(5) When preparing the questions, think about how you intend to tabulate and analyze the responses.

5.6a The sampled population will exclude those who avoid large department stores in favor or smaller shops, as well as those who consider their time too valuable to spend participating in a survey. The sampled population will therefore differ from the target population of all customers who regularly shop at the mall.

b The sampled population will contain a disproportionate number of thick books, because of the manner in which the sample is selected.

c The sampled population consists of those eligible voters who are at home in the afternoon, thereby excluding most of those with full-time jobs (or at school).

5.7a The *Literary Digest* was a popular magazine in the 1920s and 1930s which had correctly predicted the outcome of many presidential elections. To help predict the outcome of the 1936 presidential election, the *Literary Digest* mailed sample ballots to 10 million prospective voters. Based on the results of the ballots returned, the magazine predicted that the Republican candidate, Alfred Landon, would defeat the Democratic incumbent, Franklin D. Roosevelt, by a 3 to 2 margin. In fact, Roosevelt won a landslide victory, capturing 62% of the votes.

b The main reason for the poll being so wrong was *nonresponse bias* resulting from a self-selected sample, causing the sample to be unrepresentative of the target population. (Only 2.3 million ballots were returned.) The second reason was *selection bias*, resulting from poor sampling design, causing the sampled population and the target population to differ. Most of those to whom a ballot was sent were selected from the *Literary Digest's* subscription list and from telephone directories. These people tended to be wealthier than average and tended to vote Republican.

5.8a A self-selected sample is a sample formed primarily on the basis of voluntary inclusion, with little control by the designer of the survey.

b Choose any recent radio or television poll based on responses of listeners who phone in on a volunteer basis.

c Self-selected samples are usually biased, because those who participate are more interested in the issue than those who don't, and therefore probably have a different opinion.

5.9 We should ignore the results because this is an example of a self-selected sample.

5.10 No, because the sampled population consists of the responses about the professor's course. We cannot make draw inferences about all courses.

5.11 We used Excel to generate 40 three-digit random numbers. Because we will ignore all randomly generated numbers over 800, we can expect to ignore about 20% (or about 8 to 10) of the randomly generated numbers. We will also ignore any duplications. We therefore chose to generate 40 three-digit random numbers, and will use the first 25 unique random numbers less than 801 to select our sample. The 40 numbers generated are shown below, with a stroke through those to be ignored.

6	357	456	449	~~862~~	154	55	412	475	430
~~999~~	~~912~~	60	207	717	651	10	294	327	165
576	~~871~~	~~990~~	354	390	540	~~893~~	181	496	~~870~~
738	~~820~~	32	~~963~~	160	32	231	86	~~970~~	46

5.12 We used Excel to generate 30 six-digit random numbers. Because we will ignore any duplicate numbers generated, we generated 30 six-digit random numbers and will use the first 20 unique random numbers to select our sample. The 30 numbers generated are shown below.

169,470	744,530	22,554	918,730	320,262	503,129
318,858	698,203	822,383	938,262	800,806	56,643
836,116	123,936	80,539	154,211	391,278	940,154
110,630	856,380	222,145	692,313	949,828	561,511
909,269	811,274	288,553	749,627	858,944	39,308

5.13 The operations manager can select stratified random samples where the strata are the four departments. Simple random sampling can be conducted in each department.

5.14 Use cluster sampling, letting each city block represent a cluster.

5.17a Sampling error refers to an inaccuracy in a statement about a population that arises because the statement is based only on sample data. We expect this type of error to occur because we are making a statement based on incomplete information. Nonsampling error refers to mistakes made in the acquisition of data or due to the sample observations being selected improperly.
b Nonsampling error is more serious because, unlike sampling error, it cannot be diminished by taking a larger sample.

5.18 Three types of nonsampling errors:

 (1) Error due to incorrect responses

 (2)Nonresponse error, which refers to error introduced when responses are not obtained from some members of the sample. This may result in the sample being unrepresentative of the target population.

 (3)Error due to selection bias, which arises when the sampling plan is such that some members of the target population cannot possibly be selected for inclusion in the sample.

5.19 Yes. A census will likely contain significantly more nonsampling errors than a carefully conducted sample survey.

Chapter 6

6.1 a Relative frequency approach

b If the conditions today repeat themselves an infinite number of days rain will fall on 10% of the next days.

6.2 a Subjective approach

b If all the teams in major league baseball have exactly the same players the New York Yankees will win 25% of all World Series.

6.3 a {a is correct, b is correct, c is correct, d is correct, e is correct}

b P(a is correct) = P(b is correct) = P(c is correct) = P(d is correct) = P(e is correct) = .2

c Classical approach

d In the long run all answers are equally likely to be correct.

6.4 a Subjective approach

b The Dow Jones Industrial Index will increase on 60% of the days if economic conditions remain unchanged.

6.5 a P(even number) = P(2) + P(4) + P(6) = 1/6 + 1/6 + 1/6 = 3/6 = 1/2

b P(number less than or equal to 4) = P(1) + P(2) + P(3) + P(4) = 1/6 + 1/6 + 1/6 +1/6 = 4/6 = 2/3

c P(number greater than or equal to 5) = P(5) + P(6) = 1/6 + 1/6 = 2/6 = 1/3

6.6 {Adams wins. Brown wins, Collins wins, Dalton wins}

6.7a P(Adams loses) = P(Brown wins) + P(Collins wins) + P(Dalton wins) = .09 + .27 + .22 = .58

b P(either Brown or Dalton wins) = P(Brown wins) + P(Dalton wins) = .09 + .22 = .31

c P(either Adams, Brown, or Collins wins) = P(Adams wins) + P(Brown wins) + P(Collins wins)

   = .42 + .09 + .27 = .78

6.8 a {0, 1, 2, 3, 4, 5}

b {4, 5}

c P(5) = .10

d P(2, 3, or 4) = P(2) + P(3) + P(4) = .26 + .21 + .18 = .65

e P(6) = 0

6.9 {Contractor 1 wins, Contractor 2 wins, Contractor 3 wins}

6.10 P(Contractor 1 wins) = 2/6, P(Contractor 2 wins) = 3/6, P(Contractor 3 wins) = 1/6

6.11 a {Shopper pays cash, shopper pays by credit card, shopper pays by debit card}

b P(Shopper pays cash) = .30, P(Shopper pays by credit card) = .60, P(Shopper pays by debit card) = .10

c Relative frequency approach

6.12 a P(shopper does not use credit card) = P(shopper pays cash) + P(shopper pays by debit card)

   = .30 + .10 = .40

b P(shopper pays cash or uses a credit card) = P(shopper pays cash) + P(shopper pays by credit card)

   = .30 + .60 = .90

6.13 {single, divorced, widowed}

6.14 a P(single) = .15, P(married) = .50, P(divorced) = .25, P(widowed) = .10

b Relative frequency approach

6.15 a P(single) = .15

b P(adult is not divorced) = P(single) + P(married) + P(widowed) = .15+ .50 + .10 = .75

c P(adult is either widowed or divorced) = P(divorced) + P(widowed) = .25 + .10 = .35

6.16 $P(A_1) = .1 + .2 = .3, P(A_2) = .3 + .1 = .4, P(A_3) = .2 + .1 = .3.$

$P(B_1) = .1 + .3 + .2 = .6, P(B_2) = .2 + .1 + .1 = .4.$

6.17 $P(A_1) = .4 + .2 = .6, P(A_2) = .3 + .1 = .4. P(B_1) = .4 + .3 = .7, P(B_2) = .2 + .1 = .3.$

6.18 a $P(A_1 \mid B_1) = \dfrac{P(A_1 \text{ and } B_1)}{P(B_1)} = \dfrac{.4}{.7} = .5714$

b $P(A_2 \mid B_1) = \dfrac{P(A \text{ and } B_1)}{P(B_1)} = \dfrac{3}{.7} = .4286$

c Yes. It is not a coincidence. Given B_1 the events A_1 and A_2 constitute the entire sample space.

6.19 a $P(A_1 \mid B_2) = \dfrac{P(A_1 \text{ and } B_2)}{P(B_2)} = \dfrac{.2}{.3} = .6667$

b $P(B_2 \mid A_1) = \dfrac{P(A_1 \text{ and } B_2)}{P(A_1)} = \dfrac{.2}{.6} = .3333$

c One of the conditional probabilities would be greater than 1, which is not possible.

6.20 The events are not independent because $P(A_1 \mid B_2) \neq P(A_1)$.

6.21 a $P(A_1 \text{ or } B_1) = P(A_1) + P(B_1) - P(A_1 \text{ and } B_1) = .6 + .7 - .4 = .9$

b $P(A_1 \text{ or } B_2) = P(A_1) + P(B_2) - P(A_1 \text{ and } B_2) = .6 + .3 - .2 = .7$

c $P(A_1 \text{ or } A_2) = P(A_1) + P(A_2) = .6 + .4 = 1$

6.22 $P(A_1 \mid B_1) = \dfrac{P(A_1 \text{ and } B_1)}{P(B_1)} = \dfrac{.20}{.20 + .60} = .25$; $P(A_1) = .20 + .05 = .25$; the events are

independent.

6.23 $P(A_1 \mid B_1) = \dfrac{P(A_1 \text{ and } B_1)}{P(B_1)} = \dfrac{.20}{.20 + .15} = .5714$; $P(A_1) = .20 + .60 = .80$; the events are

dependent.

6.24 $P(A_1) = .15 + .25 = .40$, $P(A_2) = .20 + .25 = .45$, $P(A_3) = .10 + .05 = .15$.

$P(B_1) = .15 + 20 + .10 = .45$, $P(B_2) = .25 + .25 + .05 = .55$.

6.25 a $P(A_2 \mid B_2) = \dfrac{P(A_2 \text{ and } B_2)}{P(B_2)} = \dfrac{.25}{.55} = .4545$.

b $P(B_2 \mid A_2) = \dfrac{P(A_2 \text{ and } B_2)}{P(A_2)} = \dfrac{.25}{.45} = .5556$

c $P(B_1 \mid A_2) = \dfrac{P(A_2 \text{ and } B_1)}{P(A_2)} = \dfrac{.20}{.45} = .4444$

6.26 a $P(A_1 \text{ or } A_2) = P(A_1) + P(A_2) = .40 + .45 = .85$.

b $P(A_2 \text{ or } B_2) = P(A_2) + P(B_2) - P(A_2 \text{ and } B_2) = .45 + .55 - .25 = .75$

c $P(A_3 \text{ or } B_1) = P(A_3) + P(B_1) - P(A_3 \text{ and } B_1) = .15 + .45 - .10 = .50$

6.27 a $P(\text{promoted} \mid \text{female}) = \dfrac{P(\text{promoted and female})}{P(\text{female})} = \dfrac{.03}{.03 + .12} = .20$

b $P(\text{promoted} \mid \text{male}) = \dfrac{P(\text{promoted and male})}{P(\text{male})} = \dfrac{.17}{.17 + .68} = .20$

c No, because promotion and gender are independent events.

6.28 a $P(\text{debit card}) = .04 + .18 + .14 = .36$

b $P(\text{over \$100} \mid \text{credit card}) = \dfrac{P(\text{credit card and over \$100}}{P(\text{credit card})} = \dfrac{.23}{.03 + .21 + .23} = .4894$

c $P(\text{credit card or debit card}) = P(\text{credit card}) + P(\text{debit card}) = .47 + .36 = .83$

6.29 a $P(\text{voted}) = .25 + .18 = .43$

b $P(\text{voted} \mid \text{female}) = \dfrac{P(\textit{voted and female})}{P(\textit{female})} = \dfrac{.25}{.25 + .33} = .4310, P(\text{voted}) = .43,$ Subject to rounding

the events are independent.

6.30 a $P(\text{He is a smoker}) = .12 + .19 = .31$

b $P(\text{He does not have lung disease}) = .19 + .66 = .85$

c $P(\text{He has lung disease} \mid \text{he is a smoker}) = \dfrac{P(\text{he has lung disease and he is a smo ker})}{P(\text{he is a smo ker})} = \dfrac{.12}{.31} = .3871$

d $P(\text{He has lung disease} \mid \text{he does not smoke}) =$

$\dfrac{P(\text{he has lung disease and he does not smoke})}{P(\text{he does not smoke})} = \dfrac{.03}{.69} = .0435$

6.31 The events are dependent because P(he has lung disease) = .15, P(he has lung disease | he is a smoker) = .3871

6.32 a $P(\text{manual} \mid \text{math-stats}) = .23/(.23 + .36) = .23/.59 = .3898$

b $P(\text{computer}) = .36 + .30 = .66$

c No, because P(manual) = .23 + .11 = .34, which is not equal to P(manual | math-stats).

6.33 a P(customer says that they will return and rate the restaurant's food as Good) =.35

b P(customer rates the restaurant's food as good| says will return)

$= .35/(.02 + .08 + .35 + .20) = .35/.65 = .538$

c P(Customer says will return| customer rates the restaurant's food as good)

$= .35/(.35 + .14) = .35/.49 = .714$

d (a) is the joint probability and (b) and (c) are conditional probabilities

6.34 a $P(\text{ulcer}) = .01 + .03 + .03 + .04 = .11$

b $P(\text{ulcer} \mid \text{none}) = .01/(.01 + .22) = .01/.23 = .0435$

c $P(\text{none} \mid \text{ulcer}) = .01/(.01 + .03 + .03 + .04) = .01/.11 = .0909$

d No, because P(ulcer) = .11 and P(ulcer | none) = .0435

6.35 a $P(\text{ask for instructions} \mid \text{male}) = .12/(.25 + .12 + .13) = .12/.50 = .24$

b $P(\text{consult a map}) = .25 + .14 = .39$

93

c No, because P(consult map | male) = .25/(.25 + .12 + .13) = .25/.50 = .50, which is not equal to P(consult map)

6.36 a P(remember) = .15 + .18 = .33
b P(remember | violent) = .15/(.15 + .35) = .15/.50 = .30
c Yes, the events are dependent.

6.37 a P(above average testosterone | murderer) = .27/(.27 + .21) = .563
b No, because P(above average testosterone) = .27 + .24 = .51, which is not equal to P(above average testosterone | murderer).

6.38 a P(uses a spreadsheet) = .298 + .209 = .507
b P(uses a spreadsheet | male) = .209/(.209 + .265) = .441
c b P(female | spreadsheet user) = .298/(.298 + .209) = .588

6.39 No, because P(worker uses a spreadsheet) ≠ P(worker uses a spreadsheet | male)

6.40 a P(provided by employer) = .166 + .195 + .230 = .591
b P(provided by employer | professional/technical) = .166/(.166 + .094) = .638
c Yes, because P(provided by employer) ≠ P(provided by employer | professional/technical)

6.41 a P(new | overdue) = .06/(.06 + .52) = .103
b P(overdue | new) = .06/(.06 + .13) = .316
c Yes, because P(new) = .19 ≠ P(new | overdue)

6.42 a P(under 20) = .2307 + .0993 + .5009 = .8309
b P(retail) = .5009 + .0876 + .0113 = .5998
c P(20 to 99 | construction) = .0189/(.2307 + .0189 + .0019) = .0751

6.43 a P(fully repaid) = .19 + .64 = .83
b P(fully repaid | under 400) = .19/(.19 + .13) = .594
c P(fully repaid | 400 or more) = .64/(.64 + .04) = .941
d No, because P(fully repaid) ≠ P(fully repaid | under 400)

6.44 P(purchase | see ad) = .18/(.18 + .42) = .30; P(purchase | do not see ad) = .12/(.12 + .28) = .30; the ads are not effective.

6.45 a P(unemployed | high school graduate) = .0128/(.3108 + .0128) = .0396

b P(employed) = .0975 + .3108 + .1785 + .0849 + .1959 + .0975 = .9651

c P(advanced degree | unemployed) = .0015/(.0080 + .0128 + .0062 + .0023 + .0041 + .0015) = .0430

d P(not a high school graduate) = .0975 + .0080 = .1055

6.46 a P(bachelor's degree | west) = .0418/(.0359 + .0608 + .0456 + .0181 + .0418 + .0180) = .1898

b P(northwest | high school graduate) = .0711/(.0711 + .0843 + .1174 + .0608) = .2131

c P(south) = .0683 + .1174 + .0605 + .0248 + .0559 + .0269 = .3538

d No because P(bachelor's degree) = .0350 + .0368 + .0559 + .0418 = .1695 ≠ P(bachelor's degree | west)

6.47

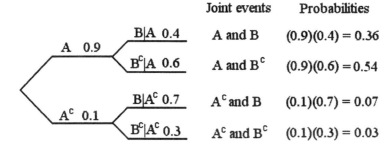

6.48

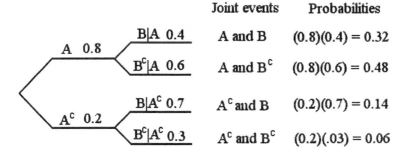

6.49

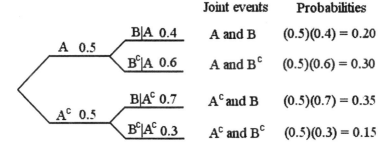

6.50

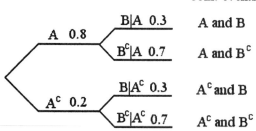

Joint events	Probabilities
A and B	(0.8)(0.3) = 0.24
A and B^c	(0.8)(0.7) = 0.56
A^c and B	(0.2)(.03) = 0.06
A^c and B^c	(0.2)(0.7) = 0.14

6.51

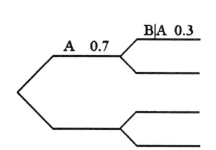

Joint events	Probabilities
A and B	(0.7)(0.3) = 0.21

6.52

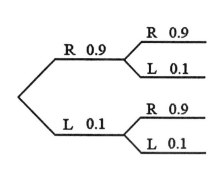

Joint events	Probabilities
R and R	(0.9)(0.9) = 0.81
R and L	(0.9)(0.1) = 0.09
L and R	(0.1)(0.9) = 0.09
L and L	(0.1)(0.1) = 0.01

a P(R and R) = .81

b P(L and L) = .01

c P(R and L) + P(L and R) = .09 + .09 = .18

d P(Rand L) + P(L and R) + P(R and R) = .09 + .09 + .81 = .99

6.53 a & b

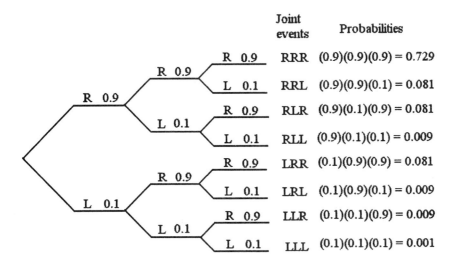

			Joint events	Probabilities
		R 0.9	RRR	(0.9)(0.9)(0.9) = 0.729
	R 0.9	L 0.1	RRL	(0.9)(0.9)(0.1) = 0.081
R 0.9		R 0.9	RLR	(0.9)(0.1)(0.9) = 0.081
	L 0.1	L 0.1	RLL	(0.9)(0.1)(0.1) = 0.009
	R 0.9	R 0.9	LRR	(0.1)(0.9)(0.9) = 0.081
		L 0.1	LRL	(0.1)(0.9)(0.1) = 0.009
L 0.1	L 0.1	R 0.9	LLR	(0.1)(0.1)(0.9) = 0.009
		L 0.1	LLL	(0.1)(0.1)(0.1) = 0.001

c   0 right-handers   1

      1 right-hander   3

      2 right-handers   3

      3 right-handers   1

d P(0 right-handers) = .001

P(1 right-hander) = 3(.009) = .027

P(2 right-handers) = 3(.081) = .243

P(3 right-handers) = .729

6.54a

		Joint events	Probabilities
	R|R 89/99	R R	(90/100)(89/99) = 0.8091
R 90/100	L|R 10/99	R L	(90/100)(10/99) = 0.0909
	R|L 90/99	L R	(10/100)(90/99) = 0.0909
L 10/100	L|L 9/99	L L	(10/100)(9/99) = 0.0091

b P(RR) = .8091

c P(LL) = .0091

d P(RL) + P(LR) = .0909 + .0909 = .1818

e P(RL) + P(LR) + P(RR) = .0909 + .0909 + .8091 = .9909

6.55a

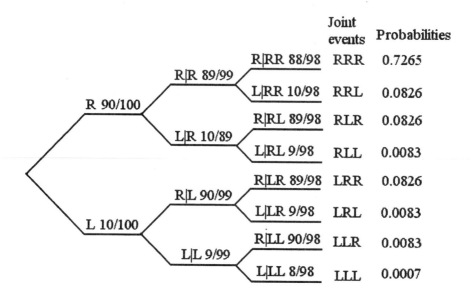

			Joint events	Probabilities
		R|RR 88/98	RRR	0.7265
	R|R 89/99	L|RR 10/98	RRL	0.0826
R 90/100		R|RL 89/98	RLR	0.0826
	L|R 10/89	L|RL 9/98	RLL	0.0083
		R|LR 89/98	LRR	0.0826
	R|L 90/99	L|LR 9/98	LRL	0.0083
L 10/100		R|LL 90/98	LLR	0.0083
	L|L 9/99	L|LL 8/98	LLL	0.0007

P(0 right-handers) = (10/100)(9/99)(8/98) = .0007

P(1 right-hander) = 3(90/100)(10/99)(9/98) = .0249

P)2 right-handers) = 3(90/100)(89/99)(10/98) = .2478

P(3 right-handers) = (90/100)(89/99)(88/98)= .7265

6.56

First contract	Second contract	Joint events	Probabilities
	win|win 0.7	win and win	(0.4)(0.7) = 0.28
win 0.4	lose|win 0.3	win and lose	(0.4)(0.3) = 0.12
lose 0.6	win|lose 0.5	lose and win	(0.6)(0.5) = 0.3
	lose|lose 0.5	lose and lose	(0.6)(0.5) = 0.3

a P(win both) = .28

b P(lose both) = .30

c P(win only one) = .12 + .30 = .42

6.57

No Ans.   0.2
or Busy

Joint events   Probabilities

0.2

Answer 0.8

Sale 0.05
No Sale 0.95

Answer
and Sale

$(0.8)(0.05) = 0.04$

P(sale) = .04

6.58

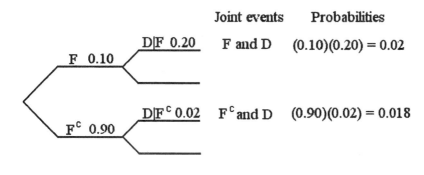

Joint events   Probabilities

F   0.10

D|F 0.20

F and D $(0.10)(0.20) = 0.02$

F^c 0.90

D|F^c 0.02

F^c and D $(0.90)(0.02) = 0.018$

P(D) = .02 + .018 = .038

6.59

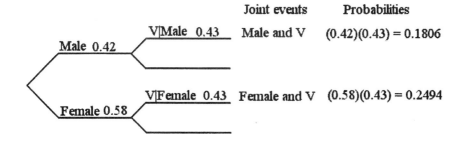

Joint events   Probabilities

Male 0.42

V|Male 0.43

Male and V $(0.42)(0.43) = 0.1806$

Female 0.58

V|Female 0.43

Female and V $(0.58)(0.43) = 0.2494$

a P(vote in last election and male) = .1806

b P(vote in last election and female) = .2494

6.60

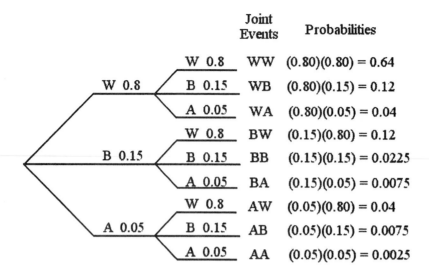

	Joint Events	Probabilities
WW	(0.80)(0.80) = 0.64
WB	(0.80)(0.15) = 0.12
WA	(0.80)(0.05) = 0.04
BW	(0.15)(0.80) = 0.12
BB	(0.15)(0.15) = 0.0225
BA	(0.15)(0.05) = 0.0075
AW	(0.05)(0.80) = 0.04
AB	(0.05)(0.15) = 0.0075
AA	(0.05)(0.05) = 0.0025

Diversity index = .12 + .04 + .12 + .0075 + .04 + .0075 = .335

6.61

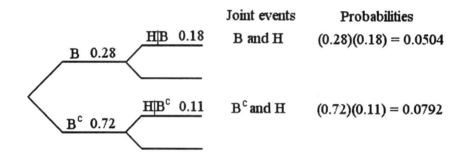

	Joint events	Probabilities
	B and H	(0.28)(0.18) = 0.0504
	B^c and H	(0.72)(0.11) = 0.0792

P(heart attack) = .0504 + .0792 = .1296

6.62

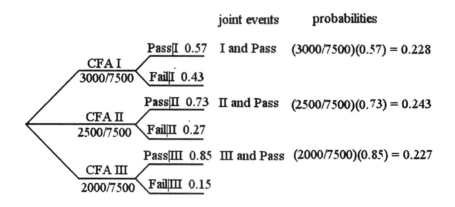

	joint events	probabilities
	I and Pass	(3000/7500)(0.57) = 0.228
	II and Pass	(2500/7500)(0.73) = 0.243
	III and Pass	(2000/7500)(0.85) = 0.227

P(pass) = .228 + .243 + .227 = .698

6.63

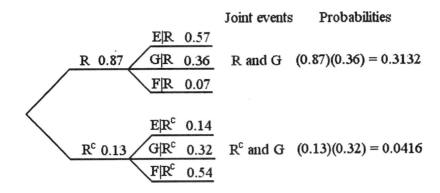

Joint events   Probabilities

E|R 0.57

R 0.87   G|R 0.36   R and G   (0.87)(0.36) = 0.3132

F|R 0.07

E|R^c 0.14

R^c 0.13   G|R^c 0.32   R^c and G   (0.13)(0.32) = 0.0416

F|R^c 0.54

P(good) = .3132 + .0416 = .3548

6.64

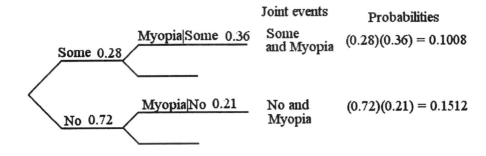

Joint events   Probabilities

Myopia|Some 0.36   Some   (0.28)(0.36) = 0.1008
Some 0.28   and Myopia

Myopia|No 0.21   No and   (0.72)(0.21) = 0.1512
No 0.72   Myopia

P(myopic) = .1008 + .1512 = .2520

6.65

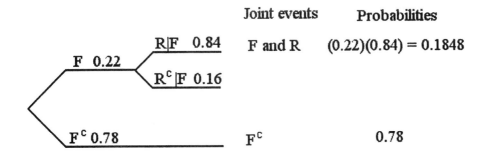

Joint events   Probabilities

R|F 0.84   F and R   (0.22)(0.84) = 0.1848
F 0.22

R^c|F 0.16

F^c 0.78   F^c 0.78

P(does not have to be discarded) = .1848 + .78 = .9648

6.66 Let A = mutual fund outperforms the market in the first year

B = mutual outperforms the market in the second year

$P(A \text{ and } B) = P(A)P(B \mid A) = (.15)(.22) = .033$

6.67 Let A = DJIA increase and B = NASDAQ increase

$P(A) = .60$ and $P(B \mid A) = .77$

$P(A \text{ and } B) = P(A)P(B \mid A) = (.60)(.77) = .462$

6.68 Define the events:

M: The main control will fail.

B_1: The first backup will fail.

B_2: The second backup will fail

The probability that the plane will crash is

$P(M \text{ and } B_1 \text{ and } B_2) = [P(M)][P(B_1)][P(B_2)]$

$= (.0001)(.01)(.01)$

$= .00000001$

We have assumed that the 3 systems will fail independently of one another.

6.69 P(wireless Web user uses it primarily for e-mail) = .69

P(3 wireless Web users use it primarily for e-mail) = (.69)(.69)(.69) = .3285

6.70

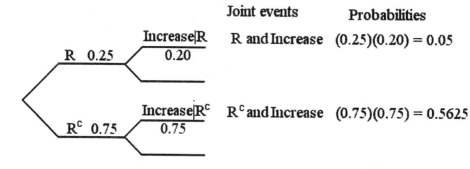

		Joint events	Probabilities
	Increase|R	R and Increase	(0.25)(0.20) = 0.05
R 0.25	0.20		
	Increase|R^c	R^c and Increase	(0.75)(0.75) = 0.5625
R^c 0.75	0.75		

P(Increase) = .05 + .5625 = .6125

6.71 $P(A \text{ and } B) = .36$, $P(B) = .36 + .07 = .43$

$P(B \mid A) = P(A \text{ and } B)/P(B) = .36/.43 = .837$

6.72 $P(A \text{ and } B) = .32$, $P(A^C \text{ and } B) = .14$, $P(B) = .46$, $P(B^C) = .54$

a $P(A \mid B) = P(A \text{ and } B)/P(B) = .32/.46 = .696$

b $P(A^C \mid B) = P(A^C \text{ and } B)/P(B) = .14/.46 = .304$

102

c $P(A \text{ and } B^C) = .48$; $P(A \mid B^C) = P(A \text{ and } B^C)/ P(B^C) = .48/.54 = .889$

d $P(A^C \text{ and } B^C) = .06$; $P(A^C \mid B^C) = P(A^C \text{ and } B^C)/ P(B^C) = .06/.54 = .111$

6.73a $P(PT) = P(D \text{ and } PT) + P(D^C \text{ and } PT) = (.04)(.98) + (.96)(.01) = .0392 + .0096 = .0488$

$P(D \mid PT) = .0392/.0488 = .8033$

b $P(PT) = P(D \text{ and } PT) + P(D^C \text{ and } PT) = (.04)(.70) + (.96)(.15) = .0280 + .1440 = .1720$

$P(D \mid PT) = .0280/.1720 = .1628$

6.74 $P(F \mid D) = P(F \text{ and } D)/P(D) = .020/.038 = .526$

6.75 Define events: A = crash with fatality, B = BAC is greater than .09)

$P(A) = .01$, $P(B \mid A) = .084$, $P(B) = .12$

$P(A \text{ and } B) = (.01)(.084) = .00084$

$P(A \mid B) = P(A \text{ and } B)/P(B) = .00084/.12 = .007$

6.76 $P(CFA\ I \mid passed) = P(CFA\ I \text{ and } passed)/P(Passed) = .228/.698 = .327$

6.77 Define events: A = heart attack, B = periodontal disease

$P(A) = .10$, $P(B \mid A) = .85$, $P(B \mid A^C) = .29$

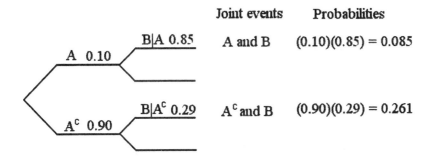

	Joint events	Probabilities
B|A 0.85	A and B	(0.10)(0.85) = 0.085
B|A^c 0.29	A^c and B	(0.90)(0.29) = 0.261

$P(B) = .085 + .261 = .346$

$P(A \mid B) = P(A \text{ and } B)/P(B) = .085/.346 = .246$

6.78 $P(A) = .40$, $P(B \mid A) = .85$, $P(B \mid A^C) = .29$

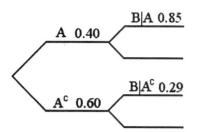

	Joint events	Probabilities
B|A 0.85	A and B	(0.40)(0.85) = 0.34
B|A^c 0.29	A^c and B	(0.60)(0.29) = 0.174

P(B) = .34 + .174 = .514

P(A | B) = P(A and B)/P(B) = .34/.514 = .661

6.79

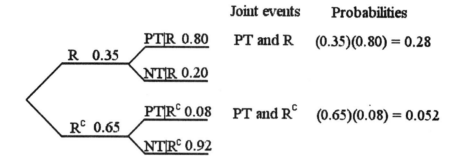

	Joint events	Probabilities
PT|R 0.80	PT and R	(0.35)(0.80) = 0.28
PT|R^c 0.08	PT and R^c	(0.65)(0.08) = 0.052

P(PT) = .28 + .052 = .332

P(R | PT) = P(R and PT) /P(R) = .28/.332 = .843

6.80 Define events: A = smoke, B_1 = did not finish high school, B_2 = high school graduate, B_3 = some college, no degree, B_4 = completed a degree

P(A | B_1) = .40, P(A | B_2) = .34, P(A | B_3) = .24, P(A | B_4) = .14

From Exercise 6.45: P(B_1) = .1055, P(B_2) = .3236, P(B_3) = .1847, P(B_4) = .3862

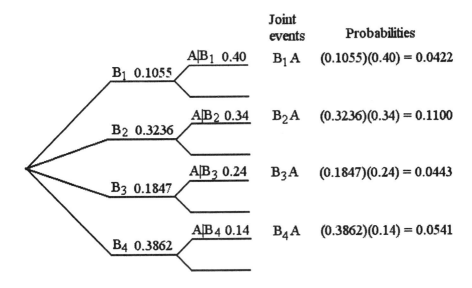

Joint events	Probabilities
$B_1 A$	$(0.1055)(0.40) = 0.0422$
$B_2 A$	$(0.3236)(0.34) = 0.1100$
$B_3 A$	$(0.1847)(0.24) = 0.0443$
$B_4 A$	$(0.3862)(0.14) = 0.0541$

$P(A) = .0422 + .1100 + .0443 + .0541 = .2506$

$P(B_4 | A) = .0541/.2506 = .2159$

6.81 Define events: A, B, C = airlines A, B, and C, D = on time

$P(A) = .50, P(B) = .30, P(C) = .20, P(D | A) = .80, P(D | B) = .65, P(D | C) = .40$

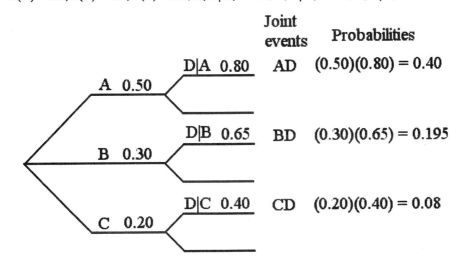

Joint events	Probabilities
AD	$(0.50)(0.80) = 0.40$
BD	$(0.30)(0.65) = 0.195$
CD	$(0.20)(0.40) = 0.08$

$P(D) = .40 + .195 + .08 = .675$

$P(A | D) = PA \text{ and } D)/P(D) = .40/.675 = .593$

6.82 Define events: A = win series, B = win first game

$P(A) = .60, P(B | A) = .70, P(B | A^C) = .25$

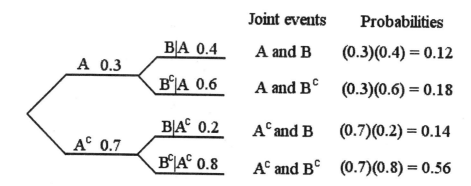

Joint events   Probabilities

B|A 0.7

A 0.6

B^c|A 0.3   A and B^c $(0.60)(0.30) = 0.18$

B|A^c 0.25

A^c 0.4

B^c|A^c 0.75   A^c and B^c $(0.40)(0.75) = 0.30$

$P(B^C) = .18 + .30 = .48$

$P(A \mid B^C) = P(A \text{ and } B^C)/P(B^C) = .18/.48 = .375$

6.83 a P(Marketing-A) $= .06 + .23 = .29$

b P(Marketing-A | Statistics-not A)

     = P(Marketing-A and Statistics-not A)/P(Statistics-not A)

     = .23/(.23 + .58) = .23/.81 = .2840

c No, the probabilities in (a) and (b) differ

6.84 Define events: A = win contract A and B = win contract B

Joint events   Probabilities

B|A 0.4   A and B $(0.3)(0.4) = 0.12$

A 0.3

B^c|A 0.6   A and B^c $(0.3)(0.6) = 0.18$

B|A^c 0.2   A^c and B $(0.7)(0.2) = 0.14$

A^c 0.7

B^c|A^c 0.8   A^c and B^c $(0.7)(0.8) = 0.56$

$P(B^{C)} = P(A \text{ and } B^C) + P(A^C \text{ and } B^C) = .18 + .56 = .74$

$P(A^C | B^C) = P(A^C \text{ and } B^C)/P(B^C) = .56/.74 = .757$

6.85 a P(Second) $= .05 + .14 = .19$

b P(Successful | −8 or less) = P(Successful and −8 or less)/P(−8 or less)

     = .15/(.15 + .14) = .15/.29 = .517

c No, because P(Successful) $= .66 + .15 = .81$, which is not equal to P(Successful | −8 or less) .

6.86 Define events: A = woman, B = drug is effective

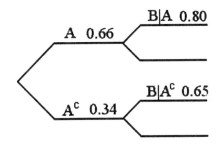

Joint events   Probabilities

B|A 0.80   A and B $(0.66)(0.80) = 0.528$

A 0.66

B|A^c 0.65   A^c and B $(0.34)(0.65) = 0.221$

A^c 0.34

$P(B) = .528 + .221 = .749$

6.87 $P(A^C \mid B) = P(A^C \text{ and } B)/P(B) = .221/.749 = .295$

6.88 P(Idle roughly)

= P(at least one spark plug malfunctions) = 1- P(all function) = $1 - (.90^4) = 1-.6561 = .3439$

6.89

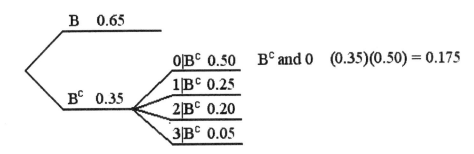

B   0.65

0|B^c 0.50   B^c and 0 $(0.35)(0.50) = 0.175$

1|B^c 0.25

B^c 0.35

2|B^c 0.20

3|B^c 0.05

$P(\text{no sale}) = .65 + .175 = .825$

6.90 a P(pass) = .86 + .03 = .89

b P(pass | miss 5 or more classes) = .03/(.09 + .03) = .250

c P(pass | miss less than 5 classes) = .86/(.86 + .02) = .977

d No since P(pass) $\neq$ P(pass | miss 5 or more classes)

6.91

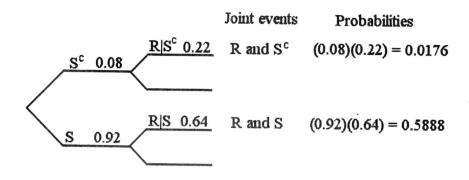

Joint events | Probabilities

R 0.27

D|R 0.41   R and D $(0.27)(0.41) = 0.1107$

D^c|R 0.59   R and D^c $(0.27)(0.59) = 0.1593$

R^c 0.73

D|R^c 0.31   R^c and D $(0.73)(0.31) = 0.2263$

D^c|R^c 0.69   R^c and D^c $(0.73)(0.69) = 0.5037$

a P(D) = P(R and D) + P(R^C and D) = .1107 + .2263 = .3370

P(R| D) = P(R and D)/P(D) = .1107/.3370) = .3285

b P(D^C) = P(R and D^C) + P(R^C and D^C) = .1593 + .5037 = .6630

P(R| D^C) = P(R and D^C)/P(D^C) = .1593/.6630) = .2403

6.92 a P(excellent) = .27 + .22 = .49

b P(excellent | man) = .22/(.22 + .10 + .12 + .06) = .44

c P(man | excellent) = .22/(.27 + .22) = .449

d No, since P(excellent) ≠ P(excellent | man)

6.93

Joint events | Probabilities

S^c 0.08

R|S^c 0.22   R and S^c $(0.08)(0.22) = 0.0176$

S 0.92

R|S 0.64   R and S $(0.92)(0.64) = 0.5888$

P(R) = .0176 + .5888 = .6064

P(S^C | R) = .5888/.6064 = .9710

6.94 Define events: A_1 = Low-income earner, A_2 = medium-income earner, A_3 = high-income earner,

B = die of a heart attack

probabilities

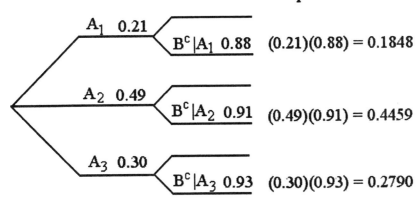

$B^c | A_1$ 0.88   (0.21)(0.88) = 0.1848

$B^c | A_2$ 0.91   (0.49)(0.91) = 0.4459

$B^c | A_3$ 0.93   (0.30)(0.93) = 0.2790

$P(B^C) = .1848 + .4459 + .2790 = .9097$

$P(A_1 | B^C) = .1848/.9097 = .2031$

6.95 Define the events: A_1 = The envelope containing two Maui brochures is selected, A_2 = The envelope containing two Oahu brochures is selected, A_3 = The envelope containing one Maui and one Oahu brochures is selected. B = A Maui brochure is removed from the selected envelope.

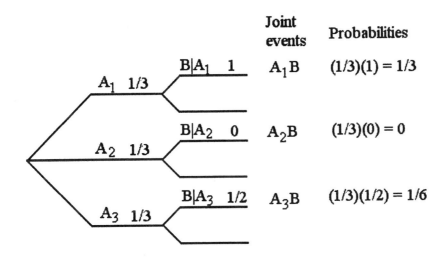

	Joint events	Probabilities
$B|A_1$ 1	A_1B	(1/3)(1) = 1/3
$B|A_2$ 0	A_2B	(1/3)(0) = 0
$B|A_3$ 1/2	A_3B	(1/3)(1/2) = 1/6

$P(B) = 1/3 + 0 + 1/6 = 1/2$

$P(A_1 | B) = P(A_1 \text{ and } B)/ P(B) = (1/3) / (1/2) = 2/3$

6.96 Define events: A = purchase extended warranty, B = regular price

a $P(A | B) = P(A \text{ and } B)/P(B) = .21/(.21 + .57) = .2692$

b $P(A) = .21 + .14 = .35$

c No, because $P(A) \neq P(A | B)$

6.97 Define events: A = company fail, B = predict bankruptcy

$P(A) = .08, P(B \mid A) = .85, P(B^C \mid A^C) = .74$

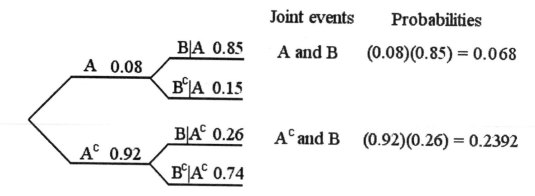

Joint events   Probabilities

B|A 0.85   A and B   (0.08)(0.85) = 0.068

B^C|A 0.15

B|A^C 0.26   A^C and B   (0.92)(0.26) = 0.2392

B^C|A^C 0.74

$P(B) = .068 + .2392 = .3072$

$P(A \mid B) = P(A \text{ and } B)/P(B) = .068/.3072 = .2214$

6.98 Define events: A = job security is an important issue, B = pension benefits is an important issue

$P(A) = .74, P(B) = .65, P(A \mid B) = .60$

a $P(A \text{ and } B) = P((B)P(A \mid B) = (.65)(.60) = .39$

b $P(A \text{ or } B) = .74 + .65 - .39 = 1$

6.99 Probabilities of outcomes: $P(HH) = .25, P(HT) = .25, P(TH) = .25, P(TT) .25$

$P(TT \mid HH \text{ is not possible}) = .25/(.25 + .25 + .25) = .333$

6.100 $P(T) = .5$

Case 6.1

1.

Events	Prior Probability	Likelihood Probability	Joint Probability	Posterior Probability
He has prostate cancer .1472	.08	.268	.02144	.02144/.14564 =
He does not have prostate cancer	.92	.135	.12420	
Probability of elevated level			.14564	

110

2.

Events	Prior Probability	Likelihood Probability	Joint Probability	Posterior Probability
He has prostate cancer	.15	.268	.0402	.0402/.15495 = .2594
He does not have prostate cancer	.85	.135	.11475	
Probability of elevated level			.15495	

3.

Events	Prior Probability	Likelihood Probability	Joint Probability	Posterior Probability
He has prostate cancer	.19	.268	.05092	.05092/.16027 = .3177
He does not have prostate cancer	.81	.135	.10935	
Probability of elevated level			.16027	

4.

Events	Prior Probability	Likelihood Probability	Joint Probability	Posterior Probability
He has prostate cancer	.21	.268	.05628	.05628/.16293 = .3454
He does not have prostate cancer	.79	.135	.10665	
Probability of elevated level			.16293	

Case 6.2

1. P(Curtain A) = 1/3, P(Curtain B) = 1/3
2. P(Curtain A) = 1/3, P(Curtain B) = 2/3

Case 6.3

Outcome	Probability of outcome	Bases Occupied	Outs	Probability of scoring	Joint Probability
1	.75	2nd	1	.42	.3150
2	.10	1st	1	.26	.0260
3	.10	none	2	.07	.0070
4	.05	1st and 2nd	0	.59	.0295
				P(scoring) =	.3775

Chapter 7

7.1 a 0, 1, 2, …

b Yes, we can identify the first value (0), the second (1), and so on.

c It is finite, because the number of cars is finite.

d The variable is discrete because it is countable.

7.2 a any value between 0 and several hundred miles

b No, because we cannot identify the second value or any other value larger than 0.

c No, uncountable means infinite.

d The variable is continuous.

7.3 a The values in cents are 0 ,1 ,2, …

b Yes, because we can identify the first ,second, etc.

c Yes, it is finite because students cannot earn an infinite amount of money.

d Technically, the variable is discrete.

7.4 a 0, 1, 2, …, 100

b Yes.

c Yes, there are 101 values.

d The variable is discrete because it is countable.

7.5 a No the sum of probabilities is not equal to 1.

b Yes, because the probabilities lie between 0 and 1 and sum to 1.

c No, because the probabilities do not sum to 1.

7.6 $p(x) = 1/6$ for $x = 1, 2 ,3 ,4 ,5,$ and 6

7.7 a

x	p(x)
0	24,750/165,000 = .15
1	37,950/165,000 = .23
2	59,400/165,000 = .36
3	29,700/165,000 = .18
4	9,900/165,000 = .06
5	3,300/165,000 = .02

b (i) $P(X \leq 2) = p(0) + p(1) + p(2) = .15 + .23 + .36 = .74$

(ii) $P(X > 2) = p(3) + p(4) + p(5) = .18 + .06 + .02 = .26$

(iii) $P(X \geq 4) = p(4) + p(5) = .06 + .02 = .08$

7.8 a $P(2 \leq X \leq 5) = p(2) + p(3) + p(4) + p(5) = .310 + .340 + .220 + .080 = .950$

b $P(X > 5) = p(6) + p(7) = .019 + .001 = .020$

c $P(X < 4) = p(0) + p(1) + p(2) + p(3) = .005 + .025 + .310 + .340 = .680$

7.9 $p(0) = p(1) = p(2) = \ldots = p(10) = 1/11 = .091$

7.10 a $P(X > 0) = p(2) + p(6) + p(8) = .3 + .4 + .1 = .8$

b $P(X \geq 1) = p(2) + p(6) + p(8) = .3 + .4 + .1 = .8$

c $P(X \geq 2) = p(2) + p(6) + p(8) = .3 + .4 + .1 = .8$

d $P(2 \leq X \leq 5) = p(2) = .3$

7.11 $P(X \geq 2) = p(2) + p(3) = .4 + .2 = .6$

7.12 a $P(X < 2) = p(0) + p(1) = .05 + ..43 = .48$

b $P(X > 1) = p(2) + p(3) = .31 + .21 = .52$

7.13

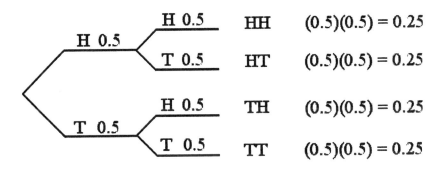

a $P(HH) = .25$

b $P(HT) = .25$

c $P(TH) = .25$

d $P(TT) = .25$

7.14 a $P(0 \text{ heads}) = P(TT) = 1/4$

b $P(1 \text{ head}) = P(HT) + P(TH) = 1/4 + 1/4 = 1/2$

c $P(2 \text{ heads}) = P(HH) = 1/4$

d $P(\text{at least 1 head}) = P(1 \text{ head}) + P(2 \text{ heads}) = 1/2 + 1/4 = 3/4$

7.15

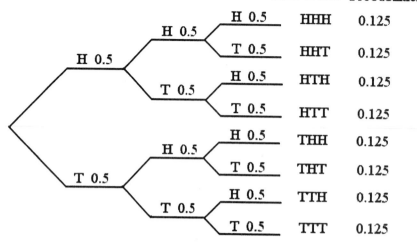

			Joint events	Probabilities

H 0.5

H 0.5

H 0.5   HHH   0.125

T 0.5   HHT   0.125

T 0.5

H 0.5   HTH   0.125

T 0.5   HTT   0.125

T 0.5

H 0.5

H 0.5   THH   0.125

T 0.5   THT   0.125

T 0.5

H 0.5   TTH   0.125

T 0.5   TTT   0.125

7.16 a P(2 heads) = P(HHT) + P(HTH) + P(THH) = 1/8 + 1/8 + 1/8 = 3/8

b P(1 heads) = P(HTT) + P(THT) = P(TTH) = 1/8 + 1/8 + 1/8 = 3/8

c P(at least 1 head) = P(1 head) + P(2 heads) + P(3 heads) = 3/8 + 3/8 + P(HHH)

$\quad$ = 3/8 + 3/8 + 1/8 = 7/8

d P(at least 2 heads) = P(2 heads) + P(3 heads) = 3/8 + 1/8 = 4/8 = 1/2

7.17 a P(X > 4) = p(5) + p(6) + p(7) = .20 + .10 + .10 = .40

b P(X $\geq$ 2) = 1- P(X $\leq$ 1) = 1 – p(1) = 1 - .05 = .95

7.18 a P(4 books) = p(4) = .06

b P(8 books) = p(8) = 0

c P(no books) = p(0) = .35

d P(at least 1 book) = 1 – p(0) = 1 - .35 = .65

7.19 a P(X $\geq$ 20) = p(20) + p(25) + p(30) + p(40) + p(50) + p(75) + P(100)

$\quad$ = .08 + .05 + .04 + .04 + .03 + .03 + .01 = .28

b P(X = 60) = 0

c P(X > 50) = P(75) + P(100) = .03 + .01 = .04

d P(X > 100) = 0

7.20 a P(X = 3) = p(3) = .21

b b P(X $\geq$ 5) = p(5) + p(6) + p(7) + p(8) = .12 + .08 + .06 + .05 = .31

c P(5 $\leq$ X $\leq$ 7) = p(5) + p(6) + p(7) = .12 + .08 + .06 = .26

7.21 a $P(X > 1) = p(2) + p(3) + p(4) = .17 + .06 + .01 = .24$

b $P(X = 0) = .45$

c $P(1 \le X \le 3) = p(1) + p(2) + p(3) = .31 + .17 + .06 = .54$

7.22 $\mu = E(X) = \sum xp(x) = -2(.59) + 5(.15) + 7(.25) + 8(.01) = 1.4$

$\sigma^2 = V(X) = \sum (x-\mu)^2 p(x) = (-2-1.4)^2 (.59) + (5-1.4)^2 (.15) + (7-1.4)^2 (.25) + (8-1.4)^2 (.01)$

$= 17.04$

$\sigma = \sqrt{\sigma^2} = \sqrt{17.04} = 4.13$

7.23 $\mu = E(X) = \sum xp(x) = 0(.4) + 1(.3) + 2(.2) + 3(.1) = 1.0$

$\sigma^2 = V(X) = \sum (x-\mu)^2 p(x) = (0-1.0)^2 (.4) + (1-1.0)^2 (.3) + (2-1.0)^2 (.2) + (3-1.0)^2 (.1)$

$= 1.0$

$\sigma = \sqrt{\sigma^2} = \sqrt{1.0} = 1.0$

7.24

x	0	1	2	3
y = 3x + 2	2	5	8	11
Probability	.4	.3	.2	.1

7.25 $\mu = E(Y) = \sum yp(y) = 2(.4) + 5(.3) + 8(.2) + 11(.1) = 5.0$

$\sigma^2 = V(Y) = \sum (y-\mu)^2 p(y) = (2-5.0)^2 (.4) + (5-5.0)^2 (.3) + (8-5.0)^2 (.2) + (11-5.0)^2 (.1)$

$= 9.0$

$\sigma = \sqrt{\sigma^2} = \sqrt{9.0} = 3.0$

7.26 $E(Y) = E(3X + 2) = 3E(X) + 2 = 3(1.0) + 2 = 5.0$

$V(Y) = V(3X + 2) = 3^2 V(X) = 9(1.0) = 9.0$

$\sigma = \sqrt{\sigma^2} = \sqrt{9.0} = 3.0$

7.27 $\mu = E(X) = \sum xp(x) = 0(.15) + 1(.23) + 2(.36) + 3(.18) + 4(.06) + 5(.02) = 1.83$

$\sigma^2 = V(X) = \sum (x-\mu)^2 p(x) = (0-1.83)^2 (.15) \ (1-1.83)^2 (.23) + (2-1.83)^2 (.36) + (3-1.83)^2 (.18)$

$+ (4-1.83)^2 (.06) + (5-1.83)^2 (.02) = 1.40$

$\sigma = \sqrt{\sigma^2} = \sqrt{1.40} = 1.18$

7.28 $\mu = E(X) = \sum xp(x) = 0(.1) + 1(.3) + 2(.4) + 3(.2) = 1.7$

$\sigma^2 = V(X) = \sum (x-\mu)^2 p(x) = (0-1.7)^2 (.1) + (1-1.7)^2 (.3) + (2-1.7)^2 (.4) + (3-1.7)^2 (.2) = .81$

$\sigma = \sqrt{\sigma^2} = \sqrt{.81} = .9$

7.29 $Y = 3X, E(Y) = 3E(X) = 3(1.7) = 5.1$

$V(Y) = V(3X) = 3^2 V(X) = 9(.81) = 7.29$

$\sigma = \sqrt{\sigma^2} = \sqrt{7.29} = 2.7$

7.30

x	1	2	3	4	5	6	7
y	.25	.50	.75	1.00	1.25	1.50	1.75
p(y)	.05	.15	.15	.25	.20	.10	.10

7.31 $\mu = E(Y) = \sum yp(y) = .25(.05) + .50(.15) + .75(.15) + 1.00(.25) + 1.25(.20) + 1.50(.10) +$
1.75(.10)

$= 1.025$

$\sigma^2 = V(Y) = \sum (y-\mu)^2 p(y) = (.25-1.025)^2 (.05) + (.50-1.025)^2 (.15) + (.75-1.025)^2 (.15)$

$+ (1.00-1.025)^2 (.25) + (1.25-1.025)^2 (.20) + (1.50-1.025)^2 (.10) + (1.75-1.1025)^2 (.10) = .168$

$\sigma = \sqrt{\sigma^2} = \sqrt{.168} = .410$

7.32 $\mu = E(X) = \sum xp(x) = 1(.05) + + 2(.15) + 3(.15) + 4(.25) + 5(.20) + 6(.10) + 7(.10) = 4.1$

$\sigma^2 = V(X) = \sum (x-\mu)^2 p(x) = (1-4.1)^2 (.05) + (2-4.1)^2 (.15) + (3-4,1)^2 (.15) + (4-4.1)^2 (.25)$

$+ (5-4.1)^2 (.20) + (6-4.1)^2 (.10) + (7-4.1)^2 (.10) = 2.69$

$\sigma = \sqrt{\sigma^2} = \sqrt{2.69} = 1.64$

$Y = .25, E(Y) = .25E(X) = .25(4.1) = 1.025$

$V(Y) = V(.25X) = .25^2 V(X) = .0625(2.69) = .168$

$\sigma = \sqrt{\sigma^2} = \sqrt{1.68} = .410$

7.33 $\mu = E(X) = \sum xp(x) = 0(.04) + 1(.19) + 2(.22) + 3(.28) + 4(.12) + 5(.09) + 6(.06)$

$= 2.76$

$\sigma^2 = V(X) = \sum (x-\mu)^2 p(x) = (1-2.76)^2 (.04) + (2-2.76)^2 (.19) + (3-2.76)^2 (.28)$

116

$$+ (4\text{-}2.76)^2 (.12) + (5\text{-}2.76)^2 (.09) + (6\text{-}2.76)^2 (.06) = 2.302$$

$$\sigma = \sqrt{\sigma^2} = \sqrt{2.302} = 1.52$$

7.34 $Y = 10X$

$E(Y) = E(10X) = 10E(X) = 10(2.76) = 27.6$

$V(Y) = V(10X) = 10^2 V(X) = 100(2.302) = 230.2$

$\sigma = \sqrt{\sigma^2} = \sqrt{230.2} = 15.17$

7.35 $\mu = E(X) = \sum xp(x) = 0(.35) + 1(.25) + 2(.20) + 3(.08) + 4(.06) + 5(.03) + 6(.02)$

$$+ 7(.01) = 1.47$$

$$\sigma^2 = V(X) = \sum (x - \mu)^2 p(x) = (0\text{-}1.47)^2 (.35) + (1\text{-}1.47)^2 (.25) + (2\text{-}1.47)^2 (.20)$$

$$+ (3\text{-}1.47)^2 (.08) + (4\text{-}1.47)^2 (.06) + (5\text{-}1.47)^2 (.03) + (6\text{-}1.47)^2 (.02)$$

$$+ (7\text{-}1.47)^2 (.01) = 2.529$$

$\sigma = \sqrt{\sigma^2} = \sqrt{2.59} = 1.59$

7.36 $\mu = E(X) = \sum xp(x) = 1(.24) + 2(.18) + 3(.13) + 4(.10) + 5(.07) + 6(.04)$

$$+ 7(.04) + 8(.20) = 3.86$$

$$\sigma^2 = V(X) = \sum (x - \mu)^2 p(x) = (1\text{-}3.86)^2 (.24) + (2\text{-}3.86)^2 (.18) + (3\text{-}3.86)^2 (.13)$$

$$+ (4\text{-}3.86)^2 (.10) + (5\text{-}3.86)^2 (.07) + (6\text{-}3.86)^2 (.04) + (7\text{-}3.86)^2 (.04)$$

$$+ (8\text{-}3.86)^2 (.20) = 6.78$$

$\sigma = \sqrt{\sigma^2} = \sqrt{6.78} = 2.60$

7.37 $E(\text{Revenue}) = E(2.50X) = 2.50E(X) = 2.50(3.86) = 9.65$

$V(\text{Revenue}) = V(2.50X) = 2.50^2 (V(X) = 6.25(6.78) = 42.38$

$\sigma = \sqrt{\sigma^2} = \sqrt{42.38} = 6.51$

7.38 $E(\text{Value of coin}) = 400(.40) + 900(.30) + 100(.30) = 460.$ Take the \$500.

7.39 $\mu = E(X) = \sum xp(x) = 0(.10) + 1(.25) + 2(.40) + 3(.20) + 4(.05) = 1.85$

7.40 Profit $= 4(X)$; Expected profit $= 4E(X) = 4(1.85) = \$7.40$

7.41 Breakeven point = $15,000/(7.40 - 3.00) = 3409$

7.42 E(damage costs) = $.01(400) + .02(200) + .10(100) + .87(0) = 18$. The owner should pay up to $18 for the device.

7.43 a

x	p(x)
1	.6
2	.4

b

y	p(y)
1	.6
2	.4

c $\mu = E(X) = \sum xp(x) = 1(.6) + 2(.4) = 1.4$

$\sigma^2 = V(X) = \sum (x - \mu)^2 p(x) = (1-1.4)^2 (.6) + (2-1.4)^2 (.4) = .24$

d $\mu = 1.4$, $\sigma^2 = .24$

7.44 a $\sum_{all\ x} \sum_{all\ y} xyp(x, y) = (1)(1)(.5) + (1)(2)(.1) + (2)(1)(.1) + (2)(2)(.3) = 2.1$

$COV(X, Y) = \sum_{all\ x} \sum_{all\ y} xyp(x, y) - \mu_x\mu_y = 2.1 - (1.4)(1.4) = .14$

$\sigma_x = \sqrt{\sigma_x^2} = \sqrt{.24} = .49$, $\sigma_y = \sqrt{\sigma_y^2} = \sqrt{.24} = .49$

$\rho = \dfrac{COV(X,Y)}{\sigma_x\sigma_y} = \dfrac{.14}{(.49)(.49)} = .58$

7.45 $E(X + Y) = E(X) + E(Y) = 1.4 + 1.4 = 2.8$

$V(X + Y) = V(X) + V(Y) + 2COV(X, Y) = .24 + .24 + 2(.14) = .76$

7.46 a

x + y	p(x + y)
2	.5
3	.2
4	.3

b $\mu_{x+y} = E(X+Y) = \sum (x+y)p(x+y) = 2(.5) + 3(.2) + 4(.3) = 2.8$

$\sigma_{x+y}^2 = V(X+Y) = \sum [(x+y) - \mu_{x+y}]^2 p(x+y) = (2-2.8)^2 (.5) + (3-2.8)^2 (.2) + (4-2.8)^2 (.3) = .76$

c Yes

7.47 a

x	p(x)
1	.4
2	.6

b

y	p(y)
1	.7
2	.3

c $\mu = E(X) = \sum xp(x) = 1(.4) + 2(.6) = 1.6$

$\sigma^2 = V(X) = \sum (x - \mu)^2 p(x) = (1\text{-}1.6)^2 (.4) + (2\text{-}1.6)^2 (.6) = .24$

d $\mu = E(Y) = \sum yp(y) = 1(.7) + 2(.3) = 1.3$

$\sigma^2 = V(Y) = \sum (y - \mu)^2 p(y) = (1\text{-}1.3)^2 (.7) + (2\text{-}1.3)^2 (.3) = .21$

7.48 a $\sum_{all\ x} \sum_{all\ y} xyp(x, y) = (1)(1)(.28) + (1)(2)(.12) + (2)(1)(.42) + (2)(2)(.18) = 2.08$

$COV(X, Y) = \sum_{all\_x} \sum_{all\_y} xyp(x, y) - \mu_x\mu_y = 2.08 - (1.6)(1.3) = 0$

$\sigma_x = \sqrt{\sigma_x^2} = \sqrt{.24} = .49,\ \sigma_y = \sqrt{\sigma_y^2} = \sqrt{.21} = .46$

$\rho = \dfrac{COV(X,Y)}{\sigma_x\sigma_y} = \dfrac{0}{(.49)(.46)} = 0$

7.49 $E(X + Y) = E(X) + E(Y) = 1.6 + 1.3 = 2.9$

$V(X + Y) = V(X) + V(Y) + 2COV(X, Y) = .24 + .21 + 2(0) = .45$

7.50 a

x + y	p(x + y)
2	.28
3	.54
4	.18

b $\mu_{x+y} = E(X+Y) = \sum (x + y)p(x + y) = 2(.28) + 3(.54) + 4(.18) = 2.9$

$\sigma_{x+y}^2 = V(X+Y) = \sum [(x+y) - \mu_{x+y}]^2 p(x+y) = (2\text{-}2.9)^2 (.28) + (3\text{-}2.9)^2 (.54) + (4\text{-}2.9)^2 (18) = .45$

c Yes

119

7.51 a

x	p(x)		y	p(y)
1	.7		1	.6
2	.2		2	.4
3	.1			

b $\mu_x = E(X) = \sum xp(x) = 1(.7) + 2(.2) + 3(.1) = 1.4$

$\sigma^2 = V(X) = \sum (x-\mu)^2 p(x) = (1-1.4)^2(.7) + (2-1.4)^2(.6) + (3-1.4)^2(.1) = .44$

$\mu_y = E(Y) = \sum yp(y) = 1(.6) + 2(.4) = 1.4$

$\sigma^2 = V(Y) = \sum (y-\mu)^2 p(y) = (1-1.4)^2(.6) + (2-1.4)^2(.4) = .25$

$\sum\limits_{all\ x} \sum\limits_{all\ y} xyp(x,y) = (1)(1)(.42) + (1)(2)(.28) + (2)(1)(.12) + (2)(2)(.08) + (3)(1)(.06)$

$+ (3)(2)(.04) = 1.96$

$COV(X,Y) = \sum\limits_{all\ x} \sum\limits_{all\ y} xyp(x,y) - \mu_x\mu_y = 1.94 - (1.4)(1.4) = 0$

$\sigma_x = \sqrt{\sigma_x^2} = \sqrt{.44} = .66, \ \sigma_y = \sqrt{\sigma_y^2} = \sqrt{.25} = .5$

$\rho = \dfrac{COV(X,Y)}{\sigma_x\sigma_y} = \dfrac{0}{(.66)(.5)} = 0$

c

x + y	p(x + y)
2	.42
3	.40
4	.14
5	.04

7.52

		x	
y	0	1	2
1	.42	.21	.07
2	.18	.09	.03

7.53

	x	
y	0	1
1	.04	.16
2	.08	.32
3	.08	.32

7.54 a
Refrigerators, x	p(x)
0	.22
1	.49
2	.29

b
Stoves, y	p(y)
0	.34
1	.39
2	.27

c $\mu_x = E(X) = \sum xp(x) = 0(.22) + 1(.49) + 2(.29) = 1.07$

$\sigma^2 = V(X) = \sum (x-\mu)^2 p(x) = (0-1.07)^2 (.22) + (1-1.07)^2 (.49) + (2-1.07)^2 (.29) = .505$

d $\mu_y = E(Y) = \sum yp(y) = 0(.34) + 1(.39) + 2(.27) = .93$

$\sigma^2 = V(Y) = \sum (y-\mu)^2 p(y) = (0-.93)^2 (.34) + (1-.93)^2 (.39) + (2-.93)^2 (.27) = .605$

e $\sum_{all\ x} \sum_{all\ y} xyp(x, y) = (0)(1)(.08) + (0)(1)(.09) + (0)(2)(.05) + (1)(0)(.14) + (1)(1)(.17)$

$+ (1)(2)(18) + (2)(0)(.12) + (21)(1)(13) + (2)(2)(.04) = .95$

$COV(X, Y) = \sum_{all\ x} \sum_{all\ y} xyp(x, y) - \mu_x\mu_y = .95 - (1.07)(.93) = -.045$

$\sigma_x = \sqrt{\sigma_x^2} = \sqrt{.505} = .711, \sigma_y = \sqrt{\sigma_y^2} = \sqrt{.605} = .778$

$\rho = \dfrac{COV(X,Y)}{\sigma_x\sigma_y} = \dfrac{-.045}{(.711)(.778)} = -.081$

7.55 a
Bottles, x	p(x)
0	.72
1	.28

b
Cartons, y	p(y)
0	.81
1	.19

c $\mu_x = E(X) = \sum xp(x) = 0(.72) + 1(.28) = .28$

$\sigma^2 = V(X) = \sum (x-\mu)^2 p(x) = (0-.28)^2 (.72) + (1-.28)^2 (.28) = .202$

d $\mu_y = E(Y) = \sum yp(y) = 0(.81) + 1(.19) = .19$

$\sigma^2 = V(Y) = \sum (y-\mu)^2 p(y) = (0-.19)^2 (.81) + (1-.28)^2 (.19) = .154$

e $\sum_{all\ x} \sum_{all\ y} xyp(x, y) = (0)(0)(.63) + (0)(1)(.09) + (1)(0)(.18) + (1)(1)(.10) = .100$

$$COV(X, Y) = \sum_{all\_x} \sum_{all\_y} xyp(x, y) - \mu_x\mu_y = .100 - (.28)(.19) = .0468$$

$$\sigma_x = \sqrt{\sigma_x^2} = \sqrt{.202} = .449, \ \sigma_y = \sqrt{\sigma_y^2} = \sqrt{.154} = .392$$

$$\rho = \frac{COV(X,Y)}{\sigma_x\sigma_y} = \frac{.100}{(.449)(.392)} = .266$$

7.56 a $P(X = 1 \mid Y = 0) = P(X = 1 \text{ and } Y = 0)/P(Y = 0) = .14/.34 = .412$

b $P(Y = 0 \mid X = 1) = P(X = 1 \text{ and } Y = 0)/P(X = 1) = .14/.49 = .286$

c $P(X = 2 \mid Y = 2) = P(X = 2 \text{ and } Y = 2)/P(Y = 2) = .04/.27 = .148$

7.57 $E\left(\sum X_i\right) = \sum E(X_i) = 18 + 12 + 27 + 8 = 65$

$V\left(\sum X_i\right) = \sum V(X_i) = 8 + 5 + 6 + 2 = 21$

7.58 $E\left(\sum X_i\right) = \sum E(X_i) = 35 + 20 + 20 + 50 + 20 = 145$

$V\left(\sum X_i\right) = \sum V(X_i) = 8 + 5 + 4 + 12 + 2 = 31$

$\sigma = \sqrt{31} = 5.57$

7.59 $E\left(\sum X_i\right) = \sum E(X_i) = 8 + 14 + 5 + 3 + 30 + 30 + 10 = 100$

$V\left(\sum X_i\right) = \sum V(X_i) = 2 + 5 + 1 + 1 + 8 + 10 + 3 = 30$

7.60 $E\left(\sum X_i\right) = \sum E(X_i) = 10 + 3 + 30 + 5 + 100 + 20 = 168$

$V\left(\sum X_i\right) = \sum V(X_i) = 3^2 + 0^2 + 10^2 + 1^2 + 20^2 + 8^2 = 574$

$\sigma = \sqrt{574} = 24.0$

7.61 $E(R_p) = w_1 E(R_1) + w_2 E(R_2) = (.30)(.12) + (.70)(.25) = .211$

$V(R_p) = w_1^2 \sigma_1^2 + w_2^2 \sigma_2^2 + 2 w_1 w_2 \rho \sigma_1 \sigma_2$

$\quad\quad = (.30)^2(.02)^2 + (.70)^2(.15^2) + 2(.30)(.70)(.5)(.02)(.15)$

$\quad\quad = .0117$

$\sigma_{R_p} = \sqrt{.0117} = .1081$

7.62 $E(R_p) = .211$

$$V(R_p) = w_1^2 \sigma_1^2 + w_2^2 \sigma_2^2 + 2w_1 w_2 \rho \sigma_1 \sigma_2$$

$$= (.30)^2(.02)^2 + (.70)^2(.15^2) + 2(.30)(.70)(.25)(.02)(.15)$$

$$= .0114$$

$$\sigma_{R_p} = \sqrt{.0114} = .1067$$

7.63 $E(R_p) = .211$

$$V(R_p) = w_1^2 \sigma_1^2 + w_2^2 \sigma_2^2 + 2w_1 w_2 \rho \sigma_1 \sigma_2$$

$$= (.30)^2(.02)^2 + (.70)^2(.15^2) + 2(.30)(.70)(0)(.02)(.15)$$

$$= .0111$$

$$\sigma_{R_p} = \sqrt{.0111} = .1054$$

7.64 The expected value does not change. The standard deviation decreases.

7.65 a She should choose stock 2 because its expected value is higher.

b. She should choose stock 1 because its standard deviation is smaller.

7.66 $E(R_p) = w_1 E(R_1) + w_2 E(R_2) = (.60)(.09) + (.40)(.13) = .1060$

$$V(R_p) = w_1^2 \sigma_1^2 + w_2^2 \sigma_2^2 + 2w_1 w_2 \rho \sigma_1 \sigma_2$$

$$= (.60)^2(.15)^2 + (.40)^2(.21^2) + 2(.60)(.40)(.4)(.15)(.21)$$

$$= .0212$$

7.67 $E(R_p) = w_1 E(R_1) + w_2 E(R_2) = (.30)(.09) + (.70)(.13) = .1180$

$$V(R_p) = w_1^2 \sigma_1^2 + w_2^2 \sigma_2^2 + 2w_1 w_2 \rho \sigma_1 \sigma_2$$

$$= (.30)^2(.15)^2 + (.70)^2(.21^2) + 2(.30)(.70)(.4)(.15)(.21)$$

$$= .0289$$

The statistics used in Exercises 7.68 to 7.80 were computed by Excel. The variances were taken from the variance-covariance matrix. As a result they are the population parameters. To convert to statistics multiply the variance of the portfolio returns by n/(n-1).

7.68 a

	Stock		
	1	2	3
Means	.0463	.1293	-.0016
Variances	.0148	.0100	.0039

b Invest all your money in stock 2; it has the largest mean return.

c Invest all your money in stock 3; it has the smallest variance.

7.69 a

Portfolio of 3 Stocks				
		Stock 1	Stock 2	Stock 3
Variance-Covariance Matrix	Stock 1	0.0148		
	Stock 2	0.0037	0.0100	
	Stock 3	0.0015	-0.0012	0.0039
Expected Returns		0.0463	0.1293	-0.0016
Weights		0.333333	0.333333	0.333333
Portfolio Return				
Expected Value	0.0580			
Variance	0.0041			
Standard Deviation	0.0640			

b The mean return on the portfolio is greater than the mean returns on stocks 1 and 3, but smaller than that of stock 2. The variance of the returns on the portfolio is smaller than that for stocks 1 and 2 and slightly larger than that of stock 3.

7.70 a

Portfolio of 3 Stocks				
		Stock 1	Stock 2	Stock 3
Variance-Covariance Matrix	Stock 1	0.0148		
	Stock 2	0.0037	0.0100	
	Stock 3	0.0015	-0.0012	0.0039
Expected Returns		0.0463	0.1293	-0.0016
Weights		0.5	0.3	0.2
Portfolio Return				
Expected Value	0.0616			
Variance	0.0060			
Standard Deviation	0.0777			

b The mean return on this portfolio is greater than the mean returns on stocks 1 and 3 and the portfolio in Exercise 7.69, but smaller than that of stock 2. The variance of the returns on this portfolio is smaller than that for stocks 1 and 2 and larger than that of stock 3 and the portfolio in Exercise 7.69.

7.71 a   Stock

	1	2	3
Means	.0232	.0601	.0136
Variances	.0957	.2345	.0515

b Invest all your money in stock 2; it has the largest mean return.

c Invest all your money in stock 3; it has the smallest variance.

7.72 a

Portfolio of 3 Stocks				
		Stock 1	Stock 2	Stock 3
Variance-Covariance Matrix	Stock 1	0.0957		
	Stock 2	-0.0288	0.2345	
	Stock 3	0.0004	0.0243	0.0515
Expected Returns		0.0232	0.0601	0.0136
Weights		0.3	0.4	0.3
Portfolio Return				
Expected Value	0.0351			
Variance	0.0498			
Standard Deviation	0.2231			

b The mean return on the portfolio is greater than the mean returns on stocks 1 and 3, but smaller than that of stock 2. The variance of the returns on the portfolio is smaller than that for the three stocks.

7.73 a

Portfolio of 3 Stocks				
		Stock 1	Stock 2	Stock 3
Variance-Covariance Matrix	Stock 1	0.0957		
	Stock 2	-0.0288	0.2345	
	Stock 3	0.0004	0.0243	0.0515
Expected Returns		0.0232	0.0601	0.0136
Weights		0.1	0.1	0.8
Portfolio Return				
Expected Value	0.0192			
Variance	0.0397			
Standard Deviation	0.1991			

b The mean return on this portfolio is greater than the mean return on stock 3, but smaller than that of stocks 1 and 2 and the portfolio in Exercise 7.72. The variance of the returns on this portfolio is smaller than that for all three stocks and the portfolio in Exercise 7.72.

7.74 a

	Stock			
	1	2	3	4
Means	.0187	-.0176	.0153	.0495
Variances	.0615	.0232	.0228	.0517

b Invest all your money in stock 4; it has the largest mean return.

c Invest all your money in stock 3; it has the smallest variance.

7.75 a

Portfolio of 4 Stocks					
		Stock 1	Stock 2	Stock 3	Stock 4
Variance-Covariance Matrix	Stock 1	0.0615			
	Stock 2	-0.0012	0.0232		
	Stock 3	0.0168	-0.0022	0.0228	
	Stock 4	0.0129	0.0179	-0.0005	0.0517
Expected Returns		0.0187	-0.0176	0.0153	0.0495
Weights		0.25	0.25	0.25	0.25
Portfolio Return					
Expected Value	0.0165				
Variance	0.0154				
Standard Deviation	0.1241				

b The mean return on the portfolio is greater than the mean returns on stocks 2 and 3, but smaller than that of stocks 1 and 4. The variance of the returns on the portfolio is smaller than that for the four stocks.

7.76 a

Portfolio of 4 Stocks					
		Stock 1	Stock 2	Stock 3	Stock 4
Variance-Covariance Matrix	Stock 1	0.0615			
	Stock 2	-0.0012	0.0232		
	Stock 3	0.0168	-0.0022	0.0228	
	Stock 4	0.0129	0.0179	-0.0005	0.0517
Expected Returns		0.0187	-0.0176	0.0153	0.0495
Weights		0.20	0.20	0.10	0.50
Portfolio Return					
Expected Value	0.0265				
Variance	0.0231				
Standard Deviation	0.1521				

b The mean return on this portfolio is greater than the mean return on stocks 1, 2, and 3, and the mean return on the portfolio in Exercise 7.75. It is smaller than the mean return on stock 4. The variance of the returns on this portfolio is smaller than that for stocks 1, 2, and 4, but larger than the variance on the returns of stock 3 and the variance of the returns on the portfolio in Exercise 7.75.

7.77 a

	GE	Seagram	Coca-Cola	McDonald's
Means	.0231	.0148	.0213	.0156
Variances	.0019	.0043	.0017	.0025

Stock (heading above GE/Seagram/Coca-Cola/McDonald's)

b Invest all your money in General Electric; it has the largest mean return.

c Invest all your money in Coca-Cola; it has the smallest variance.

7.78 a

	GE	SEAGRAM	COKE	MCDONALDS
GE	0.0019			
SEAGRAM	0.0004	0.0043		
COKE	0.0004	-0.0005	0.0017	
MCDONALDS	0.0004	0.0011	0.0002	0.0025

b Invest in General Electric and Coca-Cola.

7.79

Portfolio of 4 Stocks		GE	SEAGRAM	COKE	MCDONALDS
Variance-Covariance Matrix	GE	0.0019			
	SEAGRAM	0.0004	0.0043		
	COKE	0.0004	-0.0005	0.0017	
	MCDONALDS	0.0004	0.0011	0.0002	0.0025
Expected Returns		0.0231	0.0148	0.0213	0.0156
Weights		0.40	0.25	0.20	0.15
Portfolio Return					
Expected Value	0.0195				
Variance	0.0009				
Standard Deviation	0.0305				

7.80 We created a portfolio with the following weights

General Electric	40%
Seagram	10%
Coca-Cola	40%
McDonald's	10%

Portfolio of 4 Stocks		GE	SEAGRAM	COKE	MCDONALDS
Variance-Covariance Matrix	GE	0.0019			
	SEAGRAM	0.0004	0.0043		
	COKE	0.0004	-0.0005	0.0017	
	MCDONALDS	0.0004	0.0011	0.0002	0.0025
Expected Returns		0.0231	0.0148	0.0213	0.0156
Weights		0.40	0.10	0.40	0.10
Portfolio Return					
Expected Value	0.0208				
Variance	0.0008				
Standard Deviation	0.0289				

7.81 $P(X = x) = \dfrac{n!}{x!(n-x)!} \, p^x (1-p)^{n-x}$

a $P(X = 3) = \dfrac{10!}{3!(10-3)!} \, (.3)^3 (1-.3)^{10-3} = .2668$

b $P(X = 5) = \dfrac{10!}{5!(10-5)!} \, (.3)^5 (1-.3)^{10-5} = .1029$

c $P(X = 8) = \dfrac{10!}{8!(10-8)!} \, (.3)^8 (1-.3)^{10-8} = .0014$

7.82 a $P(X = 3) = P(X \leq 3) - P(X \leq 2) = .650 - .383 = .267$

b $P(X = 5) = P(X \leq 5) - P(X \leq 4) = .953 - .850 = .103$

c $P(X = 8) = P(X \leq 8) - P(X \leq 7) = 1.000 - .998 = .002$

7.83 a .26683

b .10292

c .00145

7.84 $P(X = x) = \dfrac{n!}{x!(n-x)!} \, p^x (1-p)^{n-x}$

a $P(X = 0) = \dfrac{5!}{0!(5-0)!} \, (.4)^0 (1-.4)^{5-0} = .0778$

b a $P(X = 2) = \dfrac{5!}{2!(5-2)!} \, (.4)^2 (1-.4)^{5-2} = .3456$

c $P(X \leq 3) = p(0) + p(1) + p(2) + p(3) = .0778 + .2592 + .3456 + .2304 = .9130$

d $P(X \geq 2) = p(2) + p(3) + p(4) + p(5) = .3456 + .2304 + .0768 + .01024 = .6630$

7.85 a $P(X = 0) = P(X \leq 0) = .078$

b $P(X = 2) = P(X \leq 2) - P(X \leq 1) = .683 - .337 = .346$

c $P(X \leq 3) = .913$

d $P(X \geq 2) = 1 - P(X \leq 1) = 1 - .337 = .663$

7.86 a .07776

b .34560

c .91296

d .66304

7.87 a $P(X = 18) = P(X \leq 18) - P(X \leq 17) = .659 - .488 = .171$

b $P(X = 15) = P(X \leq 15) - P(X \leq 14) = .189 - .098 = .091$

c $P(X \leq 20) = .910$

d $P(X \geq 16) = 1 - P(X \leq 15) = 1 - .189 = .811$

7.88 a .17119

b .09164

c .90953

d .81056

7.89 a .0830

b .8028

c .7220

7.90 Binomial distribution with p = .25

a $P(X = 1) = \dfrac{4!}{1!(4-1)!} (.25)^1 (1 - .25)^{4-1} = .4219$

b Table 1 with n = 8: $p(2) = P(X \leq 2) - P(X \leq 1) = .679 - .367 = .312$

c Excel: $p(10) = .14436$

7.91a Excel with n = 10 and p = 244/495: $P(X \geq 5) = 1 - P(X \leq 4) = 1 - .39447 = .60553$

b $E(X) = np = 100(244/495) = 49.29$

7.92 a $P(X = 2) = \dfrac{5!}{2!(5-2)!} (.45)^2 (1 - .45)^{5-2} = .3369$

b Excel with n = 25 and p = .45: $P(X \geq 10) = 1 - P(X \leq 9) = 1 - .2424 = .7576$

7.93 a Table 1 with n = 5 and p = .5: $P(X = 2) = P(X \leq 2) - P(X \leq 1) = .5 - .187 = .313$

b: Table 1 with n = 25 and p = .5: $P(X \geq 10) = 1 - P(X \leq 9) = 1 - .115 = .885$

7.94 a $P(X = 2) = \dfrac{5!}{2!(5-2)!}(.52)^2(1-.52)^{5-2} = .2990$

b Excel with n = 25 and p = .52: $P(X \geq 10) = 1 - P(X \leq 9) = 1 - .08033 = .91967$

7.95 a Excel with n = 25 and p = 2/38: $P(X \geq 2) = 1 - P(X \leq 1) = 1 - .61826 = .38174$

b Excel with n = 25 and p = 2/38: $P(X = 0)) = .25880$

c Excel with n = 25 and p = 18/38: $P(X \geq 15) = 1 - P(X \leq 14) = 1 - .85645 = .14355$

d Excel with n = 25 and p = 18/38: $P(X \leq 10) = .29680$

7.96 Table 1 with n = 25 and p = .3: $P(X \leq 10) = .902$

7.97 Table 1 with n = 25 and p = .90

a $P(X = 20) = P(X \leq 20) - P(X \leq 19) = .098 - .033 = .065$

b $P(X \geq 20) = 1 - P(X \leq 19) = 1 - .033 = .967$

c $P(X \leq 24) = .928$

d $E(X) = np = 25(.90) = 22.5$

7.98 Table 1 with n = 25 and p = .75: $P(X \geq 15) = 1 - P(X \leq 14) = 1 - .030 = .970$

7.99 a Excel with n = 100 and p = .52: $P(X \geq 50) = 1 - P(X \leq 49) = 1 - .30815 = .69185$

b Excel with n = 100 and p = .36: $P(X \leq 30) = .12519$

c Excel with n = 100 and p = .06: $P(X \leq 5) = .44069$

7.100 $P(X = 0) = \dfrac{4!}{01!(4-0)!}(.7)^0(1-.7)^{4-0} = .0081$

7.101 Excel with n = 20 and p = .38: $P(X \geq 10) = 1 - P(X \leq 9) = 1 - .81032 = .18968$

7.102 Table 1 with n = 25 and p = .10

a $P(X = 0) = P(X \leq 0) = .072$

b $P(X < 5) = P(X \leq 4) = .902$

c $P(X > 2) = P(X \geq 3) = 1 - P(X \leq 2) = 1 - .537 = .463$

7.103 $P(X = 0) = \dfrac{25!}{01!(25-0)!} (.08)^0 (1-.08)^{25-0} = .1244$

7.104 Excel with n = 100 and p = .20: $P(X > 40) = P(X \geq 41) = 1 - P(X \leq 40) = 1 - .999999 = .000001$

7.105 a Excel with n = 200 and p = .45: $P(X \geq 100) = 1 - P(X \leq 99) = 1 - .91130 = .08870$

b Excel with n = 200 and p = .25: $P(X \leq 55) = .81618$

c Excel with n = 200 and p = .30: $P(50 \leq X \leq 75) = P(X \leq 75) - P(X \leq 49) = .99062 - .05059 = .94003$

7.106 a $P(X = 0) = \dfrac{e^{-\mu}\mu^x}{x!} = \dfrac{e^{-2}2^0}{0!} = .1353$

b $P(X = 3) = \dfrac{e^{-\mu}\mu^x}{x!} = \dfrac{e^{-2}2^3}{3!} = .1804$

c $P(X = 5) = \dfrac{e^{-\mu}\mu^x}{x!} = \dfrac{e^{-2}2^5}{5!} = .0361$

7.107 $P(X = 0) = P(X \leq 0) = .135$

b $P(X = 3) = P(X \leq 3) - P(X \leq 2) = .857 - .677 = .180$

c $P(X = 5) = P(X \leq 5) - P(X \leq 4) = .983 - .947 = .036$

7.108 a .13534

b .18045

c .03609

7.109 a $P(X = 0) = \dfrac{e^{-\mu}\mu^x}{x!} = \dfrac{e^{-.5}.5^0}{0!} = .6065$

b $P(X = 1) = \dfrac{e^{-\mu}\mu^x}{x!} = \dfrac{e^{-.5}.5^1}{1!} = .3033$

c $P(X = 2) = \dfrac{e^{-\mu}\mu^x}{x!} = \dfrac{e^{-.5}.5^2}{2!} = .0758$

7.110 a $P(X = 0) = P(X \leq 0) = .607$

b $P(X = 1) = P(X \leq 1) - P(X \leq 0) = .910 - .607 = .303$

c $P(X = 2) = P(X \leq 2) - P(X \leq 1) = .986 - .910 = .076$

7.111 a .60653

b .30327

c .07582

7.112 a Table 2 with $\mu = 3.5$: $P(X = 0) = P(X \leq 0) = .030$

b Table 2 with $\mu = 3.5$: $P(X \geq 5) = 1 - P(X \leq 4) = 1 - .725 = .275$

c Table 2 with $\mu = 3.5/7$: $P(X = 1) = P(X \leq 1) - P(X \leq 0) = .910 - .607 = .303$

7.113 a $P(X = 5$ with $\mu = 14/3) = \dfrac{e^{-\mu}\mu^{x}}{x!} = \dfrac{e^{-14/3}(14/3)^{5}}{5!} = .1734$

b $P(X = 1$ with $\mu = 1/3) =) = \dfrac{e^{-\mu}\mu^{x}}{x!} = \dfrac{e^{-1/3}(1/3)^{1}}{1!} = .2388$

7.114 a $P(X = 0$ with $\mu = 2) = \dfrac{e^{-\mu}\mu^{x}}{x!} = \dfrac{e^{-2}(2)^{0}}{0!} = .1353$

b $P(X = 10$ with $\mu = 14) = \dfrac{e^{-\mu}\mu^{x}}{x!} = \dfrac{e^{-14}(14)^{10}}{10!} = .0663$

7.115 a Table 2 with $\mu = 5$: $P(X \geq 10) = 1 - P(X \leq 9) = 1 - .968 = .032$

b Table 2 with $\mu = 10$: $P(X \geq 20) = 1 - P(X \leq 19) = 1 - .997 = .003$

7.116 $P(X = 0$ with $\mu = 2) = \dfrac{e^{-\mu}\mu^{x}}{x!} = \dfrac{e^{-2}(2)^{0}}{0!} = .1353$

7.117 a Excel with $\mu = 1.8$: $P(X \geq 3) = 1 - P(X \leq 2) = 1 - .73062 = .26938$

b Table 2 with $\mu = 9$: $P(10 \leq X \leq 15) = P(X \leq 15) - P(X \leq 9) = .978 - .587 = .391$

7.118 $P(X = 0$ with $\mu = 80/200) = \dfrac{e^{-\mu}\mu^{x}}{x!} = \dfrac{e^{-.4}(.4)^{0}}{0!} = .6703$

7.119 a Table 2 with $\mu = 5$: $P(X \geq 10) = 1 - P(X \leq 9) = 1 - .968 = .032$

b Excel: $P(X \geq 25$ with $\mu = 25) = 1 - P(X \leq 24) = 1 - .47340 = .52660$

7.120 a Table 2 with $\mu = 1.5$: $P(X \geq 2) = 1 - P(X \leq 1) = 1 - .558 = .442$

b Table 2 $\mu = 6$: $P(X < 4) = P(X \leq 3) = .151$

7.121 a $P(X = 1$ with $\mu = 5) = \dfrac{e^{-\mu}\mu^{x}}{x!} = \dfrac{e^{-5}(5)^{1}}{1!} = .0337$

b Table 2 with $\mu = 15$: $P(X > 20) = P(X \geq 21) = 1 - P(X \leq 20) = 1 - .917 = .083$

7.122 a $P(X = 0$ with $\mu = 1.5) = \dfrac{e^{-\mu}\mu^{x}}{x!} = \dfrac{e^{-1.5}(1.5)^{0}}{0!} .2231$

b Table 2 with $\mu = 4.5$: $P(X \leq 5) = .703$

c Table 2 with $\mu = 3.0$: $P(X \geq 3) = 1 - P(X \leq 2 = 1 - .423 = .577$

7.123 $P(X = 5) = (.774)^{5} = .2778$

7.124 a $E(X) = np = 40(.02) = .8$

b $P(X = 0) = \dfrac{40!}{0!(40-0)!}(.02)^{0}(1-.02)^{40-0} = .4457$

7.125 a $\mu = E(X) = \sum xp(x) = 0(.48) + 1(.35) + 2(.08) + 3(.05) + 4(.04) = .82$

$\sigma^{2} = V(X) = \sum (x - \mu)^{2} p(x) = (0-.82)^{2}(.48) + (1-.82)^{2}(.35) + (2-.82)^{2}(.08)$

$\qquad + (3-.82)^{2}(.05) + (4-.82)^{2}(.04) = 1.0876$

$\sigma = \sqrt{\sigma^{2}} = \sqrt{1.0876} = 1.04$

7.126 a $P(X = 10$ with $\mu = 8) = \dfrac{e^{-\mu}\mu^{x}}{x!} = \dfrac{e^{-8}(8)^{10}}{10!} = .0993$

b Table 2 with $\mu = 8$: $P(X > 5) = P(X \geq 6) = 1 - P(X \leq 5) = 1 - .191 = .809$

c Table 2 with $\mu = 8$: $P(X < 12) = P(X \leq 11) = .888$

7.127 a $E(X) = np = 100(.15) = 15$

b $\sigma = \sqrt{np(1-p)} = \sqrt{100(.15)(1-.15)} = 3.57$

c Excel with $n = 100$ and $p = .15$: $P(X \geq 20) = 1 - P(X \leq 19) = 1 - .8935 = .1065$

7.128 Table 1 with $n = 10$ and $p = .3$: $P(X > 5) = P(X \geq 6) = 1 - P(X \leq 5) = 1 - .953 = .047$

7.129 a $\mu = E(X) = \sum xp(x) = 5(.05) + 6(.16) + 7(.41) + 8(.27) + 9(.07) + 10(.04) = 7.27$

$\sigma^{2} = V(X) = \sum (x - \mu)^{2} p(x) = (5-7.27)^{2}(.05) + (6-7.27)^{2}(.16) + (7-7.27)^{2}(.41)$

$\qquad + (8-7.27)^{2}(.27) + (9-7.27)^{2}(.07) + (10-7.27)^{2}(.04) = 1.1971$

133

$$\sigma = \sqrt{\sigma^2} = \sqrt{1.1971} = 1.09$$

7.130 Table 1 with n = 10 and p = .20: $P(X \geq 6) = 1 - P(X \leq 5) = 1 - .994 = .006$

7.131 a $P(X = 2) = \dfrac{10!}{2!(10-2)!}\,(.05)^2(1-.05)^{10-2} = .0746$

b Excel with n = 400 and p = .05: $P(X = 25) = .0446$

c .05

7.132 a Excel with n = 80 and p = .70: $P(X > 65) = P(X \geq 66) = 1 - P(X \leq 65) = 1 - .99207 = .00793$

b $E(X) = np = 80(.70) = 56$

c $\sigma = \sqrt{np(1-p)^2} = \sqrt{80(.70)(1-.70)} = 4.10$

7.133 $\mu = E(X) = \sum xp(x) = 0(.35) + 1(.25) + 2(.18) + 3(.13) + 4(.09) = 1.36$

$\sigma^2 = V(X) = \sum (x - \mu)^2 p(x) = (0\text{-}1.36)^2(.35) + (1\text{-}1.36)^2(.25) + (2\text{-}1.36)^2(.18)$

$\qquad + (3\text{-}1.36)^2(.13) + (4\text{-}1.36)^2(.09) = 1.73$

$\sigma = \sqrt{\sigma^2} = \sqrt{1.73} = 1.32$

7.134 Table 1 with n = 25 and p = .40:

a $P(X = 10) = P(X \leq 10) - P(X \leq 9) = .586 - .425 = .161$

b $P(X < 5) = P(X \leq 4) = .009$

c $P(X > 15) = P(X \geq 16) = 1 - P(X \leq 15) = 1 - .987 = .013$

7.135 Excel with n = 100 and p = .45:

a $P(X > 50) = P(X \geq 49) = 1 - P(X \leq 50) = 1 - .86542 = .13458$

b $P(X < 44) = P(X \leq 43) = .38277$

c $P(X = 45) = .07999$

7.136 a $\mu = E(X) = \sum xp(x) = 0(.36) + 1(.22) + 2(.20) + 3(.09) + 4(.08) + 5(.05) = 1.46$

$\sigma^2 = V(X) = \sum (x - \mu)^2 p(x) = (0\text{-}1.46)^2(.36) + (1\text{-}1.46)^2(.22) + (2\text{-}1.46)^2(.20)$

$\qquad + (3\text{-}1.46)^2(.09) + (4\text{-}1.46)^2(.08) + (5\text{-}1.46)^2(.05) = 2.23$

$\sigma = \sqrt{\sigma^2} = \sqrt{2.23} = 1.49$

b $\mu = E(X) = \sum xp(x) = 0(.15) + 1(.18) + 2(.23) + 3(.26) + 4(.10) + 5(.08) = 2.22$

$\sigma^2 = V(X) = \sum (x-\mu)^2 p(x) = (0\text{-}2.22)^2 (.15) + (1\text{-}2.22)^2 (.18) + (2\text{-}2.22)^2 (.23)$

$$+ (3\text{-}2.22)^2 (.26) + (4\text{-}2.22)^2 (.10) + (5\text{-}2.22)^2 (.08) = 2.11$$

$\sigma = \sqrt{\sigma^2} = \sqrt{2.11} = 1.45$

c Viewers of nonviolent shows remember more about the product that was advertised.

7.137 Excel with n = 25 and p = 1/3: $P(X \geq 10) = 1 - P(X \leq 9) = 1\text{-} .69560 = .30440$

7.138 p = .08755 because $P(X \geq 1) = 1\text{-} P(X = 0$ with n = 10 and p = .08755$) = 1\text{-} .40 = .60$

7.139 Excel with n = 100 and p = .60: $P(X > 50) = P(X \geq 51) = 1 - P(X \leq 50) = 1\text{-} .02710 = .97290$

7.140 Binomial with n = 5 and p = .01.

x	p(x)
0	.95099
1	.04803
2	.00097
3	.00001
4	0
5	0

Case 7.1

Outcome	Probability	Bases Occupied	Outs	Expected Number of Runs	
1	.75	2nd	1	.69	.5175
2	.10	1st	1	.52	.0520
3	.10	none	2	.10	.0100
4	.05	1st and 2nd	0	1.46	.0730

Expected number of runs = .6255

Chapter 8

8.1a $P(30 < X < 45) \approx \dfrac{(45-30)\times 146}{400\times 15} = .365$

b $P(90 < X < 120) \approx \dfrac{(105-90)\times 11}{400\times 15} + \dfrac{(120-105)\times 6}{400\times 15} = .0425$

c $P(40 < X < 80) \approx \dfrac{(45-40)\times 146}{400\times 15} + \dfrac{(60-45)\times 110}{400\times 15} + \dfrac{(75-60)\times 68}{400\times 15} + \dfrac{(80-75)\times 24}{400\times 15} = .5867$

d $P(X > 100) \approx \dfrac{(105-100)\times 11}{400\times 15} + \dfrac{(120-105)\times 6}{400\times 15} + \dfrac{(135-120)\times 3}{400\times 15} + \dfrac{(150-135)\times 0}{400\times 15} + \dfrac{(165-150)\times 1}{400\times 15}$

$= .0342$

8.2 a $P(X > 45) \approx \dfrac{(60-45)\times 2}{50\times 15} + \dfrac{(75-60)\times 2}{50\times 15} = .0800$

b $P(10 < X < 40) \approx \dfrac{(15-10)\times 17}{50\times 15} + \dfrac{(30-15)\times 7}{50\times 15} + \dfrac{(40-30)\times 6}{50\times 15} = .3333$

c $P(X < 25) \approx \dfrac{(-15-[-30])\times 6}{50\times 15} + \dfrac{(0-[-15])\times 10}{50\times 15} + \dfrac{(15-0)\times 17}{50\times 15} + \dfrac{(25-15)\times 7}{50\times 15} = .7533$

d $P(35 < X < 65) \approx \dfrac{(45-35)\times 6}{50\times 15} + \dfrac{(60-45)\times 2}{50\times 15} + \dfrac{(65-60)\times 2}{50\times 15} = .1333$

8.3 a $P(55 < X < 80) \approx \dfrac{(60-55)\times 16}{60\times 10} + \dfrac{(70-60)\times 5}{60\times 10} + \dfrac{(80-70)\times 24}{60\times 10} = .6167$

b $P(X > 65) \approx \dfrac{(70-65)\times 5}{60\times 10} + \dfrac{(80-70)\times 24}{60\times 10} + \dfrac{(90-80)\times 7}{60\times 10} + \dfrac{(100-90)\times 1}{60\times 10} = .5750$

c $P(X < 85) \approx \dfrac{(50-40)\times 7}{60\times 10} + \dfrac{(60-50)\times 16}{60\times 10} + \dfrac{(70-60)\times 5}{60\times 10} + \dfrac{(80-70)\times 24}{60\times 10} + \dfrac{(85-80)\times 7}{60\times 10} = .9250$

d $P(75 < X < 85) \approx \dfrac{(80-75)\times 24}{60\times 10} + \dfrac{(85-80)\times 7}{60\times 10} = .2583$

8.4 a

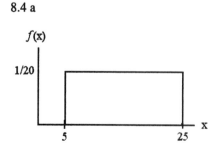

b $P(X > 25) = 0$

c $P(10 < X < 15) = (15 - 10)\dfrac{1}{20} = .25$

d $P(5.0 < X < 5.1) = (5.1 - 5)\dfrac{1}{20} = .005$

8.5 a $f(x) = \dfrac{1}{(60 - 20)} = \dfrac{1}{40}$ $20 < x < 60$

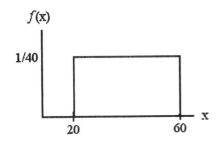

b $P(35 < X < 45) = (45\text{-}35)\ \dfrac{1}{40} = .25$

c

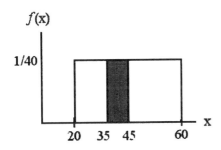

8.6 $f(x) = \dfrac{1}{(60 - 30)} = \dfrac{1}{30}\ \ 30 < x < 60$

a $P(X > 55) = (60 - 55)\dfrac{1}{30} = .1667$

b $P(30 < X < 40) = (40 - 30)\dfrac{1}{30} = .3333$

c $P(X = 37.23) = 0$

8.7 $\dfrac{1}{4} \times (60 - 30) = 7.5$; The first quartile $= 30 + 7.5 = 37.5$ minutes

8.8 $.10 \times (60 - 30) = 3$; The top decile $= 60\text{-}3 = 57$ minutes

8.9 $f(x) = \dfrac{1}{(175-110)} = \dfrac{1}{65}$ $\qquad\qquad$ $110 < x < 175$

a $P(X > 150) = (175-150)\dfrac{1}{65} = .3846$

b $P(120 < X < 160) = (160-120)\dfrac{1}{65} = .6154$

8.10 $.20(175-110) = 13$. Bottom 20% lie below $(110 + 13) = 123$

8.11 a

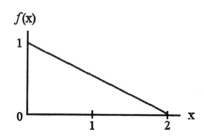

c $P(X > 1) = (.5)(2-1)(.5) = .25$

d $P(X < .5) = 1 - P(X > .5) = 1 - (.75)(1.5)(.5) = 1 - .5625 = .4375$

e $P(X = 1.5) = 0$

8.12 a

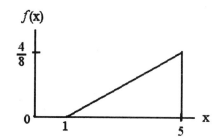

b $P(2.0 < X < 4.0) = P(X < 4) - P(X < 2) = (3)(3/8)(.5) - (1)(1/8)(.5) = .5625 - .0625 = .5$

c $P(X < 3) = (2)(2/8)(.5) = .25$

8.13a

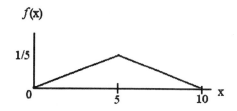

138

b $P(1 < X < 3) = P(X < 3) - P(X < 1) = \frac{1}{2} \times \frac{3}{25} \times (3 - 0) - \frac{1}{2} \times \frac{1}{25} \times (1 - 0) = .18 - .02 = .16$

c $P(4 < X < 8) = P(4 < X < 5) + P(5 < X < 8)$

$\quad P(4 < X < 5) = P(X < 5) - P(X < 4) = \frac{1}{2} \times \frac{5}{25} \times (5 - 0) - \frac{1}{2} \times \frac{4}{25} \times (4 - 0) = .5 - .32 = .18$

$\quad P(5 < X < 8) = P(X > 5) - P(X > 8) = \frac{1}{2} \times \frac{5}{25} \times (10 - 5) - \frac{1}{2} \times \frac{2}{25} \times (10 - 8) = .5 - .08 = .42$

$P(4 < X < 8) = .42 + .18 = .60$

d $P(X < 7) = 1 - P(X > 7)$

$\quad P(X > 7) = \frac{1}{2} \times \frac{3}{25} \times (10 - 7) = .18$

$P(X < 7) = 1 - .18 = .82$

e $P(X > 3) = 1 - P(X < 3)$

$\quad P(X < 3) = \frac{1}{2} \times \frac{3}{25} \times (3 - 0) = .18$

$P(X > 3) = 1 - .18 = .82$

8.14 a $f(x) = .10 - .005x \quad 0 \leq x \leq 20$
b $P(X > 10) = (10)(.05)(.5) = .25$
c $P(6 < X < 12) = P(X > 6) - PX > 12) = (14)(.07)(.5) - (8)(.04)(.5) = .49 - .16 = .33$

8.15 $P(0 < Z < 1.5) = .4332$

8.16 $P(0 < Z < 1.51) = .4345$

8.17 $P(0 < Z < 1.55) = .4394$

8.18 $P(0 < Z < 1.59) = .4441$

8.19 $P(0 < Z < 1.6) = .4452$

8.20 $P(0 < Z < 2.3) = .4893$

8.21 $P(-1.4 < Z < 0.6) = P(-1.4 < Z < 0) + P(0 < Z < .6) = P(0 < Z < 1.4) + P(0 < Z < .6)$
$\quad\quad\quad = .4192 + .2257 = .6449$

8.22 $P(Z > -1.44) = P(Z < 1.44) = .5 + P(0 < Z < 1.44) = .5 + .4251 = .9251$

8.23 $P(Z < 2.03) = .5 + P(0 < Z < 2.03) = .5 + .4788 = .9788$

8.24 $P(Z > 1.67) = .5 - P(0 < Z < 1.67) = .5 - .4525 = .0475$

8.25 $P(Z < 2.84) = .5 + P(0 < Z < 2.84) = .5 + .4977 = .9977$

8.26 $P(1.14 < Z < 2.43) = P(0 < Z < 2.43) - P(0 < Z < 1.14) = .4925 - .3729 = .1196$

8.27 $P(-0.91 < Z < -0.33) = P(0.33 < Z < .91) = P(0 < Z < .91) - P(0 < Z < .33)$
$$= .3186 - .1293 = .1893$$

8.28 $P(Z > 3.09) = .5 - P(0 < Z < 3.09) = .5 - .4990 = .0010$

8.29 $P(Z > 0) = .5$

8.30 $P(Z > 4.0) = 0$

8.31 $P(0 < Z < z_{.02}) = .5 - .02 = .4800;\ z_{.02} = 2.05$

8.32 $P(0 < Z < z_{.045}) = .5 - .045 = .4550;\ z_{.045} = 1.70$

8.33 $P(0 < Z < z_{.20}) = .5 - .20 = .3000;\ z_{.20} = .84$

8.34 $P(X > 145) = P\left(\dfrac{X - \mu}{\sigma} > \dfrac{145 - 100}{20}\right) = P(Z > 2.25) = .5 - P(0 < Z < 2.25)$
$$= .5 - .4878 = .0122$$

8.35 $P(0 < Z < z_{.15}) = .5 - .15 = .3500;\ z_{.15} = 1.04$
$$z_{.15} = \dfrac{x - \mu}{\sigma};\ 1.04 = \dfrac{x - 250}{40};\ x = 291.6$$

8.36 $P(800 < X < 1100) = P\left(\dfrac{800 - 1000}{250} < \dfrac{X - \mu}{\sigma} < \dfrac{1100 - 1000}{250}\right) = P(-.8 < Z > .4)$
$$= P(0 < Z < .4) + P(0 < Z < .8) = .1554 + .2881 = .4435$$

8.37 $P(-z_{.08} < Z < 0) = .5 - .08 = .4200;\ -z_{.08} = -1.41$

$$-z_{.08} = \frac{x-\mu}{\sigma};\ -1.41 = \frac{x-50}{8};\ x = 38.72$$

8.38 a $P(5 < X < 10) = P\left(\frac{5-6.3}{2.2} < \frac{X-\mu}{\sigma} < \frac{10-6.3}{2.2}\right) = P(-.59 < Z > 1.68)$

$$= P(0 < Z < 1.68) + P(0 < Z < .59 = .4535 + .2224 = .6759$$

b $P(X > 7) = P\left(\frac{X-\mu}{\sigma} > \frac{7-6.3}{2.2}\right) = P(Z > .32) = .5 - P(0 < Z < .32)$

$$= .5 - .1255 = .3745$$

c $P(X < 4) = P\left(\frac{X-\mu}{\sigma} < \frac{4-6.3}{2.2}\right) = P(Z < -1.05) = .5 - P(0 < Z < 1.05)$

$$= .5 - .3531 = .1469$$

8.39 $P(0 < Z < z_{.10}) = .5 - .10 = .4000;\ z_{.10} = 1.28$

$$z_{.10} = \frac{x-\mu}{\sigma};\ 1.28 = \frac{x-6.3}{2.2};\ x = 9.116$$

8.40 $P(X > 5000) = P\left(\frac{X-\mu}{\sigma} > \frac{5000-5100}{200}\right) = P(Z > -.5) = .5 + P(0 < Z < .5)$

$$= .5 + .1915 = .6915$$

8.41 $P(-z_{.02} < Z < 0) = .5 - .02 = .4800;\ -z_{.02} = -2.05$

$$-z_{.02} = \frac{x-\mu}{\sigma};\ -2.05 = \frac{x-5100}{200};\ x = 4690$$

8.42 a $P(X > 12000) = P\left(\frac{X-\mu}{\sigma} > \frac{12000-10000}{2400}\right) = P(Z > .83) = .5 - P(0 < Z < .83)$

$$= .5 - .2967 = .2033$$

b $P(X < 9000) = P\left(\frac{X-\mu}{\sigma} < \frac{9000-10000}{2400}\right) = P(Z < -.42) = .5 - P(0 < Z < .42)$

$$= .5 - .1628 = .3372$$

8.43 $P(0 < Z < z_{.001}) = .5 - .001 = .4990;\ z_{.001} = 3.08$

$$z_{.001} = \frac{x - \mu}{\sigma} \; ; \; 3.08 = \frac{x - 10000}{2,400} \; ; \; x = 17,392$$

8.44 a $P(X > 70) = P\left(\frac{X - \mu}{\sigma} > \frac{70 - 65}{4} \right) = P(Z > 1.25) = .5 - P(0 < Z < 1.25)$

$$= .5 - .3944 = .1056$$

b $P(X < 60) = P\left(\frac{X - \mu}{\sigma} < \frac{60 - 65}{4} \right) = P(Z < -1.25) = .5 - P(0 < Z < 1.25)$

$$= .5 - .3944 = .1056$$

c $P(55 < X < 70) = P\left(\frac{55 - 65}{4} < \frac{X - \mu}{\sigma} < \frac{70 - 65}{4} \right) = P(-2.50 < Z < 1.25)$

$$= P(0 < Z < 2.50) + P(0 < Z < 1.25) = .4938 + .3944 = .8882$$

8.45 a $P(X < 70000) = P\left(\frac{X - \mu}{\sigma} < \frac{70000 - 82000}{6400} \right) = P(Z < -1.88) = .5 - P(0 < Z < 1.88)$

$$= .5 - .4699 = .0301$$

b $P(X > 100000) = P\left(\frac{X - \mu}{\sigma} > \frac{100000 - 82000}{6400} \right) = P(Z > 2.81) = .5 - P(0 < Z < 2.81)$

$$= .5 - .4975 = .0025$$

8.46 Top 5%: $P(0 < Z < z_{.05}) = .5 - .05 = .4500; \; z_{.05} = 1.645$

$$z_{.05} = \frac{x - \mu}{\sigma} \; ; \; 1.645 = \frac{x - 32}{1.5} \; ; \; x = 34.4675$$

Bottom 5%: $P(-z_{.05} < Z < 0) = .5 - .05 = .4500; \; -z_{.05} = -1.645$

$$-z_{.05} = \frac{x - \mu}{\sigma} \; ; \; -1.645 = \frac{x - 32}{1.5} \; ; \; x = 29.5325$$

8.47 a $P(X > 36) = P\left(\frac{X - \mu}{\sigma} > \frac{36 - 32}{1.5} \right) = P(Z > 2.67) = .5 - P(0 < Z < 2.67)$

$$= .5 - .4962 = .0038$$

b $P(X < 34) = P\left(\frac{X - \mu}{\sigma} < \frac{34 - 32}{1.5} \right) = P(Z < 1.33) = .5 + P(0 < Z < 1.33)$

$$= .5 + .4082 = .9082$$

c $P(30 < X < 33) = P\left(\frac{30 - 32}{1.5} < \frac{X - \mu}{\sigma} < \frac{33 - 32}{1.5} \right) = P(-1.33 < Z < .67)$

$$= P(0 < Z < 1.33) + P(0 < Z < .67) = .4082 + .2486 = .6568$$

8.48 $P(X > 8) = P\left(\dfrac{X-\mu}{\sigma} > \dfrac{8-7.2}{.667}\right) = P(Z > 1.2) = .5 - P(0 < Z < 1.2)$

$\qquad = .5 - .3849 = .1151$

8.49 $P(0 < Z < z_{.25}) = .5 - .25 = .2500;\ \ z_{.25} = .67;$

$\qquad z_{.25} = \dfrac{x-\mu}{\sigma};\ .67 = \dfrac{x-7.2}{.67};\ x = 7.65$ hours

8.50 a $P(X > 10) = P\left(\dfrac{X-\mu}{\sigma} > \dfrac{10-7.5}{2.1}\right) = P(Z > 1.19) = .5 - P(0 < Z < 1.19)$

$\qquad = .5 - .3830 = .1170$

b $P(7 < X < 9) = P\left(\dfrac{7-7.5}{2.1} < \dfrac{X-\mu}{\sigma} < \dfrac{9-7.5}{2.1}\right) = P(-.24 < Z < .71)$

$\qquad = P(0 < Z < .24) + P(0 < Z < .71) = .0948 + .2611 = .3559$

c $P(X < 3) = P\left(\dfrac{X-\mu}{\sigma} < \dfrac{3-7.5}{2.1}\right) = P(Z < -2.14) = .5 - P(0 < Z < 2.14)$

$\qquad = .5 - .4838 = .0162$

d $P(-z_{.05} < Z < 0) = .5 - .05 = .4500;\ \ -z_{.05} = -1.645;$

$\qquad -z_{.05} = \dfrac{x-\mu}{\sigma};\ \ -1.645 = \dfrac{x-7.5}{2.1};\ x = 4.05$ hours

8.51 a $P(X > 12,000) = P\left(\dfrac{X-\mu}{\sigma} > \dfrac{12,000-11,500}{800}\right) = P(Z > .63) = .5 - P(0 < Z < .63)$

$\qquad = .5 - .2357 = .2643$

b $P(X < 10,000) = P\left(\dfrac{X-\mu}{\sigma} < \dfrac{10,000-11,500}{800}\right) = P(Z < -1.88) = .5 - P(0 < Z < 1.88)$

$\qquad = .5 - .4699 = .0301$

8.52 $P(-z_{.01} < Z < 0) = .5 - .01 = .4900;\ \ -z_{.01} = -2.33$

$\qquad -z_{.01} = \dfrac{x-\mu}{\sigma};\ \ -2.33 = \dfrac{x-11500}{800};\ x = 9,636$

8.53 a $P(24 < X < 28) = P\left(\dfrac{24-26}{2.5} < \dfrac{X-\mu}{\sigma} < \dfrac{28-26}{2.5}\right) = P(-.8 < Z < .8)$

$\qquad = 2P(0 < Z < .8) = 2(.2881) = .5762$

b $P(X > 28) = P\left(\dfrac{X-\mu}{\sigma} > \dfrac{28-26}{2.5}\right) = P(Z > .8) = .5 - P(0 < Z < .8) = .5 - .2881 = .2119$

c $P(X < 24) = P\left(\dfrac{X-\mu}{\sigma} < \dfrac{24-26}{2.5}\right) = P(Z < -.8) = .5 - P(0 < Z < .8) = .5 - .2881 = .2119$

8.54 a $P(X > 30) = P\left(\dfrac{X-\mu}{\sigma} > \dfrac{30-27}{7}\right) = P(Z > .43) = .5 - P(0 < Z < .43)$

$$= .5 - .1664 = .3336$$

b $P(X > 40) = P\left(\dfrac{X-\mu}{\sigma} > \dfrac{40-27}{7}\right) = P(Z > 1.86) = .5 - P(0 < Z < 1.86)$

$$= .5 - .4686 = .0314$$

c $P(X < 15) = P\left(\dfrac{X-\mu}{\sigma} < \dfrac{15-27}{7}\right) = P(Z < -1.71) = .5 - P(0 < Z < 1.71)$

$$= .5 - .4564 = .0436$$

d $P(0 < Z < z_{.20}) = .5 - .20 = .3000;\ z_{.20} = .84$

$$z_{.20} = \frac{x-\mu}{\sigma};\ .84 = \frac{x-27}{7};\ x = 32.88$$

8.55 a $P(X < 4) = P\left(\dfrac{X-\mu}{\sigma} < \dfrac{4-7.5}{1.2}\right) = P(Z < -2.92) = .5 - P(0 < Z < 2.92)$

$$= .5 - .4982 = .0018$$

b $P(7 < X < 10) = P\left(\dfrac{7-7.5}{1.2} < \dfrac{X-\mu}{\sigma} < \dfrac{10-7.5}{1.2}\right) = P(-.42 < Z < 2.08)$

$$= P(0 < Z < .42) + P(0 < Z < 2.08) = .1628 + .4812 = .6440$$

8.56 a $P(X < 10) = P\left(\dfrac{X-\mu}{\sigma} < \dfrac{10-16.40}{2.75}\right) = P(Z < -2.33) = .5 - P(0 < Z < 2.33)$

$$= .5 - .4901 = .0099$$

b $P(-z_{.10} < Z < 0) = .5 - .10 = .4000;\ -z_{.10} = -1.28$

$$-z_{.10} = \frac{x-\mu}{\sigma};\ -1.28 = \frac{x-16.40}{2.75};\ x = 12.88$$

8.57 A: $P(0 < Z < z_{.10}) = .5 - .10 = .4000;\ z_{.10} = 1.28$

$$z_{.10} = \frac{x-\mu}{\sigma};\ 1.28 = \frac{x-70}{10};\ x = 82.8$$

B: $P(0 < Z < z_{.40}) = .5 - .40 = .1000;\ z_{.40} = .25$

$$z_{.40} = \frac{x - \mu}{\sigma}; \; .25 = \frac{x - 70}{10}; \; x = 72.5$$

C: $P(-z_{.20} < Z < 0) = .5 - .20 = .3000; \; -z_{.20} = -.84$

$$-z_{.20} = \frac{x - \mu}{\sigma}; \; -.84 = \frac{x - 70}{10}; \; x = 61.6$$

D: $P(-z_{.05} < Z < 0) = .5 - .05 = .4500; \; -z_{.05} = -1.645$

$$-z_{.05} = \frac{x - \mu}{\sigma}; \; -1.645 = \frac{x - 70}{10}; \; x = 53.55$$

8.58 $P(0 < Z < z_{.02}) = .5 - .02 = .4800; \; z_{.02} = 2.05$

$$z_{.02} = \frac{x - \mu}{\sigma}; \; 2.05 = \frac{x - 100}{16}; \; x = 132.80 \text{ (rounded to 133)}$$

8.59 $P(-z_{.01} < Z < 0) = .5 - .01 = .4900; \; -z_{.01} = -2.33$

$$-z_{.01} = \frac{x - \mu}{\sigma}; \; -2.33 = \frac{x - 75}{8}; \; x = 56.36$$

8.60 $P(0 < Z < z_{.06}) = .5 - .06 = .4400; \; z_{.06} = 1.55$

$$z_{.06} = \frac{x - \mu}{\sigma}; \; 1.55 = \frac{x - 200}{30}; \; x = 246.5 \text{ (rounded to 247)}$$

8.61 $P(0 < Z < z_{.20}) = .5 - .20 = .3000; \; z_{.20} = .84$

$$z_{.20} = \frac{x - \mu}{\sigma}; \; .84 = \frac{x - 150}{25}; \; x = 171$$

8.62 $P(0 < Z < z_{.30}) = .5 - .30 = .2000; \; z_{.30} = .52$

$$z_{.30} = \frac{x - \mu}{\sigma}; \; .52 = \frac{x - 850}{90}; \; x = 896.8 \text{ (rounded to 897)}$$

8.63 $P(0 < Z < z_{.40}) = .5 - .40 = .1000; \; z_{.40} = .25$

$$z_{.40} = \frac{x - \mu}{\sigma}; \; .25 = \frac{x - 850}{90}; \; .x = 872.5 \text{ (rounded to 873)}$$

8.64 From Exercise 7.57: $\mu = 65$, $\sigma^2 = 21$, and $\sigma = 4.58$

$$P(X > 60) = P\left(\frac{X - \mu}{\sigma} > \frac{60 - 65}{4.58} \right) = P(Z > -1.09) = .5 + .3621 = .8621$$

8.65 From Exercise 7.58: $\mu = 145$, $\sigma^2 = 31$, and $\sigma = 5.57$

$$P(X < 150) = P\left(\frac{X - \mu}{\sigma} < \frac{150 - 145}{5.57}\right) = P(Z < .90) = .5 + .3159 = .8159$$

8.66 From Exercise 7.59: $\mu = 100$, $\sigma^2 = 30$, and $\sigma = 5.48$

$$P(X < 110) = P\left(\frac{X - \mu}{\sigma} < \frac{110 - 100}{5.48}\right) = P(Z < 1.82) = .5 + .4656 = .9656$$

8.67 From Exercise 7.60: $\mu = 168$, $\sigma^2 = 574$, and $\sigma = 24$

$$P(X > 180) = P\left(\frac{X - \mu}{\sigma} > \frac{180 - 168}{24}\right) = P(Z > .5) = .5 - .1915 = .3085$$

8.68 a $P(X > 25) = P\left(\dfrac{X - \mu}{\sigma} > \dfrac{25 - 14}{18}\right) = P(Z > .61) = .5 - .2291 = .2709$

b $P(X < 0) = P\left(\dfrac{X - \mu}{\sigma} < \dfrac{0 - 14}{18}\right) = P(Z < -.78) = .5 - .2823 = .2177$

8.69 a $P(X > 25) = P\left(\dfrac{X - \mu}{\sigma} > \dfrac{25 - 14}{9}\right) = P(Z > 1.22) = .5 - .3888 = .1112$

b $P(X < 0) = P\left(\dfrac{X - \mu}{\sigma} < \dfrac{0 - 14}{9}\right) = P(Z < -.1.56) = .5 - .4406 = .0594$

8.70 a $P(X < 0) = P\left(\dfrac{X - \mu}{\sigma} < \dfrac{0 - .12}{02}\right) = P(Z < -6.00) = 0$

b $P(X > .20) = P\left(\dfrac{X - \mu}{\sigma} > \dfrac{.20 - .12}{.02}\right) = P(Z > 4.00) = 0$

c $P(X < 0) = P\left(\dfrac{X - \mu}{\sigma} < \dfrac{0 - .25}{.15}\right) = P(Z < -1.67) = .5 - .4525 = .0475$

d $P(X > .20) = P\left(\dfrac{X - \mu}{\sigma} > \dfrac{.20 - .25}{.15}\right) = P(Z > -.33) = .5 + .1293 = .6293$

8.71 a $P(X < 0) = P\left(\dfrac{X - \mu}{\sigma} < \dfrac{0 - .211}{.1067}\right) = P(Z < -1.98) = .5 - .4761 = .0239$

b $P(X > .20) = P\left(\dfrac{X - \mu}{\sigma} > \dfrac{.20 - .211}{.1067}\right) = P(Z > -.10) = .5 + .0398 = .5398$

8.72 The probability of losing money is greater than that for stock 1 but less than that for stock 2. The probability of returning more that 20% is greater than that for stock 1 but less than that for stock 2.

8.73 a $P(X < 0) = P\left(\dfrac{X - \mu}{\sigma} < \dfrac{0 - .09}{.15}\right) = P(Z < -.60) = .5 - .2257 = .2743$

b $P(X > .15) = P\left(\dfrac{X - \mu}{\sigma} > \dfrac{.15 - .09}{.15}\right) = P(Z > .40) = .5 - .1554 = .3446$

c $P(X < 0) = P\left(\dfrac{X - \mu}{\sigma} < \dfrac{0 - .13}{.21}\right) = P(Z < -.62) = .5 - .2324 = .2676$

d $P(X > .15) = P\left(\dfrac{X - \mu}{\sigma} > \dfrac{.15 - .13}{.21}\right) = P(Z > .10) = .5 - .0398 = .4602$

8.74 a $P(X < 0) = P\left(\dfrac{X - \mu}{\sigma} < \dfrac{0 - .106}{.1456}\right) = P(Z < -.73) = ..5 - .2673 = .2327$

b $P(X > .15) = P\left(\dfrac{X - \mu}{\sigma} > \dfrac{.15 - .106}{.1456}\right) = P(Z > .30) = .5 - .1179 = .3821$

8.75 The disadvantage is that the portfolio has a smaller probability of returning more than 15% compared to both stocks. The advantage is that the portfolio has a smaller probability of losing money compared to both stocks.

The statistics used in Exercises 7.68 to 7.80 were computed by Excel. The variances were taken from the variance-covariance matrix. As a result they are the population parameters. These values were used in producing the solutions to Exercises 8.76 to 8.79

8.76 a $P(X < 0) = P\left(\dfrac{X - \mu}{\sigma} < \dfrac{0 - .058}{.064}\right) = P(Z < -.91) = .5 - .3186 = .1814$

b $P(X > .20) = P\left(\dfrac{X - \mu}{\sigma} > \dfrac{.20 - .058}{.064}\right) = P(Z > 2.22) = .5 - .4868 = .0132$

8.77 a $P(X < 0) = P\left(\dfrac{X - \mu}{\sigma} < \dfrac{0 - .0616}{.0777}\right) = P(Z < -.79) = .5 - .2852 = .2148$

b $P(X > .20) = P\left(\dfrac{X - \mu}{\sigma} > \dfrac{.20 - .0616}{.0777}\right) = P(Z > 1.78) = .5 - .4625 = .0375$

147

8.78 a $P(X < 0) = P\left(\dfrac{X-\mu}{\sigma} < \dfrac{0-.0351}{.2231}\right) = P(Z < -.16) = .5 - .0636 = .4364$

b $P(X > .40) = P\left(\dfrac{X-\mu}{\sigma} > \dfrac{.40-.0351}{.2231}\right) = P(Z > 1.64) = .5 - .4495 = .0505$

8.79 a $P(X < 0) = P\left(\dfrac{X-\mu}{\sigma} < \dfrac{0-.0192}{.1991}\right) = P(Z < -.10) = .5 - .0398 = .4602$

b $P(X > .40) = P\left(\dfrac{X-\mu}{\sigma} > \dfrac{.40-.0192}{.1991}\right) = P(Z > 1.91) = .5 - .4719 = .0281$

8.80

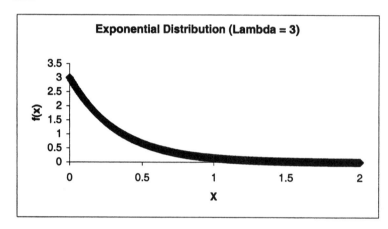

8.81

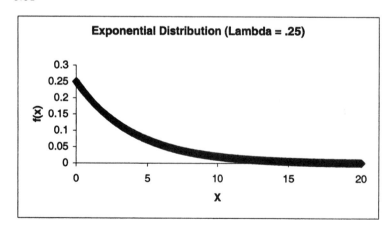

8.82 a $P(X > 1) = e^{-.5(1)} = e^{-.5} = .6065$

a $P(X > .4) = e^{-.5(.4)} = e^{-.2} = .8187$

c $P(X < .5) = 1 - e^{-.5(.5)} = 1 - e^{-.25} = 1 - .7788 = .2212$

d $P(X < 2) = 1 - e^{-.5(2)} = 1 - e^{-1} = 1 - .3679 = .6321$

8.83 a $P(X > 1) = e^{-1.5(1)} = e^{-1.5} = .2231$

b $P(X < 3) = 1 - e^{-1.5(3)} = 1 - e^{-4.5} = 1 - .0111 = .9889$

c $P(2 < X < 4) = e^{-1.5(2)} - e^{-1.5(4)} = e^{-3} - e^{-6} = .0498 - .0025 = .0473$

d $P(X > .5) = e^{-1.5(.5)} = e^{-.75} = .4724$

8.84 a $P(X > 2) = e^{-.3(2)} = e^{-.6} = .5488$

b $P(X < 4) = 1 - e^{-.3(4)} = 1 - e^{-1.2} = 1 - .3012 = .6988$

c $P(1 < X < 2) = e^{-.3(1)} - e^{-.3(2)} = e^{-.3} - e^{-.6} = .7408 - .5488 = .1920$

d $P(X = 3) = 0$

8.85 $\lambda = 6$ kilograms/hour $= .1$ kilogram/minute

$P(X > 15) = e^{-.1(15)} = e^{-1.5} = .2231$

8.86 $\mu = 1/\lambda = 25$ hours; $\lambda = .04$ breakdowns/hour

$P(X > 50) = e^{-.04(50)} = e^{-2} = .1353$

8.87 $\lambda = 10$ trucks/hour $= .167$ truck/minute

$P(X > 15) = e^{-.167(15)} = e^{-2.5} = .0821$

8.88 $\mu = 1/\lambda = 5$ minutes; $\lambda = .2$ customer/minute

$P(X < 10) = 1 - e^{-.2(10)} = 1 - e^{-2} = 1 - .1353 = .8647$

8.89 $\mu = 1/\lambda = 2.7$ minutes; $\lambda = .37$ service/minute

$P(X < 3) = 1 - e^{-.37(3)} = 1 - e^{-1.11} = 1 - .3296 = .6704$

8.90 $\mu = 1/\lambda = 7.5$ minutes; $\lambda = .133$ service/minute

$P(X < 5) = 1 - e^{-.133(5)} = 1 - e^{-.665} = 1 - .5143 = .4857$

8.91 $\mu = 1/\lambda = 125$ seconds; $\lambda = .008$ transactions/second $= .48$ transactions/minute

$P(X > 3) = e^{-.48(3)} = e^{-1.44} = .2369$

8.92 $\mu = 1/\lambda = 6$ minutes; $\lambda = .167$ customers/minute

$P(X > 10) = e^{-.167(10)} = e^{-1.67} = .1889$

8.93	a 1.341	b 1.319	c 1.990	d 1.653
8.94	a 2.724	b 1.282	c 2.132	d 2.528
8.95	a 1.3406	b 1.3195	c 1.9890	d 1.6527
8.96	a 1.6556	b 2.6810	c 1.9600	d 1.6602
8.97	a .0189	b .0341	c .0927	d .0324
8.98	a .1744	b .0231	c .0251	d .0267
8.99	a 9.23635	b 135.807	c 9.39046	d 37.4848
8.100	a 17.2919	b 50.8922	c 2.70554	d 53.5400
8.101	a 73.3441	b 102.946	c 16.3382	d 24.7690
8.102	a 33.5705	b 866.911	c 24.3976	d 261.058
8.103	a .2688	b 1.0	c .9903	d 1.0
8.104	a .4881	b .9158	c .9988	d .9077
8.105	a 4.35	b 8.89	c 3.29	d 2.50
8.106	a 2.84	b 1.93	c 3.60	d 3.37
8.107	a 1.4857	b 1.7633	c 1.8200	d 1.1587
8.108	a 1.5204	b 1.5943	c 2.8397	d 1.1670
8.109	a .0510	b .1634	c .0222	d .2133
8.110	a .1050	b .1576	c .0001	d .0044

Chapter 9

9.1 a, b, c, & d 1/6

9.2 a $P(\overline{X} = 3) = P(1,5) + P(2,4) + P(3,3) + P(4,2) + P(5,1) = 5(1/36) = 5/36$

b $P(\overline{X} = 4) = P(2,6) + P(3,5) + P(4,4) + P(5,3) + P(6,2) = 5(1/36) = 5/36$

c $P(\overline{X} = 1) = P(1,1) = 1/36$

d $P(\overline{X} = 6) = P(6,6) = 1/36$

9.3 Var ($\overline{X}$) < Var (X)

9.4 a $P(\overline{X} = 1) = (1/6)^5 = .0001286$

b $P(\overline{X} = 6) = (1/6)^5 = .0001286$

9.5 The sampling distribution of the mean is normal with a mean of 40 and a standard deviation of $12/\sqrt{100} = 1.2$.

9.6 No because of the central limit theorem.

9.7 a $P(\overline{X} > 1050) = P\left(\dfrac{\overline{X} - \mu}{\sigma/\sqrt{n}} > \dfrac{1050 - 1000}{200/\sqrt{16}}\right) = P(Z > 1.00) = .5 - P(0 < Z < 1.00)$

$= .5 - .3413 = .1587$

b $P(\overline{X} < 960) = P\left(\dfrac{\overline{X} - \mu}{\sigma/\sqrt{n}} < \dfrac{960 - 1000}{200/\sqrt{16}}\right) = P(Z < -.80) = .5 - P(0 < Z < .80)$

$= .5 - .2881 = .2119$

c $P(\overline{X} > 1100) = P\left(\dfrac{\overline{X} - \mu}{\sigma/\sqrt{n}} > \dfrac{1100 - 1000}{200/\sqrt{16}}\right) = P(Z > 2.00) = .5 - P(0 < Z < 2.00)$

$= .5 - .4772 = .0228$

9.8 a $P(\overline{X} > 1050) = P\left(\dfrac{\overline{X} - \mu}{\sigma/\sqrt{n}} > \dfrac{1050 - 1000}{200/\sqrt{25}}\right) = P(Z > 1.25) = .5 - P(0 < Z < 1.25)$

$= .5 - .3944 = .1056$

b $P(\overline{X} < 960) = P\left(\dfrac{\overline{X} - \mu}{\sigma/\sqrt{n}} < \dfrac{960 - 1000}{200/\sqrt{25}}\right) = P(Z < -1.00) = .5 - P(0 < Z < 1.00)$

$$= .5 - .3413 = .1587$$

c $P(\overline{X} > 1100) = P\left(\dfrac{\overline{X} - \mu}{\sigma / \sqrt{n}} > \dfrac{1100 - 1000}{200 / \sqrt{25}}\right) = P(Z > 2.50) = .5 - P(0 < Z < 2.50)$

$$= .5 - .4938 = .0062$$

9.9 a $P(\overline{X} > 1050) = P\left(\dfrac{\overline{X} - \mu}{\sigma / \sqrt{n}} > \dfrac{1050 - 1000}{200 / \sqrt{100}}\right) = P(Z > 2.50) = .5 - P(0 < Z < 2.50)$

$$= .5 - .4938 = .0062$$

b $P(\overline{X} < 960) = P\left(\dfrac{\overline{X} - \mu}{\sigma / \sqrt{n}} < \dfrac{960 - 1000}{200 / \sqrt{100}}\right) = P(Z < -2.00) = .5 - P(0 < Z < 2.00)$

$$= .5 - .4772 = .0228$$

c $P(\overline{X} > 1100) = P\left(\dfrac{\overline{X} - \mu}{\sigma / \sqrt{n}} > \dfrac{1100 - 1000}{200 / \sqrt{100}}\right) = P(Z > 5.00) = 0$

9.10 a $P(49 < \overline{X} < 52) = P\left(\dfrac{49 - 50}{5 / \sqrt{4}} < \dfrac{\overline{X} - \mu}{\sigma / \sqrt{n}} < \dfrac{52 - 50}{5 / \sqrt{4}}\right) = P(-.40 < Z < .80)$

$$= P(0 < Z < .40) + P(0 < Z < .80) = .1554 + .2881 = .4435$$

b $P(49 < \overline{X} < 52) = P\left(\dfrac{49 - 50}{5 / \sqrt{16}} < \dfrac{\overline{X} - \mu}{\sigma / \sqrt{n}} < \dfrac{52 - 50}{5 / \sqrt{16}}\right) = P(-.80 < Z < 1.60)$

$$= P(0 < Z < .80) + P(0 < Z < 1.60) = .2881 + .4452 = .7333$$

c $P(49 < \overline{X} < 52) = P\left(\dfrac{49 - 50}{5 / \sqrt{25}} < \dfrac{\overline{X} - \mu}{\sigma / \sqrt{n}} < \dfrac{52 - 50}{5 / \sqrt{25}}\right) = P(-1.00 < Z < 2.00)$

$$= P(0 < Z < 1.00) + P(0 < Z < 2.00) = .3413 + .4772 = .8185$$

9.11 a $P(49 < \overline{X} < 52) = P\left(\dfrac{49 - 50}{10 / \sqrt{4}} < \dfrac{\overline{X} - \mu}{\sigma / \sqrt{n}} < \dfrac{52 - 50}{10 / \sqrt{4}}\right) = P(-.20 < Z < .40)$

$$= P(0 < Z < .20) + P(0 < Z < .40) = .0793 + .1554 = .2347$$

b $P(49 < \overline{X} < 52) = P\left(\dfrac{49 - 50}{10 / \sqrt{16}} < \dfrac{\overline{X} - \mu}{\sigma / \sqrt{n}} < \dfrac{52 - 50}{10 / \sqrt{16}}\right) = P(-.40 < Z < .80)$

$$= P(0 < Z < .40) + P(0 < Z < .80) = .1554 + .2881 = .4435$$

c $P(49 < \overline{X} < 52) = P\left(\dfrac{49 - 50}{10 / \sqrt{25}} < \dfrac{\overline{X} - \mu}{\sigma / \sqrt{n}} < \dfrac{52 - 50}{10 / \sqrt{25}}\right) = P(-.50 < Z < 1.00)$

$$= P(0 < Z < .50) + P(0 < Z < 1.00) = .1915 + .3413 = .5328$$

9.12 a $P(49 < \bar{X} < 52) = P\left(\dfrac{49-50}{20/\sqrt{4}} < \dfrac{\bar{X}-\mu}{\sigma/\sqrt{n}} < \dfrac{52-50}{20/\sqrt{4}}\right) = P(-.10 < Z < .20)$

$\qquad\qquad = P(0 < Z < .10) + P(0 < Z < .20) = .0398 + .0793 = .1191$

b $P(49 < \bar{X} < 52) = P\left(\dfrac{49-50}{20/\sqrt{16}} < \dfrac{\bar{X}-\mu}{\sigma/\sqrt{n}} < \dfrac{52-50}{20/\sqrt{16}}\right) = P(-.20 < Z < .40)$

$\qquad\qquad = P(0 < Z < .20) + P(0 < Z < .40) = .0793 + .1554 = .2347$

c $P(49 < \bar{X} < 52) = P\left(\dfrac{49-50}{20/\sqrt{25}} < \dfrac{\bar{X}-\mu}{\sigma/\sqrt{n}} < \dfrac{52-50}{20/\sqrt{25}}\right) = P(-.25 < Z < .50)$

$\qquad\qquad = P(0 < Z < .25) + P(0 < Z < .50) = .0987 + .1915 = .2902$

9.13 a $P(X > 66) = P\left(\dfrac{X-\mu}{\sigma} > \dfrac{66-64}{2}\right) = P(Z > 1.00) = .5 - P(0 < Z < 1.00)$

$\qquad = .5 - .3413 = .1587$

b $P(\bar{X} > 66) = P\left(\dfrac{\bar{X}-\mu}{\sigma/\sqrt{n}} > \dfrac{66-64}{2/\sqrt{4}}\right) = P(Z > 2.00) = .5 - P(0 < Z < 2.00)$

$\qquad = .5 - .4772 = .0228$

c $P(\bar{X} > 66) = P\left(\dfrac{\bar{X}-\mu}{\sigma/\sqrt{n}} > \dfrac{66-64}{2/\sqrt{100}}\right) = P(Z > 10.00) = 0$

9.14 We can answer part (c) and possibly part (b) depending on how nonnormal the population is.

9.15 a $P(X > 120) = P\left(\dfrac{X-\mu}{\sigma} > \dfrac{120-117}{5.2}\right) = P(Z > 0.58) = .5 - P(0 < Z < .58)$

$\qquad = .5 - .2190 = .2810$

b $P(\bar{X} > 120) = P\left(\dfrac{\bar{X}-\mu}{\sigma/\sqrt{n}} > \dfrac{120-117}{5.2/\sqrt{4}}\right) = P(Z > 1.15) = .5 - P(0 < Z < 1.15)$

$\qquad = .5 - .3749 = .1251$

c $[P(X > 120)]^4 = [.2810]^4 = .00623$

9.16 a $P(X > 60) = P\left(\dfrac{X-\mu}{\sigma} > \dfrac{60-52}{6}\right) = P(Z > 1.33) = .5 - P(0 < Z < 1.33)$

$\qquad = .5 - .4082 = .0918$

b $P(\bar{X} > 60) = P\left(\dfrac{\bar{X}-\mu}{\sigma/\sqrt{n}} > \dfrac{60-52}{6/\sqrt{3}}\right) = P(Z > 2.31) = .5 - P(0 < Z < 2.31)$

$\qquad = .5 - .4896 = .0104$

c $[P(X > 60)]^3 = [.0918]^3 = .00077$

9.17 a $P(X > 12) = P\left(\dfrac{X - \mu}{\sigma} > \dfrac{12 - 10}{3}\right) = P(Z > .67) = .5 - P(0 < Z < .67)$

$= .5 - .2486 = .2514$

b $P(\overline{X} > 275 / 25) = P(\overline{X} > 11) = P\left(\dfrac{\overline{X} - \mu}{\sigma / \sqrt{n}} > \dfrac{11 - 10}{3 / \sqrt{25}}\right) = P(Z > 1.67)$

$= .5 - P(0 < Z < 1.67) = .5 - .4525 = .0475$

9.18 a $P(X < 75) = P\left(\dfrac{X - \mu}{\sigma} < \dfrac{75 - 78}{6}\right) = P(Z < -.50) = .5 - P(0 < Z < .50)$

$= .5 - .1915 = .3085$

b $P(\overline{X} < 75) = P\left(\dfrac{\overline{X} - \mu}{\sigma / \sqrt{n}} < \dfrac{75 - 78}{6 / \sqrt{50}}\right) = P(Z < -3.54) = .5 - P(0 < Z < 3.54) = .5 - .5 = 0$

9.19 a $P(X > 7) = P\left(\dfrac{X - \mu}{\sigma} > \dfrac{7 - 6}{1.5}\right) = P(Z > .67) = .5 - P(0 < Z < .67)$

$= .5 - .2486 = .2514$

b $P(\overline{X} > 7) = P\left(\dfrac{\overline{X} - \mu}{\sigma / \sqrt{n}} > \dfrac{7 - 6}{1.5 / \sqrt{5}}\right) = P(Z > 1.49) = .5 - P(0 < Z < 1.49)$

$= .5 - .4319 = .0681$

c $[P(X > 7)]^5 = [.2514]^5 = .00100$

9.20 a $P(\overline{X} < 5.97) = P\left(\dfrac{\overline{X} - \mu}{\sigma / \sqrt{n}} < \dfrac{5.97 - 6.05}{.18 / \sqrt{36}}\right) = P(Z < -2.67) = .5 - P(0 < Z < 2.67)$

$= .5 - .4962 = .0038$

b It appears to be false.

9.21 $P(\overline{X} > 10,000 / 16) = P(\overline{X} > 625) = P\left(\dfrac{\overline{X} - \mu}{\sigma / \sqrt{n}} > \dfrac{625 - 600}{200 / \sqrt{16}}\right) = P(Z > .50)$

$= .5 - P(0 < Z < .50) = .5 - .1915 = .3085$

9.22 The professor needs to know the mean and standard deviation of the population of the weights of elevator users and that the distribution is not extremely nonnormal.

9.23 $P(\overline{X} > 1,140 / 16) = P(\overline{X} > 71.25) = P\left(\dfrac{\overline{X} - \mu}{\sigma / \sqrt{n}} > \dfrac{71.25 - 75}{10 / \sqrt{16}}\right) = P(Z > -1.50)$

$$= .5 + P(0 < Z < 1.50) = .5 + .4332 = .9332$$

9.24 $P(\text{Total time} > 300) = P(\overline{X} > 300 / 60) = P(\overline{X} > 5) = P\left(\dfrac{\overline{X} - \mu}{\sigma / \sqrt{n}} > \dfrac{5 - 4.8}{1.3 / \sqrt{60}}\right) = P(Z > 1.19)$

$$= .5 - P(0 < Z < 1.19) = .5 - .3830 = .1170$$

9.25, No because the central limit theorem says that the sample mean is approximately normally distributed.

9.26 $P(\overline{X} < 53,000) = P\left(\dfrac{\overline{X} - \mu}{\sigma / \sqrt{n}} < \dfrac{53,000 - 55,000}{4,600 / \sqrt{38}}\right) = P(Z < -2.68)$

$$= .5 - P(0 < Z < 2.68) = .5 - .4963 = .0037$$

9.27 The dean's claim appears to be incorrect.

9.28 $P(\hat{P} > .60) = P\left(\dfrac{\hat{P} - p}{\sqrt{p(1 - p) / n}} > \dfrac{.60 - .5}{\sqrt{(.5)(1 - .5) / 300}}\right) = P(Z > 3.46) = 0$

9.29 $P(\hat{P} > .60) = P\left(\dfrac{\hat{P} - p}{\sqrt{p(1 - p) / n}} > \dfrac{.60 - .55}{\sqrt{(.55)(1 - .55) / 300}}\right) = P(Z > 1.74)$

$$= .5 - P(0 < Z < 1.74) = .5 - .4591 = .0409$$

9.30 $P(\hat{P} > .60) = P\left(\dfrac{\hat{P} - p}{\sqrt{p(1 - p) / n}} > \dfrac{.60 - .6}{\sqrt{(.6)(1 - .6) / 300}}\right) = P(Z > 0) = .5$

9.31 $P(\hat{P} < .22) = P\left(\dfrac{\hat{P} - p}{\sqrt{p(1 - p) / n}} > \dfrac{.22 - .25}{\sqrt{(.25)(1 - .25) / 500}}\right) = P(Z < -1.55)$

$$= .5 - P(0 < Z < 1.55) = .5 - .4394 = .0606$$

9.32 $P(\hat{P} < .22) = P\left(\dfrac{\hat{P} - p}{\sqrt{p(1 - p) / n}} > \dfrac{.22 - .25}{\sqrt{(.25)(1 - .25) / 800}}\right) = P(Z < -1.96)$

$$= .5 - P(0 < Z < 1.96) = .5 - .4750 = .0250$$

9.33 $P(\hat{P} < .22) = P\left(\dfrac{\hat{P}-p}{\sqrt{p(1-p)/n}} > \dfrac{.22-.25}{\sqrt{(.25)(1-.25)/1000}}\right) = P(Z < -2.19)$

$$= .5 - P(0 < Z < 2.19) = .5 - .4857 = .0143$$

9.34 $P(\hat{P} < .49) = P\left(\dfrac{\hat{P}-p}{\sqrt{p(1-p)/n}} < \dfrac{.49-.55}{\sqrt{(.55)(1-.55)/500}}\right) = P(Z < -2.70)$

$$= .5 - P(0 < Z < 2.70) = .5 - .4965 = .0035$$

9.35 $P(\hat{P} > .04) = P\left(\dfrac{\hat{P}-p}{\sqrt{p(1-p)/n}} > \dfrac{.04-.02}{\sqrt{(.02)(1-.02)/800}}\right) = P(Z > 4.04) = 0;$

The defective appears to be larger than 2%.

9.36 $P(\hat{P} < .50) = P\left(\dfrac{\hat{P}-p}{\sqrt{p(1-p)/n}} < \dfrac{.50-.53}{\sqrt{(.53)(1-.53)/400}}\right) = P(Z < -1.20)$

$$= .5 - P(0 < Z < 1.20) = .5 - .3849 = .1151;\ \text{the claim may be true}$$

9.37 $P(\hat{P} < .50) = P\left(\dfrac{\hat{P}-p}{\sqrt{p(1-p)/n}} < \dfrac{.50-.53}{\sqrt{(.53)(1-.53)/1000}}\right) = P(Z < -1.90)$

$$= .5 - P(0 < Z < 1.90) = .5 - .4713 = .0287;\ \text{the claim appears to be false.}$$

9.38 $P(\hat{P} > .10) = P\left(\dfrac{\hat{P}-p}{\sqrt{p(1-p)/n}} > \dfrac{.10-.05}{\sqrt{(.05)(1-.05)/400}}\right) = P(Z > 4.59) = 0;\ \text{the claim appears to be}$

false

9.39 $P(\hat{P} > .32) = P\left(\dfrac{\hat{P}-p}{\sqrt{p(1-p)/n}} > \dfrac{.32-.30}{\sqrt{(.30)(1-.30)/1,000}}\right) = P(Z > 1.38)$

$$= .5 - P(0 < Z < 1.38) = .5 - .4162 = .0838$$

9.40 a $P(\hat{P} < .45) = P\left(\dfrac{\hat{P}-p}{\sqrt{p(1-p)/n}} < \dfrac{.45-.50}{\sqrt{(.50)(1-.50)/600}}\right) = P(Z < -2.45)$

$$= .5 - P(0 < Z < 2.45) = .5 - .4929 = .0071$$

b The claim appears to be false.

$$9.41\ \mathrm{P}(\hat{P} < .75) = P\left(\frac{\hat{P} - p}{\sqrt{p(1-p)/n}} < \frac{.75 - .80}{\sqrt{(.80)(1-.80)/350}}\right) = \mathrm{P}(Z < -2.34)$$

$$= .5 - \mathrm{P}(0 < Z < 2.34) = .5 - .4904 = .0096$$

$$9.42\ \mathrm{P}(\hat{P} < .70) = P\left(\frac{\hat{P} - p}{\sqrt{p(1-p)/n}} < \frac{.70 - .75}{\sqrt{(.75)(1-.75)/460}}\right) = \mathrm{P}(Z < -2.48)$$

$$= .5 - \mathrm{P}(0 < Z < 2.48) = .5 - .4934 = .0066$$

$$9.43\ \mathrm{P}(\hat{P} > .28) = P\left(\frac{\hat{P} - p}{\sqrt{p(1-p)/n}} > \frac{.28 - .25}{\sqrt{(.25)(1-.25)/1215}}\right) = \mathrm{P}(Z > 2.40)$$

$$= .5 - \mathrm{P}(0 < Z < 2.40) = .5 - .4918 = .0082$$

9.44 The claim appears to be false.

$$9.45\ P(\overline{X}_1 - \overline{X}_2 > 25) = P\left(\frac{(\overline{X}_1 - \overline{X}_2) - (\mu_1 - \mu_2)}{\sqrt{\dfrac{\sigma_1^2}{n_1} + \dfrac{\sigma_2^2}{n_2}}} > \frac{25 - (280 - 270)}{\sqrt{\dfrac{25^2}{10} + \dfrac{30^2}{10}}}\right) = \mathrm{P}(Z > 1.21)$$

$$= .5 - \mathrm{P}(0 < Z < 1.21) = .5 - .3869 = .1131$$

$$9.46\ P(\overline{X}_1 - \overline{X}_2 > 25) = P\left(\frac{(\overline{X}_1 - \overline{X}_2) - (\mu_1 - \mu_2)}{\sqrt{\dfrac{\sigma_1^2}{n_1} + \dfrac{\sigma_2^2}{n_2}}} > \frac{25 - (280 - 270)}{\sqrt{\dfrac{25^2}{50} + \dfrac{30^2}{50}}}\right) = \mathrm{P}(Z > 2.72)$$

$$= .5 - \mathrm{P}(0 < Z < 2.72) = .5 - .4967 = .0033$$

$$9.47\ P(\overline{X}_1 - \overline{X}_2 > 25) = P\left(\frac{(\overline{X}_1 - \overline{X}_2) - (\mu_1 - \mu_2)}{\sqrt{\dfrac{\sigma_1^2}{n_1} + \dfrac{\sigma_2^2}{n_2}}} > \frac{25 - (280 - 270)}{\sqrt{\dfrac{25^2}{100} + \dfrac{30^2}{100}}}\right) = \mathrm{P}(Z > 3.84) = 0$$

$$9.48\ P(\overline{X}_1 - \overline{X}_2 > 0) = P\left(\frac{(\overline{X}_1 - \overline{X}_2) - (\mu_1 - \mu_2)}{\sqrt{\dfrac{\sigma_1^2}{n_1} + \dfrac{\sigma_2^2}{n_2}}} > \frac{0 - (40 - 38)}{\sqrt{\dfrac{6^2}{25} + \dfrac{8^2}{25}}}\right) = \mathrm{P}(Z > -1.00)$$

$$= .5 + P(0 < Z < 1.00) = .5 + .3413 = .8413$$

$$9.49 \quad P(\overline{X}_1 - \overline{X}_2 > 0) = P\left(\frac{(\overline{X}_1 - \overline{X}_2) - (\mu_1 - \mu_2)}{\sqrt{\frac{\sigma_1^2}{n_1} + \frac{\sigma_2^2}{n_2}}} > \frac{0 - (40 - 38)}{\sqrt{\frac{12^2}{25} + \frac{16^2}{25}}}\right) = P(Z > -.50)$$

$$= .5 + P(0 < Z < .50) = .5 + .1915 = .6915$$

$$9.50 \quad P(\overline{X}_1 - \overline{X}_2 > 0) = P\left(\frac{(\overline{X}_1 - \overline{X}_2) - (\mu_1 - \mu_2)}{\sqrt{\frac{\sigma_1^2}{n_1} + \frac{\sigma_2^2}{n_2}}} > \frac{0 - (140 - 138)}{\sqrt{\frac{6^2}{25} + \frac{8^2}{25}}}\right) = P(Z > -1.00)$$

$$= .5 + P(0 < Z < 1.00) = .5 + .3413 = .8413$$

$$9.51 \text{ a } \quad P(X_1 - X_2 > 0) = P\left(\frac{(X_1 - X_2) - (\mu_1 - \mu_2)}{\sqrt{\sigma_1^2 + \sigma_2^2}} > \frac{0 - (75 - 65)}{\sqrt{20^2 + 21^2}}\right) = P(Z > -.34)$$

$$= .5 + P(0 < Z < .34) = .5 + .1331 = .6331$$

$$\text{b } \quad P(\overline{X}_1 - \overline{X}_2 > 0) = P\left(\frac{(\overline{X}_1 - \overline{X}_2) - (\mu_1 - \mu_2)}{\sqrt{\frac{\sigma_1^2}{n_1} + \frac{\sigma_2^2}{n_2}}} > \frac{0 - (75 - 65)}{\sqrt{\frac{20^2}{5} + \frac{21^2}{5}}}\right) = P(Z > -.77)$$

$$= .5 + P(0 < Z < .77) = .5 + .2794 = .7794$$

$$9.52 \text{ a } \quad P(X_1 - X_2 > 0) = P\left(\frac{(X_1 - X_2) - (\mu_1 - \mu_2)}{\sqrt{\sigma_1^2 + \sigma_2^2}} > \frac{0 - (73 - 77)}{\sqrt{12^2 + 10^2}}\right) = P(Z > .26)$$

$$= .5 - P(0 < Z < .26) = .5 - .1026 = .3974$$

$$\text{b } \quad P(\overline{X}_1 - \overline{X}_2 > 0) = P\left(\frac{(\overline{X}_1 - \overline{X}_2) - (\mu_1 - \mu_2)}{\sqrt{\frac{\sigma_1^2}{n_1} + \frac{\sigma_2^2}{n_2}}} > \frac{0 - (73 - 77)}{\sqrt{\frac{12^2}{4} + \frac{10^2}{4}}}\right) = P(Z > .51)$$

$$= .5 - P(0 < Z < .51) = .5 - .1950 = .3050$$

$$9.53\ P(\overline{X}_1 - \overline{X}_2 > 0) = P\left(\frac{(\overline{X}_1 - \overline{X}_2) - (\mu_1 - \mu_2)}{\sqrt{\dfrac{\sigma_1^2}{n_1} + \dfrac{\sigma_2^2}{n_2}}} > \frac{0 - (18 - 15)}{\sqrt{\dfrac{3^2}{10} + \dfrac{3^2}{10}}} \right) = P(Z > \text{-}2.24)$$

$$= .5 + P(0 < Z < 2.24) = .5 + .4875 = .9875$$

$$9.54\ \ P(\overline{X}_1 - \overline{X}_2 < 0) = P\left(\frac{(\overline{X}_1 - \overline{X}_2) - (\mu_1 - \mu_2)}{\sqrt{\dfrac{\sigma_1^2}{n_1} + \dfrac{\sigma_2^2}{n_2}}} < \frac{0 - (10 - 15)}{\sqrt{\dfrac{3^2}{25} + \dfrac{3^2}{25}}} \right) = P(Z < 5.89) = 1$$

Chapter 10

10.1 An unbiased estimator of a parameter is an estimator whose expected value equals the parameter.

10.2

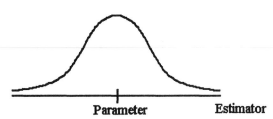

10.3

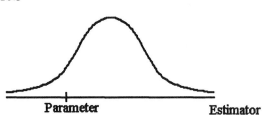

10.4 An unbiased estimator is consistent if the difference between the estimator and the parameter grows smaller as the sample size grows.

10.5 The mean is consistent because it is unbiased and the standard error grows smaller as n increases.

10.6

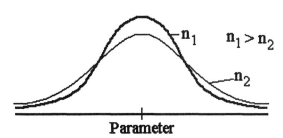

10.7 If there are two unbiased estimators of a parameter, the one whose variance is smaller is relatively efficient.

10.8

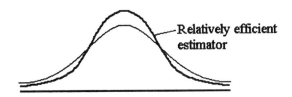

Relatively efficient estimator

10.9 $\bar{x} \pm z_{\alpha/2}\sigma/\sqrt{n} = 100 \pm 1.96(25/\sqrt{50}) = 100 \pm 6.93$; LCL = 93.07, UCL = 106.93

10.10 $\bar{x} \pm z_{\alpha/2}\sigma/\sqrt{n} = 100 \pm 1.645(25/\sqrt{50}) = 100 \pm 5.82$; LCL = 94.18, UCL = 105.82

10.11 $\bar{x} \pm z_{\alpha/2}\sigma/\sqrt{n} = 100 \pm 2.575(25/\sqrt{50}) = 100 \pm 9.11$; LCL = 90.89, UCL = 109.11

10.12 The interval widens.

10.13 $\bar{x} \pm z_{\alpha/2}\sigma/\sqrt{n} = 100 \pm 1.96(10/\sqrt{50}) = 100 \pm 2.77$; LCL = 97.23, UCL = 102.77

10.14 $\bar{x} \pm z_{\alpha/2}\sigma/\sqrt{n} = 100 \pm 1.96(50/\sqrt{50}) = 100 \pm 13.86$; LCL = 86.14, UCL = 113.86

10.15 The interval widens.

10.16 $\bar{x} \pm z_{\alpha/2}\sigma/\sqrt{n} = 100 \pm 1.96(25/\sqrt{25}) = 100 \pm 9.80$; LCL = 90.20, UCL = 109.80

10.17 $\bar{x} \pm z_{\alpha/2}\sigma/\sqrt{n} = 100 \pm 1.96(25/\sqrt{400}) = 100 \pm 2.45$; LCL = 97.55, UCL = 102.45

10.18 The interval narrows.

10.19 $\bar{x} \pm z_{\alpha/2}\sigma/\sqrt{n} = 30 \pm 1.96(25/\sqrt{50}) = 30 \pm 6.93$; LCL = 23.07, UCL = 36.93

10.20 $\bar{x} \pm z_{\alpha/2}\sigma/\sqrt{n} = 200 \pm 1.96(25/\sqrt{50}) = 200 \pm 6.93$; LCL = 193.07, UCL = 206.93

10.21 The width of the interval is unchanged.

10.22 $\bar{x} \pm z_{\alpha/2}\sigma/\sqrt{n} = 500 \pm 1.645(12/\sqrt{50}) = 500 \pm 2.79$; LCL = 497.21, UCL = 502.79

10.23 $\bar{x} \pm z_{\alpha/2}\sigma/\sqrt{n} = 500 \pm 1.96(12/\sqrt{50}) = 500 \pm 3.33$; LCL = 496.67, UCL = 503.33

10.24 $\bar{x} \pm z_{\alpha/2}\sigma/\sqrt{n} = 500 \pm 2.575(12/\sqrt{50}) = 500 \pm 4.37$; LCL = 495.63, UCL = 504.37

10.25 The interval narrows.

10.26 $\bar{x} \pm z_{\alpha/2}\sigma/\sqrt{n} = 500 \pm 1.645(10/\sqrt{50} = 500 \pm 2.33$; LCL = 497.67, UCL = 502..33

10.27 $\bar{x} \pm z_{\alpha/2}\sigma/\sqrt{n} = 500 \pm 1.645(14/\sqrt{50} = 500 \pm 3.26$; LCL = 496.74, UCL = 503.26

10.28 The interval narrows.

10.29 $\bar{x} \pm z_{\alpha/2}\sigma/\sqrt{n} = 500 \pm 1.645(12/\sqrt{100}) = 500 \pm 1.97$; LCL = 498.03, UCL = 501.97

10.30 $\bar{x} \pm z_{\alpha/2}\sigma/\sqrt{n} = 500 \pm 1.645(12/\sqrt{200}) = 500 \pm 1.40$; LCL = 498.60, UCL = 501.40

10.31 The interval widens.

10.32 $\bar{x} \pm z_{\alpha/2}\sigma/\sqrt{n} = 100 \pm 1.645(12/\sqrt{50}) = 100 \pm 2.79$; LCL = 97.21, UCL 102.79

10.33 The width of the interval is unchanged.

10.34 Yes, because the expected value of the sample median is equal to the population mean.

10.35 Yes, because as the sample size increases the variance decreases, which means that the difference between the estimator and the parameter grows smaller as the sample size grows larger.

10.36 Because the variance of the sample mean is less than the variance of the sample median, the sample mean is relatively more efficient than the sample median.

10.37 $sample\ median \pm z_{\alpha/2}\dfrac{1.2533\sigma}{\sqrt{n}}$

10.38 $sample\ median \pm z_{\alpha/2}\dfrac{1.2533\ \sigma}{\sqrt{n}} = 500 \pm 1.645\dfrac{1.2533(12)}{\sqrt{50}} = 500 \pm 3.50$

10.39 The 90% confidence interval estimate of the population mean using the sample mean is

500 ± 2.79.

The 90% confidence interval of the population mean using the sample median is wider than that using the sample mean because the variance of the sample median is larger.

10.40 The median is calculated by placing all the observations in order. Thus, the median loses the potential information contained in the actual values in the sample. This results in a wider interval estimate.

10.41 $\bar{x} \pm z_{\alpha/2} \sigma / \sqrt{n} = 6.89 \pm 1.645(2/\sqrt{9}) = 6.89 \pm 1.10$; LCL = 5.79, UCL = 7.99

10.42 $\bar{x} \pm z_{\alpha/2} \sigma / \sqrt{n} = 43.75 \pm 1.96(10/\sqrt{8}) = 43.75 \pm 6.93$; LCL = 36.82, UCL = 50.68

10.43 $\bar{x} \pm z_{\alpha/2} \sigma / \sqrt{n} = 22.83 \pm 1.96(7/\sqrt{12}) = 22.83 \pm 3.96$; LCL = 18.87, UCL = 26.79

10.44 $\bar{x} \pm z_{\alpha/2} \sigma / \sqrt{n} = 9.85 \pm 1.645(8/\sqrt{20}) = 9.85 \pm 2.94$; LCL = 6.91, UCL = 12.79

10.45 $\bar{x} \pm z_{\alpha/2} \sigma / \sqrt{n} = 75 \pm 1.96(15/\sqrt{400}) = 75 \pm 1.47$; LCL = 73.53, UCL = 76.47. We estimate that the mean number of cars sold annually by all used car salespersons lies between 73.53 and 76.47. This type of estimate is correct 95% of the time.

10.46 $\bar{x} \pm z_{\alpha/2} \sigma / \sqrt{n} = 22 \pm 2.575(5/\sqrt{100}) = 22 \pm 1.29$; LCL = 20.71, UCL = 23.29

10.47 $\bar{x} \pm z_{\alpha/2} \sigma / \sqrt{n} = 125 \pm 1.96(20/\sqrt{100}) = 125 \pm 3.92$; LCL = 121.08, UCL = 128.92

10.48 $\bar{x} \pm z_{\alpha/2} \sigma / \sqrt{n} = 25 \pm 1.645(6/\sqrt{50}) = 25 \pm 1.40$; LCL = 23.60, UCL = 26.40

10.49 $\bar{x} \pm z_{\alpha/2} \sigma / \sqrt{n} = 52{,}000 \pm 2.575(7{,}500/\sqrt{16}) = 52{,}000 \pm 4{,}830$; LCL = 47,170, UCL = 56,830

10.50 $\bar{x} \pm z_{\alpha/2} \sigma / \sqrt{n} = 252.38 \pm 1.96(30/\sqrt{400}) = 252.38 \pm 2.94$; LCL = 249.44, UCL = 255.32

10.51 $\bar{x} \pm z_{\alpha/2} \sigma / \sqrt{n} = 1810.16 \pm 1.96(400/\sqrt{64}) = 1810.16 \pm 98.00$; LCL = 1712.16, UCL = 1908.16

10.52 $\bar{x} \pm z_{\alpha/2}\sigma / \sqrt{n} = 12.10 \pm 1.645(2.1/\sqrt{200}) = 12.10 \pm .24$; LCL = 11.86, UCL = 12.34. We estimate that the mean rate of return on all real estate investments lies between 11.86% and 12.34%. This type of estimate is correct 90% of the time.

10.53 $\bar{x} \pm z_{\alpha/2}\sigma / \sqrt{n} = 10.21 \pm 2.575(2.20/\sqrt{100}) = 10.21 \pm .57$; LCL = 9.64, UCL = 10.78

10.54 $\bar{x} \pm z_{\alpha/2}\sigma / \sqrt{n} = .510 \pm 2.575(.1/\sqrt{250}) = .510 \pm .16$; LCL = .494, UCL = .526. We estimate that the mean growth rate of this type of grass lies between .494 and .526 inch . This type of estimate is correct 99% of the time.

10.55 $\bar{x} \pm z_{\alpha/2}\sigma / \sqrt{n} = 26.81 \pm 1.96(1.3/\sqrt{50}) = 26.81 \pm .36$; LCL = 26.45, UCL = 27.17. We estimate that the mean time to assemble a cell phone lies between 26.45 and 27.17 minutes. This type of estimate is correct 95% of the time.

10.56 $\bar{x} \pm z_{\alpha/2}\sigma / \sqrt{n} = 19.28 \pm 1.645(6/\sqrt{250}) = 19.28 \pm .62$; LCL = 18.66, UCL = 19.90. We estimate that the mean leisure time per week of Japanese middle managers lies between 18.66 and 19.90 hours. This type of estimate is correct 90% of the time.

10.57 $\bar{x} \pm z_{\alpha/2}\sigma / \sqrt{n} = 15.00 \pm 2.575(2.3/\sqrt{100}) = 15.00 \pm .59$; LCL = 14.41, UCL = 15.59. We estimate that the mean pulse-recovery time lies between 14.41 and 15.59 minutes. This type of estimate is correct 99% of the time.

10.58 $\bar{x} \pm z_{\alpha/2}\sigma / \sqrt{n} = 585,063 \pm 1.645(30,000/\sqrt{80}) = 585,063 \pm 5,518$; LCL = 579,545, UCL = 590,581. We estimate that the mean annual income of all company presidents lies between $579,545 and $590,581. This type of estimate is correct 90% of the time.

10.59 $\bar{x} \pm z_{\alpha/2}\sigma / \sqrt{n} = 14.98 \pm 1.645(3/\sqrt{250}) = 14.98 \pm .31$; LCL = 14.67, UCL = 15.29

10.60 $\bar{x} \pm z_{\alpha/2}\sigma / \sqrt{n} = 27.19 \pm 1.96(8/\sqrt{100}) = 27.19 \pm 1.57$; LCL = 25.62, UCL = 28.76

10.61 $\quad n = \left(\dfrac{z_{\alpha/2}\sigma}{W}\right)^2 = \left(\dfrac{1.645 \times 50}{10}\right)^2 = 68$

10.62 $\quad n = \left(\dfrac{z_{\alpha/2}\sigma}{W} \right)^2 = \left(\dfrac{1.645 \times 100}{10} \right)^2 = 271$

10.63 $\quad n = \left(\dfrac{z_{\alpha/2}\sigma}{W} \right)^2 = \left(\dfrac{1.96 \times 50}{10} \right)^2 = 97$

10.64 $\quad n = \left(\dfrac{z_{\alpha/2}\sigma}{W} \right)^2 = \left(\dfrac{1.645 \times 50}{20} \right)^2 = 17$

10.65 a The sample size increases.

b The sample size increases.

c The sample size decreases.

10.66 $\quad n = \left(\dfrac{z_{\alpha/2}\sigma}{W} \right)^2 = \left(\dfrac{2.575 \times 250}{50} \right)^2 = 166$

10.67 $\quad n = \left(\dfrac{z_{\alpha/2}\sigma}{W} \right)^2 = \left(\dfrac{2.575 \times 50}{50} \right)^2 = 7$

10.68 $\quad n = \left(\dfrac{z_{\alpha/2}\sigma}{W} \right)^2 = \left(\dfrac{1.96 \times 250}{50} \right)^2 = 97$

10.69 $\quad n = \left(\dfrac{z_{\alpha/2}\sigma}{W} \right)^2 = \left(\dfrac{2.575 \times 250}{10} \right)^2 = 4145$

10.70 a The sample size decreases.

b the sample size decreases.

c The sample size increases.

10.71 $\quad n = \left(\dfrac{z_{\alpha/2}\sigma}{W} \right)^2 = \left(\dfrac{1.645 \times 10}{1} \right)^2 = 271$

10.72 150 ± 1

10.73 $\bar{x} \pm z_{\alpha/2} \dfrac{\sigma}{\sqrt{n}} = 150 \pm 1.645 \dfrac{5}{\sqrt{271}} = 150 \pm .5$

10.74 $\bar{x} \pm z_{\alpha/2} \dfrac{\sigma}{\sqrt{n}} = 150 \pm 1.645 \dfrac{20}{\sqrt{271}} = 150 \pm 2$

10.75 a The width of the confidence interval estimate is equal to what was specified.

b The width of the confidence interval estimate is narrower than what was specified.

c The width of the confidence interval estimate is wider than what was specified.

10.76 $\quad n = \left(\dfrac{z_{\alpha/2}\sigma}{W}\right)^2 = \left(\dfrac{1.96 \times 200}{10}\right)^2 = 1537$

10.77 500 ± 10

10.78 $\bar{x} \pm z_{\alpha/2} \dfrac{\sigma}{\sqrt{n}} = 500 \pm 1.96 \dfrac{100}{\sqrt{1537}} = 500 \pm 5$

10.79 $\bar{x} \pm z_{\alpha/2} \dfrac{\sigma}{\sqrt{n}} = 500 \pm 1.96 \dfrac{400}{\sqrt{1537}} = 500 \pm 20$

10.80 a The width of the confidence interval estimate is equal to what was specified.

b The width of the confidence interval estimate is narrower than what was specified.

c The width of the confidence interval estimate is wider than what was specified.

10.81 $\quad n = \left(\dfrac{z_{\alpha/2}\sigma}{W}\right)^2 = \left(\dfrac{1.645 \times 10}{2}\right)^2 = 68$

10.82 $\quad n = \left(\dfrac{z_{\alpha/2}\sigma}{W}\right)^2 = \left(\dfrac{2.575 \times 360}{20}\right)^2 = 2149$

10.83 $\quad n = \left(\dfrac{z_{\alpha/2}\sigma}{W}\right)^2 = \left(\dfrac{1.96 \times 12}{2}\right)^2 = 139$

10.84 $\quad n = \left(\dfrac{z_{\alpha/2}\sigma}{W}\right)^2 = \left(\dfrac{1.645 \times 20}{1}\right)^2 = 1083$

10.85 $\quad n = \left(\dfrac{z_{\alpha/2}\sigma}{W} \right)^2 = \left(\dfrac{1.96 \times 25}{5} \right)^2 = 96$

10.86 $\quad n = \left(\dfrac{z_{\alpha/2}\sigma}{W} \right)^2 = \left(\dfrac{1.96 \times 15}{2} \right)^2 = 217$

Chapter 11

11.1 H_0: The drug is not safe and effective

         H_1: The drug is safe and effective

11.2 H_0: I will complete the Ph.D.

         H_1: I will not be able to complete the Ph.D.

11.3 H_0: The batter will hit one deep

         H_1: The batter will not hit one deep

11.4 H_0: Risky investment is more successful

         H_1: Risky investment is not more successful

11.5 H_0: The plane is on fire

         H_1: The plane is not on fire

11.6 The defendant in both cases was O. J. Simpson. The verdicts were logical because in the criminal trial the amount of evidence to convict is greater than the amount of evidence required in a civil trial. The two juries concluded that there was enough (preponderance of) evidence in the civil trial, but not enough evidence (beyond a reasonable doubt) in the criminal trial.

11.7 Rejection region: $z < -z_{\alpha/2} = -z_{.005} = -2.575$ or $z > z_{\alpha/2} = z_{.005} = 2.575$

$$z = \frac{\bar{x} - \mu}{\sigma / \sqrt{n}} = \frac{980 - 1000}{200 / \sqrt{100}} = -1.00$$

p-value = $2P(Z < -1.00) = 2(.5 - .3413) = 2(.1587) = .3174$

There is not enough evidence to infer that $\mu \neq 1000$.

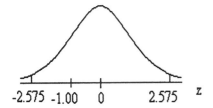

11.8 Rejection region: $z > z_\alpha = z_{.03} = 1.88$

$$z = \frac{\bar{x} - \mu}{\sigma / \sqrt{n}} = \frac{51 - 50}{5 / \sqrt{9}} = .60$$

p-value = P(Z > .60) = .5 - .2257 = .2743

There is not enough evidence to infer that $\mu > 50$.

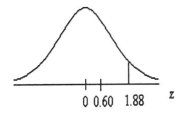

11.9 Rejection region: $z < -z_\alpha = -z_{.10} = -1.28$

$$z = \frac{\bar{x} - \mu}{\sigma / \sqrt{n}} = \frac{14.3 - 15}{2 / \sqrt{25}} = -1.75$$

p-value = P(Z < -1.75) = .5 - .4599 = .0401

There is enough evidence to infer that $\mu < 15$.

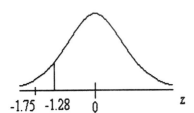

11.10 Rejection region: $z < -z_{\alpha/2} = -z_{.025} = -1.96$ or $z > z_{\alpha/2} = z_{.025} = 1.96$

$$z = \frac{\bar{x} - \mu}{\sigma / \sqrt{n}} = \frac{100 - 100}{10 / \sqrt{100}} = 0$$

p-value = 2P(Z > 0) = 2(.5) = 1.00

There is not enough evidence to infer that $\mu \neq 100$.

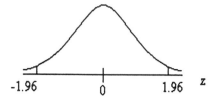

-1.96   0   1.96   z

11.11 Rejection region: $z > z_\alpha = z_{.01} = 2.33$

$$z = \frac{\bar{x} - \mu}{\sigma/\sqrt{n}} = \frac{80 - 70}{20/\sqrt{100}} = 5.00$$

p-value = p(z > 5.00) = 0

There is enough evidence to infer that $\mu > 70$.

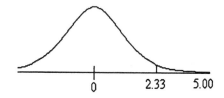

0   2.33   5.00

11.12 Rejection region: $z < -z_\alpha = -z_{.05} = -1.645$

$$z = \frac{\bar{x} - \mu}{\sigma/\sqrt{n}} = \frac{48 - 50}{15/\sqrt{100}} = -1.33$$

p-value = P(Z < -1.33) = .5 - .4082 = .0918

There is not enough evidence to infer that $\mu < 50$.

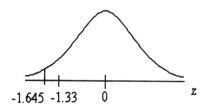

-1.645 -1.33   0   z

11.13 $z = \frac{\bar{x} - \mu}{\sigma/\sqrt{n}} = \frac{52 - 50}{5/\sqrt{9}} = 1.20$

p-value = P(Z > 1.20) = .5 - .3849 = .1151

11.14 $z = \frac{\bar{x} - \mu}{\sigma/\sqrt{n}} = \frac{52 - 50}{5/\sqrt{25}} = 2.00$

p-value = P(Z > 2.00) = .5 - .4772 = .0228.

11.15 $z = \dfrac{\bar{x} - \mu}{\sigma / \sqrt{n}} = \dfrac{52 - 50}{5 / \sqrt{100}} = 4.00$

p-value = P(Z > 4.00) = 0.

11.16 The value of the test statistic increases and the p-value decreases.

11.17 $z = \dfrac{\bar{x} - \mu}{\sigma / \sqrt{n}} = \dfrac{52 - 50}{10 / \sqrt{9}} = .60$

p-value = P(Z > .60) = .5 - .2257 = .2743.

11.18 $z = \dfrac{\bar{x} - \mu}{\sigma / \sqrt{n}} = \dfrac{52 - 50}{20 / \sqrt{9}} = .30$

p-value = P(Z > .30) = .5 - .1179 = .3821.

11.19 The value of the test statistic decreases and the p-value increases.

11.20 $z = \dfrac{\bar{x} - \mu}{\sigma / \sqrt{n}} = \dfrac{54 - 50}{5 / \sqrt{9}} = 2.40$

p-value = P(Z > 2.40) = .5 - .4918 = .0082.

11.21 $z = \dfrac{\bar{x} - \mu}{\sigma / \sqrt{n}} = \dfrac{56 - 50}{5 / \sqrt{9}} = 3.60$

.p-value = P(Z > 3.60) = 0.

11.22 The value of the test statistic increases and the p-value decreases.

11.23 $z = \dfrac{\bar{x} - \mu}{\sigma / \sqrt{n}} = \dfrac{99 - 100}{8 / \sqrt{100}} = -1.25$

p-value = P(Z < -1.25) = .5 - .3944 = .1056.

11.24 $z = \dfrac{\bar{x} - \mu}{\sigma / \sqrt{n}} = \dfrac{99 - 100}{8 / \sqrt{50}} = -.88$

p-value = P(< -.88) = .5 - .3106 = .1894

11.25 $z = \dfrac{\bar{x} - \mu}{\sigma / \sqrt{n}} = \dfrac{99 - 100}{8 / \sqrt{20}} = -.56$

p-value $= P(Z < -.56) = .5 - .2123 = .2877$

11.26 The value of the test statistic increases (becomes less negative) and the p-value increases.

11.27 $z = \dfrac{\bar{x} - \mu}{\sigma / \sqrt{n}} = \dfrac{99 - 100}{12 / \sqrt{100}} = -.83$

p-value $= P(Z < -.83) = .5 - .2967 = .2033.$

11.28 $z = \dfrac{\bar{x} - \mu}{\sigma / \sqrt{n}} = \dfrac{99 - 100}{15 / \sqrt{100}} = -.67$

p-value $= P(Z < -.67) = .5 - .2486 = .2514.$

11.29 The value of the test statistic increases (it becomes less negative) and the p-value increases.

11.30 $z = \dfrac{\bar{x} - \mu}{\sigma / \sqrt{n}} = \dfrac{98 - 100}{8 / \sqrt{100}} = -2.50$

p-value $= P(Z < -2.50) = .5 - .4938 = .0062$

11.31 $z = \dfrac{\bar{x} - \mu}{\sigma / \sqrt{n}} = \dfrac{96 - 100}{8 / \sqrt{100}} = -5.00$

p-value $= P(Z < -5.00) = 0.$

11.32 The value of the test statistic decreases (it becomes more negative) and the p-value decreases.

11.33 a $z = \dfrac{\bar{x} - \mu}{\sigma / \sqrt{n}} = \dfrac{178 - 170}{65 / \sqrt{200}} = 1.74$

p-value $= P(Z > 1.74) = .5 - .4591 = .0409.$

b $z = \dfrac{\bar{x} - \mu}{\sigma / \sqrt{n}} = \dfrac{178 - 170}{65 / \sqrt{100}} = 1.23$

p-value $= P(Z > 1.23) = .5 - .3907 = .1093.$

The value of the test statistic increases and the p-value decreases.

11.34 a $z = \dfrac{\bar{x} - \mu}{\sigma / \sqrt{n}} = \dfrac{178 - 170}{35 / \sqrt{400}} = 4.57$

p-value $= P(Z > 4.57) = 0.$

b $z = \dfrac{\bar{x} - \mu}{\sigma / \sqrt{n}} = \dfrac{178 - 170}{100 / \sqrt{400}} = 1.60$

p-value = P(Z > 1.60) = .5 - .4452 = .0548.

The value of the test statistic decreases and the p-value increases.

11.35 See Table 11.1 in the book.

11.36 a $z = \dfrac{\bar{x} - \mu}{\sigma / \sqrt{n}} = \dfrac{21.63 - 22}{6 / \sqrt{100}} = -.62$

p-value = P(Z < -.62) = .5 - .2324 = .2676

b $z = \dfrac{\bar{x} - \mu}{\sigma / \sqrt{n}} = \dfrac{21.63 - 22}{6 / \sqrt{500}} = -1.38$

p-value = P(Z < -1.38) = .5 - .4162 = .0838.

The value of the test statistic decreases (it becomes more negative) and the p-value decreases.

11.37 a $z = \dfrac{\bar{x} - \mu}{\sigma / \sqrt{n}} = \dfrac{21.63 - 22}{3 / \sqrt{220}} = -1.83$

p-value = P(Z < -1.83) = .5 - .4664 = .0336.

b $z = \dfrac{\bar{x} - \mu}{\sigma / \sqrt{n}} = \dfrac{21.63 - 22}{12 / \sqrt{220}} = -.46$

p-value = P(Z < -.46) = .5 - .1772 = .3228.

The value of the test statistic increases (it becomes less negative) and the p-value increases.

11.38	$\bar{x}$	$z = \dfrac{\bar{x} - 22}{6 / \sqrt{220}}$	p-value
	22.0	0	.5
	21.8	-.49	.3121
	21.6	-.99	.1611
	21.4	-1.48	.0694
	21.2	-1.98	.0239
	21.0	-2.47	.0062
	20.8	-2.97	.0015
	20.6	-3.46	0
	20.4	-3.96	0

11.39 a $z = \dfrac{\bar{x} - \mu}{\sigma / \sqrt{n}} = \dfrac{17.55 - 17.09}{3.87 / \sqrt{50}} = .84$

p-value = 2P(Z > .84) = 2(.5 - .2995) = 2(.2005) = .4010.

b $z = \dfrac{\bar{x} - \mu}{\sigma / \sqrt{n}} = \dfrac{17.55 - 17.09}{3.87 / \sqrt{400}} = 2.38$

p-value = $2P(Z > 2.38) = 2(.5 - .4913) = 2(.0087) = .0174$.

The value of the test statistic increases and the p-value decreases.

11.40 a $z = \dfrac{\bar{x} - \mu}{\sigma / \sqrt{n}} = \dfrac{17.55 - 17.09}{2 / \sqrt{100}} = 2.30$

p-value = $2P(Z > 2.30) = 2(.5 - .4893) = 2(.0107) = .0214$.

b $z = \dfrac{\bar{x} - \mu}{\sigma / \sqrt{n}} = \dfrac{17.55 - 17.09}{10 / \sqrt{100}} = .46$

p-value = $2P(Z > .46) = 2(.5 - .1772) = 2(.3228) = .6456$.

The value of the test statistic decreases and the p-value increases.

11.41 a

$\bar{x}$	$z = \dfrac{\bar{x} - 17.09}{3.87 / \sqrt{100}}$	p-value
15.0	-5.40	0
15.5	-4.11	0
16.0	-2.82	.0048
16.5	-1.52	.1286
17.0	-.23	.8180
17.5	1.06	.2892
18.0	2.35	.0188
18.5	3.64	0
19.0	4.94	0

11.42 $H_0 : \mu = 50$

$H_1 : \mu > 50$

$z = \dfrac{\bar{x} - \mu}{\sigma / \sqrt{n}} = \dfrac{59.17 - 50}{10 / \sqrt{18}} = 3.89$

p-value = $P(Z > 3.89) = 0$

There is enough evidence to infer that the mean is greater than 50 minutes.

11.43 $H_0 : \mu = 36$

$H_1 : \mu < 36$

$z = \dfrac{\bar{x} - \mu}{\sigma / \sqrt{n}} = \dfrac{34.25 - 36}{8 / \sqrt{12}} = -.76$

p-value = $P(Z < -.76) = .5 - .2764 = .2236$.

There is not enough evidence to infer that the average student spent less time than recommended.

11.44　　$H_0 : \mu = .50$

$H_1 : \mu \neq .50$

$$z = \frac{\bar{x} - \mu}{\sigma / \sqrt{n}} = \frac{.493 - .50}{.05 / \sqrt{10}} = -.44$$

p-value = $2P(Z < -.44) = 2(.5 - .1700) = 2(.3300) = .6600$

There is not enough evidence to infer that the mean diameter is not .50 inch.

11.45　　$H_0 : \mu = 5000$

$H_1 : \mu > 5000$

$$z = \frac{\bar{x} - \mu}{\sigma / \sqrt{n}} = \frac{5065 - 5000}{400 / \sqrt{100}} = 1.62$$

p-value = $P(Z > 1.62) = .5 - .4474 = .0526$

There is not enough evidence to conclude that the claim is true.

11.46　　$H_0 : \mu = 30000$

$H_1 : \mu < 30000$

$$z = \frac{\bar{x} - \mu}{\sigma / \sqrt{n}} = \frac{29,120 - 30,000}{8000 / \sqrt{350}} = -2.06$$

p-value = $(P(Z < -2.06) = .5 - .4803 = .0197$

There is enough evidence to infer that the president is correct

11.47　　$H_0 : \mu = 560$

$H_1 : \mu > 560$

$$z = \frac{\bar{x} - \mu}{\sigma / \sqrt{n}} = \frac{569 - 560}{50 / \sqrt{20}} = .81$$

p-value = $P(Z > .81) = .5 - .2910 = .2090$

There is not enough evidence to conclude that the dean's claim is true.

11.48a　　$H_0 : \mu = 17.85$

$H_1 : \mu > 17.85$

$$z = \frac{\bar{x} - \mu}{\sigma / \sqrt{n}} = \frac{19.13 - 17.85}{3.87 / \sqrt{25}} = 1.66$$

p-value = $P(Z > 1.66) = .5 - .4515 = .0485$

There is enough evidence to infer that the campaign was successful.

b We must assume that the population standard deviation is unchanged.

11.49 $H_0 : \mu = 0$

$H_1 : \mu < 0$

$$z = \frac{\bar{x} - \mu}{\sigma / \sqrt{n}} = \frac{-1.20 - 0}{5 / \sqrt{50}} = -1.70$$

p-value = $P(Z < -1.70) = .5 - .4554 = .0446$

There is enough evidence to conclude that the safety equipment is effective.

11.50 $H_0 : \mu = 55$

$H_1 : \mu > 55$

$$z = \frac{\bar{x} - \mu}{\sigma / \sqrt{n}} = \frac{55.8 - 55}{5 / \sqrt{200}} = 2.26$$

p-value = $P(Z > 2.26) = .5 - .4881 = .0119$

There is not enough evidence to support the officer's belief.

11.51 $H_0 : \mu = 4$

$H_1 : \mu > 4$

$$z = \frac{\bar{x} - \mu}{\sigma / \sqrt{n}} = \frac{5.04 - 4}{1.5 / \sqrt{50}} = 4.90$$

p-value = $P(Z > 4.90) = 0$

There is enough evidence to infer that the expert is correct.

11.52 $H_0 : \mu = 20$

$H_1 : \mu < 20$

$$z = \frac{\bar{x} - \mu}{\sigma / \sqrt{n}} = \frac{19.39 - 20}{3 / \sqrt{36}} = -1.22$$

p-value = $P(Z < -1.22) = .5 - .3888 = .1112$

There is not enough evidence to infer that the manager is correct.

11.53 $H_0 : \mu = 100$

$H_1 : \mu > 100$

$$z = \frac{\bar{x} - \mu}{\sigma / \sqrt{n}} = \frac{105.7 - 100}{12 / \sqrt{100}} = 3.00$$

p-value = $P(Z > 3.00) = .5 - .4987 = .0013$

There is enough evidence to infer that the site is acceptable.

11.54 $H_0 : \mu = 4$

$H_1 : \mu \neq 4$

$z = \dfrac{\bar{x} - \mu}{\sigma / \sqrt{n}} = \dfrac{4.84 - 4}{2 / \sqrt{63}} = 3.34$

p-value = 2P(Z > 3.34) = 0

There is enough evidence to infer that the average Alpine skier does not ski 4 times per year.

11.55 $H_0 : \mu = 5$

$H_1 : \mu > 5$

$z = \dfrac{\bar{x} - \mu}{\sigma / \sqrt{n}} = \dfrac{5.64 - 5}{2 / \sqrt{25}} = 1.60$

p-value = P(Z > 1.60) = .5 - .4452 = .0548.

There is enough evidence to infer that the golf professional's claim is true.

11.56 $H_0 : \mu = 32$

$H_1 : \mu < 32$

$z = \dfrac{\bar{x} - \mu}{\sigma / \sqrt{n}} = \dfrac{29.92 - 32}{6 / \sqrt{110}} = -3.64$

p-value = P(Z < -3.64) = 0

There is enough evidence to infer that there has been a decrease in the mean time away from desks. A type I error occurs when we conclude that the plan decreases the mean time away from desks when it actually does not. This error is quite expensive. Consequently we demand a low p-value. The p-value is small enough to infer that there has been a decrease.

11.57 $H_0 : \mu = 230$

$H_1 : \mu > 230$

$z = \dfrac{\bar{x} - \mu}{\sigma / \sqrt{n}} = \dfrac{231.56 - 230}{10 / \sqrt{100}} = 1.56$

p-value = P(Z > 1.56) = .5 - .4406 = .0594.

The costs of type I and type II errors are hard to assess. Using a 5% significance level we conclude that there is not enough evidence to infer that Nike is correct.

11.58 Rejection region: $\dfrac{\bar{x} - \mu}{\sigma / \sqrt{n}} > z_{\alpha/2}$ or $\dfrac{\bar{x} - \mu}{\sigma / \sqrt{n}} < -z_{\alpha/2}$

$\dfrac{\bar{x} - 200}{10 / \sqrt{100}} > z_{.025} = 1.96$ or $\dfrac{\bar{x} - 200}{10 / \sqrt{100}} < -1.96$

$\bar{x} > 201.96$ or $\bar{x} < 198.04$

$\beta = P(198.04 < \bar{x} < 201.96 \text{ given } \mu = 203)$

$$= P\left(\frac{198.04 - 203}{10/\sqrt{100}} < \frac{\bar{x} - \mu}{\sigma/\sqrt{n}} < \frac{201.96 - 203}{10/\sqrt{100}}\right) = P(-4.96 < z < -1.04) = .5 - .3508 = .1492$$

11.59 Rejection region: $\dfrac{\bar{x} - \mu}{\sigma/\sqrt{n}} > z_\alpha$

$\dfrac{\bar{x} - 1000}{50/\sqrt{25}} > z_{.01} = 2.33$

$\bar{x} > 1023.3$

$\beta = P(\bar{x} < 1023.3 \text{ given } \mu = 1050) = P\left(\dfrac{\bar{x} - \mu}{\sigma/\sqrt{n}} < \dfrac{1023.3 - 1050}{50/\sqrt{25}}\right) = P(z < -2.67) = .5 - .4962 = .0038$

11.60 Rejection region: $\dfrac{\bar{x} - \mu}{\sigma/\sqrt{n}} < -z_\alpha$

$\dfrac{\bar{x} - 50}{10/\sqrt{40}} < -z_{.05} = -1.645$

$\bar{x} < 47.40$

$\beta = P(\bar{x} > 47.40 \text{ given } \mu = 48) = P\left(\dfrac{\bar{x} - \mu}{\sigma/\sqrt{n}} > \dfrac{47.40 - 48}{10/\sqrt{40}}\right) = P(z > -.38) = .5 + .1480 = .6480$

11.61

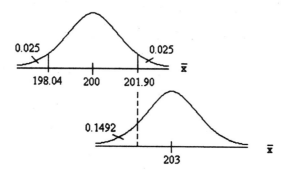

11.62

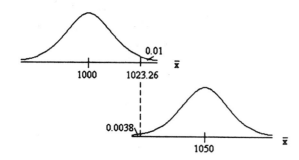

11.63

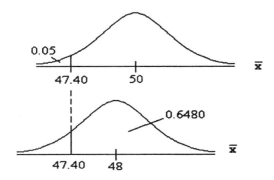

11.64 a Rejection region: $\dfrac{\bar{x} - \mu}{\sigma / \sqrt{n}} < -z_\alpha$

$\dfrac{\bar{x} - 22}{6 / \sqrt{220}} < -z_{.10} = -1.28$

$\bar{x} < 21.48$

$\beta = P(\bar{x} > 21.48 \text{ given } \mu = 21.5) = P\left(\dfrac{\bar{x} - \mu}{\sigma / \sqrt{n}} > \dfrac{21.48 - 21.5}{6 / \sqrt{220}} \right) = P(z > -.05) = .5 + .0199 = .5199$

b Rejection region: $\dfrac{\bar{x} - \mu}{\sigma / \sqrt{n}} < -z_\alpha$

$\dfrac{\bar{x} - 22}{6 / \sqrt{220}} < -z_{.10} = -1.28$

$\bar{x} < 21.33$

$\beta = P(\bar{x} > 21.48 \text{ given } \mu = 21) = P\left(\dfrac{\bar{x} - \mu}{\sigma / \sqrt{n}} > \dfrac{21.48 - 21}{6 / \sqrt{220}} \right) = P(z > 1.19 = .5 - .3830 = .1170$

c As μ decreases β decreases.

11.65a Rejection region: $\dfrac{\bar{x} - \mu}{\sigma / \sqrt{n}} < -z_\alpha$

$\dfrac{\bar{x} - 22}{6 / \sqrt{220}} < -z_{.05} = -1.645$

$\bar{x} < 21.33$

$\beta = P(\bar{x} > 21.33 \text{ given } \mu = 21.0) = P\left(\dfrac{\bar{x} - \mu}{\sigma / \sqrt{n}} > \dfrac{21.33 - 21.0}{6 / \sqrt{220}} \right) = P(z > .82) = .5 - .2939 = .2061$

b Rejection region: $\dfrac{\bar{x} - \mu}{\sigma / \sqrt{n}} < -z_\alpha$

$\dfrac{\bar{x} - 22}{6 / \sqrt{220}} < -z_{.01} = -2.33$

$\bar{x} < 21.06$

$\beta = P(\bar{x} > 21.06 \text{ given } \mu = 21.0) = P\left(\dfrac{\bar{x} - \mu}{\sigma/\sqrt{n}} > \dfrac{21.06 - 21.0}{6/\sqrt{220}}\right) = P(z > .15) = .5 - .0596 = .4404$

c As α decreases, β increases.

11.66 a Rejection region: $\dfrac{\bar{x} - \mu}{\sigma/\sqrt{n}} < -z_\alpha$

$\dfrac{\bar{x} - 22}{6/\sqrt{300}} < -z_{.10} = -1.28$

$\bar{x} < 21.56$

$\beta = P(\bar{x} > 21.56 \text{ given } \mu = 21.0) = P\left(\dfrac{\bar{x} - \mu}{\sigma/\sqrt{n}} > \dfrac{21.56 - 21.0}{6/\sqrt{300}}\right) = P(z > 1.62) = .5 - .4474 = .0526$

b Rejection region: $\dfrac{\bar{x} - \mu}{\sigma/\sqrt{n}} < -z_\alpha$

$\dfrac{\bar{x} - 22}{6/\sqrt{400}} < -z_{.10} = -1.28$

$\bar{x} < 21.62$

$\beta = P(\bar{x} > 21.62 \text{ given } \mu = 21.0) = P\left(\dfrac{\bar{x} - \mu}{\sigma/\sqrt{n}} > \dfrac{21.62 - 21.0}{6/\sqrt{400}}\right) = P(z > 2.07) = .5 - .4808 = .0192$

c As n increases β decreases.

11.67 a Rejection region: $\dfrac{\bar{x} - \mu}{\sigma/\sqrt{n}} > z_{\alpha/2}$ or $\dfrac{\bar{x} - \mu}{\sigma/\sqrt{n}} < -z_{\alpha/2}$

$\dfrac{\bar{x} - 17.09}{3.87/\sqrt{100}} > z_{.025} = 1.96$ or $\dfrac{\bar{x} - 17.09}{3.87/\sqrt{100}} < -1.96$

$\bar{x} > 17.85$ or $\bar{x} < 16.33$

$\beta = P(16.33 < \bar{x} < 17.85 \text{ given } \mu = 17.80)$

$= P\left(\dfrac{16.33 - 17.80}{3.87/\sqrt{100}} < \dfrac{\bar{x} - \mu}{\sigma/\sqrt{n}} < \dfrac{17.85 - 17.80}{3.87/\sqrt{100}}\right) = P(-3.80 < z < .13) = .5 + .0517 = .5517$

b Rejection region: $\dfrac{\bar{x} - \mu}{\sigma/\sqrt{n}} > z_{\alpha/2}$ or $\dfrac{\bar{x} - \mu}{\sigma/\sqrt{n}} < -z_{\alpha/2}$

$\dfrac{\bar{x} - 17.09}{3.87/\sqrt{100}} > z_{.025} = 1.96$ or $\dfrac{\bar{x} - 17.09}{3.87/\sqrt{100}} < -1.96$

$\bar{x} > 17.85$ or $\bar{x} < 16.33$

$\beta = P(16.33 < \bar{x} < 17.85 \text{ given } \mu = 18.00)$

$= P\left(\dfrac{16.33 - 18.00}{3.87/\sqrt{100}} < \dfrac{\bar{x} - \mu}{\sigma/\sqrt{n}} < \dfrac{17.85 - 18.00}{3.87/\sqrt{100}}\right) = P(-4.32 < z < -39) = .5 - .1517 = .3483$

c As μ increases β decreases.

11.68 a Rejection region: $\dfrac{\bar{x}-\mu}{\sigma/\sqrt{n}} > z_{\alpha/2}$ or $\dfrac{\bar{x}-\mu}{\sigma/\sqrt{n}} < -z_{\alpha/2}$

$\dfrac{\bar{x}-17.09}{3.87/\sqrt{100}} > z_{.0375} = 1.78$ or $\dfrac{\bar{x}-17.09}{3.87/\sqrt{100}} < -1.78$

$\bar{x} > 17.78$ or $\bar{x} < 16.40$

$\beta = P(16.40 < \bar{x} < 17.78 \text{ given } \mu = 18.00)$

$= P\left(\dfrac{16.40-18.00}{3.87/\sqrt{100}} < \dfrac{\bar{x}-\mu}{\sigma/\sqrt{n}} < \dfrac{17.78-18.00}{3.87/\sqrt{100}}\right) = P(-4.13 < z < -.57) = .5 - .2157 = .2843$

b Rejection region: $\dfrac{\bar{x}-\mu}{\sigma/\sqrt{n}} > z_{\alpha/2}$ or $\dfrac{\bar{x}-\mu}{\sigma/\sqrt{n}} < -z_{\alpha/2}$

$\dfrac{\bar{x}-17.09}{3.87/\sqrt{100}} > z_{.05} = 1.645$ or $\dfrac{\bar{x}-17.09}{3.87/\sqrt{100}} < -1.645$

$\bar{x} > 17.73$ or $\bar{x} < 16.45$

$\beta = P(16.45 < \bar{x} < 17.73 \text{ given } \mu = 18.00)$

$= P\left(\dfrac{16.45-18.00}{3.87/\sqrt{100}} < \dfrac{\bar{x}-\mu}{\sigma/\sqrt{n}} < \dfrac{17.73-18.00}{3.87/\sqrt{100}}\right) = P(-4.01 < z < -.70) = .5 - .2580 = .2420$

c As α increases β decreases.

11.69a Rejection region: $\dfrac{\bar{x}-\mu}{\sigma/\sqrt{n}} > z_{\alpha/2}$ or $\dfrac{\bar{x}-\mu}{\sigma/\sqrt{n}} < -z_{\alpha/2}$

$\dfrac{\bar{x}-17.09}{3.87/\sqrt{150}} > z_{.025} = 1.96$ or $\dfrac{\bar{x}-17.09}{3.87/\sqrt{150}} < -1.96$

$\bar{x} > 17.71$ or $\bar{x} < 16.47$

$\beta = P(16.47 < \bar{x} < 17.71 \text{ given } \mu = 18.00)$

$= P\left(\dfrac{16.47-18.00}{3.87/\sqrt{150}} < \dfrac{\bar{x}-\mu}{\sigma/\sqrt{n}} < \dfrac{17.71-18.00}{3.87/\sqrt{150}}\right) = P(-4.80 < z < -.92) = .5 - .3212 = .1788$

b Rejection region: $\dfrac{\bar{x}-\mu}{\sigma/\sqrt{n}} > z_{\alpha/2}$ or $\dfrac{\bar{x}-\mu}{\sigma/\sqrt{n}} < -z_{\alpha/2}$

$\dfrac{\bar{x}-17.09}{3.87/\sqrt{200}} > z_{.025} = 1.96$ or $\dfrac{\bar{x}-17.09}{3.87/\sqrt{200}} < -1.96$

$\bar{x} > 17.63$ or $\bar{x} < 16.55$

$\beta = P(16.55 < \bar{x} < 17.63 \text{ given } \mu = 18.00)$

$= P\left(\dfrac{16.55-18.00}{3.87/\sqrt{200}} < \dfrac{\bar{x}-\mu}{\sigma/\sqrt{n}} < \dfrac{17.63-18.00}{3.87/\sqrt{200}}\right) = P(-5.30 < z < -1.35) = .5 - .4115 = .0885$

c As n increases β decreases.

11.70

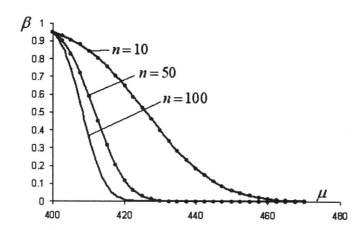

11.71

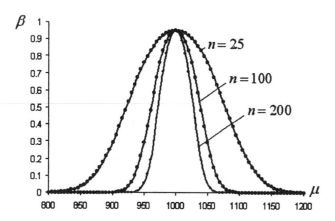

11.72 Rejection region: $\dfrac{\bar{x}-\mu}{\sigma/\sqrt{n}} > z_\alpha$

$\dfrac{\bar{x}-5000}{400/\sqrt{100}} > z_{.05} = 1.645$

$\bar{x} > 5065.8$

$\beta = P(\bar{x} < 5065.8 \text{ given } \mu = 5100) = P\left(\dfrac{\bar{x}-\mu}{\sigma/\sqrt{n}} < \dfrac{5065.8-5100}{400/\sqrt{100}}\right) = P(z < -.86) = .5 - .3051 = .1949$

11.73 Rejection region: $\dfrac{\bar{x}-\mu}{\sigma/\sqrt{n}} < -z_\alpha$

$\dfrac{\bar{x}-30{,}000}{8000/\sqrt{350}} < -z_{.05} = -1.645$

$\bar{x} < 29{,}297$

$\beta = P(\bar{x} > 29{,}297 \text{ given } \mu = 28{,}500) = P\left(\dfrac{\bar{x}-\mu}{\sigma/\sqrt{n}} > \dfrac{29{,}297-28{,}500}{8000/\sqrt{350}}\right) = P(z > 1.86) = .5 - .4686 =$

.0314

11.74 Rejection region: $\dfrac{\bar{x}-\mu}{\sigma/\sqrt{n}} > z_\alpha$

$\dfrac{\bar{x}-560}{50/\sqrt{20}} > z_{.05} = 1.645$

$\bar{x} > 578.4$

$\beta = P(\bar{x} < 578.4 \text{ given } \mu = 600) = P\left(\dfrac{\bar{x}-\mu}{\sigma/\sqrt{n}} < \dfrac{578.4-600}{50/\sqrt{20}}\right) = P(z < -1.93) = .5 - .4732 = .0268$

11.75

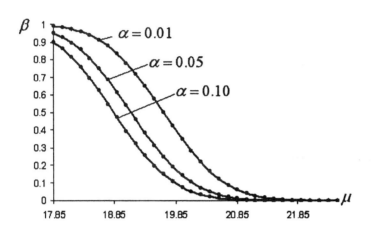

11.76

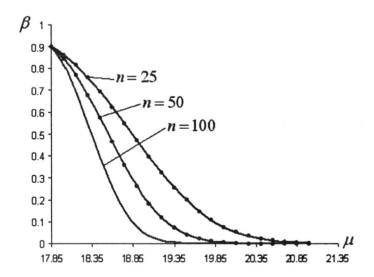

11.77 Rejection region: $\dfrac{\bar{x}-\mu}{\sigma/\sqrt{n}} < -z_\alpha$

$\dfrac{\bar{x}-0}{5/\sqrt{50}} < -z_{.10} = -1.28$

$\bar{x} < -.91$

$\beta = P(\bar{x} > -.91 \text{ given } \mu = -3) = P\left(\dfrac{\bar{x}-\mu}{\sigma/\sqrt{n}} > \dfrac{-.91-(-3)}{5/\sqrt{50}}\right) = P(z > 2.96) = .5 - .4985 = .0015$

11.78 Rejection region: $\dfrac{\bar{x}-\mu}{\sigma/\sqrt{n}} > z_\alpha$

$\dfrac{\bar{x}-55}{5/\sqrt{200}} > z_{.01} = 2.33$

$\bar{x} > 55.8$

$\beta = P(\bar{x} < 55.8 \text{ given } \mu = 57) = P\left(\dfrac{\bar{x}-\mu}{\sigma/\sqrt{n}} < \dfrac{55.8-57}{5/\sqrt{200}}\right) = P(z < -3.39) = 0$

11.79 Rejection region: $\dfrac{\bar{x}-\mu}{\sigma/\sqrt{n}} > z_\alpha$

$\dfrac{\bar{x}-4}{1.5/\sqrt{50}} > z_{.10} = 1.28$

$\bar{x} > 4.27$

$\beta = P(\bar{x} < 4.27 \text{ given } \mu = 5) = P\left(\dfrac{\bar{x}-\mu}{\sigma/\sqrt{n}} < \dfrac{4.27-5}{1.5/\sqrt{50}}\right) = P(z < -3.44) = 0$

11.80 Rejection region: $\dfrac{\bar{x}-\mu}{\sigma/\sqrt{n}} < -z_\alpha$

$\dfrac{\bar{x}-20}{3/\sqrt{36}} < -z_{.05} = -1.645$

$\bar{x} < 19.18$

$\beta = P(\bar{x} > 19.18 \text{ given } \mu = 18.5) = P\left(\dfrac{\bar{x}-\mu}{\sigma/\sqrt{n}} > \dfrac{19.18-18.5}{3/\sqrt{36}}\right) = P(z > 1.36) = .5 - .4131 = .0869$

11.81

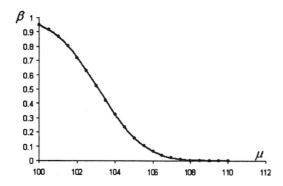

184

11.82

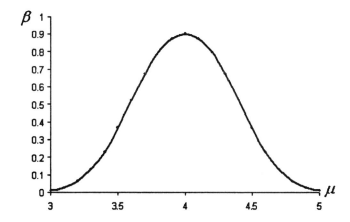

11.83

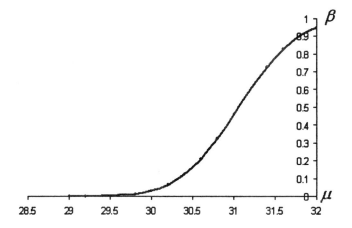

11.84 $H_0 : \mu = 170$

$H_1 : \mu < 170$

A Type I error occurs when we conclude that the new system is not cost effective when it actually is.
A Type II error occurs when we conclude that the new system is cost effective when it actually is not.

The test statistic is the same. However, the p-value equals 1 minus the p-value calculated Example
10.1. That is,

p-value = 1 - .0069 = .9931

We conclude that there is no evidence to infer that the mean is less than 170. That is, there is no
evidence to infer that the new system will not be cost effective.

11.85 i Rejection region: $\dfrac{\overline{x}-\mu}{\sigma/\sqrt{n}} < -z_\alpha$

$\dfrac{\overline{x}-10}{3/\sqrt{100}} < -z_{.01} = -2.33$

$\overline{x} < 9.30$

$\beta = P(\overline{x} > 9.30 \text{ given } \mu = 9) = P\left(\dfrac{\overline{x}-\mu}{\sigma/\sqrt{n}} > \dfrac{9.30-9}{3/\sqrt{100}}\right) = P(z > 1) = .5 - .3413 = .1587$

ii Rejection region: $\dfrac{\overline{x}-\mu}{\sigma/\sqrt{n}} < -z_\alpha$

$\dfrac{\overline{x}-10}{3/\sqrt{75}} < -z_{.05} = -1.645$

$\overline{x} < 9.43$

$\beta = P(\overline{x} > 9.43 \text{ given } \mu = 9) = P\left(\dfrac{\overline{x}-\mu}{\sigma/\sqrt{n}} > \dfrac{9.43-9}{3/\sqrt{75}}\right) = P(z > 1.24) = .5 - .3925 = .1075$

iii Rejection region: $\dfrac{\overline{x}-\mu}{\sigma/\sqrt{n}} < -z_\alpha$

$\dfrac{\overline{x}-10}{3/\sqrt{50}} < -z_{.10} = -1.28$

$\overline{x} < 9.46$

$\beta = P(\overline{x} > 9.46 \text{ given } \mu = 9) = P\left(\dfrac{\overline{x}-\mu}{\sigma/\sqrt{n}} > \dfrac{9.46-9}{3/\sqrt{50}}\right) = P(z > 1.08) = .5 - .3599 = .1401$

Plan ii has the lowest probability of a type II error.

Chapter 12

12.1 $\bar{x} \pm t_{\alpha/2} s / \sqrt{n} = 510 \pm 2.009(125/\sqrt{50}) = 510 \pm 35.51;$ LCL = 474.49, UCL = 545.51

12.2 $\bar{x} \pm t_{\alpha/2} s / \sqrt{n} = 510 \pm 1.984(125/\sqrt{100}) = 510 \pm 24.80;$ LCL = 485.20, UCL = 534.80

12.3 $\bar{x} \pm t_{\alpha/2} s / \sqrt{n} = 510 \pm 2.064(125/\sqrt{25}) = 510 \pm 51.60;$ LCL = 458.40, UCL = 561.60

12.4 The interval narrows as the sample size increases.

12.5 $\bar{x} \pm t_{\alpha/2} s / \sqrt{n} = 510 \pm 2.009(200/\sqrt{50}) = 510 \pm 56.82;$ LCL = 453.18, UCL = 566.82

12.6 $\bar{x} \pm t_{\alpha/2} s / \sqrt{n} = 510 \pm 2.009(75/\sqrt{50}) = 510 \pm 21.31;$ LCL = 488.69, UCL = 531.31

12.7 As the sample standard deviation decreases, the interval narrows.

12.8 $\bar{x} \pm t_{\alpha/2} s / \sqrt{n} = 510 \pm 1.676(125/\sqrt{50}) = 510 \pm 29.63;$ LCL = 480.37, UCL = 539.63

12.9 $\bar{x} \pm t_{\alpha/2} s / \sqrt{n} = 510 \pm 2.678(125/\sqrt{50}) = 510 \pm 47.34;$ LCL = 462.66, UCL = 557.34

12.10 As the confidence level increases the interval widens.

12.11 to 12.20 $H_0 : \mu = 20$

               $H_1 : \mu > 20$

12.11 Rejection region: $t > t_{\alpha,n-1} = t_{.05,19} = 1.729$

$t = \dfrac{\bar{x} - \mu}{s / \sqrt{n}} = \dfrac{23 - 20}{9 / \sqrt{20}} = 1.49$, p-value = .0762 (Excel). There is not enough evidence to infer that the

population mean is greater than 20.

12.12 Rejection region: $t > t_{\alpha,n-1} = t_{.05,9} = 1.833$

$t = \dfrac{\bar{x} - \mu}{s / \sqrt{n}} = \dfrac{23 - 20}{9 / \sqrt{10}} = 1.05$ p-value = .1597 (Excel). There is not enough evidence to infer that the

population mean is greater than 20.

12.13 Rejection region: $t > t_{\alpha,n-1} = t_{.05,49} \approx 1.676$

$t = \dfrac{\bar{x} - \mu}{s / \sqrt{n}} = \dfrac{23 - 20}{9 / \sqrt{50}} = 2.36$, p-value = .0112 (Excel). There is enough evidence to infer that the

population mean is greater than 20.

12.14 As the sample size increases the test statistic increases [and the p-value decreases].

12.15 Rejection region: $t > t_{\alpha,n-1} = t_{.05,19} = 1.729$

$t = \dfrac{\bar{x} - \mu}{s / \sqrt{n}} = \dfrac{23 - 20}{5 / \sqrt{20}} = 2.68$, p-value = .0074 (Excel). There is enough evidence to infer that the

population mean is greater than 20.

12.16 Rejection region: $t > t_{\alpha,n-1} = t_{.05,19} = 1.729$

$t = \dfrac{\bar{x} - \mu}{s / \sqrt{n}} = \dfrac{23 - 20}{29 / \sqrt{20}} = .67$, p-value = .2552 (Excel). There is not enough evidence to infer that the

population mean is greater than 20.

12.17 The t-statistic increases [and the p-value decreases] as the sample standard deviation decreases.

12.18 $t = \dfrac{\bar{x} - \mu}{s / \sqrt{n}} = \dfrac{21 - 20}{9 / \sqrt{20}} = .50$, p-value = .3125 (Excel). There is not enough evidence to infer that

the population mean is greater than 20.

12.19 $t = \dfrac{\bar{x} - \mu}{s / \sqrt{n}} = \dfrac{26 - 20}{9 / \sqrt{20}} = 2.98$, p-value = .0038 (Excel). There is enough evidence to infer that the

population mean is greater than 20.

12.20 When the sample mean increases, the test statistic increases [and the p-value decreases].

12.21 $\bar{x} \pm t_{\alpha/2} s / \sqrt{n} = 50 \pm 2.262(15/\sqrt{10}) = 50 \pm 10.73$; LCL = 39.27, UCL = 60.73

12.22 $\bar{x} \pm z_{\alpha/2} \sigma / \sqrt{n} = 50 \pm 1.96(15/\sqrt{10}) = 50 \pm 9.30$; LCL = 40.70, UCL = 59.30

12.23 The student t distribution is more widely dispersed than the standard normal; thus, $z_{\alpha/2}$ is smaller than $t_{\alpha/2}$.

12.24 and 12.25 $H_0 : \mu = 100$

$H_1 : \mu < 100$

12.24 Rejection region: $t < -t_{\alpha, n-1} = -t_{.10,7} = -1.415$

$t = \dfrac{\bar{x} - \mu}{s / \sqrt{n}} = \dfrac{75 - 100}{50 / \sqrt{8}} = -1.41$, p-value = .1001 (Excel). There is not enough evidence to infer that the

population mean is less than 100.

12.25 Rejection region: $z < -z_{\alpha} = -z_{.10} = -1.28$

$z = \dfrac{\bar{x} - \mu}{\sigma / \sqrt{n}} = \dfrac{75 - 100}{50 / \sqrt{8}} = -1.41$, p-value = .0786 (Excel). There is enough evidence to infer that the

population mean is less than 100.

12.26 The Student t distribution is more dispersed than the standard normal.

12.27 $\bar{x} \pm t_{\alpha/2} s / \sqrt{n} = 15,500 \pm 1.645(9950 / \sqrt{1000}) = 15,500 \pm 517.59$; LCL = 14,982.41, UCL = 16,017.59

12.28 $\bar{x} \pm z_{\alpha/2} \sigma / \sqrt{n} = 15,500 \pm 1.645(9950 / \sqrt{1000}) = 15,500 \pm 517.59$; LCL = 14,982.41, UCL = 16,017.59

12.29 With n = 1000 the student t distribution with 999 degrees of freedom is almost identical to the

standard normal distribution.

12.30 $H_0 : \mu = 6$

$H_1 : \mu < 6$

Rejection region: $t < -t_{\alpha, n-1} = -t_{.05,11} = -1.796$

$t = \dfrac{\bar{x} - \mu}{s / \sqrt{n}} = \dfrac{5.69 - 6}{1.58 / \sqrt{12}} = -.69$, p-value = .2538 (Excel). There is not enough evidence to support the

courier's advertisement.

12.31 $\bar{x} \pm t_{\alpha/2} s / \sqrt{n} = 24,051 \pm 2.145(17,386) / \sqrt{15} = 24,051 \pm 9629$; LCL = 14,422, UCL = 33,680

12.32 $H_0 : \mu = 20$

$H_1 : \mu > 20$

Rejection region: $t > t_{\alpha,n-1} = t_{.05,19} = 1.729$

$t = \dfrac{\bar{x} - \mu}{s / \sqrt{n}} = \dfrac{20.85 - 20}{6.76 / \sqrt{20}} = .56$, p-value = .2903 (Excel). There is not enough evidence to infer that the

doctor's claim is true.

12.33 $H_0 : \mu = 8$

   $H_1 : \mu < 8$

Rejection region: $t < -t_{\alpha,n-1} = -t_{.10,17} = -1.333$

$t = \dfrac{\bar{x} - \mu}{s / \sqrt{n}} = \dfrac{7.91 - 8}{.085 / \sqrt{18}} = -.4.31$, p-value = .0002 (Excel). There is enough evidence to conclude that

the average container is mislabeled.

12.34 $\bar{x} \pm t_{\alpha/2} s / \sqrt{n} = 7.15 \pm 1.972(1.65/\sqrt{200}) = 7.15 \pm .23$; LCL = 6.92, UCL = 7.38

12.35 $\bar{x} \pm t_{\alpha/2} s / \sqrt{n} = 4.66 \pm 2.576(2.37/\sqrt{240}) = 4.66 \pm .39$; LCL = 4.27, UCL = 5.05

LCL = 100 million (4.27) = 427 million, UCL = 100 million (5.05) = 505 million

12.36 $H_0 : \mu = 60$

   $H_1 : \mu > 60$

Rejection region: $t > t_{\alpha,n-1} = t_{.05,161} = 1.654$

$t = \dfrac{\bar{x} - \mu}{s / \sqrt{n}} = \dfrac{63.70 - 60}{18.94 / \sqrt{162}} = 2.48$, p-value = .0070 (Excel). There is enough evidence to infer that the

mean time exceeds 60 minutes.

12.37 $H_0 : \mu = 45$

   $H_1 : \mu > 45$

Rejection region: $t > t_{\alpha,n-1} = t_{.05,143} \approx 1.656$

$t = \dfrac{\bar{x} - \mu}{s / \sqrt{n}} = \dfrac{53.78 - 45}{4.05 / \sqrt{144}} = 26.02$, p-value = 0. There is enough evidence to infer that the mean time

exceeds 45 hours.

12.38 $\bar{x} \pm t_{\alpha/2} s / \sqrt{n} = 2.67 \pm 1.973(2.50/\sqrt{188}) = 2.67 \pm .36$; LCL = 2.31, UCL = 3.03

12.39 LCL = 200 million (2.31) = 461 million, UCL = 200 million (3.03) = 606 million

12.40 a $\bar{x} \pm t_{\alpha/2} s / \sqrt{n} = 62.79 \pm 2.052(5.32/\sqrt{28}) = 62.79 \pm 2.06$; LCL = 60.73, UCL = 64.85

b Prices are required to be normally distributed. The histogram (not shown) is bell shaped.

12.41 $\bar{x} \pm t_{\alpha/2} s / \sqrt{n} = 29.14 \pm 2.009(4.62/\sqrt{49}) = 29.14 \pm 1.33$; LCL = 27.81, UCL = 30.47

12.42 $\bar{x} \pm t_{\alpha/2} s / \sqrt{n} = 13.94 \pm 1.960(2.16/\sqrt{212}) = 13.94 \pm .29$; LCL = 13.65, UCL = 14.23

LCL = 13.65(10) = 136.5 days, UCL = 14.23(10) = 142.3 days.

12.43 $H_0 : \mu = 15$

   $H_1 : \mu > 15$

Rejection region: $t > t_{\alpha,n-1} = t_{.05,115} \approx 1.980$

$t = \dfrac{\bar{x} - \mu}{s / \sqrt{n}} = \dfrac{15.27 - 15}{5.72/\sqrt{116}} = .50$, p-value = .3080 (Excel). There is not enough evidence to infer that the

mean number of commercials is greater than 15.

12.44 $\bar{x} \pm t_{\alpha/2} s / \sqrt{n} = 3.44 \pm 1.960(3.33/\sqrt{471}) = 3.44 \pm .30$; LCL = 3.14, UCL = 3.74

12.45 $H_0 : \mu = 85$

   $H_1 : \mu > 85$

Rejection region: $t > t_{\alpha,n-1} = t_{.05,84} \approx 1.664$

$t = \dfrac{\bar{x} - \mu}{s / \sqrt{n}} = \dfrac{89.27 - 85}{17.30/\sqrt{85}} = 2.27$, p-value = .0128 (Excel). There is enough evidence to infer that an e-

grocery will be successful.

12.46 $H_0 : \mu = 2$

   $H_1 : \mu > 2$

Rejection region: $t > t_{\alpha,n-1} = t_{.01,99} \approx 2.364$

$t = \dfrac{\bar{x} - \mu}{s / \sqrt{n}} = \dfrac{2.10 - 2}{.76/\sqrt{100}} = 1.32$, p-value = .1001. There is not enough evidence to infer that the

recycling plant will be profitable.

12.47 & 12.48 $H_0 : \sigma^2 = 300$

   $H_1 : \sigma^2 \neq 300$

12.47 Rejection region: $\chi^2 < \chi^2_{1-\alpha/2,n-1} = \chi^2_{.975,99} \approx 74.2219$ or $\chi^2 > \chi^2_{\alpha/2,n-1} = \chi^2_{.025,99} \approx 129.561$

$$\chi^2 = \frac{(n-1)s^2}{\sigma^2} = \frac{(100-1)(220)}{300} = 72.60,\ \text{p-value} = .0427\ (\text{Excel}).\ \text{There is enough evidence to infer}$$

that the population variance differs from 300.

12.48 Rejection region: $\chi^2 < \chi^2_{1-\alpha/2,n-1} = \chi^2_{.975,49} \approx 32.3574$ or $\chi^2 > \chi^2_{\alpha/2,n-1} = \chi^2_{.025,49} \approx 71.4202$

$$\chi^2 = \frac{(n-1)s^2}{\sigma^2} = \frac{(50-1)(220)}{300} = 35.93,\ \text{p-value} = .1643\ (\text{Excel}).\ \text{There is not enough evidence to}$$

infer that the population variance differs from 300. Decreasing the sample size decreases the test statistic and increases the p-value of the test.

12.49 & 12.50 $H_0 : \sigma^2 = 100$

$H_1 : \sigma^2 < 100$

12.49 Rejection region: $\chi^2 < \chi^2_{1-\alpha,n-1} = \chi^2_{.99,49} \approx 29.7067$

$$\chi^2 = \frac{(n-1)s^2}{\sigma^2} = \frac{(50-1)(80)}{100} = 39.20,\ \text{p-value} = .1596\ (\text{Excel}).\ \text{There is not enough evidence to infer}$$

that the population variance is less than 100.

12.50 Rejection region: $\chi^2 < \chi^2_{1-\alpha,n-1} = \chi^2_{.99,99} \approx 70.0648$

$$\chi^2 = \frac{(n-1)s^2}{\sigma^2} = \frac{(100-1)(80)}{100} = 79.20,\ \text{p-value} = .0714\ (\text{Excel}).\ \text{There is not enough evidence to infer}$$

that the population variance is less than 100. Increasing the sample size increases the test statistic and decreases the p-value.

12.51 $\text{LCL} = \dfrac{(n-1)s^2}{\chi^2_{\alpha/2,n-1}} = \dfrac{(n-1)s^2}{\chi^2_{.05,14}} = \dfrac{(15-1)(12)}{23.6848} = 7.09,$

$\text{UCL} = \dfrac{(n-1)s^2}{\chi^2_{1-\alpha/2,n-1}} = \dfrac{(n-1)s^2}{\chi^2_{.95,14}} \dfrac{(15-1)(12)}{6.57063} = 25.57$

12.52 $\text{LCL} = \dfrac{(n-1)s^2}{\chi^2_{\alpha/2,n-1}} = \dfrac{(n-1)s^2}{\chi^2_{.05,29}} = \dfrac{(30-1)(12)}{42.5569} = 8.18,$

$\text{UCL} = \dfrac{(n-1)s^2}{\chi^2_{1-\alpha/2,n-1}} = \dfrac{(n-1)s^2}{\chi^2_{.95,29}} = \dfrac{(15-1)(12)}{17.7083} = 19.65;$ increasing the sample size narrows the interval.

12.53 LCL = $\dfrac{(n-1)s^2}{\chi^2_{\alpha/2,n-1}} = \dfrac{(n-1)s^2}{\chi^2_{.05,7}} = \dfrac{(8-1)(.00093)}{14.0671} = .0005,$

UCL = $\dfrac{(n-1)s^2}{\chi^2_{1-\alpha/2,n-1}} = \dfrac{(n-1)s^2}{\chi^2_{.95,7}} = \dfrac{(8-1)(.00093)}{2.16735} = .0030$

12.54 $H_0 : \sigma^2 = .001$

$\quad\quad H_1 : \sigma^2 < .001$

Rejection region: $\chi^2 < \chi^2_{1-\alpha,n-1} = \chi^2_{.95,7} = 2.16735$

$\chi^2 = \dfrac{(n-1)s^2}{\sigma^2} = \dfrac{(8-1)(.00093)}{.001} = 6.49,$ p-value = .4841 (Excel). There is not enough evidence to

infer that the population variance is less than .001.

12.55 LCL = $\dfrac{(n-1)s^2}{\chi^2_{\alpha/2,n-1}} = \dfrac{(n-1)s^2}{\chi^2_{.025,17}} = \dfrac{(18-1)(.0072)}{30.1910} = .0040,$

UCL = $\dfrac{(n-1)s^2}{\chi^2_{1-\alpha/2,n-1}} = \dfrac{(n-1)s^2}{\chi^2_{.975,17}} = \dfrac{(18-1)(.0072)}{7.56418} = .0161$

12.56 LCL = $\dfrac{(n-1)s^2}{\chi^2_{\alpha/2,n-1}} = \dfrac{(n-1)s^2}{\chi^2_{.025,11}} = \dfrac{(12-1)(2.4976)}{21.9200} = 1.2533,$

UCL = $\dfrac{(n-1)s^2}{\chi^2_{1-\alpha/2,n-1}} = \dfrac{(n-1)s^2}{\chi^2_{.975,11}} = \dfrac{(12-1)(2.4976)}{3.81575} = 7.2000$

12.57 LCL = $\dfrac{(n-1)s^2}{\chi^2_{\alpha/2,n-1}} = \dfrac{(n-1)s^2}{\chi^2_{.025,143}} = \dfrac{(144-1)(16.4079)}{177.998} = 13.1818,$

UCL = $\dfrac{(n-1)s^2}{\chi^2_{1-\alpha/2,n-1}} = \dfrac{(n-1)s^2}{\chi^2_{.975,143}} = \dfrac{(144-1)(16.4079)}{111.787} = 20.9893$

12.58 a $H_0 : \sigma^2 = 250$

$\quad\quad H_1 : \sigma^2 \neq 250$

Rejection region: $\chi^2 < \chi^2_{1-\alpha/2,n-1} = \chi^2_{.975,24} = 12.4011$ or $\chi^2 > \chi^2_{\alpha/2,n-1} = \chi^2_{.025,24} = 39.3641$

$$\chi^2 = \frac{(n-1)s^2}{\sigma^2} = \frac{(25-1)(270.58)}{250} = 25.9760, \text{ p-value} = .7088 \text{ (Excel). There is not enough evidence}$$

to infer that the population variance is not equal to 250.

b Demand is required to be normally distributed.

c The histogram is approximately bell shaped.

$$12.59 \text{ LCL} = \frac{(n-1)s^2}{\chi^2_{\alpha/2,n-1}} = \frac{(n-1)s^2}{\chi^2_{.025,24}} = \frac{(25-1)(270.58)}{39.3641} = 164.9728,$$

$$\text{UCL} = \frac{(n-1)s^2}{\chi^2_{1-\alpha/2}} = \frac{(n-1)s^2}{\chi^2_{.975,24}} = \frac{(25-1)(270.5833)}{12.4011} = 523.6613$$

$$12.60 \text{ a LCL} = \frac{(n-1)s^2}{\chi^2_{\alpha/2,n-1}} = \frac{(n-1)s^2}{\chi^2_{.05,199}} = \frac{(200-1)(2.7111)}{232.912} = 2.3163,$$

$$\text{UCL} = \frac{(n-1)s^2}{\chi^2_{1-\alpha/2,n-1}} = \frac{(n-1)s^2}{\chi^2_{.95,199}} = \frac{(200-1)(2.7111)}{167.361} = 3.2236$$

b The histogram is bell shaped.

12.61　　$H_0 : \sigma^2 = 18$

　　　　$H_1 : \sigma^2 > 18$

Rejection region: $\chi^2 > \chi^2_{\alpha,n-1} = \chi^2_{.10,244} = 272.704$

$$\chi^2 = \frac{(n-1)s^2}{\sigma^2} = \frac{(245-1)(22.56)}{18} = 305.85; \text{ p-value} = .0044 \text{ (Excel). There is enough evidence to}$$

infer that the population variance is greater than 18.

12.62　　$H_0 : \sigma^2 = 200$

　　　　$H_1 : \sigma^2 < 200$

Rejection region: $\chi^2 < \chi^2_{1-\alpha,n-1} = \chi^2_{.95,99} \approx 77.9295$

$$\chi^2 = \frac{(n-1)s^2}{\sigma^2} = \frac{(100-1)(174.47)}{200} = 86.36; \text{ p-value} = .1863 \text{ (Excel). There is not enough evidence to}$$

infer that the population variance is less than 200. Replace the bulbs as they burn out.

12.63　$\hat{p} \pm z_{\alpha/2}\sqrt{\hat{p}(1-\hat{p})/n} = .48 \pm 1.96\sqrt{.48(1-.48)/500} = .48 \pm .0438$

12.64 $\hat{p} \pm z_{\alpha/2}\sqrt{\hat{p}(1-\hat{p})/n} = .48 \pm 1.96\sqrt{.48(1-.48)/200} = .48 \pm .0692$

12.65 $\hat{p} \pm z_{\alpha/2}\sqrt{\hat{p}(1-\hat{p})/n} = .48 \pm 1.96\sqrt{.48(1-.48)/1000} = .48 \pm .0310$

12.66 The interval narrows when the sample size increases.

12.67 $\hat{p} \pm z_{\alpha/2}\sqrt{\hat{p}(1-\hat{p})/n} = .33 \pm 1.96\sqrt{.33(1-.33)/500} = .33 \pm .0412$

12.68 $\hat{p} \pm z_{\alpha/2}\sqrt{\hat{p}(1-\hat{p})/n} = .10 \pm 1.96\sqrt{.10(1-.10)/500} = .10 \pm .0263$

12.69 Reducing the sample proportion narrows the interval.

12.70 to 12.76 $H_0 : p = .60$

$H_1 : p > .60$

12.70 $z = \dfrac{\hat{p}-p}{\sqrt{p(1-p)/n}} = \dfrac{.63-.60}{\sqrt{.60(1-.60)/100}} = .61$, p-value $= P(Z > .61) = .5 - .2291 = .2709$

12.71 $z = \dfrac{\hat{p}-p}{\sqrt{p(1-p)/n}} = \dfrac{.63-.60}{\sqrt{.60(1-.60)/200}} = .87$, p-value $= P(Z > .87) = .5 - .3078 = .1932$

12.72 $z = \dfrac{\hat{p}-p}{\sqrt{p(1-p)/n}} = \dfrac{.63-.60}{\sqrt{.60(1-.60)/400}} = 1.22$, p-value $= P(Z > 1.22) = .5 - .3888 = .1112$

12.73 As the sample size increases the value of the test statistic increases and the p-value decreases.

12.74 $z = \dfrac{\hat{p}-p}{\sqrt{p(1-p)/n}} = \dfrac{.62-.60}{\sqrt{.62(1-.62)/100}} = .41$, p-value $= P(Z > .41) = .5 - 1591 = .3409$

12.75 $z = \dfrac{\hat{p}-p}{\sqrt{p(1-p)/n}} = \dfrac{.61-.60}{\sqrt{.61(1-.61)/100}} = .20$, p-value $= P(Z > .20) = .5 - .0793 = .4207$

12.76 Decreasing the sample proportion decreases the value of the test statistic and increases the p-value.

12.77 $n = \left(\dfrac{z_{\alpha/2} \sqrt{\hat{p}(1-\hat{p})}}{B} \right)^2 = \left(\dfrac{1.645 \sqrt{.5(1-.5)}}{.03} \right)^2 = 752$

12.78 a .5 $\pm$ .03

b Yes, because the sample size was chosen to produce this interval.

12.79 a $\hat{p} \pm z_{\alpha/2} \sqrt{\hat{p}(1-\hat{p})/n} = .75 \pm 1.645 \sqrt{.75(1-.75)/752} = .75 \pm .0260$

b The interval is narrower.

c Yes, because the interval estimate is better than specified.

12.80 $n = \left(\dfrac{z_{\alpha/2} \sqrt{\hat{p}(1-\hat{p})}}{B} \right)^2 = \left(\dfrac{1.645 \sqrt{.75(1-.75)}}{.03} \right)^2 = 564$

12.81 a .75 $\pm$ .03

b Yes, because the sample size was chosen to produce this interval.

12.82 a $\hat{p} \pm z_{\alpha/2} \sqrt{\hat{p}(1-\hat{p})/n} = .92 \pm 1.645 \sqrt{.92(1-.92)/564} = .92 \pm .0188$

b The interval is narrower.

c Yes, because the interval estimate is better than specified.

12.83 a $\hat{p} \pm z_{\alpha/2} \sqrt{\hat{p}(1-\hat{p})/n} = .5 \pm 1.645 \sqrt{.5(1-.5)/564} = .5 \pm .0346$

b The interval is wider.

c No because the interval estimate is wider than specified.

12.84 $\hat{p} \pm z_{\alpha/2} \sqrt{\hat{p}(1-\hat{p})/n} = .84 \pm 1.645 \sqrt{.84(1-.84)/600} = .84 \pm .0246$

12.85 $\hat{p} \pm z_{\alpha/2} \sqrt{\hat{p}(1-\hat{p})/n} = .3 \pm 2.575 \sqrt{.3(1-.3)/250} = .3 \pm .0747$

12.86 $H_0 : p = .50$

$H_1 : p > .50$

$z = \dfrac{\hat{p} - p}{\sqrt{p(1-p)/n}} = \dfrac{.59 - .5}{\sqrt{.5(1-.5)/100}} = 1.80$, p-value = P(Z > 1.80) = .5 - .4641 = .0359. There is

enough evidence to infer that p is greater than .5.

12.87 & 12.88 $H_0 : p = .65$

$H_1 : p > .65$

$z = \dfrac{\hat{p} - p}{\sqrt{p(1-p)/n}} = \dfrac{.70 - .65}{\sqrt{.65(1-.65)/200}} = 1.48$, p-value = P(Z > 1.48) = .5 - .4306 = .0694

There is not enough evidence to conclude that the proportion of successes is greater than 65%.

12.89 $\hat{p} \pm z_{\alpha/2} \sqrt{\hat{p}(1-\hat{p})/n} = .7584 \pm 1.96 \sqrt{.7584(1-.7584)/567} = .7584 \pm .0352$; LCL = .7232, UCL = .7936

12.90 $H_0 : p = .90$

$H_1 : p < .90$

$z = \dfrac{\hat{p} - p}{\sqrt{p(1-p)/n}} = \dfrac{.8644 - .90}{\sqrt{.90(1-.90)/177}} = -1.58$, p-value = P(Z < -1.58) = .5 - .4429 = .0571. There is

not enough evidence to infer that the satisfaction rate is less than 90%.

12.91 $\hat{p} \pm z_{\alpha/2} \sqrt{\hat{p}(1-\hat{p})/n} = .4211 \pm 1.96 \sqrt{.4211(1-.4211)/722} = .4211 \pm .0360$; LCL = .3851, UCL = .4571.

Total number: LCL = 280 million (.3851) = 107.8 million, UCL = 280 million (.4571) = 128.0 million

12.92 $H_0 : p = .80$

$H_1 : p > .80$

$z = \dfrac{\hat{p} - p}{\sqrt{p(1-p)/n}} = \dfrac{.8225 - .80}{\sqrt{.80(1-.80)/400}} = 1.13$, p-value = P(Z > 1.13) = .5 - .3708 = .1292. There is

not enough evidence to infer that the claim is true.

12.93 $H_0 : p = .567$

$H_1 : p < .567$

$z = \dfrac{\hat{p} - p}{\sqrt{p(1-p)/n}} = \dfrac{.5265 - .567}{\sqrt{.567(1-.567)/226}} = -1.23$, p-value = P(Z < -1.23) = .5 - .3907 = .1093. There

is not enough evidence to infer that private school students have less access to computers at school.

12.94 $H_0 : p = .50$

$H_1 : p > .50$

$$z = \frac{\hat{p} - p}{\sqrt{p(1-p)/n}} = \frac{.57 - .50}{\sqrt{.50(1-.50)/100}} = 1.40, \text{ p-value} = P(Z > 1.40) = .5 - .4192 = .0808. \text{ There is}$$

enough evidence to conclude that more than 50% of all business students would rate the book as excellent.

12.95 Codes 1, 2, and 3 have been recoded to 5.

$$H_0 : p = .90$$

$$H_1 : p > .90$$

$$z = \frac{\hat{p} - p}{\sqrt{p(1-p)/n}} = \frac{.96 - .90}{\sqrt{.90(1-.90)/100}} = 2.00, \text{ p-value} = P(Z > 2.00) = .5 - .4772 = .0228. \text{ There is}$$

enough evidence to conclude that more than 90% of all business students would rate the book as at least adequate.

12.96 $\hat{p} \pm z_{\alpha/2}\sqrt{\hat{p}(1-\hat{p})/n} = .0975 \pm 1.96\sqrt{.0975(1-.0975)/2000} = .0975 \pm .0130;$ LCL = .0845, UCL = .1105

Number: LCL = 100 million (.0845) = 8.45 million, UCL = 100 million (.1105) = 11.05 million

12.97 $\hat{p} \pm z_{\alpha/2}\sqrt{\hat{p}(1-\hat{p})/n} = .0827 \pm 1.645\sqrt{.0827(1-.0827)/387} = .0827 \pm .0230;$ LCL = .0597, UCL = .1057

12.98 $H_0 : p = .12$

$H_1 : p > .12$

$$z = \frac{\hat{p} - p}{\sqrt{p(1-p)/n}} = \frac{.1475 - .12}{\sqrt{.12(1-.12)/400}} = 1.69, \text{ p-value} = P(Z > 1.69) = .5 - .4545 = .0455. \text{ There is}$$

enough evidence to infer that the proposed newspaper will be financially viable.

12.99 $\hat{p} \pm z_{\alpha/2}\sqrt{\hat{p}(1-\hat{p})/n} = .1914 \pm 1.645\sqrt{.1914(1-.1914)/810} = .1914 \pm .0227;$ LCL = .1687, UCL = .2141

Number: LCL = 270 million (.1687) = 45.55 million, UCL = 270 million (.2141) = 57.81 million

12.100 $\hat{p} \pm z_{\alpha/2}\sqrt{\hat{p}(1-\hat{p})/n} = .2031 \pm 1.96\sqrt{.2031(1-.2031)/650} = .2031 \pm .0309;$ LCL = .1722, UCL = .2340

Number: LCL = 5million (.1722) = .861 million, UCL = 5million (.2340) = 1.17 million

12.101 Codes 3 and 4 were changed to 5

$$\hat{p} \pm z_{\alpha/2}\sqrt{\hat{p}(1-\hat{p})/n} = .7305 \pm 1.96\sqrt{.7305(1-.7305)/475} = .7305 \pm .0399;\ LCL = .6906,\ UCL = .77045$$

Number: LCL = 19,108,000 (.6906) = 13,195,985, UCL = 19,108,000 (.7704) = 14,720,803

12.102 Code 2 was changed to 3.

$$\hat{p} \pm z_{\alpha/2}\sqrt{\hat{p}(1-\hat{p})/n} = .5313 \pm 1.96\sqrt{.5313(1-.5313)/320} = .5313 \pm .0547;\ LCL = .4766,\ UCL = .5860$$

Number: LCL = 14,814,000 (.4766) = 7,060,352 , UCL = 14,814,000 (.5860) = 8,681,004

12.103 a $\hat{p} \pm z_{\alpha/2}\sqrt{\hat{p}(1-\hat{p})/n} = .2919 \pm 1.96\sqrt{.2919(1-.2919)/1836} = .2919 \pm .0208;\ LCL = .2711,\ UCL = .3127$

b LCL = 101,282,000 (.2711) = 27,457,550, UCL = 101,282,000 (.3127) = 31,670,881

The answers to the chapter review exercises were produced by Excel only.

12.104 a $H_0 : \mu = 30$

$H_1 : \mu > 30$

t-Test: Mean			
			Costs
Mean			31.95
Standard Deviation			7.19
Hypothesized Mean			30
df			124
t Stat			3.04
P(T<=t) one-tail			0.0015
t Critical one-tail			1.6572
P(T<=t) two-tail			0.003
t Critical two-tail			1.9793

t = 3.04, p-value = .0015; there is enough evidence to infer that the candidate is correct.

b

t-Estimate: Mean			
			Costs
Mean			31.95
Standard Deviation			7.19
LCL			30.68
UCL			33.23

LCL = 30.68, UCL = 33.23

c The costs are required to be normally distributed.

12.105 $H_0 : \mu = 60$

$H_1 : \mu < 60$

t-Test: Mean			
			Times
Mean			57.79
Standard Deviation			6.58
Hypothesized Mean			60
df			23
t Stat			-1.64
P(T<=t) one-tail			0.0569
t Critical one-tail			1.7139
P(T<=t) two-tail			0.1138
t Critical two-tail			2.0687

t = -1.64, p-value = .0569. There is not enough evidence to conclude that the supplier's assertion is correct.

12.106 $H_0 : \sigma^2 = 17$

$H_1 : \sigma^2 > 17$

Chi Squared Test: Variance			
			Times
Sample Variance			27.47
Hypothesized Variance			17
df			19
chi-squared Stat			30.71
P (CHI<=chi) one-tail			0.0435
chi-squared Critical one tail	Left-tail		11.6509
	Right-tail		27.2036
P (CHI<=chi) two-tail			0.0869
chi-squared Critical two tail	Left-tail		10.1170
	Right-tail		30.1435

$\chi^2 = 30.71$, p-value = .0435. There is enough evidence to infer that problems are likely.

12.107

z-Estimate: Proportion	
	Resolution
Sample Proportion	0.358
Observations	215
LCL	0.304
UCL	0.412

LCL = .304, UCL = .412

12.108 a

t-Estimate: Mean			
			Marks
Mean			71.88
Standard Deviation			10.03
LCL			69.03
UCL			74.73

LCL = 69.03, UCL = 74.73

b $\qquad H_0 : \mu = 68$

$\qquad H_1 : \mu > 68$

t-Test: Mean			
			Marks
Mean			71.88
Standard Deviation			10.03
Hypothesized Mean			68
df			49
t Stat			2.74
P(T<=t) one-tail			0.0043
t Critical one-tail			1.6766
P(T<=t) two-tail			0.0086
t Critical two-tail			2.0096

t = 2.74, p-value = .0043; there is enough evidence to infer that students with a calculus background would perform better in statistics than students with no calculus?

12.109

t-Estimate: Mean			
			Points
Mean			117.54
Standard Deviation			50.24
LCL			108.19
UCL			126.89

LCL = 108.19, UCL = 126.89

12.110

z-Estimate: Proportion	
	Insurance
Sample Proportion	0.632
Observations	250
LCL	0.582
UCL	0.682

LCL = .582, UCL = .682

12.111 a

t-Estimate: Mean			
			Times
Mean			6.91
Standard Deviation			0.23
LCL			6.84
UCL			6.98

LCL = 6.84, UCL = 6.98

b The histogram is bell shaped.

c $H_0 : \mu = 7$

$H_1 : \mu < 7$

t-Test: Mean			
			Times
Mean			6.91
Standard Deviation			0.23
Hypothesized Mean			7
df			74
t Stat			-3.48
P(T<=t) one-tail			0.0004
t Critical one-tail			1.2931
P(T<=t) two-tail			0.0008
t Critical two-tail			1.6657

t = -3.48, p-value = .0004; there is enough evidence to infer that postal workers are spending less than seven hours doing their jobs.

12.112

t-Estimate: Mean			
			Time
Mean			6.35
Standard Deviation			2.16
LCL			6.05
UCL			6.65

LCL = 6.05, UCL = 6.65

12.113

t-Estimate: Mean			
			Times
Mean			5.79
Standard Deviation			2.86
LCL			5.11
UCL			6.47

LCL = 5.11, UCL = 6.47

12.114

z-Estimate: Proportion	
	Tourist
Sample Proportion	0.667
Observations	72
LCL	0.558
UCL	0.776

LCL = .558, UCL = .776

12.115 $H_0 : \sigma^2 = 4$

   $H_1 : \sigma^2 > 4$

Chi Squared Test: Variance			
			Lengths
Sample Variance			6.52
Hypothesized Variance			4
df			99
chi-squared Stat			161.25
P (CHI<=chi) one-tail			0.0001
chi-squared Critical one tail	Left-tail		77.0463
	Right-tail		123.2252
P (CHI<=chi) two-tail			0.0002
chi-squared Critical two tail	Left-tail		73.3611
	Right-tail		128.4219

$\chi^2 = 161.25$, p-value = .0001; there is enough evidence to conclude that the number of springs requiring reworking is unacceptably large.

12.116 $H_0 : p = .90$

   $H_1 : p < .90$

z-Test: Proportion		
		Springs
Sample Proportion		0.86
Observations		100
Hypothesized Proportion		0.9
z Stat		-1.33
P(Z<=z) one-tail		0.0912
z Critical one-tail		1.6449
P(Z<=z) two-tail		0.1824
z Critical two-tail		1.96

$z = -1.33$, p-value = .0912; there is enough evidence to infer that less than 90% of the springs are the correct length.

12.117

t-Estimate: Mean		
		Service
Mean		1.10
Standard Deviation		0.98
LCL		0.94
UCL		1.26

LCL = .94, UCL = 1.26

12.118 a $H_0 : \mu = 9.8$

$H_1 : \mu < 9.8$

t-Test: Mean			
			Time
Mean			9.16
Standard Deviation			2.64
Hypothesized Mean			9.8
df			149
t Stat			-2.97
P(T<=t) one-tail			0.0018
t Critical one-tail			1.6551
P(T<=t) two-tail			0.0036
t Critical two-tail			1.976

t = -2.97, p-value = .0018; there is enough evidence to infer that enclosure of preaddressed envelopes improves the average speed of payments?

b $H_0 : \sigma^2 = 10.24 \ (3.2^2)$

$H_1 : \sigma^2 < 10.24$

Chi Squared Test: Variance			
			Time
Sample Variance			6.98
Hypothesized Variance			10.24
df			149
chi-squared Stat			101.58
P (CHI<=chi) one-tail			0.0011
chi-squared Critical one tail	Left-tail		121.7870
	Right-tail		178.4853
P (CHI<=chi) two-tail			0.0021
chi-squared Critical two tail	Left-tail		117.0980
	Right-tail		184.6869

$\chi^2 = 101.58$, p-value = .0011; there is enough evidence to infer that the variability in payment speeds decreases when a preaddressed envelope is sent.

12.119 $n = \left(\dfrac{z_{\alpha/2} \sqrt{\hat{p}(1-\hat{p})}}{B} \right)^2 = \left(\dfrac{2.575\sqrt{.5(1-.5)}}{.02} \right)^2 = 4144$

12.120

z-Estimate: Proportion	
	Concert
Sample Proportion	0.153
Observations	600
LCL	0.125
UCL	0.182

Proportion: LCL = .1245, UCL = .1821

Total: LCL = 400,000(.1245) = 49,800 UCL = 400,000(.1821) = 72,840

12.121 Number of cars:

$$H_0 : \mu = 125$$

$$H_1 : \mu < 125$$

t-Test: Mean			
			Cars
Mean			125.80
Standard Deviation			3.90
Hypothesized Mean			125
df			4
t Stat			0.46
P(T<=t) one-tail			0.3351
t Critical one-tail			2.1318
P(T<=t) two-tail			0.6702
t Critical two-tail			2.7765

t = .46, p-value = .3351; there is not enough evidence to infer that the employee is stealing by lying about the number of cars.

Amount of time

$$H_0 : \mu = 3.5$$

$$H_1 : \mu > 3.5$$

t-Test: Mean			
			Time
Mean			3.61
Standard Deviation			0.40
Hypothesized Mean			3.5
df			628
t Stat			7.00
P(T<=t) one-tail			0
t Critical one-tail			1.6473
P(T<=t) two-tail			0
t Critical two-tail			1.9637

t = 7.00, p-value = 0; there is enough evidence to infer that the employee is stealing by lying about the amount of time.

Case 12.1

95% confidence interval estimate of mean weekly consumption per student:

t-Estimate: Mean			
			Cans
Mean			1.316
Standard Deviation			1.115
LCL			1.218
UCL			1.414

Estimated Mean

Number of Cans per Student	Revenue	Cost	Profit	Current Profit	Net
LCL = 1.218	$1,187,550	$487,200	$500,350	$484,000	$ 16,350
UCL = 1.414	1,378,650	565,600	613,050	484,000	129,050

Pepsi should sign the exclusivity agreement.

Case 12.2

Estimated Mean

Number of Cans per Student	Revenue	Cost	Profit	Current Profit	Net
LCL = 1.218	$1,187,550	$487,200	$500,350	$855,910	$-355,560
UCL = 1.414	1,378,650	565,600	613,050	1,071,290	-458,240

Coke would not sign the exclusivity agreement. Coke is expected to lose from the exclusivity agreement because they currently have a much larger share of the market and would not gain by paying for exclusivity.

Case 12.3

Exclude "missing" licenses:

z-Estimate: Proportion	
	Insured
Sample Proportion	0.0300
Observations	233
LCL	0.0081
UCL	0.0520

Estimated number of uninsured drivers:

$LCL = 4,505,665 \times .0081 = 36,496$

$UCL = 4,505,665 \times .0520 = 234,295$

Include "missing" licenses with uninsured:

z-Estimate: Proportion	
	Insured
Sample Proportion	0.0924
Observations	249
LCL	0.0564
UCL	0.1283

Estimated number of uninsured drivers:

$LCL = 4,505,665 \times .0564 = 254,145$

$UCL = 4,505,665 \times .1283 = 578,227$

It is quite likely that the "missing" licenses are uninsured.

Chapter 13

For all exercises in Chapters 13, 14, and 24 we employed the F-test of two variances at the 5%
significance level to decide which one of the equal-variances or unequal-variances t-test and
estimator of the difference between two means to use to solve the problem. Additionally, for exercises
that compare two populations and are accompanied by data files, our answers were derived by
defining the sample from population 1 as the data stored in the first column (often column A in Excel
and column 1 in Minitab). The data stored in the second column represent the sample from population
2. Paired differences were defined as the difference between the variable in the first column minus the
variable in the second column.

13.1 $(\bar{x}_1 - \bar{x}_2) \pm t_{\alpha/2} \sqrt{s_p^2 \left(\dfrac{1}{n_1} + \dfrac{1}{n_2} \right)} = (524 - 469) \pm 2.009 \sqrt{18,261 \left(\dfrac{1}{25} + \dfrac{1}{25} \right)} = 55 \pm 76.79$

13.2 $(\bar{x}_1 - \bar{x}_2) \pm t_{\alpha/2} \sqrt{s_p^2 \left(\dfrac{1}{n_1} + \dfrac{1}{n_2} \right)} = (524 - 469) \pm 2.009 \sqrt{79,637 \left(\dfrac{1}{25} + \dfrac{1}{25} \right)} = 55 \pm 160.35$

13.3 The interval widens.

13.4 $(\bar{x}_1 - \bar{x}_2) \pm t_{\alpha/2} \sqrt{s_p^2 \left(\dfrac{1}{n_1} + \dfrac{1}{n_2} \right)} = (524 - 469) \pm 1.972 \sqrt{18,261 \left(\dfrac{1}{100} + \dfrac{1}{100} \right)} = 55 \pm 37.69$

13.5 The interval narrows.

13.6 to 13.12 $\quad H_0 : (\mu_1 - \mu_2) = 0$

$\qquad\qquad\quad H_1 : (\mu_1 - \mu_2) \neq 0$

13.6 Rejection region: $t < -t_{\alpha/2,n-1} = -t_{.025,22} = -2.074$ or $t > t_{\alpha/2,n-1} = t_{.025,22} = 2.074$

$t = \dfrac{(\bar{x}_1 - \bar{x}_2) - (\mu_1 - \mu_2)}{\sqrt{s_p^2 \left(\dfrac{1}{n_1} + \dfrac{1}{n_2} \right)}} = \dfrac{(74 - 71) - 0}{\sqrt{275 \left(\dfrac{1}{12} + \dfrac{1}{12} \right)}} = .44$, p-value = .6617 (Excel). There is not enough

evidence to infer that the population means differ.

13.7 Rejection region: $t < -t_{\alpha/2,n-1} = -t_{.025,22} = -2.074$ or $t > t_{\alpha/2,n-1} = t_{.025,22} = 2.074$

$$t = \frac{(\bar{x}_1 - \bar{x}_2) - (\mu_1 - \mu_2)}{\sqrt{s_p^2\left(\dfrac{1}{n_1} + \dfrac{1}{n_2}\right)}} = \frac{(74-71)-0}{\sqrt{41,652\left(\dfrac{1}{12} + \dfrac{1}{12}\right)}} = .036,$$ p-value = .9716 (Excel). There is not enough

evidence to infer that the population means differ.

13.8 The value of the test statistic decreases and the p-value increases.

13.9 Rejection region: $t < -t_{\alpha/2,\nu} = -t_{.025,289} = -1.960$ or $t > t_{\alpha/2,\gamma} = t_{.025,289} = 1.960$

$$t = \frac{(\bar{x}_1 - \bar{x}_2) - (\mu_1 - \mu_2)}{\sqrt{\left(\dfrac{s_1^2}{n_1} + \dfrac{s_2^2}{n_2}\right)}} = \frac{(74-71)-0}{\sqrt{\left(\dfrac{324}{150} + \dfrac{225}{150}\right)}} = 1.57,$$ p-value = .1179 (Excel). There is not enough

evidence to infer that the population means differ.

13.10 The value of the test statistic increases and the p-value decreases.

13.11 Rejection region: $t < -t_{\alpha/2,n-1} = -t_{.025,22} = -2.074$ or $t > t_{\alpha/2,n-1} = t_{.025,22} = 2.074$

$$t = \frac{(\bar{x}_1 - \bar{x}_2) - (\mu_1 - \mu_2)}{\sqrt{s_p^2\left(\dfrac{1}{n_1} + \dfrac{1}{n_2}\right)}} = \frac{(76-71)-0}{\sqrt{275\left(\dfrac{1}{12} + \dfrac{1}{12}\right)}} = .74,$$ p-value = .4676 (Excel). There is not enough

evidence to infer that the population means differ.

13.12 The value of the test statistic increases and the p-value decreases.

13.13 $(\bar{x}_1 - \bar{x}_2) \pm t_{\alpha/2}\sqrt{\left(\dfrac{s_1^2}{n_1} + \dfrac{s_2^2}{n_2}\right)} = (63-60) \pm 1.671\sqrt{\left(\dfrac{324}{50} + \dfrac{49}{45}\right)} = 3 \pm 4.60$

13.14 $(\bar{x}_1 - \bar{x}_2) \pm t_{\alpha/2}\sqrt{\left(\dfrac{s_1^2}{n_1} + \dfrac{s_2^2}{n_2}\right)} = (63-60) \pm 1.671\sqrt{\left(\dfrac{1681}{50} + \dfrac{225}{45}\right)} = 3 \pm 10.38$

13.15 The interval widens.

13.16 $(\bar{x}_1 - \bar{x}_2) \pm t_{\alpha/2}\sqrt{\left(\dfrac{s_1^2}{n_1} + \dfrac{s_2^2}{n_2}\right)} = (63-60) \pm 1.671\sqrt{\left(\dfrac{324}{100} + \dfrac{49}{90}\right)} = 3 \pm 3.22$

13.17 The interval narrows.

13.18 to 13.24 $H_0 : (\mu_1 - \mu_2) = 0$

$H_1 : (\mu_1 - \mu_2) > 0$

13.18 Rejection region: $t > t_{\alpha,v} = t_{.05,200} = 1.653$

$$t = \frac{(\bar{x}_1 - \bar{x}_2) - (\mu_1 - \mu_2)}{\sqrt{\left(\dfrac{s_1^2}{n_1} + \dfrac{s_2^2}{n_2}\right)}} = \frac{(412 - 405) - 0}{\sqrt{\left(\dfrac{16,384}{150} + \dfrac{2,916}{150}\right)}} = .62,$$ p-value = .2689 (Excel). There is not enough

evidence to infer that μ_1 is greater than μ_2.

13.19 Rejection region: $t > t_{\alpha,v} = t_{.05,289} = 1.645$

$$t = \frac{(\bar{x}_1 - \bar{x}_2) - (\mu_1 - \mu_2)}{\sqrt{\left(\dfrac{s_1^2}{n_1} + \dfrac{s_2^2}{n_2}\right)}} = \frac{(412 - 405) - 0}{\sqrt{\left(\dfrac{961}{150} + \dfrac{676}{150}\right)}} = 2.12,$$ p-value = .0175 (Excel). There is enough evidence

to infer that μ_1 is greater than μ_2.

13.20 The value of the test statistic increases and the p-value decreases.

13.21 Rejection region: $t > t_{\alpha,v} = t_{.05,26} = 1.706$

$$t = \frac{(\bar{x}_1 - \bar{x}_2) - (\mu_1 - \mu_2)}{\sqrt{\left(\dfrac{s_1^2}{n_1} + \dfrac{s_2^2}{n_2}\right)}} = \frac{(412 - 405) - 0}{\sqrt{\left(\dfrac{16,384}{20} + \dfrac{2,916}{20}\right)}} = .23,$$ p-value = .4118 (Excel). There is not enough

evidence to infer that μ_1 is greater than μ_2.

13.22 The value of the test statistic decreases and the p-value increases.

13.23 Rejection region: $t > t_{\alpha,v} = t_{.05,200} = 1.653$

$$t = \frac{(\bar{x}_1 - \bar{x}_2) - (\mu_1 - \mu_2)}{\sqrt{\left(\dfrac{s_1^2}{n_1} + \dfrac{s_2^2}{n_2}\right)}} = \frac{(409 - 405) - 0}{\sqrt{\left(\dfrac{16,384}{150} + \dfrac{2,916}{150}\right)}} = .35,$$ p-value = .3624 (Excel). There is not enough

evidence to infer that μ_1 is greater than μ_2.

13.24 The value of the test statistic decreases and the p-value increases.

211

13.25 a Equal-variances t-test degrees of freedom = 28, Unequal-variances t-test degrees of freedom =26.4

b Equal-variances t-test degrees of freedom = 24, Unequal-variances t-test degrees of freedom = 10.7

c Equal-variances t-test degrees of freedom = 98 , Unequal-variances t-test degrees of freedom =91.2

d Equal-variances t-test degrees of freedom = 103, Unequal-variances t-test degrees of freedom = 78.5

13.26 a In all cases the equal-variances t-test degrees of freedom is greater than the unequal-variances t-test degrees of freedom.

13.27 $\quad H_0 : (\mu_1 - \mu_2) = 0$

$\qquad H_1 : (\mu_1 - \mu_2) \neq 0$

Rejection region: $t < -t_{\alpha/2,v} = -t_{.025,14} = -2.145$ or $t > t_{\alpha/2,v} = t_{.025,14} = 2.145$

$$t = \frac{(\bar{x}_1 - \bar{x}_2) - (\mu_1 - \mu_2)}{\sqrt{s_p^2 \left(\frac{1}{n_1} + \frac{1}{n_2} \right)}} = \frac{(5.88 - 5.13) - 0}{\sqrt{2.27 \left(\frac{1}{8} + \frac{1}{8} \right)}} = 1.00,\ \text{p-value} = .3361\ (\text{Excel}).\ \text{There is not enough}$$

evidence to conclude that the population means differ.

13.28 $\quad H_0 : (\mu_1 - \mu_2) = 0$

$\qquad H_1 : (\mu_1 - \mu_2) \neq 0$

Rejection region: $t < -t_{\alpha/2,v} = -t_{.025,10} = -2.228$ or $t > t_{\alpha/2,v} = t_{.025,10} = 2.228$

$$t = \frac{(\bar{x}_1 - \bar{x}_2) - (\mu_1 - \mu_2)}{\sqrt{s_p^2 \left(\frac{1}{n_1} + \frac{1}{n_2} \right)}} = \frac{(7.83 - 8.50) - 0}{\sqrt{9.03 \left(\frac{1}{6} + \frac{1}{6} \right)}} = -.38,\ \text{p-value} = .7089\ (\text{Excel}).\ \text{There is not enough}$$

evidence to conclude that the population means differ.

13.29a $\quad H_0 : (\mu_1 - \mu_2) = 0$

$\qquad H_1 : (\mu_1 - \mu_2) \neq 0$

Rejection region: $t < -t_{\alpha/2,v} = -t_{.025,380} = -1.960$ or $t > t_{\alpha/2,v} = t_{.025,380} = 1.960$

$$t = \frac{(\bar{x}_1 - \bar{x}_2) - (\mu_1 - \mu_2)}{\sqrt{s_p^2 \left(\frac{1}{n_1} + \frac{1}{n_2} \right)}} = \frac{(99.30 - 95.77) - 0}{\sqrt{565 \left(\frac{1}{165} + \frac{1}{217} \right)}} = 1.43,\ \text{p-value} = .1522\ (\text{Excel}).\ \text{There is not enough}$$

evidence to infer that the population means differ.

b $(\bar{x}_1 - \bar{x}_2) \pm t_{\alpha/2}\sqrt{s_p^2\left(\dfrac{1}{n_1}+\dfrac{1}{n_2}\right)} = (99.30 - 95.77) \pm 1.960\sqrt{565\left(\dfrac{1}{165}+\dfrac{1}{217}\right)} = 3.53 \pm 4.81;$

LCL = -1.28, UCL = 8.34

c The two populations must be normally distributed.

d The histograms (not shown here) are bell shaped.

13.30a $H_0 : (\mu_1 - \mu_2) = 0$

$H_1 : (\mu_1 - \mu_2) > 0$

Rejection region: $t > t_{\alpha,v} = t_{.10,203} \approx 1.286$

$t = \dfrac{(\bar{x}_1 - \bar{x}_2) - (\mu_1 - \mu_2)}{\sqrt{s_p^2\left(\dfrac{1}{n_1}+\dfrac{1}{n_2}\right)}} = \dfrac{(21.51 - 19.76) - 0}{\sqrt{20.33\left(\dfrac{1}{121}+\dfrac{1}{84}\right)}} = 2.72,$ p-value = .0036 (Excel). There is enough

evidence to infer that the mean of population 1 is greater than the mean of population 2.

b $(\bar{x}_1 - \bar{x}_2) \pm t_{\alpha/2}\sqrt{s_p^2\left(\dfrac{1}{n_1}+\dfrac{1}{n_2}\right)} = (21.51 - 19.76) \pm 1.653\sqrt{20.33\left(\dfrac{1}{121}+\dfrac{1}{84}\right)} = 1.75 \pm 1.06;$

LCL = .69, UCL = 2.81

c The two populations must be normally distributed.

d The histograms are bell shaped.

13.31 $H_0 : (\mu_1 - \mu_2) = 0$

$H_1 : (\mu_1 - \mu_2) < 0$

Rejection region: $t < -t_{\alpha,v} = -t_{.01,46} \approx -2.412$

$t = \dfrac{(\bar{x}_1 - \bar{x}_2) - (\mu_1 - \mu_2)}{\sqrt{\left(\dfrac{s_1^2}{n_1}+\dfrac{s_2^2}{n_2}\right)}} = \dfrac{(250.40 - 259.80) - 0}{\sqrt{\left(\dfrac{175.12}{40}+\dfrac{1893.75}{40}\right)}} = -1.31,$ p-value = .0988 (Excel). There is not

enough evidence to infer that the mean of population 2 is less than the mean of population 1.

13.32 $H_0 : (\mu_1 - \mu_2) = 0$

$H_1 : (\mu_1 - \mu_2) < 0$

Rejection region: $t < -t_{\alpha,v} = -t_{.10,485} = -1.28$

$t = \dfrac{(\bar{x}_1 - \bar{x}_2) - (\mu_1 - \mu_2)}{\sqrt{\left(\dfrac{s_1^2}{n_1}+\dfrac{s_2^2}{n_2}\right)}} = \dfrac{(72.93 - 73.99) - 0}{\sqrt{\left(\dfrac{26.32}{400}+\dfrac{241.66}{400}\right)}} = -1.30,$ p-value = .0974 (Excel). There is enough

evidence to infer that the mean of population 1 is less than the mean of population 2.

13.33a $\quad H_0 : (\mu_1 - \mu_2) = 0$

$\qquad H_1 : (\mu_1 - \mu_2) > 0$

Rejection region: $t > t_{\alpha,\nu} = t_{.05,38} \approx 1.684$

$$t = \frac{(\bar{x}_1 - \bar{x}_2) - (\mu_1 - \mu_2)}{\sqrt{s_p^2\left(\dfrac{1}{n_1} + \dfrac{1}{n_2}\right)}} = \frac{(36.93 - 31.36) - 0}{\sqrt{13.70\left(\dfrac{1}{15} + \dfrac{1}{25}\right)}} = 4.61,\ \text{p-value} = 0.\ \text{There is enough evidence to infer}$$

that Tastee is superior.

b $(\bar{x}_1 - \bar{x}_2) \pm t_{\alpha/2}\sqrt{s_p^2\left(\dfrac{1}{n_1} + \dfrac{1}{n_2}\right)} = (36.93 - 31.36) \pm 2.021 \sqrt{13.70\left(\dfrac{1}{15} + \dfrac{1}{25}\right)} = 5.57 \pm 2.44;$

LCL = 3.13, UCL = 8.01

c The histograms are somewhat bell shaped. The weight gains may be normally distributed.

13.34 $\quad H_0 : (\mu_1 - \mu_2) = 0$

$\qquad H_1 : (\mu_1 - \mu_2) < 0$

Rejection region: $t < -t_{\alpha,\nu} = -t_{.05,94} \approx -1.662$

$$t = \frac{(\bar{x}_1 - \bar{x}_2) - (\mu_1 - \mu_2)}{\sqrt{s_p^2\left(\dfrac{1}{n_1} + \dfrac{1}{n_2}\right)}} = \frac{(19.02 - 21.85) - 0}{\sqrt{33.41\left(\dfrac{1}{48} + \dfrac{1}{48}\right)}} = \text{-2.40, p-value} = .0092\ \text{(Excel). There is enough}$$

evidence to infer that taking vitamin and mineral supplements daily increases the body's immune system?

13.35 a $\quad H_0 : (\mu_1 - \mu_2) = 0$

$\qquad H_1 : (\mu_1 - \mu_2) \neq 0$

Rejection region: $t < -t_{\alpha/2,\nu} = -t_{.025,449} = -1.960$ or $t > t_{\alpha/2,\nu} = t_{.025,449} = 1.960$

$$t = \frac{(\bar{x}_1 - \bar{x}_2) - (\mu_1 - \mu_2)}{\sqrt{\left(\dfrac{s_1^2}{n_1} + \dfrac{s_2^2}{n_2}\right)}} = \frac{(58.99 - 52.96) - 0}{\sqrt{\left(\dfrac{946.97}{250} + \dfrac{1876.44}{250}\right)}} = 1.79,\ \text{p-value} = .0737\ \text{(Excel). There is not}$$

enough evidence to conclude that a difference in mean listening times exist between the two populations.

b $(\bar{x}_1 - \bar{x}_2) \pm t_{\alpha/2}\sqrt{\left(\dfrac{s_1^2}{n_1} + \dfrac{s_2^2}{n_2}\right)} = (58.99 - 52.96) \pm 1.960 \sqrt{\left(\dfrac{946.97}{250} + \dfrac{1876.44}{250}\right)} = 6.03 \pm 6.59;$

LCL = -.56, UCL = 12.62

c The histograms are bell shaped.

13.36 $H_0 : (\mu_1 - \mu_2) = 0$

$H_1 : (\mu_1 - \mu_2) < 0$

Rejection region: $t < -t_{\alpha,\nu} = -t_{.05,220} = -1.645$

$$t = \frac{(\bar{x}_1 - \bar{x}_2) - (\mu_1 - \mu_2)}{\sqrt{s_p^2 \left(\frac{1}{n_1} + \frac{1}{n_2}\right)}} = \frac{(3.19 - 4.35 - 0)}{\sqrt{14.18\left(\frac{1}{124} + \frac{1}{98}\right)}} = \text{-2.27, p-value} = .0122 \text{ (Excel). There is enough}$$

evidence to infer that the number of visits to health professionals grew between 1997 and 1998.

13.37a $H_0 : (\mu_1 - \mu_2) = 0$

$H_1 : (\mu_1 - \mu_2) \neq 0$

Rejection region: $t < -t_{\alpha/2,\nu} = -t_{.025,198} \approx -1.972$ or $t > t_{\alpha/2,\nu} = t_{.025,198} \approx 1.972$

$$t = \frac{(\bar{x}_1 - \bar{x}_2) - (\mu_1 - \mu_2)}{\sqrt{s_p^2 \left(\frac{1}{n_1} + \frac{1}{n_2}\right)}} = \frac{(10.23 - 9.66) - 0}{\sqrt{8.30\left(\frac{1}{100} + \frac{1}{100}\right)}} = 1.41, \text{ p-value} = .1606 \text{ (Excel). There is not enough}$$

evidence to infer that male and female drivers differ.

b $(\bar{x}_1 - \bar{x}_2) \pm t_{\alpha/2}\sqrt{s_p^2\left(\frac{1}{n_1} + \frac{1}{n_2}\right)} = (10.23 - 9.66) \pm 1.972\sqrt{8.30\left(\frac{1}{100} + \frac{1}{100}\right)} = .57 \pm .80; \text{LCL} = -.23,$

UCL = 1.38

c The histograms are bell shaped.

13.38 $H_0 : (\mu_1 - \mu_2) = 0$

$H_1 : (\mu_1 - \mu_2) > 0$

Rejection region: $t > t_{\alpha,\nu} = t_{.05,56} \approx 1.671$

$$t = \frac{(\bar{x}_1 - \bar{x}_2) - (\mu_1 - \mu_2)}{\sqrt{s_p^2 \left(\frac{1}{n_1} + \frac{1}{n_2}\right)}} = \frac{(115.50 - 110.32) - 0}{\sqrt{492.28\left(\frac{1}{30} + \frac{1}{28}\right)}} = .89, \text{ p-value} = .1891 \text{ (Excel). There is not enough}$$

evidence to retain supplier A—switch to supplier B.

13.39a $H_0 : (\mu_1 - \mu_2) = 0$

$H_1 : (\mu_1 - \mu_2) > 0$

Rejection region: $t > t_{\alpha,\nu} = t_{.01,42} \approx 2.423$

$$t = \frac{(\bar{x}_1 - \bar{x}_2) - (\mu_1 - \mu_2)}{\sqrt{\left(\dfrac{s_1^2}{n_1} + \dfrac{s_2^2}{n_2}\right)}} = \frac{(13.52 - 9.92) - 0}{\sqrt{\left(\dfrac{5.76}{25} + \dfrac{13.16}{25}\right)}} = 4.14, \text{ p-value} = .0001 \text{ (Excel). There is enough}$$

evidence to conclude that exercise is more effective.

b $(\bar{x}_1 - \bar{x}_2) \pm t_{\alpha/2} \sqrt{\left(\dfrac{s_1^2}{n_1} + \dfrac{s_2^2}{n_2}\right)} = (13.52 - 9.92) \pm 2.021 \sqrt{\left(\dfrac{5.76}{25} + \dfrac{13.16}{25}\right)} = 3.60 \pm 1.76;$ LCL = 1.84,

UCL = 5.36

c The histograms are bell shaped.

13.40a $\quad H_0 : (\mu_1 - \mu_2) = 0$

$\qquad H_1 : (\mu_1 - \mu_2) \neq 0$

Rejection region: $t < -t_{\alpha/2,v} = -t_{.005,29} = -2.756$ or $t > t_{\alpha/2,v} = t_{.005,29} = 2.756$

$$t = \frac{(\bar{x}_1 - \bar{x}_2) - (\mu_1 - \mu_2)}{\sqrt{\left(\dfrac{s_1^2}{n_1} + \dfrac{s_2^2}{n_2}\right)}} = \frac{(74.91 - 53.40) - 0}{\sqrt{\left(\dfrac{601.90}{23} + \dfrac{73.69}{15}\right)}} = 3.86, \text{ p-value} = .0006 \text{ (Excel). There is enough}$$

evidence to conclude that the two packages differ in the amount of time needed to learn how to use them.

b $(\bar{x}_1 - \bar{x}_2) \pm t_{\alpha/2} \sqrt{\left(\dfrac{s_1^2}{n_1} + \dfrac{s_2^2}{n_2}\right)} = (74.91 - 53.40) \pm 2.045 \sqrt{\left(\dfrac{601.90}{23} + \dfrac{73.69}{15}\right)} = 21.51 \pm 11.40;$

LCL = 10.11, UCL = 32.92

c The amount of time is required to be normally distributed.

d The histograms are somewhat bell shaped.

13.41a $\quad H_0 : (\mu_1 - \mu_2) = 0$

$\qquad H_1 : (\mu_1 - \mu_2) < 0$

Rejection region: $t < -t_{\alpha,v} = -t_{.01,277} = -2.326$

$$t = \frac{(\bar{x}_1 - \bar{x}_2) - (\mu_1 - \mu_2)}{\sqrt{\left(\dfrac{s_1^2}{n_1} + \dfrac{s_2^2}{n_2}\right)}} = \frac{(5.02 - 7.80) - 0}{\sqrt{\left(\dfrac{1.94}{200} + \dfrac{9.57}{200}\right)}} = -11.61, \text{ p-value} = 0. \text{ There is enough evidence to infer}$$

that the amount of time wasted in unsuccessful firms exceeds that of successful firms.

b $(\bar{x}_1 - \bar{x}_2) \pm t_{\alpha/2} \sqrt{\left(\dfrac{s_1^2}{n_1} + \dfrac{s_2^2}{n_2}\right)} = (5.02 - 7.80) \pm 1.960 \sqrt{\left(\dfrac{1.94}{200} + \dfrac{9.57}{200}\right)} = -2.78 \pm .47;$

LCL = -3.25, UCL = -2.31. Workers in unsuccessful companies waste on average between 2.31 and 3.25 hours per week more than workers in successful companies.

13.42 $H_0 : (\mu_1 - \mu_2) = 0$

$H_1 : (\mu_1 - \mu_2) > 0$

Rejection region: $t > t_{\alpha,\nu} = t_{.05,268} = 1.645$

$$t = \frac{(\bar{x}_1 - \bar{x}_2) - (\mu_1 - \mu_2)}{\sqrt{s_p^2\left(\frac{1}{n_1} + \frac{1}{n_2}\right)}} = \frac{(.646 - .601) - 0}{\sqrt{.00243\left(\frac{1}{125} + \frac{1}{145}\right)}} = 7.44,\ \text{p-value} = 0.\ \text{There is enough evidence to}$$

conclude that the reaction time of drivers using cell phones is slower that for non-cell phone users.

13.43 $H_0 : (\mu_1 - \mu_2) = 0$

$H_1 : (\mu_1 - \mu_2) \neq 0$

Rejection region: $t < -t_{\alpha/2,\nu} = -t_{.025,183} \approx -1.973$ or $t > t_{\alpha/2,\nu} = t_{.025,183} \approx 1.973$

$$t = \frac{(\bar{x}_1 - \bar{x}_2) - (\mu_1 - \mu_2)}{\sqrt{s_p^2\left(\frac{1}{n_1} + \frac{1}{n_2}\right)}} = \frac{(.654 - .662) - 0}{\sqrt{.00217\left(\frac{1}{95} + \frac{1}{90}\right)}} = -1.21,\ \text{p-value} = .2268\ \text{(Excel). There is not enough}$$

evidence to infer that the type of discussion affects reaction times.

13.44 $H_0 : (\mu_1 - \mu_2) = 0$

$H_1 : (\mu_1 - \mu_2) > 0$

Rejection region: $t > t_{\alpha,\nu} = t_{.05,143} \approx 1.656$

$$t = \frac{(\bar{x}_1 - \bar{x}_2) - (\mu_1 - \mu_2)}{\sqrt{s_p^2\left(\frac{1}{n_1} + \frac{1}{n_2}\right)}} = \frac{(6.18 - 5.94) - 0}{\sqrt{2.57\left(\frac{1}{64} + \frac{1}{81}\right)}} = .87,\ \text{p-value} = .1917\ \text{(Excel). There is not enough}$$

evidence to infer that people spend more time researching for a financial planner than they do for a stock broker.

13.45a $H_0 : (\mu_1 - \mu_2) = 0$

$H_1 : (\mu_1 - \mu_2) < 0$

Rejection region: $t < -t_{\alpha,\nu} = -t_{.05,373} = -1.645$

$$t = \frac{(\bar{x}_1 - \bar{x}_2) - (\mu_1 - \mu_2)}{\sqrt{\left(\frac{s_1^2}{n_1} + \frac{s_2^2}{n_2}\right)}} = \frac{(63.71 - 66.80) - 0}{\sqrt{\left(\frac{34.82}{173} + \frac{46.90}{202}\right)}} = -4.69,\ \text{p-value} = 0.\ \text{There is enough evidence to infer}$$

that students without textbooks outperform those with textbooks.

13.46 $H_0 : (\mu_1 - \mu_2) = 0$

$H_1 : (\mu_1 - \mu_2) \neq 0$

Rejection region: $t < -t_{\alpha/2,v} = -t_{.025,413} \approx -1.960$ or $t > t_{\alpha/2,v} = t_{.025,413} \approx 1.960$

$t = \dfrac{(\bar{x}_1 - \bar{x}_2) - (\mu_1 - \mu_2)}{\sqrt{s_p^2\left(\dfrac{1}{n_1} + \dfrac{1}{n_2}\right)}} = \dfrac{(149.85 - 154.43) - 0}{\sqrt{516.40\left(\dfrac{1}{213} + \dfrac{1}{202}\right)}} = -2.05$, p-value = .0407 (Excel). There is enough

evidence to conclude that there are differences in service times between the two chains.

13.47 $H_0 : (\mu_1 - \mu_2) = 0$

$H_1 : (\mu_1 - \mu_2) \neq 0$

Rejection region: $t < -t_{\alpha/2,v} = -t_{.025,168} \approx -1.975$ or $t > t_{\alpha/2,v} = t_{.025,168} \approx 1.975$

$t = \dfrac{(\bar{x}_1 - \bar{x}_2) - (\mu_1 - \mu_2)}{\sqrt{s_p^2\left(\dfrac{1}{n_1} + \dfrac{1}{n_2}\right)}} = \dfrac{(53.05 - 51.67) - 0}{\sqrt{11.44\left(\dfrac{1}{79} + \dfrac{1}{91}\right)}} = 2.65$, p-value = .0087 (Excel). There is enough

evidence to conclude that the two types of specialties differ in the time devoted to patients.

13.48 $H_0 : (\mu_1 - \mu_2) = 0$

$H_1 : (\mu_1 - \mu_2) \neq 0$

Rejection region: $t < -t_{\alpha/2,v} = -t_{.025,190} \approx -1.973$ or $t > t_{\alpha/2,v} = t_{.025,190} \approx 1.973$

$t = \dfrac{(\bar{x}_1 - \bar{x}_2) - (\mu_1 - \mu_2)}{\sqrt{\left(\dfrac{s_1^2}{n_1} + \dfrac{s_2^2}{n_2}\right)}} = \dfrac{(130.93 - 126.14) - 0}{\sqrt{\left(\dfrac{1023.36}{100} + \dfrac{675.85}{100}\right)}} = 1.16$, p-value = .2467 (Excel). There is not

enough evidence to infer that differences exist between the two types of customers.

13.49 $H_0 : (\mu_1 - \mu_2) = 0$

$H_1 : (\mu_1 - \mu_2) > 0$

Rejection region: $t > t_{\alpha,v} = t_{.05,38} \approx 1.684$

$t = \dfrac{(\bar{x}_1 - \bar{x}_2) - (\mu_1 - \mu_2)}{\sqrt{s_p^2\left(\dfrac{1}{n_1} + \dfrac{1}{n_2}\right)}} = \dfrac{(73.60 - 69.20) - 0}{\sqrt{235.11\left(\dfrac{1}{20} + \dfrac{1}{20}\right)}} = .91$, p-value = .1849 (Excel). There is not enough

evidence to infer that the new design tire lasts longer than the existing design tire.

13.50 $H_0 : (\mu_1 - \mu_2) = 0$

$H_1 : (\mu_1 - \mu_2) < 0$

Rejection region: $t < -t_{\alpha,\nu} = -t_{.05,531} = -1.645$

$$t = \frac{(\bar{x}_1 - \bar{x}_2) - (\mu_1 - \mu_2)}{\sqrt{\left(\frac{s_1^2}{n_1} + \frac{s_2^2}{n_2}\right)}} = \frac{(237.99 - 251.99) - 0}{\sqrt{\left(\frac{149.91}{263} + \frac{220.25}{279}\right)}} = -12.00, \text{ p-value} = 0. \text{ There is enough evidence to}$$

infer that British golfers play golf in less time than do American golfers.

13.51 $H_0 : (\mu_1 - \mu_2) = 0$

$H_1 : (\mu_1 - \mu_2) < 0$

Rejection region: $t < -t_{\alpha,\nu} = -t_{.05,53} \approx -1.676$

$$t = \frac{(\bar{x}_1 - \bar{x}_2) - (\mu_1 - \mu_2)}{\sqrt{s_p^2\left(\frac{1}{n_1} + \frac{1}{n_2}\right)}} = \frac{(6,345 - 6,358) - 0}{\sqrt{4,010\left(\frac{1}{28} + \frac{1}{33}\right)}} = -.84, \text{ p-value} = .2010 \text{ (Excel). There is not enough}$$

evidence to conclude that British courses are shorter than American courses.

13.52 $H_0 : (\mu_1 - \mu_2) = 0$

$H_1 : (\mu_1 - \mu_2) < 0$

Rejection region: $t < -t_{\alpha,\nu} = -t_{.05,53} \approx -1.676$

$$t = \frac{(\bar{x}_1 - \bar{x}_2) - (\mu_1 - \mu_2)}{\sqrt{\left(\frac{s_1^2}{n_1} + \frac{s_2^2}{n_2}\right)}} = \frac{(7,137 - 9,304) - 0}{\sqrt{\left(\frac{38,051}{28} + \frac{110,151}{33}\right)}} = -31.61, \text{ p-value} = 0. \text{ There is enough evidence to}$$

conclude that the total distance of American golf courses is greater than that of British courses.

13.53 The data are observational. Experimental data could be produced by randomly assigning babies to either Tastee or the competitor's product.

13.54 More affluent mothers use Tastee and babies with more affluent mothers gain weight faster.

13.55 The data are experimental.

13.56a The data are observational.

b Randomly assign students to use either of the software packages.

c Better students tend to choose Program B and better students learn how to use computer software more quickly.

13.57a Let students select the section they wish to attend and compare test results.

b Randomly assign students to either section and compare test results.

13.58a Randomly select finance and marketing MBA graduates and determine their starting salaries.

b Randomly assign some MBA students to major in finance and others to major in marketing. Compare starting salaries after they graduate.

c Better students may be attracted to finance and better students draw higher starting salaries.

13.59a The data are observational because to obtain experimental data would entail randomly assigning some people to smoke and others not to smoke.

b It is possible that some people smoke because of a genetic defect (Genetics have been associated with alcoholism.), which may also be linked to lung cancer.

c In our society the experiment described in part a is impossible.

13.60 $H_0 : \mu_D = 0$

$H_1 : \mu_D > 0$

Rejection region: $t > t_{\alpha,v} = t_{.01,4} = 3.747$

$t = \dfrac{\bar{x}_D - \mu_D}{s_D / \sqrt{n_D}} = \dfrac{3.8 - 0}{3.11 / \sqrt{5}} = 2.73$, p-value = .0263 (Excel). There is not enough evidence to infer that

the mean of population 1 exceeds the mean of population 2.

13.61 $H_0 : \mu_D = 0$

$H_1 : \mu_D \neq 0$

Rejection region: $t < -t_{\alpha/2,v} = -t_{.05,9} = -1.833$ or $t > t_{\alpha/2,v} = t_{.05,9} = 1.833$

$t = \dfrac{\bar{x}_D - \mu_D}{s_D / \sqrt{n_D}} = \dfrac{-1.30 - 0}{2.16 / \sqrt{10}} = -1.90$, p-value = .0898 (Excel). There is enough evidence to conclude

that the two population means differ

13.62 a $\bar{x}_D \pm t_{\alpha/2} \dfrac{s_D}{\sqrt{n_D}} = -2.10 \pm 1.833 \dfrac{2.23}{\sqrt{10}} = -2.10 \pm 1.29$; LCL = -3.39, UCL = -.81

b The mean difference is estimated to lie between -3.39 and -.81. This type of estimate is correct 90% of the time.

13.63a $H_0 : \mu_D = 0$

$H_1 : \mu_D \neq 0$

Rejection region: $t < -t_{\alpha/2,v} = -t_{.025,7} = -2.365$ or $t > t_{\alpha/2,v} = t_{.025,7} = 2.365$

$t = \dfrac{\bar{x}_D - \mu_D}{s_D / \sqrt{n_D}} = \dfrac{.75 - 0}{.71 / \sqrt{8}} = 2.99$, p-value = .0199 (Excel). There is enough evidence to infer that the

population means differ.

b The matched pairs experiment reduced the amount of variation and as a result the p-value decreased.

13.64a $H_0 : \mu_D = 0$

$H_1 : \mu_D \neq 0$

Rejection region: $t < -t_{\alpha/2,v} = -t_{.025,5} = -2.571$ or $t > t_{\alpha/2,v} = t_{.025,5} = 2.571$

$t = \dfrac{\bar{x}_D - \mu_D}{s_D / \sqrt{n_D}} = \dfrac{-.67 - 0}{5.16 / \sqrt{6}} = -.32$, p-value = .7646 (Excel). There is not enough evidence at the 5%

significance level to infer that the population means differ.

b The variable used to match the pairs was not strongly related to the variable being tested. As a consequence the matched pairs experiment did not reduce the variation. The smaller number of degrees of freedom produced a larger p-value.

13.65a $H_0 : \mu_D = 0$

$H_1 : \mu_D < 0$

Rejection region: $t < -t_{\alpha,v} = -t_{.05,11} = -1.796$

$t = \dfrac{\bar{x}_D - \mu_D}{s_D / \sqrt{n_D}} = \dfrac{-2.08 - 0}{3.58 / \sqrt{12}} = -2.01$, p-value = .0344 (Excel). There is enough evidence to infer that the

new fertilizer is better.

b $\bar{x}_D \pm t_{\alpha/2} \dfrac{s_D}{\sqrt{n_D}} = -2.08 \pm 2.201 \dfrac{3.58}{\sqrt{12}} = -2.08 \pm 2.27$; LCL = -4.35, UCL = .19

c The differences are required to be normally distributed

d The data are experimental.

e The data are experimental.

f The experimental design should be independent samples.

13.66 a $H_0 : \mu_D = 0$

$H_1 : \mu_D > 0$

Rejection region: $t > t_{\alpha,v} = t_{.05,11} = 1.796$

$t = \dfrac{\bar{x}_D - \mu_D}{s_D / \sqrt{n_D}} = \dfrac{3.08 - 0}{5.88 / \sqrt{12}} = 1.81$, p-value = .0484 (Excel). There is enough evidence to infer that

companies with exercise programs have lower medical expenses.

b $\bar{x}_D \pm t_{\alpha/2} \dfrac{s_D}{\sqrt{n_D}} = 3.08 \pm 2.201 \dfrac{5.88}{\sqrt{12}} = 3.08 \pm 3.74$; LCL = -.66, UCL = 6.82

c Yes because medical expenses will vary by the month of the year.

13.67a $H_0 : \mu_D = 0$

$\quad\quad H_1 : \mu_D > 0$

Rejection region: $t > t_{\alpha, v} = t_{.05, 149} \approx 1.656$

$t = \dfrac{\bar{x}_D - \mu_D}{s_D / \sqrt{n_D}} = \dfrac{12.4 - 0}{99.1 / \sqrt{150}} = 1.53$, p-value = .0638 (Excel). There is not enough evidence to infer that

mortgage payments have increases in the past 5 years.

13.68 $H_0 : \mu_D = 0$

$\quad\quad H_1 : \mu_D \neq 0$

Rejection region: $t < -t_{\alpha/2, v} = -t_{.025, 49} = -2.009$ or $t > t_{\alpha/2, v} = t_{.025, 49} = 2.009$

$t = \dfrac{\bar{x}_D - \mu_D}{s_D / \sqrt{n_D}} = \dfrac{-1.16 - 0}{2.22 / \sqrt{50}} = -3.70$, p-value = .0006 (Excel). There is enough evidence to infer that

waiters and waitresses earn different amounts in tips.

13.69a $\bar{x}_D \pm t_{\alpha/2} \dfrac{s_D}{\sqrt{n_D}} = 19.75 \pm 1.684 \dfrac{30.63}{\sqrt{40}} = 19.75 \pm 8.16$; LCL = 11.59, UCL = 27.91

b $\quad\quad H_0 : \mu_D = 0$

$\quad\quad\quad H_1 : \mu_D > 0$

Rejection region: $t > t_{\alpha, v} = t_{.05, 39} \approx 1.684$

$t = \dfrac{\bar{x}_D - \mu_D}{s_D / \sqrt{n_D}} = \dfrac{19.75 - 0}{30.63 / \sqrt{40}} = 4.08$, p-value = .0001 (Excel). There is enough evidence to conclude

that companies that advertise in the Yellow Pages have higher sales than companies that do not.

c The histogram of the differences is bell shaped.

d No, because we expect a great deal of variation between stores.

13.70 $H_0 : \mu_D = 0$

$H_1 : \mu_D < 0$

Rejection region: $t < -t_{\alpha,\nu} = -t_{.05,99} \approx -1.660$

$t = \dfrac{\bar{x}_D - \mu_D}{s_D / \sqrt{n_D}} = \dfrac{-3.6 - 0}{5.91 / \sqrt{100}} = -6.09$, p-value = 0. There is enough evidence to infer that the new drug

is effective.

13.71 $H_0 : \mu_D = 0$

$H_1 : \mu_D \neq 0$

Rejection region: $t < -t_{\alpha/2,\nu} = -t_{.025,44} = -2.014$ or $t > t_{\alpha/2,\nu} = t_{.025,44} = 2.014$

$t = \dfrac{\bar{x}_D - \mu_D}{s_D / \sqrt{n_D}} = \dfrac{-42.94 - 0}{317.16 / \sqrt{45}} = -.91$, p-value = .3686 (Excel). There is not enough evidence to infer

men and women spend different amounts on health care.

13.72 $H_0 : \mu_D = 0$

$H_1 : \mu_D < 0$

Rejection region: $t < -t_{\alpha,\nu} = -t_{.05,169} = -1.654$

$t = \dfrac{\bar{x}_D - \mu_D}{s_D / \sqrt{n_D}} = \dfrac{-183.35 - 0}{1568.94 / \sqrt{170}} = -1.52$, p-value = .0647 (Excel). There is not enough to infer stock

holdings have decreased.

13.73 $H_0 : \mu_D = 0$

$H_1 : \mu_D > 0$

Rejection region: $t > t_{\alpha,\nu} = t_{.05,37} \approx 1.690$

$t = \dfrac{\bar{x}_D - \mu_D}{s_D / \sqrt{n_D}} = \dfrac{.0422 - 0}{.1634 / \sqrt{38}} = t = 1.59$, p-value = .0597 (Excel). There is not enough evidence to

conclude that ratios are higher this year.

13.74 $H_0 : \mu_D = 0$

$H_1 : \mu_D > 0$

Rejection region: $t > t_{\alpha,\nu} = t_{.05,54} \approx 1.676$

$t = \dfrac{\bar{x}_D - \mu_D}{s_D / \sqrt{n_D}} = \dfrac{520.85 - 0}{1854.92 / \sqrt{55}} = 2.08$, p-value = .0210 (Excel). There is enough evidence to infer that

company 1's calculated tax payable is higher than company 2's.

13.75 $H_0 : \mu_D = 0$

$H_1 : \mu_D > 0$

Rejection region: $t > t_{\alpha,\nu} = t_{.05,19} = 1.729$

$t = \dfrac{\bar{x}_D - \mu_D}{s_D / \sqrt{n_D}} = \dfrac{4.55 - 0}{7.22 / \sqrt{20}} = 2.82$, p-value = .0055 (Excel). There is enough evidence to that the new

design tire lasts longer than the existing design.

13.76 The matched pairs experiment reduced the variation caused by different drivers.

13.77 $H_0 : \mu_D = 0$

$H_1 : \mu_D > 0$

Rejection region: $t > t_{\alpha,\nu} = t_{.05,24} = 1.711$

$t = \dfrac{\bar{x}_D - \mu_D}{s_D / \sqrt{n_D}} = \dfrac{4587 - 0}{22,851 / \sqrt{25}} = 1.00$, p-value = .1628 (Excel). There is not enough evidence to infer

that finance majors attract higher salary offers than do marketing majors.

13.78 $H_0 : \sigma_1^2 / \sigma_2^2 = 1$

$H_1 : \sigma_1^2 / \sigma_2^2 \neq 1$

Rejection region: $F > F_{\alpha/2,\nu_1,\nu_2} = F_{.025,29,29} \approx 2.09$ or

$F < F_{1-\alpha/2,\nu_1,\nu_2} = 1/ F_{\alpha/2,\nu_2,\nu_1} = 1/ F_{.025,29,29} \approx 1/2.09 = .48$

F = $s_1^2 / s_2^2 = 350/700 = .50$, p-value = .0669 (Excel). There is not enough evidence to conclude that

the population variances differ.

13.79 Rejection region: $F > F_{\alpha/2,\nu_1,\nu_2} = F_{.025,14,14} \approx 2.95$ or

$F < F_{1-\alpha/2,\nu_1,\nu_2} = 1/ F_{\alpha/2,\nu_2,\nu_1} = 1/ F_{.025,14,14} \approx 1/2.95 = .34$

F = $s_1^2 / s_2^2 = 350/700 = .50$, p-value = .3357 (Excel). There is not enough evidence to conclude that

the population variances differ.

13.80 The value of the test statistic is unchanged. The p-value increases.

13.81 $LCL = \left(\dfrac{s_1^2}{s_2^2}\right)\dfrac{1}{F_{\alpha/2,v_1,v_2}} = \left(\dfrac{28}{19}\right)\dfrac{1}{4.03} = .366$, $UCL = \left(\dfrac{s_1^2}{s_2^2}\right)F_{\alpha/2,v_2,v_1} = \left(\dfrac{28}{19}\right)4.03 = 5.94$

13.82 $LCL = \left(\dfrac{s_1^2}{s_2^2}\right)\dfrac{1}{F_{\alpha/2,v_1,v_2}} = \left(\dfrac{28}{19}\right)\dfrac{1}{2.27} = .649$, $UCL = \left(\dfrac{s_1^2}{s_2^2}\right)F_{\alpha/2,v_2,v_1} = \left(\dfrac{28}{19}\right)2.27 = 3.35$

13.83 The interval widens.

13.84 $\quad H_0 : \sigma_1^2/\sigma_2^2 = 1$

$\qquad H_1 : \sigma_1^2/\sigma_2^2 > 1$

Rejection region: $F > F_{\alpha,v_1,v_2} = F_{.05,19,19} \approx 2.16$

$F = s_1^2/s_2^2 = 60/25 = 2.40$, p-value = .0318 (Excel). There is enough evidence to infer that variance of

population 1 is greater than the variance of population 2.

13.85 $\quad H_0 : \sigma_1^2/\sigma_2^2 = 1$

$\qquad H_1 : \sigma_1^2/\sigma_2^2 \neq 1$

Rejection region: $F > F_{\alpha/2,v_1,v_2} = F_{.05,7,9} = 3.29$ or

$F < F_{1-\alpha/2,v_1,v_2} = 1/F_{\alpha/2,v_2,v_1} = 1/F_{.05,9,7} = 1/3.68 = .27$

$F = s_1^2/s_2^2 = 10.27/39.16 = .26$, p-value = .0914 (Excel). There is enough evidence to infer that the

population variances differ.

13.86 $\quad H_0 : \sigma_1^2/\sigma_2^2 = 1$

$\qquad H_1 : \sigma_1^2/\sigma_2^2 \neq 1$

Rejection region: $F > F_{\alpha/2,v_1,v_2} = F_{.025,9,9} = 4.03$ or

$F < F_{1-\alpha/2,v_1,v_2} = 1/F_{\alpha/2,v_2,v_1} = 1/F_{.025,9,9} = 1/4.03 = .25$

$F = s_1^2/s_2^2 = 163.88/233.38 = .70$, p-value = .6068 (Excel). There is no evidence to conclude that the

population variances differ.

13.87 $H_0 : \sigma_1^2 / \sigma_2^2 = 1$

$H_1 : \sigma_1^2 / \sigma_2^2 < 1$

Rejection region: $F < F_{1-\alpha,v_1,v_2} = 1/F_{\alpha,v_2,v_1} = 1/F_{.01,125,129} \approx 1/1.53 = .65$

$F = s_1^2 / s_2^2 = 15,800/18,734 = .84$, p-value = .1690 (Excel). There is not enough evidence to infer that the variance of population 1 is less that the variance of population 2.

13.88 $LCL = \left(\dfrac{s_1^2}{s_2^2}\right)\dfrac{1}{F_{\alpha/2,v_1,v_2}} = \left(\dfrac{15,800}{18,734}\right)\dfrac{1}{1.43} = .590$, $UCL = \left(\dfrac{s_1^2}{s_2^2}\right)F_{\alpha/2,v_2,v_1} = \left(\dfrac{15,800}{18,734}\right)1.43 = 1.21$

13.89 $H_0 : \sigma_1^2 / \sigma_2^2 = 1$

$H_1 : \sigma_1^2 / \sigma_2^2 \neq 1$

Rejection region: $F > F_{\alpha/2,v_1,v_2} = F_{.025,24,24} = 2.27$ or

$F < F_{1-\alpha/2,v_1,v_2} = 1/F_{\alpha/2,v_2,v_1} = 1/F_{.025,24,24} = 1/2.27 = .44$

$F = s_1^2 / s_2^2 = 5.76/13.16 = .438$, p-value = .0482 (Excel). There is enough evidence to conclude that the population variances are not equal.

13.90 $H_0 : \sigma_1^2 / \sigma_2^2 = 1$

$H_1 : \sigma_1^2 / \sigma_2^2 \neq 1$

Rejection region: $F > F_{\alpha/2,v_1,v_2} = F_{.05,78,90} \approx 1.43$ or

$F < F_{1-\alpha/2,v_1,v_2} = 1/F_{\alpha/2,v_2,v_1} = 1/F_{.05,90,78} \approx 1/1.53 = .65$

$F = s_1^2 / s_2^2 = 9.38/13.22 = .71$, p-value = .1214 (Excel). There is not enough evidence to conclude that the population variances are not equal.

13.91 $H_0 : \sigma_1^2 / \sigma_2^2 = 1$

$H_1 : \sigma_1^2 / \sigma_2^2 \neq 1$

Rejection region: $F > F_{\alpha/2,v_1,v_2} = F_{.025,99,99} \approx 1.43$ or

$F < F_{1-\alpha/2,v_1,v_2} = 1/F_{\alpha/2,v_2,v_1} = 1/F_{.025,99,99} \approx 1/1.43 = .70$

$F = s_1^2 / s_2^2 = 1023.36/675.85 = 1.51$, p-value = .0402 (Excel). There is enough evidence to conclude that the population variances are not equal.

13.92 $H_0 : \sigma_1^2 / \sigma_2^2 = 1$

$H_1 : \sigma_1^2 / \sigma_2^2 < 1$

Rejection region: $F < F_{1-\alpha, v_1, v_2} = 1/F_{\alpha, v_2, v_1} = 1/F_{.05, 51, 51} \approx 1/1.53 = .65$

$F = s_1^2 / s_2^2 = .026/.087 = .30$, p-value = 0 (Excel). There is enough evidence to infer that portfolio 2 is riskier than portfolio 1.

13.93 $H_0 : \sigma_1^2 / \sigma_2^2 = 1$

$H_1 : \sigma_1^2 / \sigma_2^2 \neq 1$

Rejection region: $F > F_{\alpha/2, v_1, v_2} = F_{.05, 99, 99} \approx 1.35$ or

$F < F_{1-\alpha, v_1, v_2} = 1/F_{\alpha, v_2, v_1} = 1/F_{.05, 99, 99} \approx 1/1.35 = .74$

$F = s_1^2 / s_2^2 = 3.35/10.95 = .31$, p-value = 0 (Excel). There is enough evidence to conclude that the population variances differ.

13.94 to 13.100 $H_0 : (p_1 - p_2) = 0$

$H_1 : (p_1 - p_2) \neq 0$

Rejection region: $z < -z_{\alpha/2} = -z_{.025} = -1.96$ or $z > z_{\alpha/2} = z_{.025} = 1.96$

13.94 $z = \dfrac{(\hat{p}_1 - \hat{p}_2)}{\sqrt{\hat{p}(1-\hat{p})\left(\dfrac{1}{n_1} + \dfrac{1}{n_2}\right)}} = \dfrac{(.45 - .40)}{\sqrt{.425(1-.425)\left(\dfrac{1}{100} + \dfrac{1}{100}\right)}} = .72$, p-value = 2P(Z > .72) = 2(.5 -

.2642) = .4716.

13.95 $z = \dfrac{(\hat{p}_1 - \hat{p}_2)}{\sqrt{\hat{p}(1-\hat{p})\left(\dfrac{1}{n_1} + \dfrac{1}{n_2}\right)}} = \dfrac{(.45 - .40)}{\sqrt{.425(1-.425)\left(\dfrac{1}{400} + \dfrac{1}{400}\right)}} = 1.43$, p-value = 2P(Z > 1.43)

= 2(.5 - .4236) = .1528.

13.96 The p-value decreases.

13.97 $z = \dfrac{(\hat{p}_1 - \hat{p}_2)}{\sqrt{\hat{p}(1-\hat{p})\left(\dfrac{1}{n_1} + \dfrac{1}{n_2}\right)}} = \dfrac{(.95 - .90)}{\sqrt{.925(1-.925)\left(\dfrac{1}{100} + \dfrac{1}{100}\right)}} = 1.34$, p-value = 2P(Z > 1.34)

= 2(.5 - .4099) = .1802.

13.98 The p-value decreases.

13.99 $z = \dfrac{(\hat{p}_1 - \hat{p}_2)}{\sqrt{\hat{p}(1-\hat{p})\left(\dfrac{1}{n_1}+\dfrac{1}{n_2}\right)}} = \dfrac{(.05 - .10)}{\sqrt{.075(1-.075)\left(\dfrac{1}{100}+\dfrac{1}{100}\right)}} = -1.34$, p-value = 2P(Z < -1.34)

$= 2(.5 - .4099) = .1802.$

13.100 The p-value deceases.

13.101 $(\hat{p}_1 - \hat{p}_2) \pm z_{\alpha/2}\sqrt{\dfrac{\hat{p}_1(1-\hat{p}_1)}{n_1}+\dfrac{\hat{p}_2(1-\hat{p}_2)}{n_2}} = (.18-.22) \pm 1.645\sqrt{\dfrac{.18(1-.18)}{100}+\dfrac{.22(1-.22)}{100}}$

$= -.040 \pm .093$

13.102 $(\hat{p}_1 - \hat{p}_2) \pm z_{\alpha/2}\sqrt{\dfrac{\hat{p}_1(1-\hat{p}_1)}{n_1}+\dfrac{\hat{p}_2(1-\hat{p}_2)}{n_2}} = (.48-.52) \pm 1.645\sqrt{\dfrac{.48(1-.48)}{100}+\dfrac{.52(1-.52)}{100}}$

$= -.040 \pm .116$

13.103 The interval widens.

13.104 $H_0 : (p_1 - p_2) = 0$

       $H_1 : (p_1 - p_2) > 0$

Rejection region: $z > z_\alpha = z_{.05} = 1.645$

$z = \dfrac{(\hat{p}_1 - \hat{p}_2)}{\sqrt{\hat{p}(1-\hat{p})\left(\dfrac{1}{n_1}+\dfrac{1}{n_2}\right)}} = \dfrac{(.071-.064)}{\sqrt{.068(1-.068)\left(\dfrac{1}{1604}+\dfrac{1}{1109}\right)}} = .71$, p-value = P(Z > .71) = .5 - .2611

$= .2389.$ There is not enough evidence to infer that the claim is false.

13.105a $H_0 : (p_1 - p_2) = 0$

       $H_1 : (p_1 - p_2) > 0$

Rejection region: $z > z_\alpha = z_{.05} = 1.645$

$z = \dfrac{(\hat{p}_1 - \hat{p}_2)}{\sqrt{\hat{p}(1-\hat{p})\left(\dfrac{1}{n_1}+\dfrac{1}{n_2}\right)}} = \dfrac{(.56-.46)}{\sqrt{.518(1-.518)\left(\dfrac{1}{1100}+\dfrac{1}{800}\right)}} = 4.31$, p-value = 0. There is enough

evidence to infer that the leader's popularity has decreased.

b $H_0 : (p_1 - p_2) = .05$

  $H_1 : (p_1 - p_2) > .05$

Rejection region: $z > z_\alpha = z_{.05} = 1.645$

$$z = \frac{(\hat{p}_1 - \hat{p}_2) - (p_1 - p_2)}{\sqrt{\dfrac{\hat{p}_1(1 - \hat{p}_1)}{n_1} + \dfrac{\hat{p}_2(1 - \hat{p}_2)}{n_2}}} = \frac{(.56 - .46) - .05}{\sqrt{\dfrac{.56(1 - .56)}{1100} + \dfrac{.46(1 - .46)}{800}}} = 2.16, \text{ p-value} = P(Z > 2.16) = .5 -$$

.4846 = .0154. There is enough evidence to infer that the leader's popularity has decreased by more than 5%.

c $(\hat{p}_1 - \hat{p}_2) \pm z_{\alpha/2} \sqrt{\dfrac{\hat{p}_1(1 - \hat{p}_1)}{n_1} + \dfrac{\hat{p}_2(1 - \hat{p}_2)}{n_2}} = (.56 - .46) \pm 1.96 \sqrt{\dfrac{.56(1 - .56)}{1100} + \dfrac{.46(1 - .46)}{800}} = .10$

$\pm .045$; LCL = .055, UCL = .145; we estimate that the leader's popularity has fallen by between 5.5% and 14.5%.

13.106 $H_0 : (p_1 - p_2) = -.08$

  $H_1 : (p_1 - p_2) < -.08$

Rejection region: $z < -z_\alpha = -z_{.01} = -2.33$

$$z = \frac{(\hat{p}_1 - \hat{p}_2) - (p_1 - p_2)}{\sqrt{\dfrac{\hat{p}_1(1 - \hat{p}_1)}{n_1} + \dfrac{\hat{p}_2(1 - \hat{p}_2)}{n_2}}} = \frac{(.11 - .28) - (-.08)}{\sqrt{\dfrac{.11(1 - .11)}{300} + \dfrac{.28(1 - .28)}{300}}} = -2.85, \text{ p-value} = P(Z < -2.85) = .5 -$$

.4978 = .0022. There is enough evidence to conclude that management should adopt process 1.

13.107 $H_0 : (p_1 - p_2) = 0$

  $H_1 : (p_1 - p_2) < 0$

Rejection region: $z < -z_\alpha = -z_{.05} = -1.645$

$$z = \frac{(\hat{p}_1 - \hat{p}_2)}{\sqrt{\hat{p}(1 - \hat{p})\left(\dfrac{1}{n_1} + \dfrac{1}{n_2}\right)}} = \frac{(.093 - .115)}{\sqrt{.104(1 - .104)\left(\dfrac{1}{6281} + \dfrac{1}{6281}\right)}} = -4.04, \text{ p-value} = 0. \text{ There is enough}$$

evidence to infer that Plavix is effective.

13.108 $H_0 : (p_1 - p_2) = 0$

  $H_1 : (p_1 - p_2) \neq 0$

Rejection region: $z < -z_{\alpha/2} = -z_{.05} = -1.96$ or $z > z_{\alpha/2} = z_{.05} = 1.96$

$$z = \frac{(\hat{p}_1 - \hat{p}_2)}{\sqrt{\hat{p}(1-\hat{p})\left(\dfrac{1}{n_1} + \dfrac{1}{n_2}\right)}} = \frac{(.0995 - .1297)}{\sqrt{.1132(1 - .1132)\left(\dfrac{1}{382} + \dfrac{1}{316}\right)}} = -1.26, \text{ p-value} = 2P(Z < -1.26)$$

$= 2(.5 - .3962) = .2076$. There is not enough evidence to infer differences between the two sources.

13.109 $H_0 : (p_1 - p_2) = 0$

   $H_1 : (p_1 - p_2) < 0$

Rejection region: $z < -z_\alpha = -z_{.05} = -1.645$

$$z = \frac{(\hat{p}_1 - \hat{p}_2)}{\sqrt{\hat{p}(1-\hat{p})\left(\dfrac{1}{n_1} + \dfrac{1}{n_2}\right)}} = \frac{(.5702 - .6365)}{\sqrt{.6042(1 - .109)\left(\dfrac{1}{577} + \dfrac{1}{608}\right)}} = -2.33, \text{ p-value} = P(Z < -2.33) = .5 - .4901$$

$= .0099$. There is enough evidence to infer that New Yorkers are more likely to respond no.

13.110 $H_0 : (p_1 - p_2) = 0$

   $H_1 : (p_1 - p_2) < 0$

Rejection region: $z < -z_\alpha = -z_{.05} = -1.645$

$$z = \frac{(\hat{p}_1 - \hat{p}_2)}{\sqrt{\hat{p}(1-\hat{p})\left(\dfrac{1}{n_1} + \dfrac{1}{n_2}\right)}} = \frac{(.2462 - .2691)}{\sqrt{.2579(1 - .2579)\left(\dfrac{1}{662} + \dfrac{1}{695}\right)}} = -.96, \text{ p-value} = P(Z < -.96) = .5 - .3315$$

$= .1685$. There is not enough evidence to infer that the proportion of smokers has decreased in the last 10 years.

13.111 $H_0 : (p_1 - p_2) = 0$

   $H_1 : (p_1 - p_2) > 0$

Rejection region: $z > z_\alpha = z_{.10} = 1.28$

$$z = \frac{(\hat{p}_1 - \hat{p}_2)}{\sqrt{\hat{p}(1-\hat{p})\left(\dfrac{1}{n_1} + \dfrac{1}{n_2}\right)}} = \frac{(.2632 - .0741)}{\sqrt{.11(1 - .11)\left(\dfrac{1}{38} + \dfrac{1}{162}\right)}} = 3.35, \text{ p-value} = 0. \text{ There is enough evidence to}$$

conclude that smokers have a higher incidence of heart diseases than nonsmokers.

b $(\hat{p}_1 - \hat{p}_2) \pm z_{\alpha/2}\sqrt{\dfrac{\hat{p}_1(1-\hat{p}_1)}{n_1} + \dfrac{\hat{p}_2(1-\hat{p}_2)}{n_2}} = (.2632 - 0741)$

$\pm 1.645\sqrt{\dfrac{.2632(1 - .2632)}{38} + \dfrac{.0741(1 - .0741)}{162}} = .1891 \pm .1222;$ LCL $= .0669$, UCL $= .3113$

13.112a $H_0 : (p_1 - p_2) = 0$

$H_1 : (p_1 - p_2) > 0$

Rejection region: $z > z_\alpha = z_{.10} = 1.28$

$$z = \frac{(\hat{p}_1 - \hat{p}_2)}{\sqrt{\hat{p}(1-\hat{p})\left(\frac{1}{n_1} + \frac{1}{n_2}\right)}} = \frac{(.62 - .52)}{\sqrt{.56(1-.56)\left(\frac{1}{400} + \frac{1}{500}\right)}} = 3.01, \text{p-value} = P(Z > 3.01) = .5 - .4987 =$$

.0013. There is enough evidence to infer that there has been a decrease in belief in the greenhouse effect.

$$\text{b } (\hat{p}_1 - \hat{p}_2) \pm z_{\alpha/2}\sqrt{\frac{\hat{p}_1(1-\hat{p}_1)}{n_1} + \frac{\hat{p}_2(1-\hat{p}_2)}{n_2}} = (.62-.52) \pm 1.645\sqrt{\frac{.62(1-.62)}{400} + \frac{.52(1-.52)}{500}} = .10$$

$\pm .0543$; LCL = .0457 and UCL = .1543; the change in the public's opinion is estimated to lie between 4.57 and 15.43%

13.113 $H_0 : (p_1 - p_2) = 0$

$H_1 : (p_1 - p_2) > 0$

Rejection region: $z > z_\alpha = z_{.05} = 1.645$

$$z = \frac{(\hat{p}_1 - \hat{p}_2)}{\sqrt{\hat{p}(1-\hat{p})\left(\frac{1}{n_1} + \frac{1}{n_2}\right)}} = \frac{(.3585 - .3420)}{\sqrt{.3504(1-.3504)\left(\frac{1}{477} + \frac{1}{462}\right)}} = .53, \text{p-value} = P(Z > .53) = .5 - .2019$$

= .2981.There is not enough evidence to infer that the use of illicit drugs in the United States has increased in the past decade.

13.114 $H_0 : (p_1 - p_2) = -.02$

$H_1 : (p_1 - p_2) < -.02$

Rejection region: $z < -z_\alpha = -z_{.05} = -1.645$

$$z = \frac{(\hat{p}_1 - \hat{p}_2) - (p_1 - p_2)}{\sqrt{\frac{\hat{p}_1(1-\hat{p}_1)}{n_1} + \frac{\hat{p}_2(1-\hat{p}_2)}{n_2}}} = \frac{(.055 - .11) - (-.02)}{\sqrt{\frac{.055(1-.055)}{200} + \frac{.11(1-.11)}{200}}} = -1.28, \text{p-value} = P(Z < -1.28)$$

= .5 - .3997= .1003. There is not enough evidence to choose machine A.

13.115 $H_0 : (p_1 - p_2) = 0$

$H_1 : (p_1 - p_2) > 0$

Rejection region: $z > z_\alpha = z_{.05} = 1.645$

$$z = \frac{(\hat{p}_1 - \hat{p}_2)}{\sqrt{\hat{p}(1-\hat{p})\left(\frac{1}{n_1} + \frac{1}{n_2}\right)}} = \frac{(.1385 - .0905)}{\sqrt{.1035(1-.1035)\left(\frac{1}{231} + \frac{1}{619}\right)}}$$ z = 2.05, p-value = P(Z > 2.05) = .5 -

.4798 = .0202. There is enough evidence to conclude that health conscious adults are more likely to buy Special X.

13.116 $H_0 : (p_1 - p_2) = 0$

$H_1 : (p_1 - p_2) > 0$

Rejection region: $z > z_\alpha = z_{.05} = 1.645$

$$z = \frac{(\hat{p}_1 - \hat{p}_2)}{\sqrt{\hat{p}(1-\hat{p})\left(\frac{1}{n_1} + \frac{1}{n_2}\right)}} = \frac{(.1561 - .0921)}{\sqrt{.1377(1-.1377)\left(\frac{1}{378} + \frac{1}{152}\right)}}$$ = 1.93, p-value = P(Z > 1.93) = .5 -

.4732 = .0268. There is enough evidence to infer that low-income individuals are more likely to use the company's services.

13.117 $H_0 : (p_1 - p_2) = 0$

$H_1 : (p_1 - p_2) < 0$

Rejection region: $z < -z_\alpha = -z_{.05} = -1.645$

$$z = \frac{(\hat{p}_1 - \hat{p}_2)}{\sqrt{\hat{p}(1-\hat{p})\left(\frac{1}{n_1} + \frac{1}{n_2}\right)}} = \frac{(.0095 - .0172)}{\sqrt{.01335(1-.01335)\left(\frac{1}{11000} + \frac{1}{11000}\right)}}$$ = -5.00, p-value = 0. There is

enough evidence to infer that aspirin is effective in reducing the incidence of heart attacks.

The answers to the chapter review exercises were produced by Excel only.

13.118 $H_0 : (\mu_1 - \mu_2) = 0$

$H_1 : (\mu_1 - \mu_2) \neq 0$

t-Test: Two-Sample Assuming Equal Variances		
	Oat bran	Other
Mean	10.01	9.12
Variance	19.64	19.84
Observations	120	120
Pooled Variance	19.74	
Hypothesized Mean Difference	0	
df	238	
t Stat	1.56	
P(T<=t) one-tail	0.0602	
t Critical one-tail	1.6513	
P(T<=t) two-tail	0.1204	
t Critical two-tail	1.9700	

$t = 1.56$, p-value = .1204. There is not enough evidence to infer that oat bran is different from other cereals in terms of cholesterol reduction?

13.119 $H_0 : (p_1 - p_2) = 0$

$H_1 : (p_1 - p_2) < 0$

z-Test: Two Proportions			
		$100-Limit	$3000-Limit
Sample Proportions		0.5234	0.5551
Observations		491	490
Hypothesized Difference		0	
z Stat		-1.00	
P(Z<=z) one tail		0.1598	
z Critical one-tail		1.2816	
P(Z<=z) two-tail		0.3196	
z Critical two-tail		1.6449	

$z = -1.00$, p-value = .1598. There is not enough evidence to infer that the dealer at the more expensive table is cheating.

13.120 $H_0 : (\mu_1 - \mu_2) = 0$

$H_1 : (\mu_1 - \mu_2) > 0$

t-Test: Two-Sample Assuming Equal Variances		
	During	Before
Mean	5746.07	5372.13
Variance	167289	194772
Observations	15	24
Pooled Variance	184373	
Hypothesized Mean Difference	0	
df	37	
t Stat	2.65	
P(T<=t) one-tail	0.0059	
t Critical one-tail	1.6871	
P(T<=t) two-tail	0.0119	
t Critical two-tail	2.0262	

$t = 2.65$, p-value = .0059. There is enough evidence to conclude that the campaign is successful.

13.121 Gross sales must increase by 50/.20 = $250 to pay for ads.

$$H_0 : (\mu_1 - \mu_2) = 250$$

$$H_1 : (\mu_1 - \mu_2) > 250$$

t-Test: Two-Sample Assuming Equal Variances		
	During	Before
Mean	5746.07	5372.13
Variance	167289	194772
Observations	15	24
Pooled Variance	184373	
Hypothesized Mean Difference	250	
df	37	
t Stat	0.88	
P(T<=t) one-tail	0.1931	
t Critical one-tail	1.6871	
P(T<=t) two-tail	0.3862	
t Critical two-tail	2.0262	

$t = .88$, p-value = .1931. There is not enough evidence to conclude that the ads are profitable.

13.122 $H_0 : (\mu_1 - \mu_2) = 0$

$\qquad H_1 : (\mu_1 - \mu_2) < 0$

t-Test: Two-Sample Assuming Unequal Variances		
	Group 1	Group 2
Mean	4.94	9.48
Variance	11.19	20.29
Observations	68	193
Hypothesized Mean Difference	0	
df	158	
t Stat	-8.73	
P(T<=t) one-tail	0.0000	
t Critical one-tail	1.6546	
P(T<=t) two-tail	0.0000	
t Critical two-tail	1.9751	

$t = -8.73$, p-value = 0. There is enough evidence to conclude that men and women who suffer heart attacks vacation less than those who do not suffer heart attacks.

13.123a $H_0 : \mu_D = 0$

$H_1 : \mu_D > 0$

t-Test: Paired Two Sample for Means		
	Uninsulated	Insulated
Mean	775.53	718.13
Variance	48106.3	51464.7
Observations	15	15
Pearson Correlation	0.9988	
Hypothesized Mean Difference	0	
df	14	
t Stat	16.92	
P(T<=t) one-tail	0.0000	
t Critical one-tail	1.3450	
P(T<=t) two-tail	0.0000	
t Critical two-tail	1.7613	

$t = 16.92$, p-value = 0. There is enough evidence to conclude that heating costs for insulated homes is less than that for uninsulated homes.

b

t-Estimate: Mean			
			Difference
Mean			57.40
Standard Deviation			13.14
LCL			50.12
UCL			64.68

LCL = 50.12, UCL = 64.68

c Differences are required to be normally distributed.

13.124 $H_0 : (\mu_1 - \mu_2) = 0$

$H_1 : (\mu_1 - \mu_2) \neq 0$

t-Test: Two-Sample Assuming Equal Variances		
	Vendor	Delivered
Mean	19.50	20.03
Variance	14.35	14.97
Observations	205	155
Pooled Variance	14.62	
Hypothesized Mean Difference	0	
df	358	
t Stat	-1.29	
P(T<=t) one-tail	0.0996	
t Critical one-tail	1.6491	
P(T<=t) two-tail	0.1993	
t Critical two-tail	1.9666	

t = -1.29, p-value = .1993. There is no evidence of a difference in reading time between the two groups.

13.125 $H_0 : (p_1 - p_2) = 0$

$H_1 : (p_1 - p_2) < 0$

z-Test: Two Proportions			
		Last Year	This Year
Sample Proportions		0.6758	0.7539
Observations		327	382
Hypothesized Difference		0	
z Stat		-2.30	
P(Z<=z) one tail		0.0106	
z Critical one-tail		1.6449	
P(Z<=z) two-tail		0.0212	
z Critical two-tail		1.9600	

z = -2.30, p-value = .0106. There is enough evidence to infer an increase in seatbelt use.

13.126a $H_0 : (\mu_1 - \mu_2) = 0$

$H_1 : (\mu_1 - \mu_2) < 0$

t-Test: Two-Sample Assuming Equal Variances		
	5 Years	This Year
Mean	32.42	33.72
Variance	36.92	45.52
Observations	200	200
Pooled Variance	41.22	
Hypothesized Mean Difference	0	
df	398	
t Stat	-2.02	
P(T<=t) one-tail	0.0218	
t Critical one-tail	1.2837	
P(T<=t) two-tail	0.0436	
t Critical two-tail	1.6487	

t = -2.02, p-value = .0218. There is enough evidence to infer that housing cost a percentage of total income has increased.

b The histograms are be bell shaped.

13.127a $H_0 : (\mu_1 - \mu_2) = 0$

$H_1 : (\mu_1 - \mu_2) \neq 0$

t-Test: Two-Sample Assuming Equal Variances		
	Male	Female
Mean	39.75	49.00
Variance	803.88	733.16
Observations	20	20
Pooled Variance	768.52	
Hypothesized Mean Difference	0	
df	38	
t Stat	-1.06	
P(T<=t) one-tail	0.1490	
t Critical one-tail	1.3042	
P(T<=t) two-tail	0.2980	
t Critical two-tail	1.6860	

t = -1.06, p-value = .2980. There is not enough evidence to conclude that men and women differ in the amount of time spent reading magazines.

b $H_0 : (\mu_1 - \mu_2) = 0$

$H_1 : (\mu_1 - \mu_2) < 0$

t-Test: Two-Sample Assuming Unequal Variances		
	Variable 1	Variable 2
Mean	33.10	56.84
Variance	278.69	1047.81
Observations	21	19
Hypothesized Mean Difference	0	
df	26	
t Stat	-2.87	
P(T<=t) one-tail	0.0040	
t Critical one-tail	1.3150	
P(T<=t) two-tail	0.0080	
t Critical two-tail	1.7056	

$t = -2.87$, p-value = .0040. There is enough evidence to conclude that high-income individuals devote more time to reading magazines than do low-income individuals.

13.128a $H_0 : \mu_D = 0$

$H_1 : \mu_D \neq 0$

t-Test: Paired Two Sample for Means		
	Female	Male
Mean	55.68	56.40
Variance	105.64	116.75
Observations	25	25
Pearson Correlation	0.9553	
Hypothesized Mean Difference	0	
df	24	
t Stat	-1.13	
P(T<=t) one-tail	0.1355	
t Critical one-tail	1.3178	
P(T<=t) two-tail	0.2710	
t Critical two-tail	1.7109	

$t = -1.13$, p-value = .2710. There is no evidence to infer that gender is a factor.

b A large variation within each gender group was expected.

c The histogram of the differences is somewhat bell shaped.

3.129 $H_0 : (p_1 - p_2) = 0$

$H_1 : (p_1 - p_2) > 0$

z-Test: Two Proportions		This Year	3 Years Ago
Sample Proportions		0.4351	0.3558
Observations		393	385
Hypothesized Difference		0	
z Stat		2.2605	
P(Z<=z) one tail		0.0119	
z Critical one-tail		1.2816	
P(Z<=z) two-tail		0.0238	
z Critical two-tail		1.6449	

$z = 2.26$, p-value $= .0119$. There is enough evidence to infer that Americans have become more distrustful of television and newspaper reporting this year than they were three years ago.

13.130 $H_0 : (\mu_1 - \mu_2) = 25$

$H_1 : (\mu_1 - \mu_2) > 25$

t-Test: Two-Sample Assuming Equal Variances		A Nondefectives	B Nondefectives
Mean		230.13	200.92
Variance		79.51	59.04
Observations		24	24
Pooled Variance		69.27	
Hypothesized Mean Difference		25	
df		46	
t Stat		1.75	
P(T<=t) one-tail		0.0433	
t Critical one-tail		1.6787	
P(T<=t) two-tail		0.0865	
t Critical two-tail		2.0129	

$t = 1.75$, p-value $= .0433$. There is enough evidence to conclude that machine A should be purchased.

13.131 $H_0 : (p_1 - p_2) = 0$

$H_1 : (p_1 - p_2) \neq 0$

The totals in columns A through D are 5788, 265, 5154, and 332, respectively.

z-Test of the Difference Between Two Proportions (Case 1)				
	Sample 1	Sample 2	z Stat	-4.28
Sample proportion	0.0458	0.0644	P(Z<=z) one-tail	0.0000
Sample size	5788	5154	z Critical one-tail	1.6449
Alpha	0.05		P(Z<=z) two-tail	0.0000
			z Critical two-tail	1.9600

z = -4.28, p-value = 0. There is enough evidence to infer that the defective rate differs between the two machines.

13.132 $H_0 : \mu_D = 0$

       $H_1 : \mu_D > 0$

Dry Cleaner

t-Test: Paired Two Sample for Means		
	Dry C Before	Dry C After
Mean	168.00	165.50
Variance	351.38	321.96
Observations	14	14
Pearson Correlation	0.8590	
Hypothesized Mean Difference	0	
df	13	
t Stat	0.96	
P(T<=t) one-tail	0.1780	
t Critical one-tail	1.7709	
P(T<=t) two-tail	0.3559	
t Critical two-tail	2.1604	

t = .96, p-value = .1780. There is not enough evidence to conclude that the dry cleaner sales have decreased.

Doughnut shop

t-Test: Paired Two Sample for Means		
	Donut Before	Donut After
Mean	308.14	295.29
Variance	809.67	812.07
Observations	14	14
Pearson Correlation	0.8640	
Hypothesized Mean Difference	0	
df	13	
t Stat	3.24	
P(T<=t) one-tail	0.0032	
t Critical one-tail	1.7709	
P(T<=t) two-tail	0.0065	
t Critical two-tail	2.1604	

t = 3.24, p-value = .0032. There is enough evidence to conclude that the doughnut shop sales have decreased.

Convenience store

t-Test: Paired Two Sample for Means		
	Convenience Before	Convenience After
Mean	374.64	348.14
Variance	2270.40	2941.82
Observations	14	14
Pearson Correlation	0.9731	
Hypothesized Mean Difference	0	
df	13	
t Stat	7.34	
P(T<=t) one-tail	0.0000	
t Critical one-tail	1.7709	
P(T<=t) two-tail	0.0000	
t Critical two-tail	2.1604	

$t = 7.34$, p-value = 0. There is enough evidence to conclude that the convenience store sales have decreased.

13.133a $H_0 : (\mu_1 - \mu_2) = 0$

$H_1 : (\mu_1 - \mu_2) < 0$

t-Test: Two-Sample Assuming Equal Variances		
	20-Year-old	40-year old
Mean	125.74	129.93
Variance	31.90	31.95
Observations	26	24
Pooled Variance	31.92	
Hypothesized Mean Difference	0	
df	48	
t Stat	-2.62	
P(T<=t) one-tail	0.0059	
t Critical one-tail	1.2994	
P(T<=t) two-tail	0.0119	
t Critical two-tail	1.6772	

$t = -2.62$, p-value = .0059. There is enough evidence to infer that 40-year-old men have more iron in their bodies than do 20-year-old men.

b $H_0 : (\mu_1 - \mu_2) = 0$

$H_1 : (\mu_1 - \mu_2) < 0$

t-Test: Two-Sample Assuming Equal Variances		
	20-year old	40-year old
Mean	134.02	141.11
Variance	36.15	39.47
Observations	26	24
Pooled Variance	37.74	
Hypothesized Mean Difference	0	
df	48	
t Stat	-4.08	
P(T<=t) one-tail	0.0001	
t Critical one-tail	1.2994	
P(T<=t) two-tail	0.0002	
t Critical two-tail	1.6772	

t = -4.08, p-value = .0001. There is enough evidence to infer that 40-year-old women have more iron in their bodies than do 20-year-old women.

13.134a $H_0 : (p_1 - p_2) = 0$

$H_1 : (p_1 - p_2) > 0$

z-Test: Two Proportions			
		Depressed	Not Depressed
Sample Proportions		0.2879	0.2004
Observations		132	1058
Hypothesized Difference		0	
z Stat		2.33	
P(Z<=z) one tail		0.0100	
z Critical one-tail		2.3263	
P(Z<=z) two-tail		0.0200	
z Critical two-tail		2.5758	

z = 2.33, p-value = .0100. There is enough evidence to infer that men who are clinically depressed are more likely to die from heart diseases.

b No, we cannot establish a causal relationship.

13.135 $H_0 : (\mu_1 - \mu_2) = 0$

$H_1 : (\mu_1 - \mu_2) \neq 0$

t-Test: Two-Sample Assuming Equal Variances		
	Men	Women
Mean	5.56	5.49
Variance	28.76	31.10
Observations	306	290
Pooled Variance	29.90	
Hypothesized Mean Difference	0	
df	594	
t Stat	0.15	
P(T<=t) one-tail	0.4422	
t Critical one-tail	1.6474	
P(T<=t) two-tail	0.8844	
t Critical two-tail	1.9640	

$t = .15$, p-value $= .8844$. There is no evidence of a difference in job tenures between men and women.

13.136 $H_0 : (\mu_1 - \mu_2) = 0$

$H_1 : (\mu_1 - \mu_2) < 0$

t-Test: Two-Sample Assuming Unequal Variances		
	Group 1	Group 2
Mean	7.46	8.46
Variance	25.06	12.98
Observations	50	50
Hypothesized Mean Difference	0	
df	89	
t Stat	-1.14	
P(T<=t) one-tail	0.1288	
t Critical one-tail	1.6622	
P(T<=t) two-tail	0.2575	
t Critical two-tail	1.9870	

$t = -1.14$, p-value $= .1288$. There is not enough evidence to conclude that people who exercise moderately more frequently lose weight faster

13.137 $H_0 : \mu_D = 0$

$H_1 : \mu_D < 0$

t-Test: Paired Two Sample for Means		
	Group 1	Group 2
Mean	7.53	8.57
Variance	29.77	43.37
Observations	50	50
Pearson Correlation	0.8885	
Hypothesized Mean Difference	0	
df	49	
t Stat	-2.40	
P(T<=t) one-tail	0.0100	
t Critical one-tail	1.6766	
P(T<=t) two-tail	0.0201	
t Critical two-tail	2.0096	

t = -2.40, p-value = .0100. There is enough evidence to conclude that people who exercise moderately more frequently lose weight faster

13.138 $H_0 : (p_1 - p_2) = 0$

$H_1 : (p_1 - p_2) > 0$

z-Test: Two Proportions			
		Special K	Other
Sample Proportions		0.635	0.530
Observations		200	200
Hypothesized Difference		0	
z Stat		2.13	
P(Z<=z) one tail		0.0166	
z Critical one-tail		1.6449	
P(Z<=z) two-tail		0.0332	
z Critical two-tail		1.96	

z = 2.13, p-value = .0166. There is enough evidence to conclude that Special K buyers like the ad more than non-buyers.

13.139 $H_0 : (p_1 - p_2) = 0$

$H_1 : (p_1 - p_2) > 0$

z-Test: Two Proportions			
		Special K	Other
Sample Proportions		0.575	0.515
Observations		200	200
Hypothesized Difference		0	
z Stat		1.20	
P(Z<=z) one tail		0.1141	
z Critical one-tail		1.6449	
P(Z<=z) two-tail		0.2282	
z Critical two-tail		1.96	

$z = 1.20$, p-value = .1141. There is not enough evidence to conclude that Special K buyers are more likely to think the ad is effective.

13.140 $H_0 : (\mu_1 - \mu_2) = 0$

       $H_1 : (\mu_1 - \mu_2) < 0$

t-Test: Two-Sample Assuming Unequal Variances			
		Small space	Large space
Mean		1245.68	1915.84
Variance		23811.89	65566.31
Observations		25	25
Hypothesized Mean Difference		0	
df		39	
t Stat		-11.21	
P(T<=t) one-tail		0.0000	
t Critical one-tail		1.3036	
P(T<=t) two-tail		0.0000	
t Critical two-tail		1.6849	

$t = -11.21$, p-value = 0. There is enough evidence to infer that students write in such a way as to fill the allotted space.

13.141 $H_0 : (\mu_1 - \mu_2) = 0$

       $H_1 : (\mu_1 - \mu_2) > 0$

t-Test: Two-Sample Assuming Unequal Variances		
	Computer	No Computer
Mean	69933	48246
Variance	63359040	101588525
Observations	89	61
Hypothesized Mean Difference	0	
df	109	
t Stat	14.07	
P(T<=t) one-tail	0.0000	
t Critical one-tail	1.2894	
P(T<=t) two-tail	0.0000	
t Critical two-tail	1.6590	

t = 14.07, p-value = 0. There is enough evidence to conclude that single-person businesses that use a PC earn more.

13.142 $H_0 : (p_1 - p_2) = 0$

$H_1 : (p_1 - p_2) > 0$

z-Test: Two Proportions			
		New	Older
Sample Proportions		0.948	0.92
Observations		250	250
Hypothesized Difference		0	
z Stat		1.26	
P(Z<=z) one tail		0.1037	
z Critical one-tail		1.2816	
P(Z<=z) two-tail		0.2074	
z Critical two-tail		1.6449	

z = 1.26, p-value = .1037. There is not enough evidence to conclude that the new company is better.

13.143 $H_0 : (\mu_1 - \mu_2) = 0$

$H_1 : (\mu_1 - \mu_2) > 0$

t-Test: Two-Sample Assuming Equal Variances		
	Happy	Unhappy
Mean	4.92	2.33
Variance	10.24	6.67
Observations	61	42
Pooled Variance	8.79	
Hypothesized Mean Difference	0	
df	101	
t Stat	4.35	
P(T<=t) one-tail	0.0000	
t Critical one-tail	1.6601	
P(T<=t) two-tail	0.0000	
t Critical two-tail	1.9837	

t = 4.35, p-value = 0. There is enough evidence to infer that people in happy marriages have a greater reduction in blood pressure.

13.144 $H_0 : (\mu_1 - \mu_2) = 0$

$H_1 : (\mu_1 - \mu_2) > 0$

t-Test: Two-Sample Assuming Unequal Variances		
	Teenagers	20-to-30
Mean	18.18	14.30
Variance	357.32	130.79
Observations	176	154
Hypothesized Mean Difference	0	
df	293	
t Stat	2.28	
P(T<=t) one-tail	0.0115	
t Critical one-tail	1.6501	
P(T<=t) two-tail	0.0230	
t Critical two-tail	1.9681	

t = 2.28, p-value = .0115. There is enough evidence to infer that teenagers see more movies than do twenty to thirty year olds.

Case 13.1 For ACT 241 and ACT 242 we test 0 high school courses versus 1 course and then 0 versus 2 high school courses. In each instance we test the following.

$H_0 : (\mu_1 - \mu_2) = 0$

$H_1 : (\mu_1 - \mu_2) < 0$

ACT 241 0 versus 1

t-Test: Two-Sample Assuming Equal Variances		
	ACT 241-0	*ACT 241-1*
Mean	73.49	74.54
Variance	45.62	67.91
Observations	296	24
Pooled Variance	47.23	
Hypothesized Mean Difference	0	
df	318	
t Stat	-0.72	
P(T<=t) one-tail	0.2364	
t Critical one-tail	1.6497	
P(T<=t) two-tail	0.4728	
t Critical two-tail	1.9675	

t = -.72, p-value .2364; there is not enough evidence to infer that students with 1 high school accounting course outperform students with no high school accounting in ACT 241.

ACT 241 0 versus 2

t-Test: Two-Sample Assuming Unequal Variances		
	ACT 241-0	*ACT 241-2*
Mean	73.49	80.26
Variance	45.62	26.72
Observations	296	54
Hypothesized Mean Difference	0	
df	90	
t Stat	-8.40	
P(T<=t) one-tail	0.0000	
t Critical one-tail	1.6620	
P(T<=t) two-tail	0.0000	
t Critical two-tail	1.9867	

t = -8.40, p-value = 0; there is enough evidence to infer that students with 2 high school accounting courses outperform students with no high school accounting in ACT 241.

ACT 242 0 versus 1

t-Test: Two-Sample Assuming Equal Variances		
	ACT242-0	ACT 242-1
Mean	76.89	77.60
Variance	15.09	9.97
Observations	210	15
Pooled Variance	14.77	
Hypothesized Mean Difference	0	
df	223	
t Stat	-0.70	
P(T<=t) one-tail	0.2437	
t Critical one-tail	1.6517	
P(T<=t) two-tail	0.4875	
t Critical two-tail	1.9707	

$t = -.70$, p-value = .2437; there is not enough evidence to infer that students with 1 high school accounting course outperform students with no high school accounting in ACT 242.

ACT 242 0 versus 2

t-Test: Two-Sample Assuming Equal Variances		
	ACT242-0	ACT 242-2
Mean	76.89	78.92
Variance	15.09	14.12
Observations	210	50
Pooled Variance	14.90	
Hypothesized Mean Difference	0	
df	258	
t Stat	-3.35	
P(T<=t) one-tail	0.0005	
t Critical one-tail	1.6508	
P(T<=t) two-tail	0.0009	
t Critical two-tail	1.9692	

$t = -3.35$, p-value = .0005; there is enough evidence to infer that students with 2 high school accounting course outperform students with no high school accounting in ACT 242.

Overall Conclusion

The statistical evidence suggests that students with 2 high school accounting courses should be exempted from both ACT 241 and ACT 242. No other exemptions should be allowed.

Chapter 14

14.1 Equal-variances t-test of $\mu_1 - \mu_2$

$$H_0 : (\mu_1 - \mu_2) = 0$$

$$H_1 : (\mu_1 - \mu_2) < 0$$

$$t = \frac{(\bar{x}_1 - \bar{x}_2) - (\mu_1 - \mu_2)}{\sqrt{s_p^2 \left(\dfrac{1}{n_1} + \dfrac{1}{n_2} \right)}}$$

t-Test: Two-Sample Assuming Equal Variances		
	This Year	3 Years Ago
Mean	8.29	10.36
Variance	8.13	8.43
Observations	100	100
Pooled Variance	8.28	
Hypothesized Mean Difference	0	
df	198	
t Stat	-5.09	
P(T<=t) one-tail	0.0000	
t Critical one-tail	1.6526	
P(T<=t) two-tail	0.0000	
t Critical two-tail	1.9720	

t = -5.09, p-value = 0. There is overwhelming evidence to conclude that there has been a decrease over the past three years.

14.2 a z-test of $p_1 - p_2$ (case 1)

$$H_0 : (p_1 - p_2) = 0$$

$$H_1 : (p_1 - p_2) > 0$$

$$z = \frac{(\hat{p}_1 - \hat{p}_2)}{\sqrt{\hat{p}(1 - \hat{p}) \left(\dfrac{1}{n_1} + \dfrac{1}{n_2} \right)}}$$

z-Test of the Difference Between Two Proportions (Case 1)				
	Sample 1	Sample 2	z Stat	2.83
Sample proportion	0.4336	0.2414	P(Z<=z) one-tail	0.0024
Sample size	113	87	z Critical one-tail	1.6449
Alpha	0.05		P(Z<=z) two-tail	0.0047
			z Critical two-tail	1.9600

$z = 2.83$, p-value = .0024. There is overwhelming evidence to infer that customers who see the ad are more likely to make a purchase than those who do not see the ad.

b Equal-variances t-test of $\mu_1 - \mu_2$

$$H_0 : (\mu_1 - \mu_2) = 0$$

$$H_1 : (\mu_1 - \mu_2) > 0$$

$$t = \frac{(\bar{x}_1 - \bar{x}_2) - (\mu_1 - \mu_2)}{\sqrt{s_p^2 \left(\frac{1}{n_1} + \frac{1}{n_2} \right)}}$$

t-Test: Two-Sample Assuming Equal Variances		
	Ad	No Ad
Mean	97.38	92.01
Variance	621.97	283.26
Observations	49	21
Pooled Variance	522.35	
Hypothesized Mean Difference	0	
df	68	
t Stat	0.90	
P(T<=t) one-tail	0.1853	
t Critical one-tail	1.6676	
P(T<=t) two-tail	0.3705	
t Critical two-tail	1.9955	

$t = .90$, p-value = .1853. There is not enough evidence to infer that customers who see the ad and make a purchase spend more than those who do not see the ad and make a purchase.

c z-estimator of p

$$\hat{p} \pm z_{\alpha/2} \sqrt{\frac{\hat{p}(1 - \hat{p})}{n}}$$

251

z-Estimate of a Proportion				
Sample proportion	0.4336	**Confidence Interval Estimate**		
Sample size	113	0.4336	±	0.0914
Confidence level	0.95	Lower confidence limit		0.3423
		Upper confidence limit		0.5250

We estimate that between 34.23% and 52.50% of all customers who see the ad will make a purchase.

d t-estimator of μ

$$\bar{x} \pm t_{\alpha/2} \frac{s}{\sqrt{n}}$$

t-Estimate: Mean			
			Ad
Mean			97.38
Standard Deviation			24.94
LCL			90.22
UCL			104.55

We estimate that the mean amount spent by customers who see the ad and make a purchase lies between $90.22 and $194.55.

14.3 t-test of μ_D

$$H_0 : \mu_D = 0$$

$$H_1 : \mu_D > 0$$

$$t = \frac{\bar{x}_D - \mu_D}{s_D / \sqrt{n_D}}$$

t-Test: Paired Two Sample for Means		
	Before	After
Mean	381.00	373.12
Variance	39001.33	40663.28
Observations	25	25
Pearson Correlation	0.9610	
Hypothesized Mean Difference	0	
df	24	
t Stat	0.70	
P(T<=t) one-tail	0.2438	
t Critical one-tail	1.7109	
P(T<=t) two-tail	0.4876	
t Critical two-tail	2.0639	

t = .70, p-value = .2438. There is not enough evidence to conclude that the equipment is effective.

14.4 a z-test of p

$$H_0 : p = .95$$

$$H_1 : p > .95$$

$$z = \frac{\hat{p} - p}{\sqrt{\dfrac{p(1-p)}{n}}}$$

z-Test: Proportion			
			Prority
Sample Proportion			0.9714
Observations			245
Hypothesized Proportion			0.95
z Stat			1.54
P(Z<=z) one-tail			0.0619
z Critical one-tail			1.6449
P(Z<=z) two-tail			0.1238
z Critical two-tail			1.96

z = 1.54, p-value = .0619. There is not enough evidence to infer that the spokesperson's claim is true.

b z-test of $p_1 - p_2$ (case 1)

$$H_0 : (p_1 - p_2) = 0$$

$$H_1 : (p_1 - p_2) > 0$$

$$z = \frac{(\hat{p}_1 - \hat{p}_2)}{\sqrt{\hat{p}(1-\hat{p})\left(\dfrac{1}{n_1} + \dfrac{1}{n_2}\right)}}$$

z-Test: Two Proportions			
		Prority	Ordinary
Sample Proportions		0.9714	0.9101
Observations		245	378
Hypothesized Difference		0	
z Stat		3.02	
P(Z<=z) one tail		0.0013	
z Critical one-tail		1.6449	
P(Z<=z) two-tail		0.0026	
z Critical two-tail		1.96	

z = 3.02, p-value = .0013. There is overwhelming evidence to infer that Priority Mail delivers letters within two days more frequently than does ordinary mail.

14.5 Equal-variances t-test of $\mu_1 - \mu_2$

$$H_0 : (\mu_1 - \mu_2) = 0$$

$$H_1 : (\mu_1 - \mu_2) < 0$$

$$t = \frac{(\bar{x}_1 - \bar{x}_2) - (\mu_1 - \mu_2)}{\sqrt{s_p^2 \left(\dfrac{1}{n_1} + \dfrac{1}{n_2} \right)}}$$

t-Test: Two-Sample Assuming Equal Variances		
	Discount	*No Discount*
Mean	13.06	18.22
Variance	30.26	38.13
Observations	50	50
Pooled Variance	34.20	
Hypothesized Mean Difference	0	
df	98	
t Stat	-4.41	
P(T<=t) one-tail	0.0000	
t Critical one-tail	1.6606	
P(T<=t) two-tail	0.0000	
t Critical two-tail	1.9845	

t = -4.41, p-value = 0. There is overwhelming evidence to infer that the discount plan works.

14.6 Speeds: Equal-variances t-test of $\mu_1 - \mu_2$

$$H_0 : (\mu_1 - \mu_2) = 0$$

$$H_1 : (\mu_1 - \mu_2) > 0$$

$$t = \frac{(\bar{x}_1 - \bar{x}_2) - (\mu_1 - \mu_2)}{\sqrt{s_p^2 \left(\dfrac{1}{n_1} + \dfrac{1}{n_2} \right)}}$$

t-Test: Two-Sample Assuming Equal Variances		
	Speeds Before	Speeds After
Mean	31.74	31.42
Variance	4.50	4.41
Observations	100	100
Pooled Variance	4.45	
Hypothesized Mean Difference	0	
df	198	
t Stat	1.07	
P(T<=t) one-tail	0.1424	
t Critical one-tail	1.6526	
P(T<=t) two-tail	0.2849	
t Critical two-tail	1.9720	

t = 1.07, p-value = .1424. There is not enough evidence to infer that speed bumps reduce speeds.

Proper stops: Equal-variances t-test of $\mu_1 - \mu_2$

$$H_0 : (\mu_1 - \mu_2) = 0$$

$$H_1 : (\mu_1 - \mu_2) < 0$$

$$t = \frac{(\bar{x}_1 - \bar{x}_2) - (\mu_1 - \mu_2)}{\sqrt{s_p^2 \left(\frac{1}{n_1} + \frac{1}{n_2} \right)}}$$

t-Test: Two-Sample Assuming Equal Variances		
	Stops Before	Stops After
Mean	7.82	7.98
Variance	1.83	1.84
Observations	100	100
Pooled Variance	1.83	
Hypothesized Mean Difference	0	
df	198	
t Stat	-0.84	
P(T<=t) one-tail	0.2021	
t Critical one-tail	1.6526	
P(T<=t) two-tail	0.4042	
t Critical two-tail	1.9720	

t = -.84, p-value = .2021. There is not enough evidence to infer that speed bumps increase the number of proper stops.

14.7 t-estimator of μ

$$\bar{x} \pm t_{\alpha/2} \frac{s}{\sqrt{n}}$$

t-Estimate: Mean			
			PSI
Mean			4.1950
Standard Deviation			1.9328
LCL			3.9254
UCL			4.4646

LCL = 3.9254, UCL = 4.4646. We estimate that on average tires are between 3.9254 and 4.4646 pounds per square inch below the recommended amount.

Tire life: LCL = 100(3.9254) = 392.54, UCL = 100(4.4646) = 446.46. We estimate that the average tire life is decreased by between 392.54 and 446.46 miles.

Gasoline consumption: LCL = .1(3.9254) = .39254, UCL = .1(4.4646) = .44646. We estimate that average gasoline consumption increases by between .39254 and .44646 gallons per mile.

14.8 t-test of μ_D

$$H_0 : \mu_D = 0$$

$$H_1 : \mu_D > 0$$

$$t = \frac{\bar{x}_D - \mu_D}{s_D / \sqrt{n_D}}$$

t-Test: Paired Two Sample for Means		
	Before	After
Mean	28.94	26.22
Variance	61.45	104.30
Observations	50	50
Pearson Correlation	0.8695	
Hypothesized Mean Difference	0	
df	49	
t Stat	3.73	
P(T<=t) one-tail	0.0002	
t Critical one-tail	1.6766	
P(T<=t) two-tail	0.0005	
t Critical two-tail	2.0096	

t = 3.73, p-value = .0002. There is overwhelming evidence to infer that the law discourages bicycle use.

14.9 z -test of $p_1 - p_2$ (case 1)

$$H_0 : (p_1 - p_2) = 0$$

$$H_1 : (p_1 - p_2) > 0$$

$$z = \frac{(\hat{p}_1 - \hat{p}_2)}{\sqrt{\hat{p}(1-\hat{p})\left(\dfrac{1}{n_1} + \dfrac{1}{n_2}\right)}}$$

z-Test: Two Proportions			
		Cardizem	Placebo
Sample Proportions		0.084	0.0797
Observations		607	301
Hypothesized Difference		0	
z Stat		0.22	
P(Z<=z) one tail		0.4126	
z Critical one-tail		1.6449	
P(Z<=z) two-tail		0.8252	
z Critical two-tail		1.96	

z = .22, p-value = .4126. There is not enough evidence to indicate that Cardizem users are more likely to suffer headache and dizziness side effects than non-users.

14.10 t-test of μ

$$H_0 : \mu = 200$$
$$H_1 : \mu > 200$$

$$t = \frac{\bar{x} - \mu}{s / \sqrt{n}}$$

t-Test: Mean			
			Pedestrians
Mean			209.13
Standard Deviation			60.01
Hypothesized Mean			200
df			39
t Stat			0.96
P(T<=t) one-tail			0.1711
t Critical one-tail			1.6849
P(T<=t) two-tail			0.3422
t Critical two-tail			2.0227

t = .96, p-value = .1711. There is not enough evidence to infer that the franchiser should build on this site.

14.11 a z-test of $p_1 - p_2$ (case 1)

$$H_0 : p_1 - p_2 = 0$$
$$H_1 : p_1 - p_2 > 0$$

$$z = \frac{(\hat{p}_1 - \hat{p}_2)}{\sqrt{\hat{p}(1-\hat{p})\left(\dfrac{1}{n_1} + \dfrac{1}{n_2}\right)}}$$

z-Test: Two Proportions			
		Smokers	NoSmokers
Sample Proportions		0.041	0.024
Observations		1000	1000
Hypothesized Difference		0	
z Stat		2.14	
P(Z<=z) one tail		0.0160	
z Critical one-tail		1.6449	
P(Z<=z) two-tail		0.032	
z Critical two-tail		1.96	

z = 2.14, p-value = .0160. There is evidence to infer that children in smoke-free households are less likely to be in fair to poor health than children in households with smokers.

b z-estimator of p

$$\hat{p} \pm z_{\alpha/2}\sqrt{\frac{\hat{p}(1-\hat{p})}{n}}$$

z-Estimate: Proportion	
	Smokers
Sample Proportion	0.0410
Observations	1000
LCL	0.0287
UCL	0.0533

LCL = .0287, UCL = .0533. We estimate that between 2.87% and 5.33% of all children living in households with smokers are in fair to poor health.

Number of children: LCL = 10 million(.0287) = 287,000, UCL = 10 million(.0533) = 533,000. Between 287,000 and 533,000 children living with at least one smoker are estimated to be in fair to poor health.

14.12 z-test of p

$$H_0 : p = .5$$

$$H_1 : p > .5$$

$$z = \frac{\hat{p} - p}{\sqrt{\dfrac{p(1-p)}{n}}}$$

z-Test: Proportion			
			Winner
Sample Proportion			0.5296
Observations			625
Hypothesized Proportion			0.5
z Stat			1.48
P(Z<=z) one-tail			0.0694
z Critical one-tail			1.6449
P(Z<=z) two-tail			0.1388
z Critical two-tail			1.96

$z = 1.48$, p-value = .0694. There is not enough evidence to conclude that more Floridians believe that Mr. Bush won than Floridians who believe Mr. Gore won.

14.13 t-tests of μ

45 minutes: $H_0 : \mu = 45$

$H_1 : \mu < 45$

$$t = \frac{\bar{x} - \mu}{s / \sqrt{n}}$$

t-Test: Mean			
			45 minutes
Mean			41.75
Standard Deviation			3.63
Hypothesized Mean			45
df			19
t Stat			-4.01
P(T<=t) one-tail			0.0004
t Critical one-tail			1.7291
P(T<=t) two-tail			0.0008
t Critical two-tail			2.093

60 minutes: $H_0 : \mu = 60$

$H_1 : \mu < 60$

$$t = \frac{\bar{x} - \mu}{s / \sqrt{n}}$$

t-Test: Mean			
			60 minutes
Mean			58.75
Standard Deviation			5.02
Hypothesized Mean			60
df			19
t Stat			-1.11
P(T<=t) one-tail			0.1399
t Critical one-tail			1.7291
P(T<=t) two-tail			0.2798
t Critical two-tail			2.093

80 minutes: $H_0 : \mu = 80$

$H_1 : \mu < 80$

$$t = \frac{\bar{x} - \mu}{s / \sqrt{n}}$$

t-Test: Mean			
			80 minutes
Mean			69.05
Standard Deviation			6.31
Hypothesized Mean			80
df			19
t Stat			-7.76
P(T<=t) one-tail			0
t Critical one-tail			1.7291
P(T<=t) two-tail			0
t Critical two-tail			2.093

100 minutes: $H_0 : \mu = 100$

$H_1 : \mu < 100$

$$t = \frac{\bar{x} - \mu}{s / \sqrt{n}}$$

t-Test: Mean			
			100 minutes
Mean			90.4
Standard Deviation			12.35
Hypothesized Mean			100
df			19
t Stat			-3.48
P(T<=t) one-tail			0.0013
t Critical one-tail			1.7291
P(T<=t) two-tail			0.0026
t Critical two-tail			2.093

125 minutes: $H_0 : \mu = 125$

$H_1 : \mu < 125$

$$t = \frac{\bar{x} - \mu}{s / \sqrt{n}}$$

t-Test: Mean			
			125 minutes
Mean			110.05
Standard Deviation			17.11
Hypothesized Mean			125
df			19
t Stat			-3.91
P(T<=t) one-tail			0.0005
t Critical one-tail			1.7291
P(T<=t) two-tail			0.001
t Critical two-tail			2.093

Overall Conclusion: p-values are .0004, .1399, 0, .0013, and .0005, respectively. In four of the jobs there is overwhelming evidence to conclude that the times specified by the schedule are greater than the actual times.

14.14 Unequal-variances t-test of $\mu_1 - \mu_2$

$H_0 : (\mu_1 - \mu_2) = 0$

$H_1 : (\mu_1 - \mu_2) > 0$

$$t = \frac{(\bar{x}_1 - \bar{x}_2) - (\mu_1 - \mu_2)}{\sqrt{\dfrac{s_1^2}{n_1} + \dfrac{s_2^2}{n_2}}}$$

t-Test: Two-Sample Assuming Unequal Variances		
	Quit	Did not quit
Mean	2.038	0.721
Variance	2.052	1.398
Observations	259	1626
Hypothesized Mean Difference	0	
df	316	
t Stat	14.06	
P(T<=t) one-tail	0.0000	
t Critical one-tail	1.6497	
P(T<=t) two-tail	0.0000	
t Critical two-tail	1.9675	

$t = 14.06$, p-value = 0. There is overwhelming evidence to infer that quitting smoking results in weight gains.

14.15 F-test of σ_1^2 / σ_2^2

$$H_0 : \sigma_1^2 / \sigma_2^2 = 1$$

$$H_1 : \sigma_1^2 / \sigma_2^2 > 1$$

$$F = \frac{s_1^2}{s_2^2}$$

F-Test Two-Sample for Variances		
	Brand A	Brand B
Mean	145.95	144.78
Variance	16.45	4.25
Observations	100	100
df	99	99
F	3.87	
P(F<=f) one-tail	0.0000	
F Critical one-tail	1.3941	

$F = 3.87$, p-value = 0. There is overwhelming evidence to infer that Brand B is superior to Brand A.

14.16 Equal-variances t-tests of $\mu_1 - \mu_2$

Memory:

$$H_0 : (\mu_1 - \mu_2) = 0$$

$$H_1 : (\mu_1 - \mu_2) > 0$$

$$t = \frac{(\bar{x}_1 - \bar{x}_2) - (\mu_1 - \mu_2)}{\sqrt{s_p^2 \left(\frac{1}{n_1} + \frac{1}{n_2} \right)}}$$

t-Test: Two-Sample Assuming Equal Variances		
	Memory-Player	*Memory-Non*
Mean	73.12	67.34
Variance	69.99	86.60
Observations	50	50
Pooled Variance	78.29	
Hypothesized Mean Difference	0	
df	98	
t Stat	3.27	
P(T<=t) one-tail	0.0008	
t Critical one-tail	1.6606	
P(T<=t) two-tail	0.0015	
t Critical two-tail	1.9845	

Reasoning:

$$H_0 : (\mu_1 - \mu_2) = 0$$

$$H_1 : (\mu_1 - \mu_2) > 0$$

$$t = \frac{(\bar{x}_1 - \bar{x}_2) - (\mu_1 - \mu_2)}{\sqrt{s_p^2 \left(\frac{1}{n_1} + \frac{1}{n_2} \right)}}$$

t-Test: Two-Sample Assuming Equal Variances		
	Reasoning-Player	*Reasoning-Non*
Mean	78.22	72.16
Variance	41.15	67.40
Observations	50	50
Pooled Variance	54.28	
Hypothesized Mean Difference	0	
df	98	
t Stat	4.11	
P(T<=t) one-tail	0.0000	
t Critical one-tail	1.6606	
P(T<=t) two-tail	0.0001	
t Critical two-tail	1.9845	

Reaction time:

$$H_0 : (\mu_1 - \mu_2) = 0$$

$$H_1 : (\mu_1 - \mu_2) \neq 0$$

$$t = \frac{(\bar{x}_1 - \bar{x}_2) - (\mu_1 - \mu_2)}{\sqrt{s_p^2 \left(\frac{1}{n_1} + \frac{1}{n_2} \right)}}$$

t-Test: Two-Sample Assuming Equal Variances		
	Reaction-Player	*Reaction-Non*
Mean	70.60	71.22
Variance	31.18	26.09
Observations	50	50
Pooled Variance	28.64	
Hypothesized Mean Difference	0	
df	98	
t Stat	-0.58	
P(T<=t) one-tail	0.2819	
t Critical one-tail	1.6606	
P(T<=t) two-tail	0.5637	
t Critical two-tail	1.9845	

Vocabulary:

$$H_0 : (\mu_1 - \mu_2) = 0$$

$$H_1 : (\mu_1 - \mu_2) \neq 0$$

$$t = \frac{(\bar{x}_1 - \bar{x}_2) - (\mu_1 - \mu_2)}{\sqrt{s_p^2 \left(\dfrac{1}{n_1} + \dfrac{1}{n_2} \right)}}$$

t-Test: Two-Sample Assuming Equal Variances		
	Vocabulary-Player	*Vocabulary-Non*
Mean	82.22	80.12
Variance	60.66	81.70
Observations	50	50
Pooled Variance	71.18	
Hypothesized Mean Difference	0	
df	98	
t Stat	1.24	
P(T<=t) one-tail	0.1081	
t Critical one-tail	1.6606	
P(T<=t) two-tail	0.2163	
t Critical two-tail	1.9845	

Overall Conclusion: p-values are .0008, 0, .5637, and .2163. There is overwhelming evidence to indicate that bridge-players score higher on memory and reasoning tests. There is not enough evidence of a difference in reaction time and vocabulary between players and nonplayers.

14.17 t-test of μ_D

$$H_0 : \mu_D = 0$$

$$H_1 : \mu_D < 0$$

$$t = \frac{\bar{x}_D - \mu_D}{s_D / \sqrt{n_D}}$$

t-Test: Paired Two Sample for Means		
	Price shown	Price not shown
Mean	56.15	60.31
Variance	243.68	467.71
Observations	100	100
Pearson Correlation	0.7903	
Hypothesized Mean Difference	0	
df	99	
t Stat	-3.12	
P(T<=t) one-tail	0.0012	
t Critical one-tail	1.6604	
P(T<=t) two-tail	0.0024	
t Critical two-tail	1.9842	

t = -3.12, p-value = .0012. There is overwhelming evidence to conclude that ads with no price shown are more effective in generating interest than ads that show the price.

14.18 t-estimator of μ

$$\bar{x} \pm t_{\alpha/2} \frac{s}{\sqrt{n}}$$

t-Estimate: Mean			
			Calls
Mean			0.320
Standard Deviation			0.717
LCL			0.204
UCL			0.436

LCL = .204, UCL = .436. On average, each copier is estimated to require between .204 and .436 service calls in the first year.

Total number of service calls: LCL = 1000(.204) = 204, UCL = 1000(.436) = 436. It is estimated that the company's copiers will require between 204 and 436 service calls in the first year.

14.19 z-test of $p_1 - p_2$ (case 1)

$H_0 : p_1 - p_2 = 0$

$H_1 : p_1 - p_2 > 0$

$$z = \frac{(\hat{p}_1 - \hat{p}_2)}{\sqrt{\hat{p}(1-\hat{p})\left(\dfrac{1}{n_1} + \dfrac{1}{n_2}\right)}}$$

z-Test: Two Proportions			
		Exercisers	Watchers
Sample Proportions		0.4250	0.3675
Observations		400	400
Hypothesized Difference		0	
z Stat		1.66	
P(Z<=z) one tail		0.0482	
z Critical one-tail		1.6449	
P(Z<=z) two-tail		0.0964	
z Critical two-tail		1.96	

z = 1.66, p-value = .0482. There is evidence to infer that exercisers are more likely to remember the sponsor's brand name than those who only watch.

14.20 Unequal-variances t-test of $\mu_1 - \mu_2$

$$H_0 : (\mu_1 - \mu_2) = 0$$

$$H_1 : (\mu_1 - \mu_2) < 0$$

$$t = \frac{(\bar{x}_1 - \bar{x}_2) - (\mu_1 - \mu_2)}{\sqrt{\dfrac{s_1^2}{n_1} + \dfrac{s_2^2}{n_2}}}$$

t-Test: Two-Sample Assuming Unequal Variances			
		Leftover	Returned
Mean		61.71	70.57
Variance		48.99	203.98
Observations		14	53
Hypothesized Mean Difference		0	
df		44	
t Stat		-3.27	
P(T<=t) one-tail		0.0011	
t Critical one-tail		1.6802	
P(T<=t) two-tail		0.0021	
t Critical two-tail		2.0154	

t = -3.27, p-value = .0011. There is overwhelming evidence to support the professor's theory.

14.21 Unequal-variances t-test of $\mu_1 - \mu_2$

$$H_0 : (\mu_1 - \mu_2) = 0$$

$$H_1 : (\mu_1 - \mu_2) > 0$$

$$t = \frac{(\bar{x}_1 - \bar{x}_2) - (\mu_1 - \mu_2)}{\sqrt{\dfrac{s_1^2}{n_1} + \dfrac{s_2^2}{n_2}}}$$

t-Test: Two-Sample Assuming Unequal Variances		
	Coupon used	*Coupon not used*
Mean	49.42	46.29
Variance	200.89	317.90
Observations	143	357
Hypothesized Mean Difference	0	
df	327	
t Stat	2.07	
P(T<=t) one-tail	0.0197	
t Critical one-tail	1.6495	
P(T<=t) two-tail	0.0395	
t Critical two-tail	1.9672	

t = 2.07, p-value = .0197. There is evidence to infer that shoppers with coupons spend more money on groceries than do non-coupon users.

14.22 a z-test of p

$H_0 : p = 104,320/425,000 = .245$

$H_1 : p > .245$

$$z = \frac{\hat{p} - p}{\sqrt{\dfrac{p(1-p)}{n}}}$$

z-Test: Proportion		
		Deliver
Sample Proportion		0.2825
Observations		400
Hypothesized Proportion		0.245
z Stat		1.74
P(Z<=z) one-tail		0.0406
z Critical one-tail		1.6449
P(Z<=z) two-tail		0.0812
z Critical two-tail		1.96

z = 1.74, p-value = .0406. There is evidence to indicate that the campaign will increase home delivery sales.

b z-test of p

$H_0 : p = 110,000/425,000 = .259$

$H_1 : p > .259$

$$z = \frac{\hat{p} - p}{\sqrt{\dfrac{p(1-p)}{n}}}$$

z-Test: Proportion			
			Deliver
Sample Proportion			0.2825
Observations			400
Hypothesized Proportion			0.259
z Stat			1.07
P(Z<=z) one-tail			0.1417
z Critical one-tail			1.6449
P(Z<=z) two-tail			0.2834
z Critical two-tail			1.96

z = 1.07, p-value = .1417. There is not enough evidence to conclude that the campaign will be successful.

14.23 Equal-variances t-test of $\mu_1 - \mu_2$

$$H_0 : (\mu_1 - \mu_2) = 0$$

$$H_1 : (\mu_1 - \mu_2) \neq 0$$

$$t = \frac{(\bar{x}_1 - \bar{x}_2) - (\mu_1 - \mu_2)}{\sqrt{s_p^2 \left(\dfrac{1}{n_1} + \dfrac{1}{n_2} \right)}}$$

t-Test: Two-Sample Assuming Equal Variances		
	ABS speed	No ABS speed
Mean	34.72	33.94
Variance	25.27	25.63
Observations	100	100
Pooled Variance	25.45	
Hypothesized Mean Difference	0	
df	198	
t Stat	1.09	
P(T<=t) one-tail	0.1394	
t Critical one-tail	1.6526	
P(T<=t) two-tail	0.2788	
t Critical two-tail	1.9720	

t = 1.09, p-value = .2788. There is not enough evidence that operating an ABS-equipped car changes a driver's behavior.

14.24a Equal-variances t-test of $\mu_1 - \mu_2$

$$H_0 : (\mu_1 - \mu_2) = 0$$

$$H_1 : (\mu_1 - \mu_2) < 0$$

$$t = \frac{(\bar{x}_1 - \bar{x}_2) - (\mu_1 - \mu_2)}{\sqrt{s_p^2 \left(\dfrac{1}{n_1} + \dfrac{1}{n_2} \right)}}$$

t-Test: Two-Sample Assuming Equal Variances		
	Expenses MSA	Expenses Regular
Mean	347.24	479.25
Variance	21042.80	21127.51
Observations	63	141
Pooled Variance	21101.51	
Hypothesized Mean Difference	0	
df	202	
t Stat	-6.00	
P(T<=t) one-tail	0.0000	
t Critical one-tail	1.6524	
P(T<=t) two-tail	0.0000	
t Critical two-tail	1.9718	

t = -6.00, p-value = 0. There is overwhelming evidence to infer that medical expenses for those under the MSA plan are lower than those who are not.

b z-test of $p_1 - p_2$ (case 1)

$$H_0 : p_1 - p_2 = 0$$

$$H_1 : p_1 - p_2 < 0$$

$$z = \frac{(\hat{p}_1 - \hat{p}_2)}{\sqrt{\hat{p}(1 - \hat{p}) \left(\dfrac{1}{n_1} + \dfrac{1}{n_2} \right)}}$$

z-Test: Two Proportions			
		Health MSA	Health Regular
Sample Proportions		0.7619	0.7801
Observations		63	141
Hypothesized Difference		0	
z Stat		-0.29	
P(Z<=z) one tail		0.3867	
z Critical one-tail		1.6449	
P(Z<=z) two-tail		0.7734	
z Critical two-tail		1.96	

z = -.29, p-value = .3867. There is not enough evidence to support the critics of MSA.

Case 14.1 Memory test scores: Equal-variances t-tests of $\mu_1 - \mu_2$

$$H_0 : (\mu_1 - \mu_2) = 0$$

$$H_1 : (\mu_1 - \mu_2) \neq 0$$

$$t = \frac{(\bar{x}_1 - \bar{x}_2) - (\mu_1 - \mu_2)}{\sqrt{s_p^2 \left(\dfrac{1}{n_1} + \dfrac{1}{n_2} \right)}}$$

t-Test: Two-Sample Assuming Equal Variances		
	Host Mark	Announcer Mark
Mean	7.76	6.97
Variance	4.52	6.37
Observations	121	121
Pooled Variance	5.44	
Hypothesized Mean Difference	0	
df	240	
t Stat	2.65	
P(T<=t) one-tail	0.0043	
t Critical one-tail	1.6512	
P(T<=t) two-tail	0.0087	
t Critical two-tail	1.9699	

$t = 2.65$, p-value = .0087. There is overwhelming evidence to infer that the memory test scores of the two groups of children differ.

Cereal choices: z-test of $p_1 - p_2$ (case 1) (success = 4, Canary Crunch)

$$H_0 : p_1 - p_2 = 0$$

$$H_1 : p_1 - p_2 \neq 0$$

$$z = \frac{(\hat{p}_1 - \hat{p}_2)}{\sqrt{\hat{p}(1 - \hat{p}) \left(\dfrac{1}{n_1} + \dfrac{1}{n_2} \right)}}$$

z-Test: Two Proportions			
		Host Cereal	Announcer Cereal
Sample Proportions		0.3636	0.3058
Observations		121	121
Hypothesized Difference		0	
z Stat		0.95	
P(Z<=z) one tail		0.1702	
z Critical one-tail		1.6449	
P(Z<=z) two-tail		0.3404	
z Critical two-tail		1.96	

z = .95, p-value = .3404. There is not enough evidence to infer that there is a difference in proportions between the two groups of children in their choice of the Canary Crunch.

Overall Conclusion: Children who watch the host commercials remember more about the details of the commercial but are no more (or less) likely to choose the advertised cereal than children who watch announcer commercials.

Case 14.2 a z-test of p (success = 1, vote "No")

$$H_0 : p = .5$$

$$H_1 : p > .5$$

$$z = \frac{\hat{p} - p}{\sqrt{\frac{p(1-p)}{n}}}$$

z-Test: Proportion			
			Planned vote
Sample Proportion			0.5382
Observations			641
Hypothesized Proportion			0.5
z Stat			1.94
P(Z<=z) one-tail			0.0265
z Critical one-tail			1.6449
P(Z<=z) two-tail			0.053
z Critical two-tail			1.96

z = 1.94, p-value = .0265. There is evidence to infer that if the referendum were held on the day of the poll, the majority of Quebec would vote to remain in Canada.

b z-estimator $p_1 - p_2$ (success = 2, vote "Yes")

$$(\hat{p}_1 - \hat{p}_2) \pm z_{\alpha/2} \sqrt{\frac{\hat{p}_1(1-\hat{p}_1)}{n_1} + \frac{\hat{p}_2(1-\hat{p}_2)}{n_2}}$$

z-Estimate: Two Proportions		
	Francophone	Anglophone
Sample Proportions	0.5553	0.0794
Observations	515	126
LCL	0.4123	
UCL	0.5397	

LCL = .4123, UCL = .5397. We estimate that the difference between French-speaking and English-speaking Quebecers in their support for separation lies between 41.23% and 53.97%.

Chapter 15

15.1 $\overline{\overline{x}} = \dfrac{5(10) + 5(15) + 5(20)}{5 + 5 + 5} = 15$

$\text{SST} = \sum n_j (\overline{x}_j - \overline{\overline{x}})^2 = 5(10 - 15)^2 + 5(15 - 15)^2 + 5(15 - 15)^2 = 250$

$\text{SSE} = \sum (n_j - 1) s_j^2 = (5 - 1)(50) + (5 - 1)(50) + (5 - 1)(50) = 600$

ANOVA table

Source	Degrees of Freedom	Sum of Squares	Mean Squares	F
Treatments	k - 1=3- 1=2	SST = 250	$\dfrac{SST}{k-1} = \dfrac{250}{2} = 125$	$\dfrac{MST}{MSE} = \dfrac{125}{50} = 2.50$
Error	n - k=15- 3=12	SSE = 600	$\dfrac{SSE}{n-k1} = \dfrac{600}{12} = 50$	
Total	n - 1=15 - 1=14	SS(Total) = 850		

15.2 $\overline{\overline{x}} = \dfrac{10(10) + 10(15) + 10(20)}{5 + 5 + 5} = 15$

$\text{SST} = \sum n_j (\overline{x}_j - \overline{\overline{x}})^2 = 10(10 - 15)^2 + 10(15 - 15)^2 + 10(15 - 15)^2 = 500$

$\text{SSE} = \sum (n_j - 1) s_j^2 = (10 - 1)(50) + (10 - 1)(50) + (10 - 1)(50) = 1350$

ANOVA table

Source	Degrees of Freedom	Sum of Squares	Mean Squares	F
Treatments	k- 1=3- 1=2	SST = 500	$\dfrac{SST}{k-1} = \dfrac{500}{2} = 250$	$\dfrac{MST}{MSE} = \dfrac{125}{50} = 5.00$
Error	n - k=30- 3=27	SSE = 1350	$\dfrac{SSE}{n-k1} = \dfrac{1350}{27} = 50$	
Total	n - 1=30- 1=29	SS(Total) = 1850		

15.3 The F statistic increases.

15.4 $\overline{\overline{x}} = \dfrac{5(10) + 5(15) + 5(20)}{5+5+5} = 15$

$SST = \sum n_j(\overline{x}_j - \overline{\overline{x}})^2 = 5(10-15)^2 + 5(15-15)^2 + 5(15-15)^2 = 250$

$SSE = \sum (n_j - 1)s_j^2 = (5-1)(25) + (5-1)(25) + (5-1)(25) = 300$

ANOVA table

Source	Degrees of Freedom	Sum of Squares	Mean Squares	F
Treatments	k - 1=3- 1=2	SST = 250	$\dfrac{SST}{k-1} = \dfrac{250}{2} = 125$	$\dfrac{MST}{MSE} = \dfrac{125}{25} = 5.00$
Error	n - k=15- 3=12	SSE = 300	$\dfrac{SSE}{n-k1} = \dfrac{300}{12} = 25$	
Total	n - 1=15 - 1=14	SS(Total) = 550		

15.5 The F statistic increases.

15.6 $\overline{\overline{x}} = \dfrac{5(110) + 5(115) + 5(120)}{5+5+5} = 115$

$SST = \sum n_j(\overline{x}_j - \overline{\overline{x}})^2 = 5(110-115)^2 + 5(115-115)^2 + 5(115-115)^2 = 250$

$SSE = \sum (n_j - 1)s_j^2 = (5-1)(50) + (5-1)(50) + (5-1)(50) = 600$

ANOVA table

Source	Degrees of Freedom	Sum of Squares	Mean Squares	F
Treatments	k - 1=3- 1=2	SST = 250	$\dfrac{SST}{k-1} = \dfrac{250}{2} = 125$	$\dfrac{MST}{MSE} = \dfrac{125}{50} = 2.50$
Error	n - k=15- 3=12	SSE = 600	$\dfrac{SSE}{n-k1} = \dfrac{600}{12} = 50$	
Total	n - 1=15 - 1=14	SS(Total) = 850		

15.7 The F statistic is unchanged.

15.8 $\overline{\overline{x}} = \dfrac{5(5) + 5(15) + 5(25)}{5+5+5} = 15$

$SST = \sum n_j(\overline{x}_j - \overline{\overline{x}})^2 = 5(5-15)^2 + 5(15-15)^2 + 5(25-15)^2 = 1000$

$SSE = \sum (n_j - 1)s_j^2 = (5-1)(50) + (5-1)(50) + (5-1)(50) = 600$

273

ANOVA table

Source	Degrees of Freedom	Sum of Squares	Mean Squares	F
Treatments	k - 1=3- 1=2	SST = 1000	$\dfrac{SST}{k-1} = \dfrac{1000}{2} = 500$	$\dfrac{MST}{MSE} = \dfrac{500}{50} = 10.0$
Error	n - k=15- 3=12	SSE = 600	$\dfrac{SSE}{n-k1} = \dfrac{600}{12} = 50$	
Total	n - 1=15 - 1=14	SS(Total) = 1600		

15.9 The F statistic increased fourfold.

15.10 $\overline{\overline{x}} = \dfrac{5(15) + 5(15) + 5(15)}{5+5+5} = 15$

$SST = \sum n_j (\overline{x}_j - \overline{\overline{x}})^2 = 5(15-15)^2 + 5(15-15)^2 + 5(15-15)^2 = 0$

$SSE = \sum (n_j - 1)s_j^2 = (5-1)(50) + (5-1)(50) + (5-1)(50) = 600$

ANOVA table

Source	Degrees of Freedom	Sum of Squares	Mean Squares	F
Treatments	k - 1=3- 1=2	SST = 0	$\dfrac{SST}{k-1} = \dfrac{0}{2} = 0$	$\dfrac{MST}{MSE} = \dfrac{0}{50} = 0$
Error	n - k=15- 3=12	SSE = 600	$\dfrac{SSE}{n-k1} = \dfrac{600}{12} = 50$	
Total	n - 1=15 - 1=14	SS(Total) = 600		

The sum of squares for treatments equals 0 and the F statistic equals 0.

15.11 $\overline{\overline{x}} = \dfrac{5(10) + 5(15) + 5(20)}{5+5+5} = 15$

$SST = \sum n_j (\overline{x}_j - \overline{\overline{x}})^2 = 5(10-15)^2 + 5(15-15)^2 + 5(15-15)^2 = 250$

$SSE = \sum (n_j - 1)s_j^2 = (5-1)(0) + (5-1)(0) + (5-1)(0) = 0$

ANOVA table

Source	Degrees of Freedom	Sum of Squares	Mean Squares	F
Treatments	k - 1=3- 1=2	SST = 250	$\dfrac{SST}{k-1} = \dfrac{250}{2} = 125$	$\dfrac{MST}{MSE} = \dfrac{125}{0}$
Error	n - k=15- 3=12	SSE = 0	$\dfrac{SSE}{n-k1} = \dfrac{0}{12} = 0$	

| Total | n - 1=15 - 1=14 | SS(Total) = 250 | | |

The sum of squares for error equals 0 and the F statistic becomes infinitely large.

15.12 Grand mean: $\bar{\bar{x}} = \dfrac{10(14.7) + 14(11.6) + 11(19.3)}{10 + 14 + 11} = 14.9$

$SST = \sum n_j (\bar{x}_j - \bar{\bar{x}})^2 = 10(14.7 - 14.9)^2 + 14(11.6 - 14.9)^2 + 11(19.3 - 14.9)^2 = 365.8$

$SSE = \sum (n_j - 1)s_j^2 = (10 - 1)(5.3)^2 + (14 - 1)(7.1)^2 + (11 - 1)(6.8)^2 = 1370.5$

ANOVA Table

Source	Degrees of Freedom	Sums of Squares	Mean Squares	F
Treatments	2	365.8	182.9	4.27
Error	32	1370.5	42.8	
Total	34	1736.3		

15. 13 Grand mean: $\bar{\bar{x}} = \dfrac{49(8.36) + 45(7.91) + 29(9.02)}{49 + 45 + 29} = 8.35$

$SST = \sum n_j (\bar{x}_j - \bar{\bar{x}})^2 = 49(8.36 - 8.35)^2 + 45(7.91 - 8.35)^2 + 29(9.02 - 8.35)^2 = 21.74$

$SSE = \sum (n_j - 1)s_j^2 = (49 - 1)(2.98)^2 + (45 - 1)(3.15)^2 + (29 - 1)(3.62)^2 = 1,229.77$

ANOVA Table

Source	Degrees of Freedom	Sums of Squares	Mean Squares	F
Treatments	2	21.74	10.87	1.06
Error	120	1,229.77	10.25	
Total	122	1,251.51		

Rejection region: $F > F_{\alpha, k-1, n-k} = F_{.01, 2, 120} = 4.79$

F = 1.06. There is not enough evidence to infer that the population means differ.

15.14 Grand mean: $\bar{\bar{x}} = \dfrac{9(35.0) + 13(47.3) + 8(40.2)}{9 + 13 + 8} = 41.72$

$SST = \sum n_j(\bar{x}_j - \bar{\bar{x}})^2 = 9(35.0 - 41.72)^2 + 13(47.3 - 41.72)^2 + 8(40.2 - 41.72)^2 = 829.68$

$SSE = \sum (n_j - 1)s_j^2 = (9-1)(8.3)^2 + (13-1)(6.4)^2 + (8-1)(7.7)^2 = 1457.67$

ANOVA Table

Source	Degrees of Freedom Sums	Sums of Squares	Mean Squares	F
Treatments	2	829.68	414.84	7.68
Error	27	1457.67	53.99	
Total	29	2287.35		

Rejection region: $F > F_{\alpha, k-1, n-k} = F_{.05, 2, 27} = 3.35$

F = 7.68. There is enough evidence to infer that the population means differ.

15.15a $H_0 : \mu_1 = \mu_2 = \mu_3 = \mu_4$

$H_1 :$ At least two means differ.

Anova: Single Factor						
SUMMARY						
Groups	Count	Sum	Average	Variance		
School A	20	1376.50	68.83	52.28		
School B	26	1692.00	65.08	37.38		
School C	16	992.20	62.01	63.46		
School D	19	1228.20	64.64	56.88		
ANOVA						
Source of Variation	SS	df	MS	F	P-value	F crit
Between Groups	430.95	3	143.65	2.83	0.0437	2.72
Within Groups	3903.57	77	50.70			
Total	4334.52	80				

F = 2.83, p-value = .0437. There is enough evidence to infer that there are differences in grading standards between the four high schools.

b The grades of the students at each high school are required to be normally distributed with the same variance.

c The histograms are approximately bell-shaped and the sample variances are similar.

15.16a $H_0 : \mu_1 = \mu_2 = \mu_3 = \mu_4$

H_1 : At least two means differ.

Anova: Single Factor						
SUMMARY						
Groups	Count	Sum	Average	Variance		
Form 1	30	2705	90.17	991.52		
Form 2	30	2873	95.77	900.87		
Form 3	30	3205	106.83	928.70		
Form 4	30	3335	111.17	1023.04		
ANOVA						
Source of Variation	SS	df	MS	F	P-value	F crit
Between Groups	8464.10	3	2821.37	2.94	0.0363	2.68
Within Groups	111479.87	116	961.03			
Total	119943.97	119				

F = 2.94, p-value = .0363. There is enough evidence to infer that there are differences between the completion times of the four income tax forms.

b The times for each form must be normally distributed with the same variance.

c The histograms are approximately bell-shaped and the sample variances are similar.

15.17 $H_0 : \mu_1 = \mu_2 = \mu_3 = \mu_4$

H_1 : At least two means differ.

Anova: Single Factor						
SUMMARY						
Groups	Count	Sum	Average	Variance		
Less than HS	41	8070	196.83	914.05		
HS grad	73	15168	207.78	861.12		
Some college	86	19211	223.38	1195.44		
College grad	79	18381	232.67	1079.81		
ANOVA						
Source of Variation	SS	df	MS	F	P-value	F crit
Between Groups	45495.69	3	15165.23	14.66	0.0000	2.64
Within Groups	284400.08	275	1034.18			
Total	329895.77	278				

F = 14.66, p-value = 0. There is enough evidence to infer that there are differences in test scores between children whose parents have different educational levels.

15.18 $H_0 : \mu_1 = \mu_2 = \mu_3 = \mu_4 = \mu_5$

H_1 : At least two means differ.

Anova: Single Factor						
SUMMARY						
Groups	Count	Sum	Average	Variance		
Lacquer 1	24	3935	163.96	1205.61		
Lacquer 2	25	4641	185.64	1719.91		
Lacquer 3	24	3703	154.29	1156.30		
Lacquer 4	25	4565	182.60	1657.83		
Lacquer 5	23	4111	178.74	906.02		
ANOVA						
Source of Variation	SS	df	MS	F	P-value	F crit
Between Groups	17413.89	4	4353.47	3.25	0.0144	3.49
Within Groups	155322.11	116	1338.98			
Total	172736.00	120				

F = 3.25, p-value = .0144. There is not enough evidence to allow the manufacturer to conclude that differences exist between the five lacquers.

b The times until first sign of corrosion for each lacquer must be normally distributed with a common variance.

c The histograms are approximately bell-shaped with similar sample variances.

15.19 $H_0 : \mu_1 = \mu_2 = \mu_3 = \mu_4$

H_1 : At least two means differ.

Anova: Single Factor						
SUMMARY						
Groups	Count	Sum	Average	Variance		
Over $50K	39	866	22.21	121.64		
$30 to 50K	114	2104	18.46	90.39		
$20 to 30K	81	1255	15.49	85.25		
<$20K	67	624	9.31	65.40		
ANOVA						
Source of Variation	SS	df	MS	F	P-value	F crit
Between Groups	5202.08	3	1734.03	19.83	0.0000	2.64
Within Groups	25973.30	297	87.45			
Total	31175.38	300				

F = 19.83, p-value = 0. There is enough evidence to infer that there are differences exist between the four groups.

15.20　　$H_0 : \mu_1 = \mu_2 = \mu_3$

　　　　H_1 : At least two means differ.

Anova: Single Factor						
SUMMARY						
Groups	Count	Sum	Average	Variance		
Fertilizer A	20	11030	551.50	2741.95		
Fertilizer B	20	11535	576.75	2641.14		
Fertilizer C	20	11189	559.45	3129.31		
ANOVA						
Source of Variation	SS	df	MS	F	P-value	F crit
Between Groups	6667.03	2	3333.52	1.17	0.3162	3.16
Within Groups	161735.70	57	2837.47			
Total	168402.73	59				

F = 1.17, p-value = .3162. There is not enough evidence of a difference between fertilizers in terms of crop yields.

15.21　　$H_0 : \mu_1 = \mu_2 = \mu_3$

　　　　H_1 : At least two means differ.

Anova: Single Factor						
SUMMARY						
Groups	Count	Sum	Average	Variance		
English	100	581	5.81	6.22		
Mathematics	100	530	5.30	4.05		
Political Science	100	533	5.33	3.90		
ANOVA						
Source of Variation	SS	df	MS	F	P-value	F crit
Between Groups	16.38	2	8.19	1.73	0.1783	3.03
Within Groups	1402.50	297	4.72			
Total	1418.88	299				

F = 1.73, p-value = .1783. There is not enough evidence of a difference between the three departments.

15.22　　$H_0 : \mu_1 = \mu_2 = \mu_3 = \mu_4$

　　　　H_1 : At least two means differ.

Anova: Single Factor						
SUMMARY						
Groups	Count	Sum	Average	Variance		
1st quarter	30	2223	74.10	249.96		
2nd quarter	30	2270	75.67	184.23		
3rd quarter	30	2355	78.50	233.36		
4th quarter	30	2439	81.30	242.91		
ANOVA						
Source of Variation	SS	df	MS	F	P-value	F crit
Between Groups	909.42	3	303.14	1.33	0.2675	2.68
Within Groups	26403.17	116	227.61			
Total	27312.59	119				

$F = 1.33$, p-value = .2675. There is not enough evidence of a difference between the four groups of companies.

15.23 $H_0 : \mu_1 = \mu_2 = \mu_3$

H_1 : At least two means differ.

a Leaf size

Anova: Single Factor						
SUMMARY						
Groups	Count	Sum	Average	Variance		
Size-Group 1	50	1248.4	24.97	48.23		
Size-Group 2	50	1082.37	21.65	54.54		
Size-Group 3	50	892.23	17.84	33.85		
ANOVA						
Source of Variation	SS	df	MS	F	P-value	F crit
Between Groups	1270.51	2	635.25	13.95	0.0000	3.06
Within Groups	6694.70	147	45.54			
Total	7965.21	149				

$F = 13.95$, p-value = 0. There is sufficient evidence to conclude that the leaf sizes differ between the 3 groups.

b Nicotine

Anova: Single Factor						
SUMMARY						
Groups	Count	Sum	Average	Variance		
Nicotine-Group 1	50	776.17	15.52	3.72		
Nicotine-Group 2	50	669.27	13.39	3.59		
Nicotine-Group 3	50	503.82	10.08	3.83		
ANOVA						
Source of Variation	SS	df	MS	F	P-value	F crit
Between Groups	753.17	2	376.59	101.47	0.0000	3.06
Within Groups	545.54	147	3.71			
Total	1298.71	149				

F = 101.47, p-value = 0. There is sufficient evidence to infer that the amounts of nicotine differ between the 3 groups.

15.24 $H_0 : \mu_1 = \mu_2 = \mu_3 = \mu_4$

H_1 : At least two means differ.

a Ages

Anova: Single Factor						
SUMMARY						
Groups	Count	Sum	Average	Variance		
Age 1	63	1972	31.30	28.34		
Age 2	81	2788	34.42	23.20		
Age 3	40	1495	37.38	31.16		
Age 4	111	4432	39.93	72.03		
ANOVA						
Source of Variation	SS	df	MS	F	P-value	F crit
Between Groups	3365.99	3	1122.00	25.60	0.0000	2.64
Within Groups	12751.80	291	43.82			
Total	16117.78	294				

F = 25.60, p-value = 0. There is sufficient evidence to infer that the ages of the four groups of cereal buyers differ.

b Incomes

Anova: Single Factor						
SUMMARY						
Groups	*Count*	*Sum*	*Average*	*Variance*		
Income 1	63	2345	37.22	39.82		
Income 2	81	3152	38.91	40.85		
Income 3	40	1659	41.48	61.38		
Income 4	111	4634	41.75	46.59		
ANOVA						
Source of Variation	*SS*	*df*	*MS*	*F*	*P-value*	*F crit*
Between Groups	1007.47	3	335.82	7.37	0.0001	2.64
Within Groups	13256.20	291	45.55			
Total	14263.66	294				

F = 7.37, p-value = .0001. There is sufficient evidence to conclude that incomes differ between the four groups of cereal buyers.

c Education

Anova: Single Factor						
SUMMARY						
Groups	*Count*	*Sum*	*Average*	*Variance*		
Education 1	63	740	11.75	3.93		
Education 2	81	1005	12.41	3.39		
Education 3	40	469	11.73	4.26		
Education 4	111	1320	11.89	4.30		
ANOVA						
Source of Variation	*SS*	*df*	*MS*	*F*	*P-value*	*F crit*
Between Groups	21.71	3	7.24	1.82	0.1428	2.64
Within Groups	1154.17	291	3.97			
Total	1175.88	294				

F = 1.82, p-value = .1428. There is not enough evidence to infer that education differs between the four groups of cereal buyers.

d Using the F-tests and the descriptive statistics we see that the mean ages and mean household incomes are in ascending order. For example, Sugar Smacks buyers are younger and earn less than the buyers of the other three cereals. Cheerio purchasers are older and earn the most.

15.25 $H_0 : \mu_1 = \mu_2 = \mu_3$

H_1 : At least two means differ.

Anova: Single Factor						
SUMMARY						
Groups	Count	Sum	Average	Variance		
Price-$9	20	3072	153.60	654.25		
Price-$10	20	3030	151.50	924.05		
Price-$11	20	2665	133.25	626.83		
ANOVA						
Source of Variation	SS	df	MS	F	P-value	F crit
Between Groups	5010.63	2	2505.32	3.41	0.0400	3.16
Within Groups	41897.55	57	735.04			
Total	46908.18	59				

F = 3.41, p-value = .0400. There is enough evidence to infer that sales will vary according to price.

15.26 $H_0 : \mu_1 = \mu_2 = \mu_3$

H_1 : At least two means differ.

Anova: Single Factor						
SUMMARY						
Groups	Count	Sum	Average	Variance		
12 to 14	61	1131	18.54	177.95		
15 to 16	83	1605	19.34	171.42		
17 to 19	91	1846	20.29	297.50		
ANOVA						
Source of Variation	SS	df	MS	F	P-value	F crit
Between Groups	114.48	2	57.24	0.26	0.7730	3.03
Within Groups	51508.27	232	222.02			
Total	51622.75	234				

F = .26, p-value = .7730. There is not enough evidence of a difference between the three segments.

15.27 $H_0 : \mu_1 = \mu_2 = \mu_3$

H_1 : At least two means differ.

Anova: Single Factor						
SUMMARY						
Groups	Count	Sum	Average	Variance		
Conservative	418	15931	38.11	71.50		
Traditional	536	20166	37.62	70.42		
Contemporary	881	33652	38.20	71.94		
ANOVA						
Source of Variation	SS	df	MS	F	P-value	F crit
Between Groups	115.58	2	57.79	0.81	0.4453	3.00
Within Groups	130797.22	1832	71.40			
Total	130912.80	1834				

$F = .81$, p-value $= .4453$. There is not enough evidence of a difference between the three segments.

15.28

ANOVA Table

Source	Degrees of Freedom	Sums of Squares	Mean Squares	F
Treatments	2	100	50.00	24.04
Blocks	6	50	8.33	4.00
Error	12	25	2.08	
Total	20	175		

a Rejection region: $F > F_{\alpha,k-1,n-k-b+1} = F_{.05,2,12} = 3.89$

Conclusion: $F = 24.04$. There is enough evidence to conclude that the treatment means differ.

b Rejection region: $F > F_{\alpha,b-1,n-k-b+1} = F_{.05,6,12} = 3.00$

$F = 4.00$. There is enough evidence to conclude that the block means differ.

15.29

ANOVA Table

Source	Degrees of Freedom	Sums of Squares	Mean Squares	F
Treatments	4	1500	375.00	16.50
Blocks	11	1000	90.91	4.00
Error	44	1000	22.73	
Total	59	3500		

a Rejection region: $F > F_{\alpha,k-1,n-k-b+1} = F_{.01,4,44} \approx 3.83$

$F = 16.50$. There is enough evidence to conclude that the treatment means differ.

b Rejection region: $F > F_{\alpha,b-1,n-k-b+1} = F_{.01,11,44} \approx 2.80$

Conclusion: F = 4.00. There is enough evidence to conclude that the block means differ.

15.30

ANOVA Table

Source	Degrees of Freedom	Sums of Squares	Mean Squares	F
Treatments	3	275	91.67	7.98
Blocks	9	625	69.44	6.05
Error	27	310	11.48	
Total	39	1210		

a Rejection region: $F > F_{\alpha,k-1,n-k-b+1} = F_{.01,3,27} = 4.60$

Conclusion: F = 7.98. There is enough evidence to conclude that the treatment means differ.

b Rejection region: $F > F_{\alpha,b-1,n-k-b+1} = F_{.01,9,27} = 3.15$

Conclusion: F = 6.05. There is enough evidence to conclude that the block means differ.

15.31

ANOVA						
Source of Variation	SS	df	MS	F	P-value	F crit
Rows	48.27	4	12.07	2.70	0.1080	3.84
Columns	15.60	2	7.80	1.75	0.2348	4.46
Error	35.73	8	4.47			
Total	99.60	14				

a Rejection region: $F > F_{\alpha,k-1,n-k-b+1} = F_{.05,2,8} = 4.46$

F = 1.75. There is not enough evidence to conclude that the treatment means differ.

b Rejection region: $F > F_{\alpha,b-1,n-k-b+1} = F_{.05,4,8} = 3.84$

F = 2.70. There is not enough evidence to conclude that the block means differ.

15.32

ANOVA						
Source of Variation	SS	df	MS	F	P-value	F crit
Rows	4.17	2	2.08	6.82	0.0285	5.14
Columns	8.92	3	2.97	9.73	0.0101	4.76
Error	1.83	6	0.31			
Total	14.92	11				

a Rejection region: $F > F_{\alpha,k-1,n-k-b+1} = F_{.05,3,6} = 4.76$

F = 9.73. There is enough evidence to conclude that the treatment means differ.

b Rejection region: $F > F_{\alpha,b-1,n-k-b+1} = F_{.05,2,6} = 5.14$

F = 6.82. There is enough evidence to conclude that the block means differ.

15.33 $H_0 : \mu_1 = \mu_2 = \mu_3$

   H_1 : At least two means differ.

ANOVA						
Source of Variation	SS	df	MS	F	P-value	F crit
Rows	7396.30	9	821.81	75.70	0.0000	3.60
Columns	151.27	2	75.63	6.97	0.0057	6.01
Error	195.40	18	10.86			
Total	7742.97	29				

Rejection region: $F > F_{\alpha,k-1,n-k-b+1} = F_{.01,2,18} = 6.01$

F = 6.97, p-value = .0057. There is enough evidence to conclude that the treatment means differ.

15.34

ANOVA						
Source of Variation	SS	df	MS	F	P-value	F crit
Rows	35300.00	24	1470.83	15.94	0.0000	1.67
Columns	2126.51	3	708.84	7.68	0.0002	2.73
Error	6642.24	72	92.25			
Total	44068.75	99				

a $H_0 : \mu_1 = \mu_2 = \mu_3 = \mu_4$

   H_1 : At least two means differ.

Rejection region: $F > F_{\alpha,k-1,n-k-b+1} = F_{.05,3,72} \approx 2.76$

F = 7.68, p-value = .0002. There is enough evidence to conclude that the treatment means differ.

b $H_0 : \mu_1 = \mu_2 = ... = \mu_{25}$

   H_1 : At least two means differ.

Rejection region: $F > F_{\alpha,b-1,n-k-b+1} = F_{.05,24,72} \approx 1.70$

Conclusion: F = 15.94, p-value = 0. There is enough evidence to conclude that the block means differ.

c The response is required to be normally distributed with a common variance.

d The histograms are bell shaped and the sample variances are similar.

15.35

ANOVA						
Source of Variation	SS	df	MS	F	P-value	F crit
Rows	1150.22	11	104.57	4.65	0.0011	2.26
Columns	204.22	2	102.11	4.54	0.0224	3.44
Error	495.11	22	22.51			
Total	1849.56	35				

a $H_0 : \mu_1 = \mu_2 = \mu_3$

            H_1 : At least two means differ.

F = 4.54, p-value = .0224. There is enough evidence to conclude that there are differences between the three couriers.

b $H_0 : \mu_1 = \mu_2 = \ldots = \mu_{12}$

            H_1 : At least two means differ.

F = 4.65, p-value = .0011. The block means differ; the practitioner used the correct design.

15.36

ANOVA						
Source of Variation	SS	df	MS	F	P-value	F crit
Rows	177464.60	19	9340.24	323.16	0.0000	1.87
Columns	7131.03	2	3565.52	123.36	0.0000	3.24
Error	1098.30	38	28.90			
Total	185693.93	59				

a $H_0 : \mu_1 = \mu_2 = \mu_3$

            H_1 : At least two means differ.

Rejection region: $F > F_{\alpha, k-1, n-k-b+1} = F_{.05, 2, 38} \approx 3.23$

F = 123.360, p-value = 0. There is sufficient evidence to conclude that the three fertilizers differ with respect to crop yield.

b F = 323.16, p-value = 0. There is sufficient evidence to indicate that there are differences between the plots.

15.37

ANOVA						
Source of Variation	SS	df	MS	F	P-value	F crit
Rows	3020.30	19	158.96	26.64	0.0000	1.87
Columns	10.26	2	5.13	0.86	0.4313	3.24
Error	226.71	38	5.97			
Total	3257.27	59				

a $\quad H_0 : \mu_1 = \mu_2 = \mu_3$

$\quad\quad H_1$: At least two means differ.

Rejection region: $F > F_{\alpha, k-1, n-k-b+1} = F_{.05, 2, 38} \approx 3.23$

F = .86, p-value = .4313. There is not enough evidence to conclude that there are differences in sales ability between the holders of the three degrees.

b $\quad H_0 : \mu_1 = \mu_2 = \ldots = \mu_{20}$

$\quad\quad H_1$: At least two means differ.

F = 26.64, p-value = 0. There is sufficient evidence to indicate that there are differences between the blocks of students. The independent samples design would not be recommended.

c The commissions for each type of degree are required to be normally distributed with the same variance.

d The histograms are bell shaped and the sample variances are similar.

15.38

ANOVA						
Source of Variation	SS	df	MS	F	P-value	F crit
Rows	126842.58	29	4373.88	66.02	0.0000	1.94
Columns	4206.09	3	1402.03	21.16	0.0000	4.02
Error	5763.66	87	66.25			
Total	136812.33	119				

a $\quad H_0 : \mu_1 = \mu_2 = \mu_3 = \mu_4$

$\quad\quad H_1$: At least two means differ.

Rejection region: $F > F_{\alpha, k-1, n-k-b+1} = F_{.01, 3, 87} \approx 4.13$

F = 21.16, p-value = 0. There is sufficient evidence to conclude that differences in completion times exist between the four forms.

b $\quad H_0 : \mu_1 = \mu_2 = \ldots = \mu_{30}$

$\quad\quad H_1$: At least two means differ.

F = 66.02, p-value = 0. There is sufficient evidence to indicate that there are differences between the taxpayers, which tells us that this experimental design is recommended.

15.39 $H_0 : \mu_1 = \mu_2 = \mu_3 = \mu_4 = \mu_5 = \mu_6 = \mu_7$

H_1 : At least two means differ.

ANOVA						
Source of Variation	SS	df	MS	F	P-value	F crit
Rows	209835	199	1054.45	2.63	0.0000	1.19
Columns	28674	6	4778.95	11.91	0.0000	2.11
Error	479125	1194	401.28			
Total	717633	1399				

F = 11.91, p-value = 0. There is enough evidence to conclude that there are differences in time spent listening to music between the days of the week

15.40

ANOVA						
Source of Variation	SS	df	MS	F	P-value	F crit
Rows	7309.68	35	208.85	6.36	0.0000	1.51
Columns	1406.39	4	351.60	10.72	0.0000	2.44
Error	4593.89	140	32.81			
Total	13309.97	179				

a $H_0 : \mu_1 = \mu_2 = \mu_3 = \mu_4 = \mu_5$

H_1 : At least two means differ.

F = 10.72, p-value = 0. There is enough evidence to infer differences between medical specialties.

b $H_0 : \mu_1 = \mu_2 = \ldots = \mu_{36}$

H_1 : At least two means differ.

F = 6.36, p-value = 0. There is sufficient evidence to indicate that there are differences between the physicians' ages, which tells us that this experimental design is recommended.

15.41 $H_0 : \mu_1 = \mu_2 = \mu_3 = \mu_4$

H_1 : At least two means differ.

ANOVA						
Source of Variation	SS	df	MS	F	P-value	F crit
Rows	1327.33	20	66.37	5.32	0.0000	1.75
Columns	563.82	3	187.94	15.06	0.0000	2.76
Error	748.70	60	12.48			
Total	2639.84	83				

$F = 15.06$, p-value = 0. There is enough evidence to infer differences in grading standards between the four high schools.

15.42 Source	Degrees of Freedom	Sums of Squares	Mean Squares	F
Factor A	2	1,560	780	5.85
Factor B	3	2,880	960	7.20
Interaction	6	7,605	1268	9.50
Error	228	30,405	133	
Total	239	42,450		

a Rejection region: $F > F_{\alpha,a-1,n-ab} = F_{.01,2,228} \approx 4.61$

$F = 5.85$. There is enough evidence to conclude that differences exist between the levels of factor A.

b Rejection region: $F > F_{\alpha,b-1,n-ab} = F_{.01,3,228} \approx 3.78$

$F = 7.20$. There is enough evidence to conclude that differences exist between the levels of factor B.

c Rejection region: $F > F_{\alpha,(a-1)(b-1),n-ab} = F_{.01,6,228} \approx 2.80$

$F = 9.50$. There is enough evidence to conclude that factors A and B interact.

15.43 Source	Degrees of Freedom	Sums of Squares	Mean Squares	F
Factor A	3	203	67.67	.72
Factor B	2	859	429.5	4.60
Interaction	6	513	85.5	.92
Error	84	7845	93.39	
Total	95	9420		

a Rejection region: $F > F_{\alpha,a-1,n-ab} = F_{.05,3,84} \approx 2.76$

$F = .72$. There is not enough evidence to conclude that differences exist between the levels of factor A.

b Rejection region: $F > F_{\alpha,b-1,n-ab} = F_{.05,2,84} \approx 3.15$

$F = 4.60$. There is enough evidence to conclude that differences exist between the levels of factor B.

c Rejection region: $F > F_{\alpha,(a-1)(b-1),n-ab} = F_{.05,6,84} \approx 2.25$

$F = .92$. There is not enough evidence to conclude that factors A and B interact.

15.44

ANOVA						
Source of Variation	SS	df	MS	F	P-value	F crit
Sample	5.33	1	5.33	1.23	0.2995	5.32
Columns	56.33	1	56.33	13.00	0.0069	5.32
Interaction	1.33	1	1.33	0.31	0.5943	5.32
Within	34.67	8	4.33			
Total	97.67	11				

a $F = .31$, p-value $= .5943$. There is not enough evidence to conclude that factors A and B interact.

b $F = 1.23$, p-value $= .2995$. There is not enough evidence to conclude that differences exist between the levels of factor A.

c $F = 13.00$, p-value $= .0069$. There is enough evidence to conclude that differences exist between the levels of factor B.

15.45

ANOVA						
Source of Variation	SS	df	MS	F	P-value	F crit
Sample	177.25	2	88.63	9.99	0.0012	3.55
Columns	0.38	1	0.38	0.04	0.8394	4.41
Interaction	9.25	2	4.63	0.52	0.6025	3.55
Within	159.75	18	8.88			
Total	346.63	23				

a $F = .52$, p-value $= .6025$. There is not enough evidence to conclude that factors A and B interact.

b $F = 9.99$, p-value $= .0012$. There is enough evidence to conclude that differences exist between the levels of factor A.

c $F = .04$, p-value $= .8394$. There is not enough evidence to conclude that differences exist between the levels of factor B.

15.46 a Factor A is the drug mixture and factor B is the schedule.

b The response variable is the improvement index.

c There are a = 4 drug mixtures and b = 2 schedules.

ANOVA						
Source of Variation	SS	df	MS	F	P-value	F crit
Sample	14.4	1	14.40	0.57	0.4548	4.15
Columns	581.8	3	193.93	7.71	0.0005	2.90
Interaction	548.6	3	182.87	7.27	0.0007	2.90
Within	804.8	32	25.15			
Total	1949.6	39				

d $F = .57$, p-value = .4548. There is not enough evidence to conclude that differences exist between the schedules.

e $F = 7.71$, p-value = .0005. There is sufficient evidence to conclude that differences exist between the four drug mixtures.

f $F = 7.27$, p-value = .0007. There is sufficient evidence to conclude that the schedules and drug mixtures interact.

15.47 a There are 2 factors--class configuration and time period.

b The response variable is the number of times students ask and answer questions.

c There are 2 levels of class configuration and 3 levels of time period.

ANOVA						
Source of Variation	SS	df	MS	F	P-value	F crit
Sample	13.33	1	13.33	1.58	0.2203	4.26
Columns	46.67	2	23.33	2.77	0.0826	3.40
Interaction	206.67	2	103.33	12.28	0.0002	3.40
Within	202.00	24	8.42			
Total	468.67	29				

d Class configuration: $F = 1.58$, p-value = .2203. There is not enough evidence that the class configurations differ.

Time: $F = 2.77$, p-value = .0826. There is not enough evidence to infer that the times of the day differ.

Interaction: $F = 12.28$, p-value = .0002. There is sufficient evidence to conclude that the class configuration and time interact.

15.48 a There are 12 treatments

b There are two factors, tax form and income group.

c There are $a = 4$ forms and $b = 3$ income groups.

ANOVA						
Source of Variation	SS	df	MS	F	P-value	F crit
Sample	6718.72	2	3359.36	4.11	0.0190	3.08
Columns	6279.87	3	2093.29	2.56	0.0586	2.69
Interaction	5101.88	6	850.31	1.04	0.4030	2.18
Within	88217.00	108	816.82			
Total	106317.47	119				

d F =2.56, p-value = .0586. There is not enough evidence to conclude that differences exist between the forms.

e F =4.11, p-value = .0190. There is enough evidence to conclude that differences exist between the three income groups.

f F = 1.04, p-value = .4030. There is not enough evidence to conclude that forms and income groups interact.

15.49 a Detergents and temperatures

b The response variable is the whiteness score.

c There are a = 5 detergents and b = 3 temperatures.

ANOVA						
Source of Variation	SS	df	MS	F	P-value	F crit
Sample	3937.08	2	1968.54	17.82	0.0000	3.06
Columns	2967.43	4	741.86	6.72	0.0001	2.44
Interaction	2452.05	8	306.51	2.78	0.0071	2.01
Within	14910.00	135	110.44			
Total	24266.56	149				

d F = 6.72, p-value = 0001. There is sufficient evidence to conclude that differences exist between the detergents.

e F =17.82, p-value = 0. There is sufficient evidence to conclude that differences exist between the three temperatures.

f F = 2.78, p-value = .0071. There is sufficient evidence to conclude that detergents and temperatures interact.

15.50

ANOVA						
Source of Variation	SS	df	MS	F	P-value	F crit
Sample	16.04	1	16.04	14.74	0.0005	4.11
Columns	6.77	1	6.77	6.22	0.0173	4.11
Interaction	0.025	1	0.025	0.02	0.8814	4.11
Within	39.17	36	1.09			
Total	62.00	39				

The p-values for machines, alloys, and interaction are .0173, .0005, and .8814, respectively. Both machines and alloys are sources of variation.

15.51

ANOVA						
Source of Variation	SS	df	MS	F	P-value	F crit
Sample	0.00031	3	0.000103	0.66	0.5798	2.90
Columns	0.00051	1	0.000515	3.33	0.0775	4.15
Interaction	0.00018	3	0.000061	0.39	0.7584	2.90
Within	0.00495	32	0.000155			
Total	0.00596	39				

The p-values for devices, alloys, and interaction are .0775, .5798, and .7584, respectively. There are no sources of variation.

15.52

ANOVA						
Source of Variation	SS	df	MS	F	P-value	F crit
Sample	211.78	2	105.89	21.04	0.0000	3.22
Columns	0.59	1	0.59	0.12	0.7348	4.07
Interaction	0.128	2	0.064	0.01	0.9874	3.22
Within	211.42	42	5.03			
Total	423.91	47				

The p-values for methods, skills, and interaction are .7348, 0, and .9874. The only source of variation is skill level.

15.53 $\alpha = .05$: $t_{\alpha/2,n-k} = t_{.025,27} = 2.052$

	$\bar{x}_i$	$\bar{x}_j$	$\lvert\bar{x}_i - \bar{x}_j\rvert$	$LSD = t_{\alpha/2,n-k}\sqrt{MSE\left(\dfrac{1}{n_i}+\dfrac{1}{n_j}\right)}$
$i=1, j=2$	128.7	101.4	27.3	$2.052\sqrt{700\left(\dfrac{1}{10}+\dfrac{1}{10}\right)} = 24.28$
$i=1, j=3$	128.7	133.7	5.0	$2.052\sqrt{700\left(\dfrac{1}{10}+\dfrac{1}{10}\right)} = 24.28$
$i=2, j=3$	101.4	133.7	32.3	$2.052\sqrt{700\left(\dfrac{1}{10}+\dfrac{1}{10}\right)} = 24.28$

Conclusion: μ_2 differs from μ_1 and μ_3.

15.54 $C = 3(2)/2 = 3$, $\alpha_E = .05$, $\alpha = \alpha_E/C = .0167$: $t_{\alpha/2,n-k} = t_{.0083,27} = 2.552$ (from Excel)

	$\bar{x}_i$	$\bar{x}_j$	$\lvert\bar{x}_i - \bar{x}_j\rvert$	$LSD = t_{\alpha/2,n-k}\sqrt{MSE\left(\dfrac{1}{n_i}+\dfrac{1}{n_j}\right)}$
$i=1, j=2$	128.7	101.4	27.3	$2.552\sqrt{700\left(\dfrac{1}{10}+\dfrac{1}{10}\right)} = 30.20$
$i=1, j=3$	128.7	133.7	5.0	$2.552\sqrt{700\left(\dfrac{1}{10}+\dfrac{1}{10}\right)} = 30.20$
$i=2, j=3$	101.4	133.7	32.3	$2.552\sqrt{700\left(\dfrac{1}{10}+\dfrac{1}{10}\right)} = 30.20$

Conclusion: μ_2 and μ_3 differ.

15.55 $q_\alpha(k,\nu) = q_{.05}(3,27) \approx 3.53$

	$\bar{x}_i$	$\bar{x}_j$	$\lvert\bar{x}_i - \bar{x}_j\rvert$	$\varpi = q_\alpha(k,\nu)\sqrt{\dfrac{MSE}{n_g}}$
$i=1, j=2$	128.7	101.4	27.3	$3.53\sqrt{\dfrac{700}{10}} = 29.53$
$i=1, j=3$	128.7	133.7	5.0	$3.53\sqrt{\dfrac{700}{10}} = 29.53$
$i=2, j=3$	101.4	133.7	32.3	$3.53\sqrt{\dfrac{700}{10}} = 29.53$

Conclusion: μ_2 and μ_3 differ.

15.56 $\quad \alpha = .05$: $t_{\alpha/2,n-k} = t_{.025,20} = 2.086$

	$\bar{x}_i$	$\bar{x}_j$	$\|\bar{x}_i - \bar{x}_j\|$	$LSD = t_{\alpha/2,n-k}\sqrt{MSE\left(\dfrac{1}{n_i}+\dfrac{1}{n_j}\right)}$
$i = 1, j = 2$	227	205	22	$2.086\sqrt{125\left(\dfrac{1}{5}+\dfrac{1}{5}\right)} = 14.75$
$i = 1, j = 3$	227	219	8	$2.086\sqrt{125\left(\dfrac{1}{5}+\dfrac{1}{5}\right)} = 14.75$
$i = 1, j = 4$	227	248	21	$2.086\sqrt{125\left(\dfrac{1}{5}+\dfrac{1}{5}\right)} = 14.75$
$i = 1, j = 5$	227	202	25	$2.086\sqrt{125\left(\dfrac{1}{5}+\dfrac{1}{5}\right)} = 14.75$
$i = 2, j = 3$	205	219	14	$2.086\sqrt{125\left(\dfrac{1}{5}+\dfrac{1}{5}\right)} = 14.75$
$i = 2, j = 4$	205	248	43	$2.086\sqrt{125\left(\dfrac{1}{5}+\dfrac{1}{5}\right)} = 14.75$
$i = 2, j = 5$	205	202	3	$2.086\sqrt{125\left(\dfrac{1}{5}+\dfrac{1}{5}\right)} = 14.75$
$i = 3, j = 4$	219	248	29	$2.086\sqrt{125\left(\dfrac{1}{5}+\dfrac{1}{5}\right)} = 14.75$
$i = 3, j = 5$	219	202	17	$2.086\sqrt{125\left(\dfrac{1}{5}+\dfrac{1}{5}\right)} = 14.75$
$i = 4, j = 5$	248	202	46	$2.086\sqrt{125\left(\dfrac{1}{5}+\dfrac{1}{5}\right)} = 14.75$

Conclusion: The following pairs of means differ. μ_1 and μ_2, μ_1 and μ_4, μ_1 and μ_5, μ_2 and μ_4, μ_3 and μ_4, μ_3 and μ_5, and μ_4 and μ_5.

15.57 $C = 5(4)/2 = 10, \alpha_E = .05, \alpha = \alpha_E / C = .005: t_{\alpha/2,n-k} = t_{.0025,20} = 3.153$ (from Excel)

$\bar{x}_i$	$\bar{x}_j$	$|\bar{x}_i - \bar{x}_j|$		$LSD = t_{\alpha/2,n-k}\sqrt{MSE\left(\dfrac{1}{n_i}+\dfrac{1}{n_j}\right)}$
$i = 1, j = 2$	227	205	22	$3.153\sqrt{125\left(\dfrac{1}{5}+\dfrac{1}{5}\right)} = 22.30$
$i = 1, j = 3$	227	219	8	$3.153\sqrt{125\left(\dfrac{1}{5}+\dfrac{1}{5}\right)} = 22.30$
$i = 1, j = 4$	227	248	21	$3.153\sqrt{125\left(\dfrac{1}{5}+\dfrac{1}{5}\right)} = 22.30$
$i = 1, j = 5$	227	202	25	$3.153\sqrt{125\left(\dfrac{1}{5}+\dfrac{1}{5}\right)} = 22.30$
$i = 2, j = 3$	205	219	14	$3.153\sqrt{125\left(\dfrac{1}{5}+\dfrac{1}{5}\right)} = 22.30$
$i = 2, j = 4$	205	248	43	$3.153\sqrt{125\left(\dfrac{1}{5}+\dfrac{1}{5}\right)} = 22.302$
$i = 2, j = 5$	205	202	3	$3.153\sqrt{125\left(\dfrac{1}{5}+\dfrac{1}{5}\right)} = 22.30$
$i = 3, j = 4$	219	248	29	$3.153\sqrt{125\left(\dfrac{1}{5}+\dfrac{1}{5}\right)} = 22.30$
$i = 3, j = 5$	219	202	17	$3.153\sqrt{125\left(\dfrac{1}{5}+\dfrac{1}{5}\right)} = 22.30$
$i = 4, j = 5$	248	202	46	$3.153\sqrt{125\left(\dfrac{1}{5}+\dfrac{1}{5}\right)} = 22.30$

Conclusion: The following pairs of means differ. μ_1 and μ_5, μ_2 and μ_4, μ_3 and μ_4, and μ_4 and μ_5.

15.58 $q_\alpha(k, v) = q_{.05}(5, 20) = 4.23$

	$\bar{x}_i$	$\bar{x}_j$	$|\bar{x}_i - \bar{x}_j|$	$\varpi = q_\alpha(k, v)\sqrt{\dfrac{MSE}{n_g}}$
$i = 1, j = 2$	227	205	22	$4.23\sqrt{\dfrac{125}{5}} = 21.15$
$i = 1, j = 3$	227	219	8	$4.23\sqrt{\dfrac{125}{5}} = 21.15$
$i = 1, j = 4$	227	248	21	$4.23\sqrt{\dfrac{125}{5}} = 21.15$
$i = 1, j = 5$	227	202	25	$4.23\sqrt{\dfrac{125}{5}} = 21.15$
$i = 2, j = 3$	205	219	14	$4.23\sqrt{\dfrac{125}{5}} = 21.15$
$i = 2, j = 4$	205	248	43	$4.23\sqrt{\dfrac{125}{5}} = 21.15$
$i = 2, j = 5$	205	202	3	$4.23\sqrt{\dfrac{125}{5}} = 21.15$
$i = 3, j = 4$	219	248	29	$4.23\sqrt{\dfrac{125}{5}} = 21.15$
$i = 3, j = 5$	219	202	17	$4.23\sqrt{\dfrac{125}{5}} = 21.15$
$i = 4, j = 5$	248	202	46	$4.23\sqrt{\dfrac{125}{5}} = 21.15$

Conclusion: The following pairs of means differ. μ_1 and μ_2, μ_1 and μ_5, μ_2 and μ_4, μ_3 and μ_4, and μ_4 and μ_5.

15.59 & 15.60

Multiple Comparisons				
			LSD	Omega
Treatment	Treatment	Difference	Alpha = 0.00833	Alpha = 0.05
School A	School B	3.75	5.74	5.91
	School C	6.81	6.47	5.91
	School D	4.18	6.18	5.91
School B	School C	3.06	6.13	5.91
	School D	0.43	5.82	5.91
School C	School D	-2.63	6.54	5.91

15.59 The mean grades from high schools A and C differ.

15.60 The mean grades from high schools A and C differ.

15.61 & 15.62

Multiple Comparisons				
			LSD	Omega
Treatment	Treatment	Difference	Alpha = 0.00833	Alpha = 0.05
Form 1	Form 2	-5.60	21.49	20.83
	Form 3	-16.67	21.49	20.83
	Form 4	-21.00	21.49	20.83
Form 2	Form 3	-11.07	21.49	20.83
	Form 4	-15.40	21.49	20.83
Form 3	Form 4	-4.33	21.49	20.83

15.61 The means of forms 1 and 4 differ.

15.62 No means differ.

15.63 & 15.64

Multiple Comparisons				
			LSD	Omega
Treatment	Treatment	Difference	Alpha = 0.01	Alpha = 0.05
Lacquer 1	Lacquer2	-21.68	27.39	29.17
	Lacquer3	9.67	27.66	29.17
	Lacquer4	-18.64	27.39	29.17
	Lacquer5	-14.78	27.96	29.17
Lacquer2	Lacquer3	31.35	27.39	29.17
	Lacquer4	3.04	27.10	29.17
	Lacquer5	6.90	27.69	29.17
Lacquer3	Lacquer4	-28.31	27.39	29.17
	Lacquer5	-24.45	27.96	29.17
Lacquer4	Lacquer5	3.86	27.69	29.17

15.63 The means of lacquers 2 and 3 differ

15.64. The means of lacquers 2 and 3, and 3 and 4 differ.

15.65a $H_0 : \mu_1 = \mu_2 = \mu_3 = \mu_4$

H_1 : At least two means differ.

ANOVA

Source of Variation	SS	df	MS	F	P-value	F crit
Between Groups	662.67	3	220.89	3.56	0.0236	2.87
Within Groups	2235.70	36	62.10			
Total	2898.38	39				

$F = 3.56$, p-value = .0236. There is enough evidence to infer that differences exist between the flares with respect to burning times.

b

Multiple Comparisons

Treatment	Treatment	Difference	LSD Alpha = 0.00833	Omega Alpha = 0.05
Flare A	Flare B	4.3	9.84	9.44
	Flare C	-0.2	9.84	9.44
	Flare D	9.8	9.84	9.44
Flare B	Flare C	-4.5	9.84	9.44
	Flare D	5.5	9.84	9.44
Flare C	Flare D	10	9.84	9.44

Bonferronni adjustment with $\alpha = \alpha_E / C = .05/6 = .0083$. The means of flares C and D differ.

c $\varpi = 9.44$: The means of flares C and D, and A and D differ.

15.66a $H_0 : \mu_1 = \mu_2 = \mu_3$

   H_1 : At least two means differ.

ANOVA

Source of Variation	SS	df	MS	F	P-value	F crit
Between Groups	1178.02	2	589.01	3.70	0.0286	3.10
Within Groups	13835.80	87	159.03			
Total	15013.82	89				

$F = 3.70$, p-value = .0286. There is enough evidence to infer that speed of promotion varies between the three sizes of engineering firms.

b

Multiple Comparisons

Treatment	Treatment	Difference	LSD Alpha = 0.05	Omega Alpha = 0.05
Small	Medium	3.80	6.47	7.74
	Large	8.83	6.47	7.74
Medium	Large	5.03	6.47	7.74

The means of small and large firms differ. Answer (v) is correct.

15.67a $H_0 : \mu_1 = \mu_2 = \mu_3 = \mu_4 = \mu_5$

H_1 : At least two means differ.

Anova: Single Factor						
SUMMARY						
Groups	*Count*	*Sum*	*Average*	*Variance*		
Borough A	50	413	8.26	116.40		
Borough B	50	784	15.68	103.45		
Borough C	50	722	14.44	96.70		
Borough D	50	534	10.68	84.30		
Borough E	50	610	12.20	88.61		
ANOVA						
Source of Variation	*SS*	*df*	*MS*	*F*	*P-value*	*F crit*
Between Groups	1747.42	4	436.86	4.46	0.0017	2.41
Within Groups	23983.70	245	97.89			
Total	25731.12	249				

$F = 4.46$, p-value = .0017. There is enough evidence to infer that there are differences in the effect of the new assessment system between the five boroughs.

b

Multiple Comparisons				
			LSD	Omega
Treatment	Treatment	Difference	Alpha = 0.05	Alpha = 0.05
Borough A	Borough B	-7.42	3.90	5.40
	Borough C	-6.18	3.90	5.40
	Borough D	-2.42	3.90	5.40
	Borough E	-3.94	3.90	5.40
Borough B	Borough C	1.24	3.90	5.40
	Borough D	5.00	3.90	5.40
	Borough E	3.48	3.90	5.40
Borough C	Borough D	3.76	3.90	5.40
	Borough E	2.24	3.90	5.40
Borough D	Borough E	-1.52	3.90	5.40

The mean assessments in borough A differs from the means in boroughs B and C.

c The assessments for each borough are required to be normally distributed with equal variances.

d The histograms are approximately bell-shaped and the sample variances are similar.

15.68 $H_0 : \mu_1 = \mu_2 = \mu_3 = \mu_4$

H_1 : At least two means differ.

ANOVA						
Source of Variation	SS	df	MS	F	P-value	F crit
Rows	43979.64	19	2314.72	21.58	0.0000	1.77
Columns	4437.64	3	1479.21	13.79	0.0000	2.77
Error	6113.11	57	107.25			
Total	54530.39	79				

F = 13.79, p-value = 0. There is sufficient evidence to conclude that the reading speeds differ between the four typefaces. The typeface that was read the fastest should be used.

15.69a The factors are mental outlook (2 levels) and physical condition (3 levels).

ANOVA						
Source of Variation	SS	df	MS	F	P-value	F crit
Sample	2118.43	2	1059.22	24.48	0.0000	3.17
Columns	166.67	1	166.67	3.85	0.0548	4.02
Interaction	20.03	2	10.02	0.23	0.7941	3.17
Within	2336.20	54	43.26			
Total	4641.33	59				

b F = 3.85, p-value = .0548. There is not enough evidence to conclude that differences exist between optimists and pessimists.

c F = 24.48, p-value = 0. There is sufficient evidence to conclude that differences exist between the three levels of physical condition.

15.70a $H_0 : \mu_1 = \mu_2 = \mu_3 = \mu_4$

H_1 : At least two means differ.

ANOVA						
Source of Variation	SS	df	MS	F	P-value	F crit
Between Groups	9.90	3	3.30	7.67	0.0001	2.70
Within Groups	41.33	96	0.430			
Total	51.23	99				

F = 7.67, p-value = .0001. There is sufficient evidence to infer that differences in productivity exist between the four groups of companies.

b

Multiple Comparisons				
			LSD	Omega
Treatment	Treatment	Difference	Alpha = 0.00833	Alpha = 0.05
Extensive	Some	0.534	0.500	0.483
	Little	0.722	0.500	0.483
	No	0.811	0.500	0.483
Some	Little	0.188	0.500	0.483
	No	0.277	0.500	0.483
Little	No	0.089	0.500	0.483

Using either the Bonferroni adjustment or Tukey's method we conclude that μ_1 differs from μ_2, μ_3 and μ_4. Companies that offered extensive training have productivity levels different from the other companies.

15.71

ANOVA						
Source of Variation	SS	df	MS	F	P-value	F crit
Rows	335.17	13	25.78	16.86	0.0000	2.12
Columns	10.90	2	5.45	3.57	0.0428	3.37
Error	39.76	26	1.53			
Total	385.83	41				

a $H_0 : \mu_1 = \mu_2 = \mu_3$

H_1 : At least two means differ.

F = 3.57, p-value = .0428. There is enough evidence to conclude that there are differences in waiting times between the three resorts.

b The waiting times are required to be normally distributed with the same variance at all three resorts.

c The conditions appear to be satisfied.

15.72a There are 4 levels of ranks and 4 levels of faculties for a total of 16 treatments.

b

ANOVA						
Source of Variation	SS	df	MS	F	P-value	F crit
Between Groups	1091.15	15	72.74	2.84	0.0019	1.83
Within Groups	1638.40	64	25.60			
Total	2729.55	79				

F = 2.84, p-value = .0019. There is enough evidence to infer that at least two treatment means differ.

c Factor A (columns) is the faculty. The levels are business, engineering, arts, and science. Factor B (samples) is the rank. The levels are professor, associate professor, assistant professor, and lecturer.

ANOVA						
Source of Variation	SS	df	MS	F	P-value	F crit
Sample	46.85	3	15.62	0.61	0.6109	2.75
Columns	344.65	3	114.88	4.49	0.0064	2.75
Interaction	699.65	9	77.74	3.04	0.0044	2.03
Within	1638.40	64	25.60			
Total	2729.55	79				

d $F = .61$, p-value = .6109. There is not enough evidence to conclude that differences exist between the ranks.

e $F = 4.49$, p-value = .0064. There is enough evidence to conclude that differences exist between the faculties.

f $F = 3.04$, p-value = .0044. There is evidence to conclude that ranks and faculties interact.

15.73 $H_0 : \mu_1 = \mu_2 = \mu_3$

H_1 : At least two means differ.

ANOVA						
Source of Variation	SS	df	MS	F	P-value	F crit
Between Groups	406.49	2	203.25	1.82	0.1662	3.06
Within Groups	16445.78	147	111.88			
Total	16852.27	149				

$F = 1.82$, p-value = .1662. There is not enough evidence to infer that differences in attention span exist between the three products.

15.74 $H_0 : \mu_1 = \mu_2 = \mu_3$

H_1 : At least two means differ

ANOVA						
Source of Variation	SS	df	MS	F	P-value	F crit
Rows	156.44	5	31.29	9.71	0.0014	3.33
Columns	43.11	2	21.56	6.69	0.0143	4.10
Error	32.22	10	3.22			
Total	231.78	17				

$F = 6.69$, p-value = .0143. There is enough evidence to infer that differences in attention span exist between the three products.

15.75 $H_0 : \mu_1 = \mu_2 = \mu_3 = \mu_4$

   H_1 : At least two means differ.

ANOVA						
Source of Variation	SS	df	MS	F	P-value	F crit
Between Groups	209961	4	52490	5.12	0.0006	2.42
Within Groups	1997214	195	10242			
Total	2207176	199				

F = 5.12, p-value = .0006. There is sufficient evidence to infer that the bumpers differ in their reaction to low-speed collisions.

b

Multiple Comparisons				
			LSD	Omega
Treatment	Treatment	Difference	Alpha = 0.005	Alpha = 0.05
Bumper 1	Bumper 2	49.35	64.25	61.77
	Bumper 3	-35.45	64.25	61.77
	Bumper 4	46.78	64.25	61.77
	Bumper 5	-3.85	64.25	61.77
Bumper 2	Bumper 3	-84.80	64.25	61.77
	Bumper 4	-2.57	64.25	61.77
	Bumper 5	-53.20	64.25	61.77
Bumper 3	Bumper 4	82.23	64.25	61.77
	Bumper 5	31.60	64.25	61.77
Bumper 4	Bumper 5	-50.63	64.25	61.77

Using either the Bonferroni adjustment or Tukey's method we conclude that the mean repair costs of bumpers 2 and 3, and 3 and 4 differ.

15.76

ANOVA						
Source of Variation	SS	df	MS	F	P-value	F crit
Sample	123554	1	123554	3.66	0.0576	3.91
Columns	3965110	2	1982555	58.78	0.0000	3.06
Interaction	30006	2	15003	0.44	0.6418	3.06
Within	4856578	144	33726			
Total	8975248	149				

Age: F = 58.78, p-value = 0. There is sufficient evidence to conclude that differences in offers exist between the three age groups.

Gender: F = 3.66, p-value = .0576. There is not enough evidence to conclude that differences in offers exist between males and females

Interaction: F = .44, p-value = .6418. There is not enough evidence to conclude that age and gender interact.

15.77a $H_0 : \mu_1 = \mu_2 = \mu_3$

   H_1 : At least two means differ.

ANOVA						
Source of Variation	SS	df	MS	F	P-value	F crit
Between Groups	1769.49	2	884.74	136.58	0.0000	3.02
Within Groups	2409.81	372	6.48			
Total	4179.30	374				

F = 136.58, p-value = 0. There is sufficient evidence to infer that differences exist between the effects of the three teaching approaches.

b

Multiple Comparisons				
			LSD	Omega
Treatment	Treatment	Difference	Alpha = 0.0167	Alpha = 0.05
Whole Language	Embedded	-0.856	0.774	0.754
	Pure	-4.976	0.774	0.754
Embedded	Pure	-4.120	0.774	0.754

All three means differ from one another. From the sample means we may infer that the pure method is best, followed by embedded, and by whole-language.

15.78a $H_0 : \mu_1 = \mu_2 = \mu_3$

   H_1 : At least two means differ.

ANOVA						
Source of Variation	SS	df	MS	F	P-value	F crit
Between Groups	1913.4	2	956.70	9.54	0.0002	3.10
Within Groups	8726.6	87	100.31			
Total	10640.0	89				

F = 9.54, p-value = .0002. There is sufficient evidence to infer that there are differences between the three groups.

b

Multiple Comparisons				
			LSD	Omega
Treatment	Treatment	Difference	Alpha = 0.0167	Alpha = 0.05
Mozart	*White noise*	-9.30	6.31	6.14
	Glass	-10.20	6.31	6.14
White noise	*Glass*	-0.90	6.31	6.14

The mean time of the Mozart group differs from the mean times of white noise and the Glass groups.

15.79 $H_0 : \mu_1 = \mu_2 = \mu_3 = \mu_4$

H_1 : At least two means differ.

ANOVA						
Source of Variation	*SS*	*df*	*MS*	*F*	*P-value*	*F crit*
Between Groups	5990284	3	1996761	14.47	0.0000	2.64
Within Groups	40024172	290	138014			
Total	46014456	293				

F = 14.47, p-value = 0. There is enough evidence to infer differences in debt levels between the four types of degrees.

15.80 $H_0 : \mu_1 = \mu_2 = \mu_3 = \mu_4$

H_1 : At least two means differ.

ANOVA						
Source of Variation	*SS*	*df*	*MS*	*F*	*P-value*	*F crit*
Between Groups	3263.41	3	1087.80	10.26	0.0000	2.64
Within Groups	29684.97	280	106.02			
Total	32948.39	283				

F = 10.26, p-value = 0. There is enough evidence of differences between the four groups of investors.

15.81 $H_0 : \mu_1 = \mu_2 = \mu_3 = \mu_4$

H_1 : At least two means differ.

ANOVA						
Source of Variation	SS	df	MS	F	P-value	F crit
Between Groups	3006.79	3	1002.26	13.84	0.0000	2.67
Within Groups	10576.04	146	72.44			
Total	13582.83	149				

F = 13.84, p-value = 0. There is enough evidence to infer that the length of time depends on the size of the party

15.82 $H_0 : \mu_1 = \mu_2 = \mu_3 = \mu_4$

H_1 : At least two means differ.

ANOVA						
Source of Variation	SS	df	MS	F	P-value	F crit
Between Groups	2.12	3	0.705	9.17	0.0000	2.69
Within Groups	7.99	104	0.0769			
Total	10.11	107				

F = 9.17, p-value = 0. There is sufficient evidence to infer that there are differences in changes to the TSE depending on the loss the previous day.

15.83 $H_0 : \mu_1 = \mu_2 = \mu_3$

H_1 : At least two means differ.

ANOVA						
Source of Variation	SS	df	MS	F	P-value	F crit
Between Groups	1.57	2	0.787	1.62	0.2022	3.09
Within Groups	46.98	97	0.484			
Total	48.55	99				

F = 1.62, p-value = .2022. There is no evidence to infer that at least one buy indicator is useful.

Case 15.1

Revenue growth

ANOVA						
Source of Variation	SS	df	MS	F	P-value	F crit
Between Groups	26902	2	13451	12.86	0.0000	3.13
Within Groups	73221	70	1046			
Total	100122	72				

F = 12.86, p-value = 0. There is sufficient evidence to infer that there are differences in revenue growth between the different levels of planning.

Net income growth

ANOVA						
Source of Variation	SS	df	MS	F	P-value	F crit
Between Groups	4616	2	2308	2.82	0.0666	3.13
Within Groups	57365	70	819			
Total	61981	72				

F = 2.82, p-value = .0666. There is not enough evidence to infer that there are differences in net income growth between the different levels of planning.

Present value growth

ANOVA						
Source of Variation	SS	df	MS	F	P-value	F crit
Between Groups	32801	2	16400	12.92	0.0000	3.13
Within Groups	88836	70	1269			
Total	121637	72				

F = 12.92, p-value = 0. There is sufficient evidence to infer that there are differences in present value growth between the different levels of planning.

CEO cash compensation growth

ANOVA						
Source of Variation	SS	df	MS	F	P-value	F crit
Between Groups	32830	2	16415	19.41	0.0000	3.13
Within Groups	59204	70	846			
Total	92035	72				

F = 19.41, p-value = 0. There is sufficient evidence to infer that there are differences in CEO cash compensation growth between the different levels of planning.

Case 15.2

Profit-to Sales Ratio, Levels of Diversification

ANOVA						
Source of Variation	SS	df	MS	F	P-value	F crit
Between Groups	169.78	2	84.89	6.69	0.0016	3.04
Within Groups	2359.25	186	12.68			
Total	2529.03	188				

F = 6.69, p-value = .0016. There is sufficient evidence to infer that there are differences in profit-to-sales ratio between the three levels of diversification.

Profit-to Assets Ratio, Levels of Diversification

ANOVA						
Source of Variation	SS	df	MS	F	P-value	F crit
Between Groups	185.15	2	92.57	4.85	0.0088	3.04
Within Groups	3546.81	186	19.07			
Total	3731.96	188				

F = 4.85, p-value = .0088. There is sufficient evidence to infer that there are differences in profit-to-assets ratio between the three levels of diversification.

Profit-to Sales Ratio, Degrees of Internationalization

ANOVA						
Source of Variation	SS	df	MS	F	P-value	F crit
Between Groups	43.12	4	10.78	0.80	0.5280	2.42
Within Groups	2485.91	184	13.51			
Total	2529.03	188				

F = .80, p-value = .5280. There is no evidence to infer that there are differences in profits-to-sales ratio between the five levels of internationalization.

Profit-to Assets Ratio, Degrees of Internationalization

ANOVA						
Source of Variation	SS	df	MS	F	P-value	F crit
Between Groups	21.53	4	5.38	0.27	0.8989	2.42
Within Groups	3710.43	184	20.17			
Total	3731.96	188				

F = .27, p-value = .8989. There is no evidence to infer that there are differences in profits-to-assets ratio between the five levels of internationalization.

Chapter 16

16.1 $H_0 : p_1 = .1, \ p_2 = .2, \ p_3 = .3, \ p_4 = .2, \ p_5 = .2$

H_1 : At least one p_i is not equal to its specified value.

Cell i	f_i	e_i	$(f_i - e_i)$	$(f_i - e_i)^2 / e_i$
1	24	$300(.1) = 30$	-6	1.20
2	64	$300(.2) = 60$	4	.27
3	84	$300(.3) = 90$	-6	.40
4	72	$300(.2) = 60$	12	2.40
5	56	$300(.2) = 60$	-4	.27
Total	300	300		$\chi^2 = 4.54$

Rejection region: $\chi^2 > \chi^2_{\alpha, k-1} = \chi^2_{.01, 4} = 13.2767$

$\chi^2 = 4.54$, p-value = .3386 (Excel). There is enough evidence to infer that at least one p_i is not equal to its specified value.

16.2 $H_0 : p_1 = .1, \ p_2 = .2, \ p_3 = .3, \ p_4 = .2, \ p_5 = .2$

H_1 : At least one p_i is not equal to its specified value.

Cell i	f_i	e_i	$(f_i - e_i)$	$(f_i - e_i)^2 / e_i$
1	12	$150(.1) = 15$	-3	.60
2	32	$150(.2) = 30$	2	.13
3	42	$150(.3) = 45$	-3	.20
4	36	$150(.2) = 30$	6	1.20
5	28	$150(.2) = 30$	-2	.13
Total	150	150		$\chi^2 = 2.26$

Rejection region: $\chi^2 > \chi^2_{\alpha, k-1} = \chi^2_{.01, 4} = 13.2767$

$\chi^2 = 2.26$, p-value = .6868 (Excel). There is not enough evidence to infer that at least one p_i is not equal to its specified value.

16.3 $H_0: p_1 = .1, \ p_2 = .2, \ p_3 = .3, \ p_4 = .2, \ p_5 = .2$

   H_1 : At least one p_i is not equal to its specified value.

Cell i	f_i	e_i	$(f_i - e_i)$	$(f_i - e_i)^2 / e_i$
1	6	$75(.1) = 7.5$	-1.5	.30
2	16	$75(.2) = 15$	1	.07
3	21	$75(.3) = 22.5$	-1.5	.10
4	18	$75(.2) = 15$	3	.60
5	14	$70(.2) = 15$	-1	.07
Total	75	75		$\chi^2 = 1.14$

Rejection region: $\chi^2 > \chi^2_{\alpha, k-1} = \chi^2_{.01,4} = 13.2767$

$\chi^2 = 1.14$, p-value = .8889 (Excel). There is not enough evidence to infer that at least one p_i is not equal to its specified value.

16.4 The χ^2 statistic decreases.

16.5 $H_0: p_1 = .3, \ p_2 = .3, \ p_3 = .2, \ p_4 = .2$

   H_1 : At least one p_i is not equal to its specified value.

Cell i	f_i	e_i	$(f_i - e_i)$	$(f_i - e_i)^2 / e_i$
1	38	$150(.3) = 45$	-7	1.09
2	50	$150(.3) = 45$	5	0.56
3	38	$150(.2) = 30$	8	2.13
4	24	$150(.2) = 30$	-6	1.20
Total	150	150		$\chi^2 = 4.98$

Rejection region: $\chi^2 > \chi^2_{\alpha, k-1} = \chi^2_{.05,3} = 7.81473$

$\chi^2 = 4.98$, p-value = .1734 (Excel). There is not enough evidence to infer that at least one p_i is not equal to its specified value.

16.6　　$H_0 : p_1 = .3, \; p_2 = .3, \; p_3 = .2, \; p_4 = .2$

H_1 : At least one p_i is not equal to its specified value.

Cell i	f_i	e_i	$(f_i - e_i)$	$(f_i - e_i)^2 / e_i$
1	76	$300(.3) = 90$	-14	2.18
2	100	$300(.3) = 90$	10	1.11
3	76	$300(.2) = 60$	16	4.27
4	48	$300(.2) = 60$	-12	2.40
Total	300	300		$\chi^2 = 9.96$

Rejection region: $\chi^2 > \chi^2_{\alpha, k-1} = \chi^2_{.05,3} = 7.81473$

$\chi^2 = 9.96$, p-value = .0189 (Excel). There is enough evidence to infer that at least one p_i is not equal to its specified value.

16.7　　$H_0 : p_1 = .2, \; p_2 = .2, \; p_3 = .2, \; p_4 = .2, \; p_5 = .2$

H_1 : At least one p_i is not equal to its specified value.

Cell i	f_i	e_i	$(f_i - e_i)$	$(f_i - e_i)^2 / e_i$
1	28	$100(.2) = 20$	8	3.20
2	17	$100(.2) = 20$	-3	0.45
3	19	$100(.2) = 20$	-1	0.05
4	17	$100(.2) = 20$	-3	0.45
5	19	$100(.2) = 20$	-1	0.05
Total	100	100		$\chi^2 = 4.20$

Rejection region: $\chi^2 > \chi^2_{\alpha, k-1} = \chi^2_{10,4} = 7.77944$

$\chi^2 = 4.20$, p-value = .3796 (Excel). There is not enough evidence to infer that at least one p_i is not equal to its specified value.

16.8 $H_0 : p_1 = .15, \; p_2 = .40, \; p_3 = .35, \; p_4 = .10$

H_1 : At least one p_i is not equal to its specified value.

Cell i	f_i	e_i	$(f_i - e_i)$	$(f_i - e_i)^2 / e_i$
1	41	$233(.15) = 34.95$	6.05	1.05
2	107	$233(.40) = 93.20$	13.80	2.04
3	66	$233(.35) = 81.55$	-15.55	2.97
4	19	$233(.10) = 23.30$	-4.30	0.79
Total	233	233		$\chi^2 = 6.85$

Rejection region: $\chi^2 > \chi^2_{\alpha, k-1} = \chi^2_{.05,3} = 7.81473$

$\chi^2 = 6.85$, p-value = .0769 (Excel). There is not enough evidence to infer that at least one p_i is not equal to its specified value.

16.9 $H_0 : p_1 = 1/6, \; p_2 = 1/6, \; p_3 = 1/6, \; p_4 = 1/6, \; p_5 = 1/6, \; p_6 = 1/6$

H_1 : At least one p_i is not equal to its specified value.

Cell i	f_i	e_i	$(f_i - e_i)$	$(f_i - e_i)^2 / e_i$
1	114	$600(1/6) = 100$	14	1.96
2	92	$600(1/6) = 100$	-8	0.64
3	84	$600(1/6) = 100$	-16	2.56
4	101	$600(1/6) = 100$	1	0.01
5	107	$600(1/6) = 100$	7	0.49
6	102	$600(1/6) = 100$	2	0.04
Total	600	600		$\chi^2 = 5.70$

Rejection region: $\chi^2 > \chi^2_{\alpha, k-1} = \chi^2_{.05,5} = 11.0705$

$\chi^2 = 5.70$, p-value = .3365 (Excel). There is not enough evidence to infer that the die is not fair.

16.10　$H_0: p_1 = .05,\ p_2 = .25\ p_3 = .40,\ p_4 = .25\ p_5 = .05$

H_1 : At least one p_i is not equal to its specified value.

Cell i	f_i	e_i	$(f_i - e_i)$	$(f_i - e_i)^2 / e_i$
1	11	$150(.05) = 7.5$	3.5	1.63
2	32	$150(.25) = 37.5$	-5.5	0.81
3	62	$150(.40) = 60.0$	2.0	0.07
4	29	$150(.25) = 37.5$	-8.5	1.93
5	16	$150(.05) = 7.5$	8.5	9.63
Total	150	150		$\chi^2 = 14.07$

Rejection region: $\chi^2 > \chi^2_{\alpha, k-1} = \chi^2_{.05,4} = 9.48773$

$\chi^2 = 14.07$, p-value = .0071 (Excel). There is enough evidence to infer that grades are distributed differently from grades in the past.

16.11　$H_0: p_1 = .2,\ p_2 = .2\ p_3 = .2,\ p_4 = .2\ p_5 = .2$

H_1 : At least one p_i is not equal to its specified value.

Cell i	f_i	e_i	$(f_i - e_i)$	$(f_i - e_i)^2 / e_i$
1	8	$25(.2) = 5.0$	3.0	1.80
2	4	$25(.2) = 5.0$	-1.0	0.20
3	3	$25(.2) = 5.0$	-2.0	0.80
4	8	$25(.2) = 5.0$	3.0	1.80
5	2	$25(.2) = 5.0$	-3.0	1.80
Total	25	25		$\chi^2 = 6.40$

Rejection region: $\chi^2 > \chi^2_{\alpha, k-1} = \chi^2_{.10,4} = 7.77944$

$\chi^2 = 6.40$, p-value = .1712 (Excel). There is not enough evidence to infer that the professor does not randomly distribute the correct answer over the five choices.

16.12 $H_0: p_1 = .72, \ p_2 = .15, \ p_3 = .10, \ p_4 = .03$

H_1 : At least one p_i is not equal to its specified value.

Cell i	f_i	e_i	$(f_i - e_i)$	$(f_i - e_i)^2 / e_i$
1	159	250(.72) = 180.0	-21.0	2.45
2	28	250(.15) = 37.5	-9.5	2.41
3	47	250(.10) = 25.0	22.0	19.36
4	16	250(.03) = 7.5	8.5	9.63
Total	250	250		$\chi^2 = 33.85$

Rejection region: $\chi^2 > \chi^2_{\alpha,k-1} = \chi^2_{.05,3} = 7.81473$

$\chi^2 = 33.85$, p-value = 0 (Excel). There is enough evidence to infer that the aging schedule has changed.

16.13 $H_0: p_1 = .15, \ p_2 = .25, \ p_3 = .40, \ p_4 = .20$

H_1 : At least one p_i is not equal to its specified value.

Cell i	f_i	e_i	$(f_i - e_i)$	$(f_i - e_i)^2 / e_i$
1	36	250(.15) = 29.55	6.45	1.41
2	58	250(.25) = 49.25	8.75	1.55
3	74	250(.40) = 78.80	-4.80	0.29
4	29	250(.20) = 39.40	-10.40	2.75
Total	197	197		$\chi^2 = 6.00$

Rejection region: $\chi^2 > \chi^2_{\alpha,k-1} = \chi^2_{.05,3} = 7.81473$

$\chi^2 = 6.00$, p-value = .1116 (Excel). There is not enough evidence to infer that certain sizes of cars are involved in a higher than expected percentage of accidents.

16.14 $H_0: p_1 = .31, \ p_2 = .51, \ p_3 = .18$

H_1 : At least one p_i is not equal to its specified value.

Cell i	f_i	e_i	$(f_i - e_i)$	$(f_i - e_i)^2 / e_i$
1	408	1200(.31) = 372	36	3.48
2	571	1200(.51) = 612	-41	2.75
3	221	1200(.18) = 216	5	0.12
Total	1200	1200		$\chi^2 = 6.35$

Rejection region: $\chi^2 > \chi^2_{\alpha,k-1} = \chi^2_{.10,2} = 4.60517$

$\chi^2 = 6.35$, p-value = .0419 (Excel). There is enough evidence to infer that voter support has changed since the election.

16.15　　$H_0 : p_1 = .05, \ p_2 = .07, \ p_3 = .04, \ p_4 = .84$

H_1 : At least one p_i is not equal to its specified value.

Cell i	f_i	e_i	$(f_i - e_i)$	$(f_i - e_i)^2 / e_i$
1	19	250(.05) = 12.5	6.5	3.38
2	23	250(.07) = 17.5	5.5	1.73
3	14	250(.04) = 10.0	4.0	1.60
4	194	250(.84) = 210.0	-16.0	1.22
Total	250	250		$\chi^2 = 7.93$

Rejection region: $\chi^2 > \chi^2_{\alpha, k-1} = \chi^2_{.05,3} = 7.81473$

$\chi^2 = 7.93$, p-value = .0475 (Excel). There is enough evidence to infer that the reported side effects of the placebo differ from that of the cold remedy.

16.16　　$H_0 : p_1 = .23, \ p_2 = .40, \ p_3 = .15, \ p_4 = .22$

H_1 : At least one p_i is not equal to its specified value.

Cell i	f_i	e_i	$(f_i - e_i)$	$(f_i - e_i)^2 / e_i$
1	63	320(.23) = 73.6	-10.6	1.53
2	125	320(.40) = 128.0	-3.0	0.07
3	45	320(.15) = 48.0	-3.0	0.19
4	87	320(.22) = 70.4	16.6	3.91
Total	320	320		$\chi^2 = 5.70$

Rejection region: $\chi^2 > \chi^2_{\alpha, k-1} = \chi^2_{.05,3} = 7.81473$

$\chi^2 = 5.70$, p-value = .1272 (Excel). There is not enough evidence to infer that there has been a change in proportions.

16.17 H_0 : The two variables are independent

       H_1 : The two variables are dependent

Cell i	f_i	e_i	$(f_i - e_i)$	$(f_i - e_i)^2 / e_i$
1	28	96(84)/188 = 42.89	-14.89	5.17
2	68	96(104)/188 = 53.11	14.89	4.17
3	56	92(84)/188 = 41.11	14.89	5.40
4	36	92(104)/188 = 50.89	-14.89	4.36
Total	188	188		$\chi^2 = 19.10$

Rejection region: $\chi^2 > \chi^2_{\alpha,(r-1)(c-1)} = \chi^2_{.05,1} = 3.84146$

$\chi^2 = 19.10$, p-value = 0 (Excel). There is enough evidence to infer that the two variables are dependent.

16.18 H_0 : The two variables are independent

       H_1 : The two variables are dependent

Cell i	f_i	e_i	$(f_i - e_i)$	$(f_i - e_i)^2 / e_i$
1	14	48(42)/188 = 21.45	-7.45	2.59
2	34	48(52)/188 = 26.55	7.45	2.09
3	28	46(42)/188 = 20.55	7.45	2.70
4	18	46(52)/188 = 25.45	-7.45	2.18
Total	94	94		$\chi^2 = 9.56$

Rejection region: $\chi^2 > \chi^2_{\alpha,(r-1)(c-1)} = \chi^2_{.05,1} = 3.84146$

$\chi^2 = 9.56$, p-value = .0020 (Excel). There is enough evidence to infer that the two classifications L and M are dependent.

16.19 H_0 : The two variables are independent

       H_1 : The two variables are dependent

Cell i	f_i	e_i	$(f_i - e_i)$	$(f_i - e_i)^2 / e_i$
1	7	24(21)/188 = 10.72	-3.72	1.29
2	17	24(26)/188 = 13.28	3.72	1.04
3	14	23(21)/188 = 10.28	3.72	1.35
4	9	23(26)/188 = 12.72	-3.72	1.09
Total	47	47		$\chi^2 = 4.77$

Rejection region: $\chi^2 > \chi^2_{\alpha,(r-1)(c-1)} = \chi^2_{.05,1} = 3.84146$

$\chi^2 = 4.77$, p-value = .0289 (Excel). There is enough evidence to infer that the two classifications L and M are dependent.

16.20 The χ^2 statistic decreases.

16.21 H_0 : The two variables are independent

        H_1 : The two variables are dependent

Cell i	f_i	e_i	$(f_i - e_i)$	$(f_i - e_i)^2 / e_i$
1	40	120(70)/250 = 33.60	6.40	1.22
2	32	120(80)/250 = 38.40	- 6.40	1.07
3	48	120(100)/250 = 48.00	0	0.00
4	30	130(70)/250 = 36.40	-6.40	1.13
5	48	130(80)/250 = 41.60	6.40	0.99
6	52	130(100)/250 = 52.00	0	0.00
Total	250	250		$\chi^2 = 4.41$

Rejection region: $\chi^2 > \chi^2_{\alpha,(r-1)(c-1)} = \chi^2_{.10,2} = 4.60517$

$\chi^2 = 4.41$, p-value = .1110 (Excel). There is not enough evidence to infer that the two classifications R and C are dependent.

16.22 H_0 : The two variables are independent

        H_1 : The two variables are dependent

Cell i	f_i	e_i	$(f_i - e_i)$	$(f_i - e_i)^2 / e_i$
1	67	110(130)/200 = 71.50	-4.50	0.28
2	32	110(50)/200 = 27.50	4.50	0.74
3	11	110(20)/200 = 11.00	0	0.00
4	63	90(130)/200 = 58.50	4.50	0.35
5	18	90(50)/200 = 22.50	-4.50	0.90
6	9	90(20)/200 = 9.00	0	0.00
Total	200	200		$\chi^2 = 2.27$

Rejection region: $\chi^2 > \chi^2_{\alpha,(r-1)(c-1)} = \chi^2_{.10,2} = 4.60517$

$\chi^2 = 2.27$, p-value $= .3221$ (Excel). There is not enough evidence to infer that responses differ among the three groups of employees.

16.23　H_0 : The two variables are independent

H_1 : The two variables are dependent

Cell i	f_i	e_i	$(f_i - e_i)$	$(f_i - e_i)^2 / e_i$
1	240	$570(250)/600 = 237.5$	2.5	0.03
2	191	$570(200)/600 = 190.0$	1.0	0.01
3	139	$570(150)/600 = 142.5$	-3.5	0.09
4	10	$30(250)/600 = 12.5$	-2.5	0.50
5	9	$30(200)/600 = 10.0$	-1.0	0.10
6	11	$30(150)/600 = 7.5$	3.5	1.63
Total	600	600		$\chi^2 = 2.36$

Rejection region: $\chi^2 > \chi^2_{\alpha,(r-1)(c-1)} = \chi^2_{.05,2} = 5.99147$

$\chi^2 = 2.36$, p-value $= .3087$ (Excel). There is not enough evidence to infer that there are differences in quality among the three shifts.

16.24　H_0 : The two variables are independent

H_1 : The two variables are dependent

Cell i	f_i	e_i	$(f_i - e_i)$	$(f_i - e_i)^2 / e_i$
1	101	$444(331)/1000 = 146.96$	-45.96	14.376
2	282	$444(557)/1000 = 233.99$	48.01	9.852
3	61	$444(142)/1000 = 63.05$	-2.05	0.067
4	38	$130(331)/1000 = 43.03$	-5.03	0.588
5	67	$130(557)/1000 = 68.51$	-1.51	0.033
6	25	$130(142)/1000 = 18.46$	6.54	2.317
7	131	$250(331)/1000 = 82.75$	48.25	28.134
8	88	$250(557)/1000 = 131.75$	-43.75	14.528
9	31	$250(142)/1000 = 35.50$	-4.50	0.570
10	61	$176(331)/1000 = 58.26$	2.74	0.129
11	90	$176(557)/1000 = 92.75$	-2.75	0.082
12	25	$176(142)/1000 = 24.99$	0.01	0.000
Total	1000	1000		$\chi^2 = 70.675$

Rejection region: $\chi^2 > \chi^2_{\alpha,(r-1)(c-1)} = \chi^2_{.01,6} = 16.8119$

$\chi^2 = 70.675$, p-value = 0 (Excel). There is sufficient evidence to infer that political affiliation affects support for economic options.

16.25 H_0 : The two variables are independent

H_1 : The two variables are dependent

Contingency Table					
	Program				
Thinking		1	2	3	TOTAL
	1	50	15	8	73
	2	11	42	25	78
	TOTAL	61	57	33	151
	chi-squared Stat			46.3668	
	df			2	
	p-value			0	
	chi-squared Critical			5.9915	

Rejection region: $\chi^2 > \chi^2_{\alpha,(r-1)(c-1)} = \chi^2_{.05,2} = 5.99147$

$\chi^2 = 46.3668$, p-value = 0. There is enough evidence to infer that commercials viewed during happy television programs have a different effect than those viewed during sad television programs.

16.26 H_0 : The two variables are independent

H_1 : The two variables are dependent

Contingency Table					
	Drug				
Outcome		1	2	3	TOTAL
	1	60	31	12	103
	2	65	22	13	100
	TOTAL	125	53	25	203
	chi-squared Stat			1.7243	
	df			2	
	p-value			0.4222	
	chi-squared Critical			5.9915	

Rejection region: $\chi^2 > \chi^2_{\alpha,(r-1)(c-1)} = \chi^2_{.05,2} = 5.99147$

$\chi^2 = 1.7243$, p-value = .4222. There is not enough evidence to infer that there are differences in outcomes for the children treated by the two drugs.

16.27 H_0 : The two variables are independent

H_1 : The two variables are dependent

Contingency Table				
	Smoker			
Read		1	2	3	TOTAL
	1	33	24	19	76
	2	23	17	26	66
	3	16	27	46	89
	4	14	38	57	109
	TOTAL	86	106	148	340
	chi-squared Stat			31.476	
	df			6	
	p-value			0	
	chi-squared Critical			12.5916	

Rejection region: $\chi^2 > \chi^2_{\alpha,(r-1)(c-1}} = \chi^2_{.05,6} = 12.5916$

$\chi^2 = 31.476$, p-value = 0. There is sufficient enough evidence to infer that the antismoking campaign has reason to be concerned.

16.28a H_0 : The two variables are independent

H_1 : The two variables are dependent

Contingency Table				
	Predicted			
Actual		1	2	TOTAL
	1	65	64	129
	2	39	48	87
	TOTAL	104	112	216
	chi-squared Stat		0.6434	
	df		1	
	p-value		0.4225	
	chi-squared Critical		3.8415	

Rejection region: $\chi^2 > \chi^2_{\alpha,(r-1)(c-1}} = \chi^2_{.05,1} = 3.84146$

$\chi^2 = .6434$, p-value = .4225. There is not enough evidence to infer that the predicted and actual directions of change are related.

b Ignore the what the other investors are doing.

16.29 H_0 : The two variables are independent

H_1 : The two variables are dependent

Contingency Table				
	Education			
Smoker		1	2	TOTAL
	1	34	23	57
	2	251	212	463
	3	159	248	407
	4	16	57	73
	TOTAL	460	540	1000
	chi-squared Stat			41.7645
	df			3
	p-value			0
	chi-squared Critical			7.8147

Rejection region: $\chi^2 > \chi^2_{\alpha,(r-1)(c-1)} = \chi^2_{.05,3} = 7.81473$

$\chi^2 = 41.7645$, p-value = 0. There is sufficient evidence to infer that the amount of education is a factor in determining whether a smoker will quit.

16.30 H_0 : The two variables are independent

H_1 : The two variables are dependent

Contingency Table					
	Segment				
Employment		1	2	3	TOTAL
	1	157	44	217	418
	2	219	53	264	536
	3	256	102	524	882
	TOTAL	632	199	1005	1836
	chi-squared Stat		23.0946		
	df		4		
	p-value		0.0001		
	chi-squared Critical		9.4877		

Rejection region: $\chi^2 > \chi^2_{\alpha,(r-1)(c-1)} = \chi^2_{.05,4} = 9.48773$

$\chi^2 = 23.0946$, p-value = .0001. There is sufficient evidence to infer that there are differences in employment status between the market segments.

16.31 H_0 : The two variables are independent

H_1 : The two variables are dependent

Contingency Table					
	Segment				
Value		1	2	3	TOTAL
	1	147	135	136	418
	2	221	155	160	536
	3	339	254	289	882
	TOTAL	707	544	585	1836
	chi-squared Stat			4.5122	
	df			4	
	p-value			0.3411	
	chi-squared Critical			9.4877	

Rejection region: $\chi^2 > \chi^2_{\alpha,(r-1)(c-1)} = \chi^2_{.05,4} = 9.48773$

$\chi^2 = 4.5122$, p-value = .3411. There is insufficient evidence to infer that there are differences in values definition between the three market segments.

16.32 H_0 : The two variables are independent

H_1 : The two variables are dependent

Contingency Table						
	Group					
Education		1	2	3	4	TOTAL
	1	31	62	72	104	269
	2	55	157	143	129	484
	3	39	83	74	45	241
	4	74	107	51	24	256
	TOTAL	199	409	340	302	1250
	chi-squared Stat			108.9699		
	df			9		
	p-value			0		
	chi-squared Critical			16.919		

Rejection region: $\chi^2 > \chi^2_{\alpha,(r-1)(c-1)} = \chi^2_{.05,9} = 16.9190$

$\chi^2 = 108.9699$, p-value = 0. There is sufficient evidence to infer that there are differences in educational levels between the market segments.

16.33 H_0 : The two variables are independent

       H_1 : The two variables are dependent

Contingency Table						
	Approach					
Degree		1	2	3	4	TOTAL
	1	51	8	5	11	75
	2	24	14	12	8	58
	3	26	9	19	8	62
	TOTAL	101	31	36	27	195
	chi-squared Stat		20.8929			
	df		6			
	p-value		0.0019			
	chi-squared Critical		12.5916			

Rejection region: $\chi^2 > \chi^2_{\alpha,(r-1)(c-1)} = \chi^2_{.05,6} = 12.5916$

$\chi^2 = 20.8929$, p-value $= .0019$. There is sufficient evidence to infer that there are differences in teaching approach among the four types of degree. The editor can design books and sales campaigns based on the distribution of degrees.

16.34 H_0 : The data are normally distributed

       H_1 : The data are not normally distributed

Interval	Probability	Expected Value e_i	Observed Value f_i	$f_i - e_i$	$(f_i - e_i)^2 / e_i$
$Z \leq -1.5$	.0668	6.68	10	3.32	1.65
$-1.5 < Z \leq -0.5$	.2417	24.17	18	-6.17	1.58
$-0.5 < Z \leq 0.5$	.3829	38.29	48	9.71	2.46
$0.5 < Z \leq 1.5$	.2417	24.17	16	-8.17	2.76
$Z > 1.5$	.0668	6.68	8	1.32	0.26
Total	1	100	100		$\chi^2 = 8.71$

Rejection region: $\chi^2 > \chi^2_{\alpha,k-3} = \chi^2_{.05,2} = 5.99147$

$\chi^2 = 8.71$, p-value $= .0128$ (Excel). There is enough evidence to infer that the data are not normally distributed.

16.35 H_0 : The data are normally distributed

       H_1 : The data are not normally distributed

Interval	Probability	Expected Value e_i	Observed Value f_i	$f_i - e_i$	$(f_i - e_i)^2 / e_i$
$Z \leq -1$	.1587	7.94	6	-1.94	0.47
$-1 < Z \leq 0$	.3413	17.07	27	9.93	5.78
$0 < Z \leq 1$	.3413	17.07	14	-3.07	0.55
$Z > 1$	.1587	7.94	3	-4.94	3.07
Total	1	50	50		$\chi^2 = 9.87$

Rejection region: $\chi^2 > \chi^2_{\alpha,k-3} = \chi^2_{.10,1} = 2.70554$

$\chi^2 = 9.87$, p-value = .0017. There is sufficient evidence to infer that the data are not normally distributed.

16.36 H_0 : Times are normally distributed

       H_1 : Times are not normally distributed.

Chi-Squared Test of Normality			
	Hours		
Mean	7.15		
Standard deviation	1.65		
Observations	200		
Intervals	Probability	Expected	Observed
(z <= -1.5)	0.0668	13.36	11
(-1.5 < z <= -0.5)	0.2417	48.35	55
(-0.5 < z <= 0.5)	0.3829	76.59	52
(0.5 < z <= 1.5)	0.2417	48.35	67
(z > 1.5)	0.0668	13.36	15
chi-squared Stat	16.6238		
df	2		
p-value	0.0002		
chi-squared Critical	5.9915		

$\chi^2 = 16.6238$, p-value = .0002. There is sufficient evidence to infer that the amount of time at part-time jobs is not normally distributed.

16.37 H_0 : Weights of discarded newspaper are normally distributed

   H_1 : Weights of discarded newspaper are not normally distributed

Chi-Squared Test of Normality			
	Weights		
Mean	2.10		
Standard deviation	0.76		
Observations	100		
Intervals	Probability	Expected	Observed
(z <= -1.5)	0.0668	6.68	8
(-1.5 < z <= -0.5)	0.2417	24.17	8
(-0.5 < z <= 0.5)	0.3829	38.29	55
(0.5 < z <= 1.5)	0.2417	24.17	25
(z > 1.5)	0.0668	6.68	4
chi-squared Stat	19.4748		
df	2		
p-value	0.0001		
chi-squared Critical	5.9915		

χ^2 = 19.4748, p-value = .0001. There is sufficient evidence to infer that the amount of discarded newspaper is not normally distributed.

16.38   Successful firms:

   H_0 : Productivity in successful firms is normally distributed

   H_1 : Productivity in successful firms is not normally distributed

Chi-Squared Test of Normality			
	Successful		
Mean	5.02		
Standard deviation	1.39		
Observations	200		
Intervals	Probability	Expected	Observed
($z <= -1.5$)	0.0668	13.36	12
($-1.5 < z <= -0.5$)	0.2417	48.35	52
($-0.5 < z <= 0.5$)	0.3829	76.59	72
($0.5 < z <= 1.5$)	0.2417	48.35	55
($z > 1.5$)	0.0668	13.36	9
chi-squared Stat	3.0288		
df	2		
p-value	0.2199		
chi-squared Critical	5.9915		

$\chi^2 = 3.0288$, p-value = .2199. There is not enough evidence to infer that productivity in successful firms is not normally distributed.

Unsuccessful firms:

H_0 : Productivity in unsuccessful firms is normally distributed

H_1 : Productivity in unsuccessful firms is not normally distributed

Chi-Squared Test of Normality			
	Unsuccessful		
Mean	7.80		
Standard deviation	3.09		
Observations	200		
Intervals	Probability	Expected	Observed
($z <= -1.5$)	0.0668	13.36	12
($-1.5 < z <= -0.5$)	0.2417	48.35	47
($-0.5 < z <= 0.5$)	0.3829	76.59	83
($0.5 < z <= 1.5$)	0.2417	48.35	44
($z > 1.5$)	0.0668	13.36	14
chi-squared Stat	1.1347		
df	2		
p-value	0.567		
chi-squared Critical	5.9915		

$\chi^2 = 1.1347$, p-value = .5670. There is not enough evidence to infer that productivity in unsuccessful firms is not normally distributed.

16.39 H_0 : Matched pairs differences of sales are normally distributed

H_1 : Matched pairs differences of sales are not normally distributed

Chi-Squared Test of Normality			
	Difference		
Mean	19.75		
Standard deviation	30.63		
Observations	40		
Intervals	Probability	Expected	Observed
(z <= -1)	0.1587	6.35	6
(-1 < z <= 0)	0.3413	13.65	14
(0 < z <= 1)	0.3413	13.65	14
(z > 1)	0.1587	6.35	6
chi-squared Stat	0.0553		
df	1		
p-value	0.814		
chi-squared Critical	2.7055		

$\chi^2 = .0553$, p-value = .8140. There is not enough evidence to infer that matched pairs difference of sales is not normally distributed.

16.40 $H_0 : p_1 = 1/3, \ p_2 = 1/3, \ p_3 = 1/3$

H_1 : At least one p_i is not equal to its specified value.

Cell i	f_i	e_i	$(f_i - e_i)$	$(f_i - e_i)^2 / e_i$
1	14	30(1/3) = 10	4	1.6
2	10	30(1/3) = 10	0	0.0
3	6	30(1/3) = 10	-4	1.6
Total	30	30		$\chi^2 = 3.2$

Rejection region: $\chi^2 > \chi^2_{\alpha,k-1} = \chi^2_{.10,2} = 4.60517$

$\chi^2 = 3.2$, p-value = .2019 (Excel). There is not enough evidence to infer that the game is unfair.

16.41 H_0 : The two variables are independent

H_1 : The two variables are dependent

	Summary	Gift	No Inducement	Total
Returned	80	100	120	300
Not returned	120	200	380	700
Total	200	300	500	1000

Cell i	f_i	e_i	$(f_i - e_i)$	$(f_i - e_i)^2 / e_i$
1	80	$300(200)/1000 = 60$	20	6.67
2	100	$300(300)/1000 = 90$	10	1.11
3	120	$300(500)/1000 = 150$	-30	6.00
4	120	$700(200)/1000 = 140$	-20	2.86
5	200	$700(300)/1000 = 210$	-10	0.50
6	380	$700(500)/1000 = 350$	30	2.57
Total	1000	1000		$\chi^2 = 19.71$

Rejection region: $\chi^2 > \chi^2_{\alpha,(r-1)(c-1} = \chi^2_{.05,2} = 5.99147$

Conclusion: $\chi^2 = 19.71$, p-value = 0. There is sufficient evidence to infer that the return rates differ among the different inducements.

16.42 $H_0 : p_1 = .2, \; p_2 = .2, \; p_3 = .2, \; p_4 = .2, \; p_5 = .2$

H_1 : At least one p_i is not equal to its specified value.

Cell i	f_i	e_i	$(f_i - e_i)$	$(f_i - e_i)^2 / e_i$
1	87	$362(.2) = 72.4$	14.6	2.94
2	62	$362(.2) = 72.4$	-10.4	1.49
3	71	$362(.2) = 72.4$	-1.4	0.03
4	68	$362(.2) = 72.4$	-4.4	0.27
5	74	$362(.2) = 72.4$	1.6	0.04
Total	362	362		$\chi^2 = 4.77$

Rejection region: $\chi^2 > \chi^2_{\alpha,k-1} = \chi^2_{.05,4} = 9.48773$

Conclusion: $\chi^2 = 4.77$, p-value = .3119 (Excel). There is not enough evidence to infer that absenteeism is higher on some days of the week.

16.43 H_0 : The two variables are independent

H_1 : The two variables are dependent

Cell i	f_i	e_i	$(f_i - e_i)$	$(f_i - e_i)^2 / e_i$
1	52	181(87)/362 = 43.50	8.50	1.66
2	28	181(62)/362 = 31.00	-3.00	0.29
3	37	181(71)/362 = 35.50	-1.50	0.06
4	31	181(68)/362 = 34.00	-3.00	0.27
5	33	181(74)/362 = 37.00	-4.00	0.43
6	35	181(87)/362 = 43.50	-8.50	1.66
7	34	181(62)/362 = 31.00	3.00	0.29
8	34	181(71)/362 = 35.50	-1.50	0.06
9	37	181(68)/362 = 34.00	3.00	0.26
10	41	181(74)/362 = 37.00	4.00	0.43
Total	362	362		$\chi^2 = 5.41$

Rejection region: $\chi^2 > \chi^2_{\alpha,(r-1)(c-1)} = \chi^2_{.10,4} = 7.77944$

Conclusion: $\chi^2 = 5.41$, p-value = .2465 (Excel). There is not enough evidence to infer that there is a relationship between the days an employee is absent and the shift on which the employee works.

16.44 H_0 : The two variables are independent

H_1 : The two variables are dependent

Cell i	f_i	e_i	$(f_i - e_i)$	$(f_i - e_i)^2 / e_i$
1	21	171(91)/447 = 34.81	-13.81	5.48
2	25	171(122)/447 = 46.67	-21.67	10.06
3	54	171(114)/447 = 43.61	10.39	2.48
4	71	171(120)/447 = 45.91	25.09	13.72
5	39	176(91)/447 = 35.83	3.17	0.28
6	49	176(122)/447 = 48.04	0.96	0.02
7	50	176(114)/447 = 44.89	5.11	0.58
8	38	176(120)/447 = 47.25	-9.25	1.81
9	31	100(91)/447 = 20.36	10.64	5 56
10	48	100(122)/447 = 27.29	20.71	15.71
11	10	100(114)/447 = 25.50	-15.50	9.42
12	11	100(120)/447 = 26.85	-15.85	9.35
Total	447	447		$\chi^2 = 74.47$

Rejection region: $\chi^2 > \chi^2_{\alpha,(r-1)(c-1)} = \chi^2_{.05,6} = 12.5916$

Conclusion: $\chi^2 = 74.47$, p-value = 0 (Excel). There is sufficient evidence to infer that the level of job satisfaction depends on boss/employee gender relationship.

16.45a H_0 : The two variables (sport and year) are independent

     H_1 : The two variables are dependent

Contingency Table				
	Sport			
Year		1	2	TOTAL
	1	116	122	238
	2	119	92	211
	3	29	58	87
	4	52	39	91
	5	48	34	82
	6	16	33	49
	7	26	29	55
	8	24	21	45
	9	70	72	142
	TOTAL	500	500	1000
	chi-squared Stat			23.8101
	df			8
	p-value			0.0025
	chi-squared Critical			15.5073

$\chi^2 = 23.8101$, p-value = .0025. There is enough evidence to infer that North Americans changed their favorite sport between 1985 and 1993.

b $H_0 : (p_1 - p_2) = 0$

        $H_1 : (p_1 - p_2) \neq 0$

$$z = \frac{(\hat{p}_1 - \hat{p}_2)}{\sqrt{\hat{p}(1-\hat{p})\left(\frac{1}{n_1} + \frac{1}{n_2}\right)}} = \frac{(.238 - .184)}{\sqrt{(.211)(1-.211)\left(\frac{1}{500} + \frac{1}{500}\right)}} = 2.09, \text{ p-value} = .0364$$

Rejection region: $z < -z_{\alpha/2} = -1.96$ or $z > z_{\alpha/2} = z_{.025} = 1.96$

z-Test: Two Proportions			
		Year:1985	Year:1993
Sample Proportions		0.238	0.184
Observations		500	500
Hypothesized Difference		0	
z Stat		2.09	
P(Z<=z) one tail		0.0182	
z Critical one-tail		1.6449	
P(Z<=z) two-tail		0.0364	
z Critical two-tail		1.96	

$z = 2.09$, p-value $= .0364$. There is enough evidence to infer that the popularity of baseball has changed.

16.46 H_0 : The two variables are independent

H_1 : The two variables are dependent

Contingency Table						
	Quit					
Method		1	2	3	4	TOTAL
	1	104	125	32	49	310
	2	14	17	5	9	45
	TOTAL	118	142	37	58	355
	chi-squared Stat			0.5803		
	df			3		
	p-value			0.9009		
	chi-squared Critical			7.8147		

$\chi^2 = .5803$, p-value $= .9009$. There is not enough evidence to infer that the four methods differ in their success rates.

16.47 H_0 : The two variables are independent

H_1 : The two variables are dependent

Contingency Table						
	Section					
Education		1	2	3	4	TOTAL
	1	4	21	31	14	70
	2	27	32	18	2	79
	3	1	20	42	22	85
	4	10	44	22	3	79
	TOTAL	42	117	113	41	313
	chi-squared Stat			86.6154		
	df			9		
	p-value			0		
	chi-squared Critical			16.919		

$\chi^2 = 86.6154$, p-value = 0. There is sufficient evidence to infer that educational level affects the way adults read the newspaper.

16.48a The expected frequency is 1/49.

b $H_0 : p_1 = 1/49, \ p_2 = 1/49, \ldots, \ p_{49} = 1/49$

    H_1 : At least one p_i is not equal to its specified value.

Number i	f_i	e_i	$(f_i - e_i)$	$(f_i - e_i)^2 / e_i$
1	5	312(1/49) = 6.37	-1.38	0.29
2	6	312(1/49) = 6.37	-0.38	0.02
3	7	312(1/49) = 6.37	0.63	0.06
.		.		
.		.		
.		.		
47	6	312(1/49) = 6.37	-0.37	0.02
48	10	312(1/49) = 6.37	3.63	2.07
49	6	312(1/49) = 6.37	-0.37	0.02
Total	312	312		$\chi^2 = 38.22$

Conclusion: $\chi^2 = 38.22$, p-value = .8427 (Excel). There is not enough evidence to infer that the numbers were not generated randomly.

16.49 H_0 : The two variables are independent

        H_1 : The two variables are dependent

Contingency Table							
	RRSP						
Income		1	2	3	4	5	TOTAL
	1	18	41	32	20	4	115
	2	6	16	40	21	7	90
	TOTAL	24	57	72	41	11	205
	chi-squared Stat			15.8838			
	df			4			
	p-value			0.0032			
	chi-squared Critical			9.4877			

$\chi^2 = 15.8838$, p-value = .0032. There is enough evidence to infer that there are differences in RRSP positions among the five income brackets.

16.50 Binomial probabilities with n = 5 and p = .5: $P(X = 0) = .0313$, $P(X = 1) = .1563$, $P(X = 2) = .3125$, $P(X = 3) = .3125$, $P(X = 4) = .1563$, $P(X = 5) = .0313$

$H_0: p_0 = .0313, p_1 = .1563, p_2 = .3125, p_3 = .3125, p_4 = .1563, p_5 = .0313$

$H_1:$ At least one p_i is not equal to its specified value.

Cell i	f_i	e_i	$(f_i - e_i)$	$(f_i - e_i)^2 / e_i$
0	8	200(.0313) = 6.26	1.74	0.48
1	35	200(.1563) = 31.26	3.74	0.45
2	57	200(.3125) = 62.50	-5.50	0.48
3	69	200(.3125) = 62.50	6.50	0.68
4	28	200(.1563) = 31.26	-3.26	0.34
5	3	200(.0313) = 6.26	-3.26	1.70
Total	200	200		$\chi^2 = 4.13$

$\chi^2 = 4.13$, p-value = .5310 (Excel). There is not enough evidence to infer that at the number of boys in families with 5 children is not a binomial random variable with p =.5.

16.51 H_0 : The two variables are independent

H_1 : The two variables are dependent

Contingency Table			
	Group		
Cold		1	2	TOTAL
	1	17	11	28
	2	12	13	25
	3	9	18	27
	4	16	18	34
	TOTAL	54	60	114
	chi-squared Stat		4.139
	df		3
	p-value		0.2468
	chi-squared Critical		7.8147

$\chi^2 = 4.139$, p-value = .2468. There is not enough evidence to infer there are differences between the four groups.

16.52 H_0 : The two variables are independent

H_1 : The two variables are dependent

Contingency Table			
	Results		
Financial		1	2	TOTAL
	1	29	1	30
	2	10	7	17
	3	9	14	23
	TOTAL	48	22	70
	chi-squared Stat		20.9881
	df		2
	p-value		0
	chi-squared Critical		5.9915

$\chi^2 = 20.9881$, p-value = 0. There is sufficient evidence to infer that the research findings are related to whether drug companies fund the research.

16.53 H_0 : The two variables are independent

H_1 : The two variables are dependent

Contingency Table						
	Newspaper					
Occupation		1	2	3	4	TOTAL
	1	36	4	30	8	78
	2	63	7	73	10	153
	3	29	164	23	43	259
	4	58	49	41	55	203
	TOTAL	186	224	167	116	693
	chi-squared Stat			274.62		
	df			9		
	p-value			0		
	chi-squared Critical			16.919		

$\chi^2 = 274.62$, p-value = 0. There is sufficient evidence to infer that the readership of the four daily newspapers differs in terms of the occupation of their readers.

16.54 H_0 : The two variables are independent

H_1 : The two variables are dependent

Contingency Table				
	Group			
Improvement		1	2	TOTAL
	1	42	8	50
	2	32	18	50
	3	13	37	50
	TOTAL	87	63	150
	chi-squared Stat			35.6322
	df			2
	p-value			0
	chi-squared Critical			5.9915

$\chi^2 = 35.6322$, p-value = 0. There is sufficient evidence to infer there are differences between the three groups.

Case 16.1　　H_0 : The two variables are independent

H_1 : The two variables are dependent

Contingency Table						
	Early					
Game (Early)		1	2	3	4	TOTAL
	1	57	15	33	23	128
	2	132	65	40	52	289
	TOTAL	189	80	73	75	417
	chi-squared Stat			12.6165		
	df			3		
	p-value			0.0055		
	chi-squared Critical			7.8147		

$\chi^2 = 12.6165$, p-value = .0055. There is enough evidence to infer that there are differences among the four professional sports in terms of whether early-game leaders win the game.

Contingency Table						
	Late					
Game (Late)		1	2	3	4	TOTAL
	1	39	6	21	15	81
	2	150	86	72	65	373
	TOTAL	189	92	93	80	454
	chi-squared Stat			10.5184		
	df			3		
	p-value			0.0146		
	chi-squared Critical			7.8147		

$\chi^2 = 10.5184$, p-value = .0146. There is enough evidence to infer that there are differences among the four professional sports in terms of whether late-game leaders win the game.

Case 16.2 H_0 : The two variables are independent

H_1 : The two variables are dependent

Question 1

Contingency Table				
	Question 1			
Acc/Non		1	2	TOTAL
	1	24	41	65
	2	44	91	135
	TOTAL	68	132	200
	chi-squared Stat			0.3667
	df			1
	p-value			0.5448
	chi-squared Critical			3.8415

χ^2 = .3667, p-value = .5448. There is not enough evidence to infer that the answers to Question 1 and the type of business student are related.

Question 2

Contingency Table				
	Question 2			
Acc/Non		1	2	TOTAL
	1	66	122	188
	2	2	10	12
	TOTAL	68	132	200
	chi-squared Stat			1.7092
	df			1
	p-value			0.1911
	chi-squared Critical			3.8415

χ^2 = 1.7092, p-value = .1911. There is not enough evidence to infer that the answers to Question 2 and the type of business student are related.

Question 3

Contingency Table				
	Question 3			
Acc/Non		1	2	TOTAL
	1	44	96	140
	2	24	36	60
	TOTAL	68	132	200
	chi-squared Stat			1.3751
	df			1
	p-value			0.2409
	chi-squared Critical			3.8415

$\chi^2 = 1.3751$, p-value = .2409. There is not enough evidence to infer that the answers to Question 3 and the type of business student are related.

Question 4

Contingency Table				
	Question 4			
Acc/Non		1	2	TOTAL
	1	3	10	13
	2	34	44	78
	3	31	78	109
	TOTAL	68	132	200
	chi-squared Stat			5.3892
	df			2
	p-value			0.0676
	chi-squared Critical			5.9915

$\chi^2 = 5.3892$, p-value = .0676. There is not enough evidence to infer that the answers to Question 4 and the type of business student are related.

Question 5

Contingency Table				
	Question 5			
Acc/Non		1	2	TOTAL
	1	24	56	80
	2	33	61	94
	3	3	3	6
	4	8	12	20
	TOTAL	68	132	200
	chi-squared Stat			1.627
	df			3
	p-value			0.6533
	chi-squared Critical			7.8147

$\chi^2 = 1.627$, p-value = .6533. There is not enough evidence to infer that the answers to Question 5 and the type of business student are related.

Question 6

Contingency Table				
	Question 6			
Acc/Non		1	2	TOTAL
	1	18	45	63
	2	35	57	92
	3	7	12	19
	4	3	9	12
	5	5	9	14
	TOTAL	68	132	200
	chi-squared Stat			2.0175
	df			4
	p-value			0.7325
	chi-squared Critical			9.4877

$\chi^2 = 2.0175$, p-value = .7325. There is not enough evidence to infer that the answers to Question 6 and the type of business student are related.

Chapter 17

17.1 & 17.2 H_0 : The two population locations are the same

         H_1 : The location of population 1 is different from the location of population 2

$$E(T) = \frac{n_1(n_1 + n_2 + 1)}{2} = \frac{15(15 + 15 + 1)}{2} = 232.5$$

$$\sigma_T = \sqrt{\frac{n_1 n_2 (n_1 + n_2 + 1)}{12}} = \sqrt{\frac{(15)(15)(15 + 15 + 1)}{12}} = 24.11$$

17.1 $z = \dfrac{T - E(T)}{\sigma_T} = \dfrac{250 - 232.5}{24.11} = .73$, p-value $= 2P(Z > .73) = 2(.5 - .2673) = .4654.$

17.2 $z = \dfrac{T - E(T)}{\sigma_T} = \dfrac{275 - 232.5}{24.11} = 1.76$, p-value $= 2P(Z > 1.76) = 2(.5 - .4608) = .0784.$

17.3 The value of the test statistic increases and the p-value decreases.

17.4 & 17.5 H_0 : The two population locations are the same

         H_1 : The location of population 1 is to the right of the location of population 2

Rejection region: $z > z_\alpha = z_{.01} = 2.33$

$$E(T) = \frac{n_1(n_1 + n_2 + 1)}{2} = \frac{30(30 + 40 + 1)}{2} = 1065$$

$$\sigma_T = \sqrt{\frac{n_1 n_2 (n_1 + n_2 + 1)}{12}} = \sqrt{\frac{(30)(40)(30 + 40 + 1)}{12}} = 84.26$$

17.4 $z = \dfrac{T - E(T)}{\sigma_T} = \dfrac{1205 - 1065}{84.26} = 1.66$, p-value $= P(Z > 1.66) = .5 - .4515 = .0485.$ There is not

enough evidence to infer that the location of population 1 is to the right of the location of population 2.

17.5 $z = \dfrac{T - E(T)}{\sigma_T} = \dfrac{1065 - 1065}{84.26} = 0$, p-value $= P(Z > 0) = .5.$ There is not enough evidence to infer

that the location of population 1 is to the right of the location of population 2.

17.6 The value of the test statistic decreases and the p-value increases.

17.7 H_0 : The two population locations are the same

   H_1 : The location of population 1 is to the left of the location of population 2

Rejection region: T $\leq T_L = 19$

Sample 1	Rank	Sample 2	Rank
75	5	90	9
60	1	72	3
73	4	103	10
66	2	82	8
81	7	78	6
	$T_1 = 19$		$T_2 = 36$

There is enough evidence to infer that the location of population 1 is to the left of the location of population 2.

17.8 H_0 : The two population locations are the same

   H_1 : The location of population 1 is different from the location of population 2

Rejection region: T $\geq T_U = 127$ or T $\leq T_L = 83$

Sample 1	Rank	Sample 2	Rank
15	4.0	8	2.0
7	1.0	27	18.0
22	14.0	17	7.0
20	.5	25	16.0
32	20.0	20	11.5
18	9.5	16	5.0
26	17.0	21	13.0
17	7.0	17	7.0
23	15.0	10	3.0
30	19.0	18	9.5
	$T_1 = 118$		$T_2 = 92$

There is not enough evidence to infer that the location of population 1 is different from the location of population 2.

17.9 H_0 : The two population locations are the same

        H_1 : The location of population 1 is to the left of the location of population 2

Wilcoxon Rank Sum Test			
		Rank Sum	Observations
New		623.5	25
Leading		651.5	25
z Stat		-0.27	
P(Z<=z) one-tail		0.3929	
z Critical one-tail		1.6449	
P(Z<=z) two-tail		0.7858	
z Critical two-tail		1.96	

z = -.27, p-value = .3929. There is not enough evidence to infer that the new beer is less highly rated than the leading brand.

17.10 The printout is identical to that of Exercise 17.9.

17.11 All codes that preserve the order produce the same results.

17.12 H_0 : The two population locations are the same

        H_1 : The location of population 1 is different from the location of population 2

Wilcoxon Rank Sum Test			
		Rank Sum	Observations
Business		4004	40
Economy		8086	115
z Stat		3.61	
P(Z<=z) one-tail		0.0002	
z Critical one-tail		1.6449	
P(Z<=z) two-tail		0.0004	
z Critical two-tail		1.96	

z = 3.61, p-value = .0004. There is enough evidence to infer that the business and economy class differ in their degree of satisfaction.

17.13 The printout is identical to that of Exercise 17.12.

17.14 All codes that preserve the order produce the same results.

17.15 H_0 : The two population locations are the same

   H_1 : The location of population 1 is to the right of the location of population 2

Wilcoxon Rank Sum Test			
		Rank Sum	Observations
New		276.5	15
Aspirin		188.5	15
z Stat		1.83	
P(Z<=z) one-tail		0.034	
z Critical one-tail		1.6449	
P(Z<=z) two-tail		0.068	
z Critical two-tail		1.96	

z = 1.83, p-value = .0340. There is enough evidence to infer that the new painkiller is more effective than aspirin.

17.16 The results are identical because the codes in this exercise and in Example 17.2 are ranked identically.

17.17 H_0 : The two population locations are the same

   H_1 : The location of population 1 is to the right of the location of population 2

Rejection region: $z > z_\alpha = z_{.05} = 1.645$

$$E(T) = \frac{n_1(n_1 + n_2 + 1)}{2} = \frac{82(82 + 75 + 1)}{2} = 6478$$

$$\sigma_T = \sqrt{\frac{n_1 n_2 (n_1 + n_2 + 1)}{12}} = \sqrt{\frac{(82)(75)(82 + 75 + 1)}{12}} = 284.6$$

$$z = \frac{T - E(T)}{\sigma_T} = \frac{6807 - 6478}{284.6} = 1.16,\ \text{p-value} = P(Z > 1.16) = .5 - .3770 = .1230.\ \text{There is not enough}$$

evidence to infer that members of the Mathematics department rate nonparametric techniques as more important than do members of other departments.

17.18 H_0 : The two population locations are the same

   H_1 : The location of population 1 is to the left of the location of population 2

Rejection region: $z < -z_\alpha = -z_{.05} = -1.645$

$$E(T) = \frac{n_1(n_1 + n_2 + 1)}{2} = \frac{30(30 + 30 + 1)}{2} = 915$$

$$\sigma_T = \sqrt{\frac{n_1 n_2 (n_1 + n_2 + 1)}{12}} = \sqrt{\frac{(30)(30)(30 + 30 + 1)}{12}} = 67.6$$

$$z = \frac{T - E(T)}{\sigma_T} = \frac{797 - 915}{67.6} = -1.75$$, p-value = P(Z < -1.75) = .5 - .4599 = .0401. There is enough

evidence to infer that companies that provide exercise programs should be given discounts.

17.19 H_0 : The two population locations are the same

H_1 : The location of population 1 is to the left of the location of population 2

Rejection region: $z < -z_\alpha = -z_{.05} = -1.645$

$$E(T) = \frac{n_1(n_1 + n_2 + 1)}{2} = \frac{125(125 + 125 + 1)}{2} = 15,687.5$$

$$\sigma_T = \sqrt{\frac{n_1 n_2 (n_1 + n_2 + 1)}{12}} = \sqrt{\frac{(125)(125)(125 + 125 + 1)}{12}} = 571.7$$

$$z = \frac{T - E(T)}{\sigma_T} = \frac{14,873 - 15,687.5}{571.7} = -1.42$$, p-value = P(Z < - 1.42) = .5 - .4222 = .0778. There is not

enough evidence to infer that women are doing less housework today than last year.

17.20 H_0 : The two population locations are the same

H_1 : The location of population 1 is to the right of the location of population 2

Rejection region: $z > z_\alpha = z_{.10} = 1.28$

$$E(T) = \frac{n_1(n_1 + n_2 + 1)}{2} = \frac{100(100 + 100 + 1)}{2} = 10,050$$

$$\sigma_T = \sqrt{\frac{n_1 n_2 (n_1 + n_2 + 1)}{12}} = \sqrt{\frac{(100)(100)(100 + 100 + 1)}{12}} = 409.3$$

$$z = \frac{T - E(T)}{\sigma_T} = \frac{10,691 - 10,050}{409.3} = 1.57$$, p-value = P(Z > 1.57) = .5 - .4418 = .0582. There is enough

evidence to conclude that public support has decreased between this year and last year.

17.21 H_0 : The two population locations are the same

H_1 : The location of population 1 is different from the location of population 2

Rejection region: $z < -z_{\alpha/2} = -z_{.025} = -1.96$ or $z > z_{\alpha/2} = z_{.025} = 1.96$

$$E(T) = \frac{n_1(n_1 + n_2 + 1)}{2} = \frac{50(50 + 50 + 1)}{2} = 2525$$

$$\sigma_T = \sqrt{\frac{n_1 n_2 (n_1 + n_2 + 1)}{12}} = \sqrt{\frac{(50)(50)(50 + 50 + 1)}{12}} = 145.1$$

$z = \dfrac{T - E(T)}{\sigma_T} = \dfrac{2810 - 2525}{145.1} = 1.964$, p-value = 2P(Z > 1.964), which is slightly less than 2P(Z >

1.96) = 2(.5 - .4750) = .05. There is enough evidence to infer that men and women experience

different levels of stomach upset.

17.22 H_0 : The two population locations are the same

       H_1 : The location of population 1 is to the right of the location of population 2

Rejection region: $z > z_\alpha = z_{.05} = 1.645$

$$E(T) = \dfrac{n_1(n_1 + n_2 + 1)}{2} = \dfrac{15(15 + 25 + 1)}{2} = 307.5$$

$$\sigma_T = \sqrt{\dfrac{n_1 n_2 (n_1 + n_2 + 1)}{12}} = \sqrt{\dfrac{(15)(25)(15 + 25 + 1)}{12}} = 35.8$$

$z = \dfrac{T - E(T)}{\sigma_T} = \dfrac{383.5 - 307.55}{35.8} = 2.12$, p-value = P(Z > 2.12) = .5 - .4830 = .0170. There is enough

evidence to infer that Tastee is superior.

17.23 H_0 : The two population locations are the same

       H_1 : The location of population 1 is to the right of the location of population 2

Rejection region: $z > z_\alpha = z_{.10} = 1.28$

$$E(T) = \dfrac{n_1(n_1 + n_2 + 1)}{2} = \dfrac{20(20 + 20 + 1)}{2} = 410$$

$$\sigma_T = \sqrt{\dfrac{n_1 n_2 (n_1 + n_2 + 1)}{12}} = \sqrt{\dfrac{(20)(20)(20 + 20 + 1)}{12}} = 37.0$$

$z = \dfrac{T - E(T)}{\sigma_T} = \dfrac{439.5 - 410}{37.0} = .80$, p-value = P(Z > .80) = .5 - .2881 = .2119. There is not enough

evidence to infer that women perceive another woman wearing a size 6 dress as more professional

than one wearing a size 14 dress.

17.24 H_0 : The two population locations are the same

       H_1 : The location of population 1 is to the left of the location of population 2

Rejection region: $z < -z_\alpha = -z_{.05} = -1.645$

$$E(T) = \dfrac{n_1(n_1 + n_2 + 1)}{2} = \dfrac{125(125 + 125 + 1)}{2} = 15,687.5$$

$$\sigma_T = \sqrt{\dfrac{n_1 n_2 (n_1 + n_2 + 1)}{12}} = \sqrt{\dfrac{(125)(125)(125 + 125 + 1)}{12}} = 571.7$$

$z = \dfrac{T - E(T)}{\sigma_T} = \dfrac{13,078 - 15,687.5}{571.7} = -4.56$, p-value = P(Z < -4.46) = 0. There is enough evidence to infer that changing the name of prunes to dried plums will increase the likelihood that shoppers will buy.

17.25 H_0 : The two population locations are the same

H_1 : The location of population 1 is different from the location of population 2

Rejection region: $z < -z_{\alpha/2} = -z_{.025} = -1.96$ or $z > z_{\alpha/2} = z_{.025} = 1.96$

$E(T) = \dfrac{n_1(n_1 + n_2 + 1)}{2} = \dfrac{182(182 + 163 + 1)}{2} = 31,486$

$\sigma_T = \sqrt{\dfrac{n_1 n_2(n_1 + n_2 + 1)}{12}} = \sqrt{\dfrac{(182)(163)(182 + 163 + 1)}{12}} = 924.9$

$z = \dfrac{T - E(T)}{\sigma_T} = \dfrac{32,225.5 - 31,486}{924.9} = .80$, p-value = 2P(Z > .80) = 2(.5 - .2881) = .4238.. There is not enough evidence to infer that the night and day shifts rate the service differently.

17.26 H_0 : The two population locations are the same

H_1 : The location of population 1 is different from the location of population 2

Rejection region: $z < -z_{\alpha/2} = -z_{.025} = -1.96$ or $z > z_{\alpha/2} = z_{.025} = 1.96$

$z = \dfrac{x - .5n}{.5\sqrt{n}} = \dfrac{15 - .5(45)}{.5\sqrt{45}} = -2.24$, p-value = 2P(Z < - 2.24) = 2(.5 - .4875) = .0250. There is enough evidence to infer that the population locations differ.

17.27 H_0 : The two population locations are the same

H_1 : The location of population 1 is to the left of the location of population 2

Rejection region: $z < -z_{\alpha} = -z_{.10} = -1.28$

$z = \dfrac{x - .5n}{.5\sqrt{n}} = \dfrac{28 - .5(69)}{.5\sqrt{69}} = -1.57$, p-value = P(Z < -1.57) = .5 - .4418 = .0582. There is enough evidence to infer that the location of population 1 is to the left of the location of population 2.

17.28 H_0 : The two population locations are the same

H_1 : The location of population 1 is to the right of right of the location of population 2

Rejection region: $z > z_{\alpha} = z_{.05} = 1.645$

$$z = \frac{x - .5n}{.5\sqrt{n}} = \frac{18 - .5(30)}{.5\sqrt{30}} = 1.10, \text{ p-value} = P(Z > 1.10) = .5 - .3643 = .1357. \text{ There is not enough}$$

evidence to infer that the location of population 1 is to the right of the location of population 2.

17.29 H_0 : The two population locations are the same

H_1 : The location of population 1 is to the right of the location of population 2

Pair	A	B	Sign of Difference
1	5	3	+
2	3	2	+
3	4	4	0
4	2	3	-
5	3	3	0
6	4	1	+
7	3	3	0
8	5	4	+
9	4	2	+
10	3	5	-
11	4	1	+
12	5	2	+
13	4	2	+
14	5	3	+
15	3	2	+
16	2	2	0

Rejection region: $z > z_\alpha = z_{.01} = 2.33$

$$x = 10, n = 12, \ z = \frac{x - .5n}{.5\sqrt{n}} = \frac{10 - .5(12)}{.5\sqrt{12}} = 2.31, \text{ p-value} = P(Z > 2.31) = .5 - .4896 = .0104$$

There is not enough evidence to infer that the population 1 is located to the right of population 2.

17.30 H_0 : The two population locations are the same

H_1 : The location of population 1 is different from the location of population 2

Rejection region: $z < -z_{\alpha/2} = -z_{.025} = -1.96 \text{ or } z > z_{\alpha/2} = z_{.025} = 1.96$

$$E(T) = \frac{n(n+1)}{4} = \frac{55(56)}{4} = 770; \ \sigma_T = \sqrt{\frac{n(n+1)(2n+1)}{24}} = \sqrt{\frac{55(56)(111)}{24}} = 119.35$$

$$z = \frac{T - E(T)}{\sigma_T} = \frac{660 - 770}{119.35} = -.92, \text{ p-value} = 2P(z < -.92) = 2(.5 - .3212) = .3576. \text{ There is not enough}$$

evidence to infer that the population locations differ.

17.31 H_0 : The two population locations are the same

       H_1 : The location of population 1 is to the right of the location of population 2

Rejection region: $z > z_\alpha = z_{.01} = 2.33$

$$E(T) = \frac{n(n+1)}{4} = \frac{108(109)}{4} = 2943 \, ; \; \sigma_T = \sqrt{\frac{n(n+1)(2n+1)}{24}} = \sqrt{\frac{108(109)(217)}{24}} = 326.25$$

$z = \dfrac{T - E(T)}{\sigma_T} = \dfrac{3457 - 2943}{326.25} = 1.58$, p-value = P(Z > 1.58) = .5 - .4429 = .0571. There is not enough

evidence to conclude that population 1 is located to the right of the location of population 2.

17.32 H_0 : The two population locations are the same

       H_1 : The location of population 1 is different from the location of population 2

       Rejection region: $T \geq T_U = 19$ or $T \leq T_L = 2$

Pair	Sample 1	Sample 2	Difference	|Difference|	Ranks	
1	9	5	4	4	5.5	
2	12	10	2	2	3.5	
3	13	11	2	2	3.5	
4	8	9	-1	1		1.5
5	7	3	4	4	5.5	
6	10	9	1	1	1.5	

$$T^+ = 19.5 \quad T^- = 1.5$$

T = 19.5. There is enough evidence to infer that the population locations differ.

17.33 H_0 : The two population locations are the same

       H_1 : The location of population 1 is different from the location of population 2

       Rejection region: $T \geq T_U = 39$ or $T \leq T_L = 6$

Pair	Sample 1	Sample 2	Difference	|Difference|	Ranks	
1	18.2	18.2	0	0		
2	14.1	14.1	0	0		
3	24.5	23.6	.9	.9	6.5	
4	11.9	12.1	-.2	.2		2
5	9.5	9.5	0	0		
6	12.1	11.3	.8	.8	5	
7	10.9	9.7	1.2	1.2	8	
8	16.7	17.6	-.9	.9		6.5
9	19.6	19.4	.2	.2	2	
10	8.4	8.1	.3	.3	4	
11	21.7	21.9	-.2	.2		2
12	23.4	21.6	1.8	1.8	9	

$$T^+ = 34.5 \quad T^- = 10.5$$

T = 34.5. There is not enough evidence to conclude that the population locations differ.

17.34 H_0 : The two population locations are the same

H_1 : The location of population 1 is to the right of the location of population 2

Sign Test			
Difference			New - Leading
Positive Differences			46
Negative Differences			30
Zero Differences			24
z Stat			1.84
P(Z<=z) one-tail			0.0332
z Critical one-tail			1.6449
P(Z<=z) two-tail			0.0664
z Critical two-tail			1.96

z = 1.84, p-value = .0332. There is enough evidence to indicate that the new beer is more highly rated than the leading brand.

17.35 The printout is identical to that of Exercise 17.34.

17.36 All codes that preserve the order produce the same results.

17.37 H_0 : The two population locations are the same

H_1 : The location of population 1 is to the right of the location of population 2

Sign Test			
Difference			Brand A - Brand B
Positive Differences			21
Negative Differences			15
Zero Differences			14
z Stat			1.00
P(Z<=z) one-tail			0.1587
z Critical one-tail			1.6449
P(Z<=z) two-tail			0.3174
z Critical two-tail			1.96

z = 1.00, p-value = .1587. There is no evidence to infer that Brand A is preferred.

17.38 The printout is identical to that of Exercise 17.37.

17.39 All codes that preserve the order produce the same results.

351

17.40 H_0 : The two population locations are the same

H_1 : The location of population 1 is to the right of the location of population 2

Sign Test			
Difference			European - American
Positive Differences			18
Negative Differences			5
Zero Differences			2
z Stat			2.71
P(Z<=z) one-tail			0.0034
z Critical one-tail			1.6449
P(Z<=z) two-tail			0.0068
z Critical two-tail			1.96

z = 2.71, p-value = .0034. There is enough evidence to infer that the European car is perceived to be more comfortable.

17.41 The results are identical. All codes that preserve the order produce the same results.

17.42 & 17.43 H_0 : The two population locations are the same

H_1 : The location of population 1 is different from the location of population 2

17.42

Sign Test			
Difference			Sample 1 - Sample 2
Positive Differences			51
Negative Differences			74
Zero Differences			0
z Stat			-2.06
P(Z<=z) one-tail			0.0198
z Critical one-tail			1.6449
P(Z<=z) two-tail			0.0396
z Critical two-tail			1.96

z = -2.06, p-value = .0396. There is enough evidence to infer that the population locations differ.

17.43

Wilcoxon Signed Rank Sum Test		
Difference		Sample 1 - Sample 2
T+		3726.5
T-		4148.5
Observations (for test)		125
z Stat		-0.52
P(Z<=z) one-tail		0.3016
z Critical one-tail		1.6449
P(Z<=z) two-tail		0.6032
z Critical two-tail		1.96

z = -.52, p-value = .6032. There is not enough evidence to infer that the population locations differ.

17.44 The sign test ignores the magnitudes of the paired differences whereas the Wilcoxon signed rank sum test does not.

17.45 & 17.46 H_0 : The two population locations are the same

H_1 : The location of population 1 is different from the location of population 2

17.45

Sign Test			
Difference			Sample 1 - Sample 2
Positive Differences			19
Negative Differences			29
Zero Differences			22
z Stat			-1.44
P(Z<=z) one-tail			0.0745
z Critical one-tail			1.6449
P(Z<=z) two-tail			0.149
z Critical two-tail			1.96

z = -1.44, p-value = .1490. There is not enough evidence to infer that the population locations differ.

17.46

Wilcoxon Signed Rank Sum Test		
Difference		Sample 1 - Sample 2
T+		304
T-		872
Observations (for test)		48
z Stat		-2.91
P(Z<=z) one-tail		0.0018
z Critical one-tail		1.6449
P(Z<=z) two-tail		0.0036
z Critical two-tail		1.96

$z = -2.91$, p-value = .0036. There is enough evidence to conclude that the population locations differ.

17.47 The sign test ignores the magnitudes of the paired differences whereas the Wilcoxon signed rank sum test does not.

17.48 H_0 : The two population locations are the same

H_1 : The location of population 1 is to the left of the location of population 2

Rejection region: $z < -z_\alpha = -z_{.05} = -1.645$

$$E(T) = \frac{n(n+1)}{4} = \frac{72(72+1)}{4} = 1314 ;\ \sigma_T = \sqrt{\frac{n(n+1)(2n+1)}{24}} = \sqrt{\frac{72(72+1)(2[72]+1)}{24}} = 178.2$$

$$z = \frac{T - E(T)}{\sigma_T} = \frac{378.5 - 1314}{178.2} = -5.25,$$ p-value = $P(Z < -5.25) = 0$. There is enough evidence to infer that the drug is effective.

17.49 H_0 : The two population locations are the same

H_1 : The location of population 1 is to the left of the location of population 2

Wilcoxon Signed Rank Sum Test		
Difference		This Year - Last year
T+		62
T-		758
Observations (for test)		40
z Stat		-4.68
P(Z<=z) one-tail		0
z Critical one-tail		2.3263
P(Z<=z) two-tail		0
z Critical two-tail		2.5758

Rejection region: $z < -z_\alpha = -z_{.01} = -2.33$

$$E(T) = \frac{n(n+1)}{4} = \frac{40(40+1)}{4} = 410 \; ; \; \sigma_T = \sqrt{\frac{n(n+1)(2n+1)}{24}} = \sqrt{\frac{40(40+1)(2[40]+1)}{24}} = 74.4$$

$z = \dfrac{T - E(T)}{\sigma_T} = \dfrac{62 - 410}{74.4} = -4.68$, p-value = $P(z < -4.68) = 0$. There is enough evidence to infer that

women are doing less housework now than last year.

17.50 H_0 : The two population locations are the same

H_1 : The location of population 1 is to the right of the location of population 2

Rejection region: $z > z_\alpha = z_{.05} = 1.645$

$z = \dfrac{x - .5n}{.5\sqrt{n}} = \dfrac{60 - .5(98)}{.5\sqrt{98}} = 2.22$, p-value = $P(Z > 2.22) = .5 - .4868 = .0132$. There is enough evidence

to conclude that concern about a gasoline shortage exceeded concern about an electricity shortage.

17.51 H_0 : The two population locations are the same

H_1 : The location of population 1 is different from the location of population 2

Rejection region: $z < -z_{\alpha/2} = -z_{.025} = -1.96$ or $z > z_{\alpha/2} = z_{.025} = 1.96$

$$E(T) = \frac{n(n+1)}{4} = \frac{23(23+1)}{4} = 138 \; ; \; \sigma_T = \sqrt{\frac{n(n+1)(2n+1)}{24}} = \sqrt{\frac{23(23+1)(2[23]+1)}{24}} = 32.9$$

$z = \dfrac{T - E(T)}{\sigma_T} = \dfrac{40.5 - 138}{32.9} = -2.96$, p-value = $2P(Z < -2.96) = 2(.5 - .4985) = .0030$. There is enough

evidence of a difference between machines.

17.52 H_0 : The two population locations are the same

H_1 : The location of population 1 is to the left of the location of population 2

Rejection region: $z < -z_\alpha = -z_{.05} = -1.645$

$$E(T) = \frac{n(n+1)}{4} = \frac{26(26+1)}{4} = 175.5 \; ; \; \sigma_T = \sqrt{\frac{n(n+1)(2n+1)}{24}} = \sqrt{\frac{26(26+1)(2[26]+1)}{24}} = 39.4$$

$z = \dfrac{T - E(T)}{\sigma_T} = \dfrac{111 - 175.5}{39.4} = -1.64$, p-value = $P(z < -1.64) = .5 - .4495 = .0505$. There is not enough

evidence to infer that the swimming department has higher gross sales.

17.53 H_0 : The two population locations are the same

H_1 : The location of population 1 is to the right of the location of population 2

Rejection region: $z > z_\alpha = z_{.10} = 1.28$

$z = \dfrac{x - .5n}{.5\sqrt{n}} = \dfrac{30 - .5(38)}{.5\sqrt{38}} = 3.57$, p-value = $P(Z > 3.57) = 0$. There is enough evidence to conclude that the European brand is preferred.

17.54 H_0 : The two population locations are the same

        H_1 : The location of population 1 is to the left of the location of population 2

Rejection region: $z < -z_\alpha = -z_{.01} = -2.33$

$z = \dfrac{x - .5n}{.5\sqrt{n}} = \dfrac{5 - .5(20)}{.5\sqrt{20}} = -2.24$, p-value = $P(Z < -2.24) = .5 - .4875 = .0125$. There is not enough evidence to conclude that children feel less pain.

17.55 H_0 : The two population locations are the same

        H_1 : The location of population 1 is different from the location of population 2

Rejection region: $z < -z_{\alpha/2} = -z_{.025} = -1.96$ or $z > z_{\alpha/2} = z_{.025} = 1.96$

$E(T) = \dfrac{n(n+1)}{4} = \dfrac{25(25+1)}{4} = 162.5$; $\sigma_T = \sqrt{\dfrac{n(n+1)(2n+1)}{24}} = \sqrt{\dfrac{25(25+1)(2[25]+1)}{24}} = 37.2$

$z = \dfrac{T - E(T)}{\sigma_T} = \dfrac{190 - 162.5}{37.2} = .74$, p-value = $2P(Z > .74) = .2(5 - .2704) = .4592$. There is not enough

evidence of a difference in salary offers between men and women

17.56 H_0 : The two population locations are the same

        H_1 : The location of population 1 is to the right of the location of population 2

Sign Test			
Difference			High School 1 - High School 2
Positive Differences			32
Negative Differences			21
Zero Differences			47
z Stat			1.51
P(Z<=z) one-tail			0.0654
z Critical one-tail			1.6449
P(Z<=z) two-tail			0.1308
z Critical two-tail			1.96

Rejection region: $z > z_\alpha = z_{.05} = 1.645$

$z = \dfrac{x - .5n}{.5\sqrt{n}} = \dfrac{32 - .5(53)}{.5\sqrt{53}} = 1.51$, p-value = $P(Z > 1.51) = .5 - .4345 = .0655$. There is not enough evidence to infer that preference should be given to students for high school 1.

17.57 H_0: The two population locations are the same

H_1: The location of population 1 is to the left of the location of population 2

Rejection region: $z < -z_\alpha = -z_{.05} = -1.645$

$$E(T) = \frac{n(n+1)}{4} = \frac{39(39+1)}{4} = 390; \ \sigma_T = \sqrt{\frac{n(n+1)(2n+1)}{24}} = \sqrt{\frac{39(39+1)(2[39]+1)}{24}} = 71.7$$

$z = \dfrac{T - E(T)}{\sigma_T} = \dfrac{48 - 390}{71.7} = -4.77$, p-value $= P(Z < -4.77) = 0$. There is enough evidence to support

the belief.

17.58 H_0: The locations of all 3 populations are the same.

H_1: At least two population locations differ.

Rejection region: $H > \chi^2_{\alpha, k-1} = \chi^2_{.05, 2} = 5.99147$

$$H = \left[\frac{12}{n(n+1)} \sum \frac{T_j^2}{n_j} \right] - 3(n+1) = \left[\frac{12}{88(88+1)} \left(\frac{984^2}{23} + \frac{1502^2}{36} + \frac{1430^2}{29} \right) \right] - 3(88+1) = 1.56.$$ There is

not enough evidence to conclude that the population locations differ.

17.59 H_0: The locations of all 4 populations are the same.

H_1: At least two population locations differ.

Rejection region: $H > \chi^2_{\alpha, k-1} = \chi^2_{.01, 3} = 11.3449$

$$H = \left[\frac{12}{n(n+1)} \sum \frac{T_j^2}{n_j} \right] - 3(n+1) = \left[\frac{12}{100(100+1)} \left(\frac{1207^2}{25} + \frac{1088^2}{250} + \frac{1310^2}{25} + \frac{1445^2}{25} \right) \right] - 3(100+1) =$$

3.28. There is not enough evidence to conclude that the population locations differ.

17.60 H_0: The locations of all 3 populations are the same.

H_1: At least two population locations differ.

Rejection region: $H > \chi^2_{\alpha, k-1} = \chi^2_{.10, 2} = 4.60517$

$$H = \left[\frac{12}{n(n+1)} \sum \frac{T_j^2}{n_j} \right] - 3(n+1) = \left[\frac{12}{143(143+1)} \left(\frac{3741^2}{47} + \frac{1610^2}{29} + \frac{4945^2}{67} \right) \right] - 3(143+1) = 6.30.$$

There is enough evidence to conclude that the population locations differ.

17.61 H_0: The locations of all 3 populations are the same.

H_1: At least two population locations differ.

Rejection region: $H > \chi^2_{\alpha,k-1} = \chi^2_{.05,2} = 5.99147$

1	Rank	2	Rank	3	Rank
27	8	37	14	19	6
33	12.5	12	1.5	12	1.5
18	4.5	17	3	33	12.5
29	10	22	7	41	15.5
41	15.5	30	11	28	9
52	17			18	4.5
75	18				
$T_1 = 85.5$		$T_2 = 36.5$		$T_3 = 49$	

$$H = \left[\frac{12}{n(n+1)} \sum \frac{T_j^2}{n_j} \right] - 3(n+1) = \left[\frac{12}{18(18+1)} \left(\frac{85.5^2}{7} + \frac{36.5^2}{5} + \frac{49^2}{6} \right) \right] - 3(18+1) = 3.03, \text{ p-value} = .2195$$

(Excel). There is no evidence to conclude that at least two population locations differ.

17.62 H_0 : The locations of all 3 populations are the same.

      H_1 : At least two population locations differ.

Rejection region: $H > \chi^2_{\alpha,k-1} = \chi^2_{.05,2} = 5.99147$

1	Rank	2	Rank	3	Rank
25	10.5	19	2	27	12
15	1	21	4	25	10.5
20	3	23	8.5	22	6
22	6	22	6	29	15
23	8.5	28	13.5	28	13.5
$T_1 = 29$		$T_2 = 34$		$T_3 = 57$	

$$H = \left[\frac{12}{n(n+1)} \sum \frac{T_j^2}{n_j} \right] - 3(n+1) = \left[\frac{12}{15(15+1)} \left(\frac{29^2}{5} + \frac{34^2}{5} + \frac{57^2}{5} \right) \right] - 3(15+1) = 4.46, \text{ p-value} = .1075$$

(Excel). There is not enough evidence to conclude that at least two population locations differ.

17.63 H_0 : The locations of all 4 populations are the same.

      H_1 : At least two population locations differ.

Rejection region: $H > \chi^2_{\alpha,k-1} = \chi^2_{.05,3} = 7.81473$

1	Rank	2	Rank	3	Rank	4	Rank
39	18	31	15	13	3	50	25.5
8	2	43	22	58	32	51	27
7	1	50	25.5	16	7	55	29
21	10	57	30.5	26	11.5	28	13
14	4	54	28	44	23	57	30.5
40	19	46	24	17	8	37	16.5
42	21	26	11.5	15	5.5	41	20
15	5.5	29	14	19	9	37	16.5
$T_1 = 80.5$		$T_2 = 170.5$		$T_3 = 99$		$T_4 = 178$	

$$H = \left[\frac{12}{n(n+1)} \sum \frac{T_j^2}{n_j} \right] - 3(n+1) = \left[\frac{12}{32(32+1)} \left(\frac{80.5^2}{8} + \frac{170.5^2}{8} + \frac{99^2}{8} + \frac{178^2}{8} \right) \right] - 3(32+1) = 10.43, \text{p-value} =$$

.0153 (Excel). There is enough evidence to conclude that at least two population locations differ.

17.64 H_0 : The locations of all 4 populations are the same.

       H_1 : At least two population locations differ.

Kruskal-Wallis Test		
Group	Rank Sum	Observations
Printer 1	4889.5	50
Printer 2	5350	50
Printer 3	4864.5	50
Printer 4	4996	50
H Stat		0.899
df		3
p-value		0.8257
chi-squared Critical		7.8147

H = .899, p-value = .8257. There is not enough evidence to conclude that differences exist between the ratings of the four printings.

17.65 The printout is identical to that of Exercise 17.64.

17.66 All codes that preserve the order produce the same results.

17.67 H_0 : The locations of all 4 populations are the same.

       H_1 : At least two population locations differ.

Kruskal-Wallis Test		
Group	Rank Sum	Observations
4:00-mid	186.5	10
Mid-8:00	156	10
8:00-4:00	122.5	10
H Stat		2.6445
df		2
p-value		0.2665
chi-squared Critical		5.9915

H = 2.64, p-value = .2665. There is not enough evidence of a difference in ratings between the three shifts.

17.68 All codes that preserve the order produce the same results.

17.69 H_0 : The locations of all 3 populations are the same.

H_1 : At least two population locations differ.

Rejection region: $H > \chi^2_{\alpha,k-1} = \chi^2_{.05,2} = 5.99147$

$$H = \left[\frac{12}{n(n+1)} \sum_{j=1}^{k} \frac{T_j^2}{n_j} \right] - 3(n+1) = \frac{12}{75(75+1)} \left(\frac{767.5^2}{25} + \frac{917^2}{25} + \frac{1165^2}{25} \right) - 3(75+1) = 6.81, \text{p-value} =$$

.0333 (Excel). There is enough evidence to infer that there are differences in student satisfaction

between the teaching methods.

17.70 H_0 : The locations of all 4 populations are the same.

H_1 : At least two population locations differ.

Rejection region: $H > \chi^2_{\alpha,k-1} = \chi^2_{.05,3} = 7.81473$

$$H = \left[\frac{12}{n(n+1)} \sum_{j=1}^{k} \frac{T_j^2}{n_j} \right] - 3(n+1)$$

$$= \frac{12}{401(401+1)} \left(\frac{17,116.5^2}{80} + \frac{16,816.5^2}{90} + \frac{17,277^2}{77} + \frac{29,391^2}{154} \right) - 3(401+1) = 6.65, \text{p-value} = .0838$$

(Excel). There is not enough evidence to infer that there are differences between the four groups of

GMAT scores.

17.71 H_0 : The locations of all 4 populations are the same.

H_1 : At least two population locations differ.

Rejection region: $H > \chi^2_{\alpha,k-1} = \chi^2_{.05,3} = 7.81473$

$$H = \left[\frac{12}{n(n+1)} \sum_{j=1}^{k} \frac{T_j^2}{n_j} \right] - 3(n+1) = \frac{12}{132(132+1)} \left(\frac{2195^2}{33} + \frac{1650.5^2}{34} + \frac{2830^2}{34} + \frac{2102.5^2}{31} \right) - 3(132+1)$$

= 14.04, p-value = .0029 (Excel). There is enough evidence to conclude that there are differences in

grading standards between the four high schools.

17.72a The one-way analysis of variance and the Kruskal-Wallis test should be considered.

b H_0 : The locations of all 4 populations are the same.

        H_1 : At least two population locations differ.

Rejection region: $H > \chi^2_{\alpha,k-1} = \chi^2_{.05,3} = 7.81473$

$$H = \left[\frac{12}{n(n+1)} \sum_{j=1}^{k} \frac{T_j^2}{n_j} \right] - 3(n+1) = \frac{12}{200(200+1)} \left(\frac{4180^2}{50} + \frac{5262^2}{50} + \frac{5653^2}{50} + \frac{5005^2}{50} \right) - 3(200+1) =$$

6.96, p-value = .0733 (Excel). There is not enough evidence to infer that differences exist between the speeds at which the four brands perform.

17.73 H_0 : The locations of all 3 populations are the same.

        H_1 : At least two population locations differ.

Rejection region: $H > \chi^2_{\alpha,k-1} = \chi^2_{.05,2} = 5.99147$

$$H = \left[\frac{12}{n(n+1)} \sum_{j=1}^{k} \frac{T_j^2}{n_j} \right] - 3(n+1) = \frac{12}{90(90+1)} \left(\frac{1565^2}{30} + \frac{1358.5^2}{30} + \frac{1171.5^2}{30} \right) - 3(90+1) = 3.78, \text{p-}$$

value = .1507 (Excel). There is not enough evidence to infer that Democrat's ratings of their chances changed over the 3-month period.

17.74 H_0 : The locations of all 4 populations are the same.

        H_1 : At least two population locations differ.

Rejection region: $H > \chi^2_{\alpha,k-1} = \chi^2_{.05,3} = 7.81473$

$$H = \left[\frac{12}{n(n+1)} \sum_{j=1}^{k} \frac{T_j^2}{n_j} \right] - 3(n+1)$$

$$= \frac{12}{400(400+1)} \left(\frac{21,246^2}{100} + \frac{19,784^2}{100} + \frac{20,976^2}{100} + \frac{18,194^2}{100} \right) - 3(400+1) = 4.34, \text{p-value} = .2269 \text{ (Excel)}.$$

There is not enough evidence to infer that differences in believability exist between the four ads.

17.75 H_0 : The locations of all 4 populations are the same.

        H_1 : At least two population locations differ.

Rejection region: $H > \chi^2_{\alpha,k-1} = \chi^2_{.05,3} = 7.81473$

$$H = \left[\frac{12}{n(n+1)} \sum_{j=1}^{k} \frac{T_j^2}{n_j} \right] - 3(n+1)$$

$$= \frac{12}{428(428+1)} \left(\frac{28,304^2}{123} + \frac{21,285^2}{109} + \frac{21,796^2}{102} + \frac{20,421^2}{94} \right) - 3(428+1) = 4.64, \text{p-value} = .1999$$

(Excel). There is not enough evidence to infer that there are differences in support between the four levels of students.

17.76 H_0 : The locations of all 5 populations are the same.

       H_1 : At least two population locations differ.

Rejection region: $H > \chi_{\alpha,k-1}^2 = \chi_{.05,4}^2 = 9.48773$

$$H = \left[\frac{12}{n(n+1)} \sum_{j=1}^{k} \frac{T_j^2}{n_j} \right] - 3(n+1)$$

$$= \frac{12}{133(133+1)} \left(\frac{638.5^2}{18} + \frac{1233.5^2}{14} + \frac{1814.5^2}{26} + \frac{3159.5^2}{42} + \frac{2065^2}{33} \right) - 3(133+1) = 18.73, \text{p-value} =$$

.0009 (Excel). There is enough evidence to infer that differences in perceived ease of use between the five brands of scanners.

17.77 H_0 : The locations of all 4 populations are the same.

       H_1 : At least two population locations differ.

Rejection region: $F_r > \chi_{\alpha,k-1}^2 = \chi_{.10,3}^2 = 6.25139$

			Treatment					
Block	1	Rank	2	Rank	3	Rank	4	Rank
1	10	2	12	3	15	4	9	1
2	8	2	10	3	11	4	6	1
3	13	2	14	3	16	4	11	1
4	9	1.5	9	1.5	12	3	13	4
5	7	1	8	2	14	4	10	3
		$T_1 = 8.5$		$T_2 = 12.5$		$T_3 = 19$		$T_4 = 10$

$$F_r = \left[\frac{12}{b(k)(k+1)} \sum_{j=1}^{k} T_j^2 \right] - 3b(k+1) = \left[\frac{12}{(5)(4)(5)} (8.5^2 + 12.5^2 + 19^2 + 10^2) \right] - 3(5)(5) = 7.74, \text{p-value}$$

$= .0517$ (Excel). There is enough evidence to infer that at least two population locations differ.

17.78 H_0 : The locations of all 3 populations are the same.

       H_1 : At least two population locations differ.

Rejection region: $F_r > \chi^2_{\alpha,k-1} = \chi^2_{.05,2} = 5.99147$

		Treatment				
Block	1	Rank	2	Rank	3	Rank
1	7.3	2	6.9	1	8.4	3
2	8.2	3	7.0	1	7.3	2
3	5.7	1	6.0	2	8.1	3
4	6.1	1	6.5	2	9.1	3
5	5.9	1	6.1	2	8.0	3
	$T_1 = 8$		$T_2 = 8$		$T_3 = 14$	

$$F_r = \left[\frac{12}{b(k)(k+1)}\sum_{j=1}^{k}T_j^2\right] - 3b(k+1) = \left[\frac{12}{(5)(3)(4)}(8^2 + 8^2 + 14^2)\right] - 3(5)(4) = 4.8, \text{ p-value} = .0907$$

(Excel). There is not enough evidence to infer that at least two population locations differ.

17.79 H_0: The locations of all 4 populations are the same.

H_1: At least two population locations differ.

Rejection region: $F_r > \chi^2_{\alpha,k-1} = \chi^2_{.05,3} = 7.81473$

		Orange Juice Brand						
Judge	1	Rank	2	Rank	3	Rank	4	Rank
1	3	1.5	5	4	4	3	3	1.5
2	2	1	3	2	5	4	4	3
3	4	3	4	3	3	1	4	3
4	3	2	4	3	5	4	2	1
5	2	1	4	3.5	4	3.5	3	2
6	4	2	5	3.5	5	3.5	3	1
7	3	1.5	3	1.5	4	3.5	4	3.5
8	2	1	3	3	3	3	3	3
9	4	2.5	3	1	5	4	4	2.5
10	2	1	4	3	5	4	3	2
	$T_1 = 16.5$		$T_2 = 27.5$		$T_3 = 33.5$		$T_4 = 22.5$	

$$F_r = \left[\frac{12}{b(k)(k+1)}\sum_{j=1}^{k}T_j^2\right] - 3b(k+1) = \left[\frac{12}{(10)(4)(5)}(16.5^2 + 27.5^2 + 33.5^2 + 22.5^2)\right] - 3(10)(5) = 9.42,$$

p-value = .0242 (Excel). There is enough evidence to infer that differences in sensory perception exist between the four brands of orange juice.

17.80a The randomized block experimental design of the analysis of variance and the Friedman test.

b H_0: The locations of all 3 populations are the same.

H_1: At least two population locations differ.

363

Rejection region: $F_r > \chi^2_{\alpha, k-1} = \chi^2_{.05, 2} = 5.99147$

Job Advertised	Newspaper 1	Rank	2	Rank	3	Rank
Receptionist	14	2	17	3	12	1
Systems analyst	8	2	9	3	6	1
Junior secretary	25	3	20	1	23	2
Computer programmer	12	2	15	3	10	1
Legal secretary	7	2	10	3	5	1
Office manager	5	2	9	3	4	1
	$T_1 = 13$		$T_2 = 16$		$T_3 = 7$	

$$F_r = \left[\frac{12}{b(k)(k+1)} \sum_{j=1}^{k} T_j^2 \right] - 3b(k+1) = \left[\frac{12}{(6)(3)(4)} (13^2 + 16^2 + 7^2) \right] - 3(6)(4) = 7.00, \text{ p-value} = .0302$$

(Excel). There is enough evidence to infer that differences exist between the newspapers.

17.81 H_0 : The locations of all 4 populations are the same.

   H_1 : At least two population locations differ.

Friedman Test	
Group	Rank Sum
Brand A	65
Brand B	65
Brand C	85
Brand D	85
Fr Stat	8
df	3
p-value	0.046
chi-squared Critical	7.8147

$F_r = 8.00$, p-value $= .0460$. There is enough evidence to infer that differences exist between the ratings of the four brands of coffee.

17.82 Printout is identical to that of Exercise 17.81.

17.83 Different codes produce identical results provided the codes are in order.

17.84 H_0 : The locations of all 4 populations are the same.

   H_1 : At least two population locations differ.

Friedman Test		
Group		Rank Sum
Manager 1		21
Manager 2		10
Manager 3		24.5
Manager 4		24.5
Fr Stat		10.613
df		3
p-value		0.014
chi-squared Critical		7.8147

$F_r = 10.613$, p-value = .0140. There is enough evidence to infer that differences exist between the ratings of the four managers.

17.85 The results are identical because the codes are in order.

17.86 H_0 : The locations of all 3 populations are the same.

H_1 : At least two population locations differ.

Rejection region: $F_r > \chi^2_{\alpha,k-1} = \chi^2_{.05,2} = 5.99147$

$$F_r = \left[\frac{12}{b(k)(k+1)} \sum_{j=1}^{k} T_j^2 \right] - 3b(k+1) = \left[\frac{12}{(20)(3)(4)} (33^2 + 39.5^2 + 47.5^2) \right] - 3(20)(4) = 5.28, \text{ p-value} =$$

.0715 (Excel). There is not enough evidence to infer that there are differences in the ratings of the three recipes.

17.87a The randomized block experiment of the analysis of variance and the Friedman test should be considered. The analysis of variance requires the number of pedestrians to be normally distributed.

b H_0 : The locations of all 3 populations are the same.

H_1 : At least two population locations differ.

Rejection region: $F_r > \chi^2_{\alpha,k-1} = \chi^2_{.05,2} = 5.99147$

$$F_r = \left[\frac{12}{b(k)(k+1)} \sum_{j=1}^{k} T_j^2 \right] - 3b(k+1) = \left[\frac{12}{(30)(3)(4)} (46^2 + 72^2 + 62^2) \right] - 3(30)(4) = 11.47, \text{ p-value} =$$

.0032 (Excel). There is enough evidence to infer that there are differences in the number of people passing between the three locations.

17.88 H_0 : The locations of all 3 populations are the same.

H_1 : At least two population locations differ.

Rejection region: $F_r > \chi^2_{\alpha,k-1} = \chi^2_{.05,2} = 5.99147$

$$F_r = \left[\frac{12}{b(k)(k+1)} \sum_{j=1}^{k} T_j^2 \right] - 3b(k+1) = \left[\frac{12}{(12)(3)(4)} (28.5^2 + 22.5^2 + 21^2) \right] - 3(12)(4) = 2.63, \text{p-value} =$$

.2691 (Excel). There is not enough evidence to infer that there are differences in delivery times between the three couriers.

17.89 H_0 : The locations of all 4 populations are the same.

H_1 : At least two population locations differ.

Rejection region: $F_r > \chi^2_{\alpha,k-1} = \chi^2_{.05,3} = 7.81473$

$$F_r = \left[\frac{12}{b(k)(k+1)} \sum_{j=1}^{k} T_j^2 \right] - 3b(k+1) = \left[\frac{12}{(25)(3)(4)} (84.5^2 + 88.5^2 + 49^2 + 78^2) \right] - 3(25)(4) = 19.15, \text{p-}$$

value = .0003 (Excel). There is enough evidence to infer that differences exist between the four drugs.

17.90 H_0 : The two population locations are the same

H_1 : The location of population 1 is different from the location of population 2

Wilcoxon Rank Sum Test			
		Rank Sum	Observations
Section 1		15297.5	113
Section 2		14592.5	131
z Stat		2.65	
P(Z<=z) one-tail		0.0041	
z Critical one-tail		2.3263	
P(Z<=z) two-tail		0.0082	
z Critical two-tail		2.5758	

$z = 2.65$, p-value = .0082. There is enough evidence to infer that the two teaching methods differ

17.91 H_0 : The two population locations are the same

H_1 : The location of population 1 is left of the location of population 2

Wilcoxon Rank Sum Test			
		Rank Sum	Observations
New		207.5	15
Existing		257.5	15
z Stat		-1.04	
P(Z<=z) one-tail		0.1499	
z Critical one-tail		1.2816	
P(Z<=z) two-tail		0.2998	
z Critical two-tail		1.6449	

$z = -1.04$, p-value = .1499. There is not enough evidence to infer that the new method is better.

17.92 H_0 : The locations of all 4 populations are the same.

        H_1 : At least two population locations differ.

Friedman Test		
Group		Rank Sum
Typeface 1		50.5
Typeface 2		38
Typeface 3		66
Typeface 4		45.5
Fr Stat		12.615
df		3
p-value		0.0055
chi-squared Critical		7.8147

$F_r = 12.615$, p-value = .0055. There is enough evidence to conclude that there are differences between typefaces.

17.93 H_0 : The two population locations are the same

        H_1 : The location of population 1 is to the left of the location of population 2

Sign Test			
Difference			*Drug A - Drug B*
Positive Differences			2
Negative Differences			18
Zero Differences			10
z Stat			-3.58
P(Z<=z) one-tail			0.0002
z Critical one-tail			1.6449
P(Z<=z) two-tail			0.0004
z Critical two-tail			1.96

z = -3.58, p-value = .0002. There is enough evidence to conclude that drug B is more effective.

17.94 H_0 : The two population locations are the same

H_1 : The location of population 1 is to the left of the location of population 2

Wilcoxon Signed Rank Sum Test		
Difference		*Drug A - Drug B*
T+		36
T-		342
Observations (for test)		27
z Stat		-3.68
P(Z<=z) one-tail		0.0001
z Critical one-tail		1.6449
P(Z<=z) two-tail		0.0002
z Critical two-tail		1.96

z = -3.68, p-value = .0001. There is enough evidence to conclude that drug B is more effective.

17.95a The one-way analysis of variance and the Kruskal-Wallis test should be considered. If the data are normal apply the analysis of variance, otherwise use the Kruskal-Wallis test.

b H_0 : The locations of all 3 populations are the same.

H_1 : At least two population locations differ.

Kruskal-Wallis Test		
Group	Rank Sum	Observations
Binding 1	827	25
Binding 2	1110	25
Binding 3	913	25
H Stat		3.5451
df		2
p-value		0.1699
chi-squared Critical		4.6052

$H = 3.55$, p-value $= .1699$. There is not enough evidence to infer that there are differences between bindings.

17.96 H_0 : The two population locations are the same

H_1 : The location of population 1 is to the right of the location of population 2

Wilcoxon Rank Sum Test			
		Rank Sum	Observations
New Material		2747	50
Old Material		2303	50
z Stat		1.5304	
P(Z<=z) one-tail		0.063	
z Critical one-tail		1.6449	
P(Z<=z) two-tail		0.126	
z Critical two-tail		1.96	

$z = 1.53$, p-value $= .0630$. There is not enough evidence to conclude that the new material takes longer to burst into flames.

17.97 H_0 : The locations of all 7 populations are the same.

H_1 : At least two population locations differ.

Kruskal-Wallis Test		
Group	Rank Sum	Observations
Sunday	10060	63
Monday	2977	26
Tuesday	2932.5	29
Wednesday	3834.5	31
Thursday	4060.5	30
Friday	6045	42
Saturday	6405.5	48
H Stat		14.874
df		6
p-value		0.0213
chi-squared Critical		12.5916

H = 14.87, p-value = .0213. There is enough evidence to infer that there are differences in the perceptions of speed of service between the days of the week.

17.98 H_0 : The two population locations are the same

       H_1 : The location of population 1 is different from the location of population 2

Sign Test			
Difference			*Commercial 1 - Commercial 2*
Positive Differences			15
Negative Differences			21
Zero Differences			24
z Stat			-1.00
P(Z<=z) one-tail			0.1587
z Critical one-tail			1.6449
P(Z<=z) two-tail			0.3174
z Critical two-tail			1.96

z = -1.00, p-value = .3174. There is not enough evidence to infer differences in believability between the two commercials.

17.99 H_0 : The two population locations are the same

       H_1 : The location of population 1 is to the right of the location of population 2

Wilcoxon Signed Rank Sum Test		
Difference		Men - Women
T+		324
T-		204
Observations (for test)		32
z Stat		1.12
P(Z<=z) one-tail		0.1309
z Critical one-tail		1.6449
P(Z<=z) two-tail		0.2618
z Critical two-tail		1.96

$z = 1.12$, p-value = .1309. There is not enough evidence to conclude that men lose a greater percentage of their hearing than women.

17.100　H_0 : The two population locations are the same

H_1 : The location of population 1 is to the left of the location of population 2

Wilcoxon Rank Sum Test			
		Rank Sum	Observations
This Year		37525.5	200
10 Years Ago		42674.5	200
z Stat		-2.23	
P(Z<=z) one-tail		0.013	
z Critical one-tail		1.6449	
P(Z<=z) two-tail		0.026	
z Critical two-tail		1.96	

$z = -2.23$, p-value = .0130. There is enough evidence to infer that people perceive newspapers as doing a better job 10 years ago than today.

17.101　H_0 : The two population locations are the same

H_1 : The location of population 1 is different from the location of population 2

Wilcoxon Rank Sum Test			
		Rank Sum	Observations
Males		10336.5	100
Females		9763.5	100
z Stat		0.70	
P(Z<=z) one-tail		0.242	
z Critical one-tail		1.2816	
P(Z<=z) two-tail		0.484	
z Critical two-tail		1.6449	

z = .70, p-value = .4840. There is not enough evidence to conclude that businesswomen and business men differ in the number of business trips taken per year.

17.102 H_0 : The two population locations are the same

H_1 : The location of population 1 is to the right of the location of population 2

Sign Test			
Difference			Before - After
Positive Differences			19
Negative Differences			5
Zero Differences			16
z Stat			2.86
P(Z<=z) one-tail			0.0021
z Critical one-tail			1.6449
P(Z<=z) two-tail			0.0042
z Critical two-tail			1.96

z = 2.86, p-value = .0021. There is enough evidence to infer that the midterm test negatively influences student opinion.

17.103 H_0 : The two population locations are the same

H_1 : The location of population 1 is to the right of the location of population 2

Wilcoxon Rank Sum Test		Rank Sum	Observations
		Rank Sum	Observations
2 Years Ago		10786.5	100
This Year		9313.5	100
z Stat		1.7996	
P(Z<=z) one-tail		0.036	
z Critical one-tail		1.6449	
P(Z<=z) two-tail		0.072	
z Critical two-tail		1.96	

z = 1.80, p-value = .0360. There is enough evidence to indicate that the citizens of Stratford should be concerned.

17.104 H_0 : The two population locations are the same

H_1 : The location of population 1 is to the left of the location of population 2

Wilcoxon Rank Sum Test		Rank Sum	Observations
Low		9055	100
High		11045	100
z Stat		-2.43	
P(Z<=z) one-tail	0.0075		
z Critical one-tail	1.6449		
P(Z<=z) two-tail	0.015		
z Critical two-tail	1.96		

$z = -2.43$, p-value = .0075. There is enough evidence to conclude that boys with high levels of lead are more aggressive than boys with low levels.

17.105a H_0 : The two population locations are the same

H_1 : The location of population 1 is to the right of the location of population 2

Sign Test			
Difference			Female Professor - Male Professor
Positive Differences			45
Negative Differences			7
Zero Differences			48
z Stat			5.27
P(Z<=z) one-tail			0
z Critical one-tail			1.6449
P(Z<=z) two-tail			0
z Critical two-tail			1.96

$z = 5.27$, p-value = 0. There is enough evidence to infer that female students rate female professors higher than they rate male professors.

b H_0 : The two population locations are the same

H_1 : The location of population 1 is to the left of the location of population 2

Sign Test			
Difference			Female Professor - Male Professor
Positive Differences			21
Negative Differences			31
Zero Differences			48
z Stat			-1.39
P(Z<=z) one-tail			0.0828
z Critical one-tail			1.6449
P(Z<=z) two-tail			0.1656
z Critical two-tail			1.96

$z = -1.39$, p-value = .0828. There is not enough evidence to infer that male students rate male professors higher than they rate female professors.

17.106 H_0 : The locations of all 3 populations are the same.

H_1 : At least two population locations differ.

Kruskal-Wallis Test		
Group	Rank Sum	Observations
Unattractive	16844.5	134
Neutral	13313	68
Attractive	26122.5	133
H Stat		42.5935
df		2
p-value		0
chi-squared Critical		5.9915

$H = 42.59$, p-value = 0. There is enough evidence to conclude that incomes of lawyers are affected by physical attractiveness.

17.107 H_0 : The two population locations are the same

H_1 : The location of population 1 is to the right of the location of population 2

Wilcoxon Rank Sum Test			
		Rank Sum	Observations
Telecommuters		10934.5	100
Office		9165.5	100
z Stat		2.16	
P(Z<=z) one-tail		0.0153	
z Critical one-tail		1.6449	
P(Z<=z) two-tail		0.0306	
z Critical two-tail		1.96	

z = 2.16, p-value = .0153. There is enough evidence to conclude that telecommuters are more satisfied with their jobs.

17.108 H_0 : The two population locations are the same

H_1 : The location of population 1 is to the right of the location of population 2

Day 1 versus Before

Sign Test			
Difference			Before - Day 1
Positive Differences			67
Negative Differences			0
Zero Differences			5
z Stat			8.19
P(Z<=z) one-tail			0
z Critical one-tail			1.6449
P(Z<=z) two-tail			0
z Critical two-tail			1.96

z = 8.19, p-value = 0

Day 2 versus Before

Sign Test			
Difference			Before - Day 2
Positive Differences			59
Negative Differences			0
Zero Differences			13
z Stat			7.68
P(Z<=z) one-tail			0
z Critical one-tail			1.6449
P(Z<=z) two-tail			0
z Critical two-tail			1.96

z = 7.68, p-value = 0

Day 3 versus Before

Sign Test			
Difference			Before - Day 3
Positive Differences			35
Negative Differences			0
Zero Differences			37
z Stat			5.92
P(Z<=z) one-tail			0
z Critical one-tail			1.6449
P(Z<=z) two-tail			0
z Critical two-tail			1.96

$z = 5.92$, p-value = 0

There is enough evidence to infer that exercisers who abstain from physical activity are less happy than when they are exercising.

b H_0 : The two population locations are the same

     H_1 : The location of population 1 (Day 2) is to the left of the location of population 2 (Day 3)

Sign Test			
Difference			Day 2 - Day 3
Positive Differences			3
Negative Differences			37
Zero Differences			32
z Stat			-5.38
P(Z<=z) one-tail			0
z Critical one-tail			1.6449
P(Z<=z) two-tail			0
z Critical two-tail			1.96

$z = -5.38$, p-value = 0. There is enough evidence to conclude that by the third day their moods were improving.

c 1. Exercisers who abstained were adjusting to their inactivity by the third day. 2. By the third day exercisers realized that they were closer to the end of their inactivity.

17.109 H_0 : The two population locations are the same

      H_1 : The location of population 1 is to the left of the location of population 2

Wilcoxon Rank Sum Test		
	Rank Sum	Observations
3 Hours Before	22553.5	180
Closing	42426.5	180
z Stat	-10.06	
P(Z<=z) one-tail	0	
z Critical one-tail	1.6449	
P(Z<=z) two-tail	0	
z Critical two-tail	1.96	

$z = -10.06$, p-value $= 0$. There is enough evidence to conclude that alcohol impairs judgment.

Case 17.1

a H_0 : The locations of all 3 populations are the same.

H_1 : At least two population locations differ.

Kruskal-Wallis Test		
Group	Rank Sum	Observations
Br 1 Q 2	2681.5	38
Br 2 Q 2	5330	61
Br 3 Q 2	3616.5	53
H Stat		6.2821
df		2
p-value		0.0432
chi-squared Critical		5.9915

$H = 6.28$, p-value $= .0432$. There is enough evidence to infer that customers at the three branches differ in their assessments of the quality of service at their branch.

b H_0 : The two population locations are the same

H_1 : The location of population 1 is different from the location of population 2

Branch 1

Sign Test			
Difference			*Br 1 Q 1 - Br 1 Q 2*
Positive Differences			4
Negative Differences			24
Zero Differences			10
z Stat			-3.78
P(Z<=z) one-tail			0.0001
z Critical one-tail			1.6449
P(Z<=z) two-tail			0.0002
z Critical two-tail			1.96

z = -3.78, p-value = .0002.

Branch 2

Sign Test			
Difference			*Br 2 Q 1 - Br 2 Q 2*
Positive Differences			15
Negative Differences			31
Zero Differences			15
z Stat			-2.36
P(Z<=z) one-tail			0.0092
z Critical one-tail			1.6449
P(Z<=z) two-tail			0.0184
z Critical two-tail			1.96

z = -2.36, p-value = .0184.

Branch 3

Sign Test			
Difference			*Br 3 Q 1 - Br 3 Q 2*
Positive Differences			12
Negative Differences			25
Zero Differences			16
z Stat			-2.14
P(Z<=z) one-tail			0.0163
z Critical one-tail			1.6449
P(Z<=z) two-tail			0.0326
z Critical two-tail			1.96

z = -2.14, p-value = .0326.

There is enough evidence that for each branch customers have a different opinion of their branch than of the Bank of Commerce as a whole.

378

Chapter 18

18.1 a The slope coefficient tells us that for additional inch of father's height the son's height increases on average by .516. The y-intercept is meaningless.

b On average the son will be shorter than his father.

c On average the sons will be taller than his father.

18.2 a $b_1 = \dfrac{\text{cov}(x, y)}{s_x^2} = \dfrac{7.87}{16.43} = .479$, $b_0 = \bar{y} - b_1\bar{x} = 68.70 - .479(67.14) = 36.54$. (Excel: $\hat{y} = 36.54 + .479x$).

b Nothing

c For each additional inch of father's height, the son's height increases on average by .479 inch.

18.3 $b_1 = \dfrac{\text{cov}(x, y)}{s_x^2} = \dfrac{-9.40}{.24} = -39.17$, $b_0 = \bar{y} - b_1\bar{x} = 154.0 - (-.39.17)(8.2) = 475.19$. (Excel: $\hat{y} = 475.17 - 39.17x$). The slope coefficient tells us that on average for each one-point increase in the mortgage rate the number of housing starts decreases by 39.17.

18.4 a $b_1 = \dfrac{\text{cov}(x, y)}{s_x^2} = \dfrac{.121}{2.56} = .047$, $b_0 = \bar{y} - b_1\bar{x} = 10.05 - .047(3.47) = 9.89$. (Excel: $\hat{y} = 9.88 + .048x$).

b Nothing

c The slope coefficient tells us that on average for each one-point increase in the inflation rate the return on common stocks increases by .048.

18.5 $b_1 = \dfrac{\text{cov}(x, y)}{s_x^2} = \dfrac{-8.27}{10.20} = -.81$, $b_0 = \bar{y} - b_1\bar{x} = 67.28 - (-.81)(8.18) = 73.91$. (Excel: $\hat{y} = 73.91 - .811x$). The slope coefficient tells us that for each one-point increase in the amount of work marks decrease on average by .811.

18.6 a

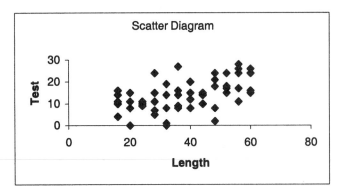

b $b_1 = \dfrac{\text{cov}(x, y)}{s_x^2} = \dfrac{51.86}{193.90} = .267$, $b_0 = \bar{y} - b_1\bar{x} = 13.80 - .267(38.00) = 3.65$. (Excel: $\hat{y} = 3.64 +$

.267x).

c $b_1 = .267$; for each additional second of commercial, the memory test score increases on average by

.267. $b_0 = 3.64$ is the y-intercept.

18.7a $b_1 = \dfrac{\text{cov}(x, y)}{s_x^2} = \dfrac{153.95}{82.01} = 1.88$, $b_0 = \bar{y} - b_1\bar{x} = 74.06 - 1.88(27.95) = 21.51$. (Excel: $\hat{y} = 21.59 +$

1.88x).

b $b_1 = 1.88$; for each additional hour of study the final mark increases on average by 1.88. $b_0 = 21.59$

is the y-intercept.

c The sign of the slope is logical. If the slope had been negative, it would indicate that on average the

more one studied the lower the final mark would be.

18.8 a $b_1 = \dfrac{\text{cov}(x, y)}{s_x^2} = \dfrac{3.08}{3.90} = .790$, $b_0 = \bar{y} - b_1\bar{x} = 6.67 - .790(11.04) = -2.05$. (Excel: $\hat{y} = -2.03 +$

.788x).

b $b_1 = .788$; for each additional year of education, Internet use increases on average by .788 hour. $b_0 =$

-2.03 is the y-intercept.

18.9 a $b_1 = \dfrac{\text{cov}(x, y)}{s_x^2} = \dfrac{-6.44}{55.11} = -.117$, $b_0 = \bar{y} - b_1\bar{x} = 26.28 - (-.117)(37.29) = 30.64$. (Excel: $\hat{y} =$

30.63 - .117x).

b $b_1 = -.117$; for each additional year of age, the employment period decreases on average by .117.

$b_0 = 30.63$ is the y-intercept.

18.10 $b_1 = \dfrac{\text{cov}(x, y)}{s_x^2} = \dfrac{2.03}{21.39} = .0949$, $b_0 = \bar{y} - b_1\bar{x} = 12.73 - .0949(34.61) = 9.45$. (Excel: $\hat{y} = 9.44 +$

.0949x). The appropriate compensation is 9.49 cents per degree API.

18.11a $b_1 = \dfrac{\text{cov}(x, y)}{s_x^2} = \dfrac{51.53}{228.26} = .226$, $b_0 = \bar{y} - b_1\bar{x} = 6.67 - .226(56.00) = -5.99$. (Excel: $\hat{y} = -5.97 +$

.226x).

b $b_1 = .226$; for each additional year of age, mean daily medical emergency expenses increase on

average by $.226 (22.6 cents) per day. $b_0 = -5.97$ is the y-intercept.

c Charge $0.25 (or so) per day per year of age.

18.12 a $b_1 = \dfrac{\text{cov}(x, y)}{s_x^2} = \dfrac{12.00}{.00323} = 3715$, $b_0 = \bar{y} - b_1\bar{x} = 500.08 - 3715(.204) = -257.8$. (Excel:

$\hat{y} = -259.6 + 3721x$).

b $b_1 = 3721$; for each additional carat of weight, the price increases on average by $3721. $b_0 = -259.6$

cannot be interpreted.

18.13 For each father's height, the sons height are normally distributed with constant variance and a

mean that is a linear function of the fathers' heights.

18.14 It is normally distributed with constant variance and a mean that is a linear function of the

quality of oil.

18.15 For each age they are normally distributed with constant variance and a mean that is a linear

function

of the ages.

18.16 a $SSE = (n-1)\left(s_y^2 - \dfrac{[\text{cov}(x, y)]^2}{s_x^2} \right) = (400-1)\left(14.14 - \dfrac{7.87^2}{16.43} \right) = 4137.7$

$s_\varepsilon = \sqrt{\dfrac{SSE}{n-2}} = \sqrt{\dfrac{4137.7}{400-2}} = 3.22$ (Excel: $s_\varepsilon = 3.22$). This statistic is an estimate of the standard

deviation of the error variable.

b $R^2 = \dfrac{[\text{cov}(x, y)]^2}{s_x^2 s_y^2} = \dfrac{7.87^2}{(16.43)(14.14)} = .2666$ (Excel: $R^2 = .2665$)

c $H_0 : \beta_1 = 0$

         $H_1 : \beta_1 \neq 0$

Rejection region: $t < -t_{\alpha/2,\nu} = -t_{.025,398} = -1.96$ or $t > t_{\alpha/2,\nu} = t_{.025,398} = 1.96$

$$s_{b_1} = \frac{s_\varepsilon}{\sqrt{(n-1)s_x^2}} = \frac{3.22}{\sqrt{(400-1)16.43}} = .040$$

$t = \frac{b_1 - \beta_1}{s_{b_1}} = \frac{.479 - 0}{.040} = .11.98$ (Excel: t = 12.03, p-value = 0). There is enough evidence to infer that

the height of sons and fathers are linearly related.

18.17 $SSE = (n-1)\left(s_y^2 - \frac{[\text{cov}(x,y)]^2}{s_x^2} \right) = (10-1)\left(1248.9 - \frac{(-9.40)^2}{.24} \right) = 7926.6$

$$s_\varepsilon = \sqrt{\frac{SSE}{n-2}} = \sqrt{\frac{7926.6}{10-2}} = 31.48 \text{ (Excel: } s_\varepsilon = 31.48).$$

b $R^2 = \frac{[\text{cov}(x,y)]^2}{s_x^2 s_y^2} = \frac{(-9.40)^2}{(.24)(1248.9)} = .2948$ (Excel: $R^2 = .2948$)

c $H_0 : \beta_1 = 0$

         $H_1 : \beta_1 \neq 0$

Rejection region: $t < -t_{\alpha/2,\nu} = -t_{.025,8} = -2.306$ or $t > t_{\alpha/2,\nu} = t_{.025,8} = 2.306$

$$s_{b_1} = \frac{s_\varepsilon}{\sqrt{(n-1)s_x^2}} = \frac{31.48}{\sqrt{(10-1).24}} = 21.42$$

$t = \frac{b_1 - \beta_1}{s_{b_1}} = \frac{-39.17 - 0}{21.42} = -1.83$ (Excel: t = -1.83, p-value = .1048). There is not enough evidence to

infer that mortgage rates and starts are linearly related.

18.18 $SSE = (n-1)\left(s_y^2 - \frac{[\text{cov}(x,y)]^2}{s_x^2} \right) = (10-1)\left(193.06 - \frac{.121^2}{2.56} \right) = 1737.49$

$$s_\varepsilon = \sqrt{\frac{SSE}{n-2}} = \sqrt{\frac{1737.48}{10-2}} = 14.74 \text{ (Excel: } s_\varepsilon = 14.74).$$

$$H_0 : \beta_1 = 0$$

$$H_1 : \beta_1 \neq 0$$

Rejection region: $t < -t_{\alpha/2,\nu} = -t_{.05,8} = -1.860$ or $t > t_{\alpha/2,\nu} = t_{.05,8} = 1.860$

$$s_{b_1} = \frac{s_\varepsilon}{\sqrt{(n-1)s_x^2}} = \frac{14.74}{\sqrt{(10-1)2.56}} = 3.07$$

$$t = \frac{b_1 - \beta_1}{s_{b_1}} = \frac{.047 - 0}{3.07} = .02 \text{ (Excel: t = .02, p-value = .9880). There is no evidence to infer that the}$$

two variables are linearly related.

$$18.19 \quad SSE = (n-1)\left(s_y^2 - \frac{[\text{cov}(x,y)]^2}{s_x^2}\right) = (300-1)\left(39.05 - \frac{.(-8.27)^2}{10.20}\right) = 9671.1$$

$$s_\varepsilon = \sqrt{\frac{SSE}{n-2}} = \sqrt{\frac{9671.1}{300-2}} = 5.70 \text{ (Excel: } s_\varepsilon = 5.70\text{).}$$

$$R^2 = \frac{[\text{cov}(x,y)]^2}{s_x^2 s_y^2} = \frac{(-8.27)^2}{(10.20)(39.05)} = .1717 \text{ (Excel: } R^2 = .1717\text{). There is a weak linear relationship.}$$

$$18.20 \text{ a } SSE = (n-1)\left(s_y^2 - \frac{[\text{cov}(x,y)]^2}{s_x^2}\right) = (60-1)\left(47.96 - \frac{51.86^2}{193.90}\right) = 2011.3$$

$$s_\varepsilon = \sqrt{\frac{SSE}{n-2}} = \sqrt{\frac{2011.3}{60-2}} = 5.89 \text{ (Excel: } s_\varepsilon = 5.89\text{). This statistic is an estimate of the standard}$$

deviation of the error variable.

b $R^2 = \dfrac{[\text{cov}(x,y)]^2}{s_x^2 s_y^2} = \dfrac{51.86^2}{(193.90)(47.96)} = .2892$ (Excel: $R^2 = .2893$). 28.93% of the variation in

memory test scores is explained by the variation in commercial lengths.

c $\qquad H_0 : \beta_1 = 0$

$\qquad H_1 : \beta_1 \neq 0$

Rejection region: $t < -t_{\alpha/2,\nu} = -t_{.025,58} \approx -2.000$ or $t > t_{\alpha/2,\nu} = t_{.025,58} \approx 2.000$

$$s_{b_1} = \frac{s_\varepsilon}{\sqrt{(n-1)s_x^2}} = \frac{5.89}{\sqrt{(60-1)193.90}} = .055$$

$$t = \frac{b_1 - \beta_1}{s_{b_1}} = \frac{.267 - 0}{.055} = 4.85 \text{ (Excel: } t = 4.86, \text{ p-value} = 0). \text{ There is enough evidence to infer that the}$$

length of commercial and memory test score are linearly related.

18.21 a $H_0 : \beta_1 = 0$

$H_1 : \beta_1 \neq 0$

Rejection region: $t < -t_{\alpha/2,v} = -t_{.05,98} \approx -1.660$ or $t > t_{\alpha/2,v} = t_{.05,98} \approx 1.660$

$$SSE = (n-1)\left(s_y^2 - \frac{[\text{cov}(x, y)]^2}{s_x^2} \right) = (100-1)\left(363.94 - \frac{153.95^2}{82.01} \right) = 7419.4$$

$$s_\varepsilon = \sqrt{\frac{SSE}{n-2}} = \sqrt{\frac{7419.4}{100-2}} = 8.70 \text{ (Excel: } s_\varepsilon = 8.70), \quad s_{b_1} = \frac{s_\varepsilon}{\sqrt{(n-1)s_x^2}} = \frac{8.70}{\sqrt{(100-1)82.01}} = .0966$$

$$t = \frac{b_1 - \beta_1}{s_{b_1}} = \frac{1.88 - 0}{.0966} = 19.46 \text{ (Excel: } t = 19.44, \text{ p-value} = 0). \text{ There is enough evidence to infer that}$$

there

is a linear relationship between final mark and study time.

b $R^2 = \frac{[\text{cov}(x, y)]^2}{s_x^2 s_y^2} = \frac{153.95^2}{(82.01)(363.94)} = .7941$ (Excel: $R^2 = .7941$). 79.41% of the variation in final

marks

is explained by the variation in study times.

18.22 a $SSE = (n-1)\left(s_y^2 - \frac{[\text{cov}(x, y)]^2}{s_x^2} \right) = (200-1)\left(22.16 - \frac{3.08^2}{3.90} \right) = 3925.8$

$$s_\varepsilon = \sqrt{\frac{SSE}{n-2}} = \sqrt{\frac{3925.8}{200-2}} = 4.45 \text{ (Excel: } s_\varepsilon = 4.45). \text{ This statistic is an estimate of the standard}$$

deviation of the error variable

b $H_0 : \beta_1 = 0$

$H_1 : \beta_1 \neq 0$

Rejection region: $t < -t_{\alpha/2,v} = -t_{.005,198} \approx -2.601$ or $t > t_{\alpha/2,v} = t_{.005,198} \approx 2.601$

$$s_{b_1} = \frac{s_\varepsilon}{\sqrt{(n-1)s_x^2}} = \frac{4.45}{\sqrt{(200-1)3.90}} = .160$$

$t = \dfrac{b_1 - \beta_1}{s_{b_1}} = \dfrac{.790 - 0}{.160} = 4.94$ (Excel: t = 4.93, p-value = 0). There is enough evidence to infer that

educational level and Internet use are linearly related.

c $R^2 = \dfrac{[\text{cov}(x, y)]^2}{s_x^2 s_y^2} = \dfrac{3.08^2}{(3.90)(22.16)} = .1098$ (Excel: $R^2 = .1094$). 10.94% of the variation in Internet

use is explained by the variation in education.

18.23 $H_0 : \beta_1 = 0$

$H_1 : \beta_1 \neq 0$

Rejection region: $t < -t_{\alpha/2, v} = -t_{.025, 78} \approx -1.990$ or $t > t_{\alpha/2, v} = t_{.025, 78} \approx 1.990$

$SSE = (n-1)\left(s_y^2 - \dfrac{[\text{cov}(x, y)]^2}{s_x^2} \right) = (80-1)\left(4.00 - \dfrac{(-6.44)^2}{55.11} \right) = 256.5$

$s_\varepsilon = \sqrt{\dfrac{SSE}{n-2}} = \sqrt{\dfrac{256.5}{80-2}} = 1.81$ (Excel: $s_\varepsilon = 1.81$), $s_{b_1} = \dfrac{s_\varepsilon}{\sqrt{(n-1)s_x^2}} = \dfrac{1.81}{\sqrt{(80-1)55.11}} = .027$

$t = \dfrac{b_1 - \beta_1}{s_{b_1}} = \dfrac{-.117 - 0}{.027} = -4.33$ (Excel: t = -4.25, p-value = .0001). There is enough evidence to infer

that length of employment is linearly related to age.

$R^2 = \dfrac{[\text{cov}(x, y)]^2}{s_x^2 s_y^2} = \dfrac{(-6.44)^2}{(55.11)(4.00)} = .1881$ (Excel: $R^2 = .1884$).

18.24 $H_0 : \beta_1 = 0$

$H_1 : \beta_1 \neq 0$

Rejection region: $t < -t_{\alpha/2, v} = -t_{.025, 11} = -2.201$ or $t > t_{\alpha/2, v} = t_{.025, 11} = 2.201$

$SSE = (n-1)\left(s_y^2 - \dfrac{[\text{cov}(x, y)]^2}{s_x^2} \right) = (13-1)\left(.21 - \dfrac{2.03^2}{21.39} \right) = .208$

$s_\varepsilon = \sqrt{\dfrac{SSE}{n-2}} = \sqrt{\dfrac{.208}{13-2}} = .138$ (Excel: $s_\varepsilon = .1325$), $s_{b_1} = \dfrac{s_\varepsilon}{\sqrt{(n-1)s_x^2}} = \dfrac{.138}{\sqrt{(13-1)21.39}} = .0086$

$t = \dfrac{b_1 - \beta_1}{s_{b_1}} = \dfrac{.0949 - 0}{.0086} = 11.02$ (Excel: t = 11.48, p-value = 0). There is enough evidence to infer that

oil quality and price are linearly related.

$$R^2 = \frac{[\text{cov}(x, y)]^2}{s_x^2 s_y^2} = \frac{2.03^2}{(21.39)(.21)} = .9174 \ (\text{Excel:} \ R^2 = .9229).$$

18.25 $H_0 : \beta_1 = 0$

       $H_1 : \beta_1 \neq 0$

Rejection region: $t < -t_{\alpha/2,\nu} = -t_{.025,1346} = -1.96$ or $t > t_{\alpha/2,\nu} = t_{.025,1346} = 1.96$

$$SSE = (n-1)\left(s_y^2 - \frac{[\text{cov}(x, y)]^2}{s_x^2} \right) = (1348-1)\left(179.99 - \frac{51.53^2}{228.26} \right) = 226,777$$

$$s_\varepsilon = \sqrt{\frac{SSE}{n-2}} = \sqrt{\frac{226,777}{1348-2}} = 12.98 \ (\text{Excel:} \ s_\varepsilon = 12.98), \quad s_{b_1} = \frac{s_\varepsilon}{\sqrt{(n-1)s_x^2}} = \frac{12.98}{\sqrt{(1348-1)228.26}} = ..023$$

$$t = \frac{b_1 - \beta_1}{s_{b_1}} = \frac{.226 - 0}{.023} = 9.82 \ (\text{Excel:} \ t = 9.65, \ \text{p-value} = 0). \ \text{There is enough evidence to infer that}$$

age and medical expense are linearly related.

$$R^2 = \frac{[\text{cov}(x, y)]^2}{s_x^2 s_y^2} = \frac{51.53^2}{(228.26)(179.88)} = .0647 \ (\text{Excel:} \ R^2 = .0647).$$

18.26 a $SSE = (n-1)\left(s_y^2 - \frac{[\text{cov}(x, y)]^2}{s_x^2} \right) = (48-1)\left(45,643 - \frac{12.00^2}{.00323} \right) = 49,865$

$$s_\varepsilon = \sqrt{\frac{SSE}{n-2}} = \sqrt{\frac{49,865}{48-2}} = 32.92 \ (\text{Excel:} \ s_\varepsilon = 31.84). \ \text{This statistic is an estimate of the standard}$$

deviation of the error variable.

b $R^2 = \frac{[\text{cov}(x, y)]^2}{s_x^2 s_y^2} = \frac{12.00^2}{(.00323)(45,643)} = .9768 \ (\text{Excel:} \ R^2 = .9783). \ 97.83\%$ of the variation in

price is explained by the variation in weight.

c $H_0 : \beta_1 = 0$

       $H_1 : \beta_1 \neq 0$

Rejection region: $t < -t_{\alpha/2,\nu} = -t_{.025,46} \approx -2.014$ or $t > t_{\alpha/2,\nu} = t_{.025,46} \approx 2.014$

$$s_{b_1} = \frac{s_\varepsilon}{\sqrt{(n-1)s_x^2}} = \frac{32.92}{\sqrt{(48-1).00323}} = 84.49$$

$$t = \frac{b_1 - \beta_1}{s_{b_1}} = \frac{3715 - 0}{84.49} = 43.97 \text{ (Excel: t =45.50, p-value = 0). There is enough evidence to infer that}$$

the price and weight of diamonds are linearly related.

18.27 a $b_1 = \dfrac{\text{cov}(x, y)}{s_x^2} = \dfrac{-10.78}{35.47} = -.30$, $b_0 = \bar{y} - b_1\bar{x} = 17.20 - (-.304)(11.33) = 20.64$. (Excel: $\hat{y} =$

20.64 - .30x).

b The slope indicates that for each additional one percentage point increase in the vacancy rate rents

on average decrease by $.30. The y-intercept is 20.64.

c $\qquad H_0 : \beta_1 = 0$

$\qquad H_1 : \beta_1 < 0$

Rejection region: $t < -t_{\alpha, v} = -t_{.05, 28} = -1.701$

$$SSE = (n - 1)\left(s_y^2 - \frac{[\text{cov}(x, y)]^2}{s_x^2}\right) = (30 - 1)\left(11.24 - \frac{(-10.78)^2}{35.47}\right) = 230.9$$

$$s_\varepsilon = \sqrt{\frac{SSE}{n - 2}} = \sqrt{\frac{230.9}{30 - 2}} = 2.87 \text{ (Excel: } s_\varepsilon = 2.87), \quad s_{b_1} = \frac{s_\varepsilon}{\sqrt{(n - 1)s_x^2}} = \frac{2.87}{\sqrt{(30 - 1)35.47}} = .089$$

$$t = \frac{b_1 - \beta_1}{s_{b_1}} = \frac{-.304 - 0}{.089} = -3.42 \text{ (Excel: t = -3.39, p-value = .0021/2 = .0011. There is enough}$$

evidence to infer that higher vacancy rates yield lower rents.

d $R^2 = \dfrac{[\text{cov}(x, y)]^2}{s_x^2 s_y^2} = \dfrac{(-10.78)^2}{(35.47)(11.24)} = .2915$ (Excel: $R^2 = .2911$). 29.11% of the variation in rents

is explained by the variation in vacancy rates.

18.28a $b_1 = \dfrac{\text{cov}(x, y)}{s_x^2} = \dfrac{1240.60}{13,641} = .0909$, $b_0 = \bar{y} - b_1\bar{x} = 27.80 - .0909(283.14) = 2.06$. (Excel: $\hat{y} =$

2.05 + .0909x).

b $b_1 = .0909$; for each additional minute of exercise, cholesterol is reduced on average by .0909. $b_0 =$

2.05 is the y-intercept.

c $\qquad H_0 : \beta_1 = 0$

$\qquad H_1 : \beta_1 < 0$

Rejection region $t < -t_{\alpha/2, v} = -t_{.025, 48} \approx -2.009$ or $t > t_{\alpha/2, v} = t_{.025, 48} \approx 2.009$

$$SSE = (n-1)\left(s_y^2 - \frac{[\text{cov}(x,y)]^2}{s_x^2}\right) = (50-1)\left(221.43 - \frac{1240.69^2}{13,641}\right) = 5321.5$$

$$s_\varepsilon = \sqrt{\frac{SSE}{n-2}} = \sqrt{\frac{5321.5}{50-2}} = 10.53 \text{ (Excel: } s_\varepsilon = 10.53\text{)}, \quad s_{b_1} = \frac{s_\varepsilon}{\sqrt{(n-1)s_x^2}} = \frac{10.53}{\sqrt{(50-1)13,641}} = .0129$$

$$t = \frac{b_1 - \beta_1}{s_{b_1}} = \frac{.0909 - 0}{.0129} = 7.05 \text{ (Excel: } t = 7.06, \text{ p-value} = 0\text{). There is enough evidence to infer that}$$

exercise and cholesterol reduction are linearly related.

$$\text{d } R^2 = \frac{[\text{cov}(x,y)]^2}{s_x^2 s_y^2} = \frac{1240.60^2}{(13,641)(221.43)} = .5095 \text{ (Excel: } R^2 = .5095\text{). The model fits moderately}$$

well.

$$18.29 \quad b_1 = \frac{\text{cov}(x,y)}{s_x^2} = \frac{.83}{1316.07} = .052, \quad b_0 = \bar{y} - b_1\bar{x} = 93.89 - .052(79.47) = 89.76. \text{ (Excel: } \hat{y} = 89.81$$

$+ .051x).$

$$H_0 : \beta_1 = 0$$

$$H_1 : \beta_1 > 0$$

Rejection region: $t > t_{\alpha,\nu} = t_{.05,43} \approx 1.679$

$$SSE = (n-1)\left(s_y^2 - \frac{[\text{cov}(x,y)]^2}{s_x^2}\right) = (45-1)\left(1.28 - \frac{.83^2}{16.07}\right) = 54.43$$

$$s_\varepsilon = \sqrt{\frac{SSE}{n-2}} = \sqrt{\frac{54.43}{450-2}} = 1.13 \text{ (Excel: } s_\varepsilon = 1.13\text{)}, \quad s_{b_1} = \frac{s_\varepsilon}{\sqrt{(n-1)s_x^2}} = \frac{1.13}{\sqrt{(45-1)16.07}} = .042$$

$$t = \frac{b_1 - \beta_1}{s_{b_1}} = \frac{.051 - 0}{.042} = 1.21 \text{ (Excel: } t = 1.21, \text{ p-value} = .2319/2 = .1160\text{). There is not enough}$$

evidence to conclude that higher test results are associated with higher percentages of nondefective units.

18.30 Intel's beta is 1.47, which means its stock is more volatile than the market. The coefficient of determination is .1480, which means that only 14.80% of the total risk is market related. The remaining 85.20% of the total risk is associated specifically with Intel.

18.31 Motorola's beta is 1.12, which means its stock is more volatile than the market. The coefficient of determination is .1142, which means that only 11.42% of the total risk is market related. The remaining 88.58% of the total risk is associated specifically with Motorola.

18.32 General Motor's beta is .8429, which means its stock is less volatile than the market. The coefficient of determination is .1280, which means that only 12.80% of the total risk is market related. The remaining 87.20% of the total risk is associated specifically with General Motors.

18.33 Gillette's beta is .777, which means its stock is less volatile than the market. The coefficient of determination is .1459, which means that only 14.59% of the total risk is market related. The remaining 85.41% of the total risk is associated specifically with Gillette.

18.34 General Electric's beta is 1.09, which means its stock is more volatile than the market. The coefficient of determination is .4049, which means that 40.49% of the total risk is market related. The remaining 59.51% of the total risk is associated specifically with General Electric.

18.35 Seagram's beta is 1.17, which means its stock is more volatile than the market. The coefficient of determination is .2022, which means that only 20.22% of the total risk is market related. The remaining 79.78% of the total risk is associated specifically with Seagram.

18.36 Coca Cola's beta is .506, which means its stock is less volatile than the market. The coefficient of determination is .0962, which means that only 9.62% of the total risk is market related. The remaining 90.38 of the total risk is associated specifically with Coca Cola.

18.37 McDonalds' beta is 1.05, which means its stock is more volatile than the market. The coefficient of determination is .2772, which means that only 27.72% of the total risk is market related. The remaining 72.28% of the total risk is associated specifically with McDonalds.

18.38 The stock that is least sensitive is Coca Cola whose beta is .506. The most sensitive is Intel with a beta of 1.47. Coca Cola's R^2 is 9.62%, which means that its firm-specific risk is 90.38%. The stock with the smallest firm-specific risk is General Electric (59.51%).

18.39 Biomira's beta is 1.51, which means its stock is more volatile than the market. The coefficient of determination is .1131, which means that only 11.31% of the total risk is market related. The remaining 88.69% of the total risk is associated specifically with Biomira.

18.40 Lorus's beta is 1.69, which means its stock is more volatile than the market. The coefficient of determination is .1145, which means that only 11.45% of the total risk is market related. The remaining 88.55% of the total risk is associated specifically with Lorus Therapeutics.

18.41 Petro Canada's beta is .539, which means its stock is less volatile than the market. The coefficient of determination is .1216, which means that only 12.16% of the total risk is market related. The remaining 87.84% of the total risk is associated specifically with Petro Canada.

18.42 Suncor's beta is .326, which means its stock is very much less volatile than the market. The coefficient of determination is .0575, which means that only 5.75% of the total risk is market related. The remaining 94.25% of the total risk is associated specifically with Suncor.

18.43 National Bank's beta is .691, which means its stock is less volatile than the market. The coefficient of determination is .3199, which means that 31.99% of the total risk is market related. The remaining 68.01% of the total risk is associated specifically with National Bank.

18.44 Laurentian Bank's beta is .485, which means its stock is less volatile than the market. The coefficient of determination is .1293, which means that only 12.93% of the total risk is market related. The remaining 87.07% of the total risk is associated specifically with Laurentian Bank.

18.45 Bombardier's beta is .709, which means its stock is less volatile than the market. The coefficient of determination is .2973, which means that only 29.73% of the total risk is market related. The remaining 70.27% of the total risk is associated specifically with Bombardier.

18.46 ATI's beta is 1.19, which means its stock is more volatile than the market. The coefficient of determination is .1541, which means that only 15.41% of the total risk is market related. The remaining 84.59% of the total risk is associated specifically with ATI.

18.47 The stock that is least sensitive is Suncor whose beta is .326. The most sensitive is Lorus with a beta of 1.69. Suncor's R^2 is 5.75%, which means that its firm-specific risk is 94.25%. The stock with the smallest firm-specific risk is National Bank (68.01%).

18.48 The prediction interval provides a prediction for a value of y. The confidence interval estimator of the expected value of y is an estimator of the population mean for a given x.

18.49 We should use the prediction interval.

$\hat{y} = 36.54 + .479x = 36.54 + .479(72) = 71.03$

$$\hat{y}\pm t_{\alpha/2,n-2}s_\varepsilon\sqrt{1+\frac{1}{n}+\frac{(x_g-\overline{x})^2}{(n-1)s_x^2}}=71.03\pm2.576(3.22)\sqrt{1+\frac{1}{400}+\frac{(72-67.14)^2}{(400-1)(16.43)}}=71.03\pm8.32$$

Excel: Lower prediction limit = 62.65, upper prediction limit = 79.40

18.50 $\hat{y}=475.19-39.17x=475.19-39.17(8)=161.83$

$$\hat{y}\pm t_{\alpha/2,n-2}s_\varepsilon\sqrt{1+\frac{1}{n}+\frac{(x_g-\overline{x})^2}{(n-1)s_x^2}}=161.83\pm2.306(31.48)\sqrt{1+\frac{1}{10}+\frac{(8-8.2)^2}{(10-1)(.24)}}=161.83\pm76.77$$

Excel: Lower prediction limit = 85.07, upper prediction limit = 238.60

18.51 $\hat{y}=3.65+.267x=3.65+.267(36)=13.26$

a $\hat{y}\pm t_{\alpha/2,n-2}s_\varepsilon\sqrt{1+\frac{1}{n}+\frac{(x_g-\overline{x})^2}{(n-1)s_x^2}}=13.26\pm2.000(5.89)\sqrt{1+\frac{1}{60}+\frac{(36-38.00)^2}{(60-1)(193.90)}}=13.26\pm11.88$

Excel: Lower prediction limit = 1.38, upper prediction limit = 25.15

b $\hat{y}\pm t_{\alpha/2,n-2}s_\varepsilon\sqrt{\frac{1}{n}+\frac{(x_g-\overline{x})^2}{(n-1)s_x^2}}=13.26\pm2.000(5.89)\sqrt{\frac{1}{60}+\frac{(36-38.00)^2}{(60-1)(193.90)}}=13.26\pm1.54$

Excel: Lower confidence limit = 11.73, upper confidence limit = 14.80

18.52 $\hat{y}=21.59+1.88x=21.59+1.88(25)=68.59$

a $\hat{y}\pm t_{\alpha/2,n-2}s_\varepsilon\sqrt{1+\frac{1}{n}+\frac{(x_g-\overline{x})^2}{(n-1)s_x^2}}=68.59\pm1.660(8.70)\sqrt{1+\frac{1}{100}+\frac{(25-27.95)^2}{(100-1)(82.01)}}=68.59\pm14.52$

Excel: Lower prediction limit = 54.00, upper prediction limit = 83.05

b $\hat{y}\pm t_{\alpha/2,n-2}s_\varepsilon\sqrt{\frac{1}{n}+\frac{(x_g-\overline{x})^2}{(n-1)s_x^2}}=68.59\pm1.660(8.70)\sqrt{\frac{1}{100}+\frac{(25-27.95)^2}{(100-1)(82.01)}}=68.59\pm1.52$

Excel: Lower confidence limit = 67.00, upper confidence limit = 70.04

18.53 $\hat{y}=-2.05+.790x=-2.05+.790(15)=9.80$

$$\hat{y}\pm t_{\alpha/2,n-2}s_\varepsilon\sqrt{\frac{1}{n}+\frac{(x_g-\overline{x})^2}{(n-1)s_x^2}}=9.80\pm1.653(4.45)\sqrt{\frac{1}{200}+\frac{(15-11.04)^2}{(200-1)(3.90)}}=9.80\pm1.17$$

Excel: Lower confidence limit = 8.62, upper confidence limit = 10.96

18.54 $\hat{y}=30.64-.117x=30.64-.117(25)=27.72$

a $\hat{y} \pm t_{\alpha/2,n-2} s_\varepsilon \sqrt{1 + \dfrac{1}{n} + \dfrac{(x_g - \bar{x})^2}{(n-1)s_x^2}} = 27.72 \pm 1.990(1.81)\sqrt{1 + \dfrac{1}{80} + \dfrac{(25 - 37.29)^2}{(80-1)(55.11)}} = 27.72 \pm 3.69$

Excel: Lower prediction limit = 24.02, upper prediction limit = 31.40

18.55 $\hat{y} = 9.45 + .0949x = 9.45 + .0949(42.0) = 13.44$

$\hat{y} \pm t_{\alpha/2,n-2} s_\varepsilon \sqrt{1 + \dfrac{1}{n} + \dfrac{(x_g - \bar{x})^2}{(n-1)s_x^2}} = 13.44 \pm 1.796(.1325)\sqrt{1 + \dfrac{1}{13} + \dfrac{(42.0 - 34.61)^2}{(13-1)(21.39)}} = 13.44 \pm .27$

Excel: Lower prediction limit = 13.16, upper prediction limit = 13.70

18.56 $\hat{y} = -5.99 + .226x = -5.99 + .226(65) = 8.70$

a $\hat{y} \pm t_{\alpha/2,n-2} s_\varepsilon \sqrt{1 + \dfrac{1}{n} + \dfrac{(x_g - \bar{x})^2}{(n-1)s_x^2}} = 8.70 \pm 1.96(12.98)\sqrt{1 + \dfrac{1}{1348} + \dfrac{(65 - 56.00)^2}{(1348-1)(228.26)}} = 8.70 \pm 25.45$

Excel: Lower prediction limit = -16.76 (increased to 0), upper prediction limit = 34.17

b $\hat{y} \pm t_{\alpha/2,n-2} s_\varepsilon \sqrt{\dfrac{1}{n} + \dfrac{(x_g - \bar{x})^2}{(n-1)s_x^2}} = 8.70 \pm 1.96(12.98)\sqrt{\dfrac{1}{1348} + \dfrac{(65 - 56.00)^2}{(1348-1)(228.26)}} = 8.70 \pm .81$

Excel: Lower confidence limit = 7.90, upper confidence limit = 9.51

18.57 $\hat{y} = -257.8 + 3715x = -257.8 + 3715(.35) = 1042.45$

$\hat{y} \pm t_{\alpha/2,n-2} s_\varepsilon \sqrt{1 + \dfrac{1}{n} + \dfrac{(x_g - \bar{x})^2}{(n-1)s_x^2}} = 1042.45 \pm 1.679(32.92)\sqrt{1 + \dfrac{1}{48} + \dfrac{(.35 - .204)^2}{(48-1)(.00323)}} = 1042.45$

± 59.56. Excel: Lower prediction limit = 985.14, upper prediction limit = 1100.33

18.58 $\hat{y} = 20.64 - .304x = 20.64 - .304(10) = 17.60$

$\hat{y} \pm t_{\alpha/2,n-2} s_\varepsilon \sqrt{1 + \dfrac{1}{n} + \dfrac{(x_g - \bar{x})^2}{(n-1)s_x^2}} = 17.60 \pm 2.048(2.87)\sqrt{1 + \dfrac{1}{30} + \dfrac{(10 - 11.33)^2}{(30-1)(35.47)}} = 17.60 \pm 5.98$

Excel: Lower prediction limit = 11.61, upper prediction limit = 23.59

18.59 a $\hat{y} = 2.06 + .0909x = 2.06 + .0909(300) = 29.33$

$\hat{y} \pm t_{\alpha/2,n-2} s_\varepsilon \sqrt{1 + \dfrac{1}{n} + \dfrac{(x_g - \bar{x})^2}{(n-1)s_x^2}} = 29.33 \pm 2.009(10.53)\sqrt{1 + \dfrac{1}{50} + \dfrac{(300 - 283.14)^2}{(50-1)(13,641)}} = 29.33 \pm 21.37$

Excel: Lower prediction limit = 7.95, upper prediction limit = 50.72

b $\hat{y} = 2.06 + .0909x = 2.06 + .0909(250) = 24.79$

$$\hat{y} \pm t_{\alpha/2,n-2} s_{\varepsilon} \sqrt{1 + \frac{1}{n} + \frac{(x_g - \bar{x})^2}{(n-1)s_x^2}} = 24.79 \pm 2.009(10.53)\sqrt{1 + \frac{1}{50} + \frac{(250-283.14)^2}{(50-1)(13,641)}} = 24.79 \pm 21.38$$

Reduction: Lower prediction limit = 3.41, upper prediction limit = 46.17 (Excel: 3.39, 46.18)

Cholesterol level prediction interval: Lower limit = 250 − 46.17 = 203.83, upper limit = 250 − 3.41 =246.59 (Excel: 203.82, 246.61)

18.60 a $H_0 : \rho = 0$

  $H_1 : \rho \neq 0$

Correlation			
X and Y			
Pearson Coefficient of Correlation			0.9375
t Stat			5.39
df			4
P(T<=t) one tail			0.0029
t Critical one tail			2.1318
P(T<=t) two tail			0.0058
t Critical two tail			2.7765

r = .9375, t = 5.39, p-value = .0058. There is enough evidence of a linear relationship.

b $H_0 : \rho_S = 0$

  $H_1 : \rho_S \neq 0$

Spearman Rank Correlation			
X and Y			
Spearman Rank Correlation			0.9429
z Stat			2.11
P(Z<=z) one tail			0.0175
z Critical one tail			1.6449
P(Z<=z) two tail			0.035
z Critical two tail			1.96

r_S = .9429, z = 2.11, p-value = .0350. There is enough evidence of a linear relationship.

18.61a $H_0 : \rho = 0$

  $H_1 : \rho \neq 0$

Correlation			
Stock 1 and Stock 2			
Pearson Coefficient of Correlation			0.3237
t Stat			1.13
df			11
P(T<=t) one tail			0.1403
t Critical one tail			1.7959
P(T<=t) two tail			0.2806
t Critical two tail			2.201

t = 1.13, p-value = .2806. There is not enough evidence to infer that the two stocks are correlated.

b $\qquad H_0 : \rho_S = 0$

$\qquad H_1 : \rho_S \neq 0$

Spearman Rank Correlation			
Stock 1 and Stock 2			
Spearman Rank Correlation			0.225
z Stat			0.78
P(Z<=z) one tail			0.2179
z Critical one tail			1.6449
P(Z<=z) two tail			0.4358
z Critical two tail			1.96

z = .78, p-value = .4358. There is not enough evidence to infer that the two stocks are correlated.

18.62 $\qquad H_0 : \rho_S = 0$

$\qquad H_1 : \rho_S \neq 0$

Spearman Rank Correlation			
Experience and Rating			
Spearman Rank Correlation			0.2336
z Stat			1.12
P(Z<=z) one tail			0.1313
z Critical one tail			1.2816
P(Z<=z) two tail			0.2626
z Critical two tail			1.6449

. z = 1.12, p-value = .2626. There is not enough evidence to infer that the two variables are related.

18.63a $\quad H_0 : \rho = 0$

$\qquad H_1 : \rho \neq 0$

Correlation			
Odometer and Price			
Pearson Coefficient of Correlation			-0.8063
t Stat			-13.49
df			98
P(T<=t) one tail			0
t Critical one tail			1.6606
P(T<=t) two tail			0
t Critical two tail			1.9845

t = -13.49, p-value = 0. There is enough evidence to infer that odometer reading and price are correlated.

b The value of the test statistic and its p-value are identical to those of Example 18.2.

18.64a The required condition is that odometer reading and price are bivariate normally distributed.

b $H_0 : \rho_S = 0$

$H_1 : \rho_S \neq 0$

Spearman Rank Correlation			
Odometer and Price			
Spearman Rank Correlation			-0.8038
z Stat			-8.00
P(Z<=z) one tail			0
z Critical one tail			1.6449
P(Z<=z) two tail			0
z Critical two tail			1.96

z = -8.00, p-value = 0. There is enough evidence to infer that odometer reading and price are related.

18.65a & b $H_0 : \rho = 0$

$H_1 : \rho \neq 0$

Correlation			
Length and Test			
Pearson Coefficient of Correlation			0.5378
t Stat			4.86
df			58
P(T<=t) one tail			0
t Critical one tail			1.6716
P(T<=t) two tail			0
t Critical two tail			2.0017

a r = .5378

b t = 4.86, p-value = 0. There is enough evidence to infer that memory test scores and commercial lengths are linearly related.

c $\qquad H_0 : \rho_S = 0$

$\qquad H_1 : \rho_S > 0$

Spearman Rank Correlation			
Length and Test			
Spearman Rank Correlation			0.546
z Stat			4.19
P(Z<=z) one tail			0
z Critical one tail			1.6449
P(Z<=z) two tail			0
z Critical two tail			1.96

z = 4.19, p-value = 0. There is enough evidence to infer that on average the longer the commercial the higher the memory test score will be.

18.66 $\qquad H_0 : \rho_S = 0$

$\qquad H_1 : \rho_S > 0$

Spearman Rank Correlation			
Time and Mark			
Spearman Rank Correlation			0.7894
z Stat			7.85
P(Z<=z) one tail			0
z Critical one tail			1.6449
P(Z<=z) two tail			0
z Critical two tail			1.96

z = 7.85, p-value = 0. There is enough evidence to infer that mark and study time are positively related.

18.67a & b $\qquad H_0 : \rho = 0$

$\qquad H_1 : \rho \neq 0$

Correlation			
Education and Internet			
Pearson Coefficient of Correlation			0.3308
t Stat			4.93
df			198
P(T<=t) one tail			0
t Critical one tail			1.2858
P(T<=t) two tail			0
t Critical two tail			1.6526

a r = .3308

b t = 4.93, p-value = 0. There is enough evidence to infer that education and Internet use are linearly related.

c $\qquad H_0 : \rho_S = 0$

$\qquad H_1 : \rho_S > 0$

Spearman Rank Correlation		
Education and Internet		
Spearman Rank Correlation		0.3657
z Stat		5.16
P(Z<=z) one tail		0
z Critical one tail		1.2816
P(Z<=z) two tail		0
z Critical two tail		1.6449

z = 5.16, p-value = 0; there is enough evidence to infer that people with more education use the Internet more often.

18.68 $\qquad H_0 : \rho_S = 0$

$\qquad H_1 : \rho_S \neq 0$

Spearman Rank Correlation			
Age and Employment			
Spearman Rank Correlation			-0.4654
z Stat			-4.14
P(Z<=z) one tail			0
z Critical one tail			1.6449
P(Z<=z) two tail			0
z Critical two tail			1.96

z = -4.14, p-value = 0. There is enough to infer that age and length of employment are related.

18.69 $H_0 : \rho_S = 0$

$H_1 : \rho_S > 0$

Spearman Rank Correlation		
Degrees and Price		
Spearman Rank Correlation		0.9381
z Stat		3.25
P(Z<=z) one tail		0.0006
z Critical one tail		1.2816
P(Z<=z) two tail		0.0012
z Critical two tail		1.6449

z = 3.25, p-value = .0006. There is enough to infer that higher prices are related to higher quality.

18.70

Correlation		
Age and Expense		
Pearson Coefficient of Correlation		0.2543
t Stat		9.65
df		1346
P(T<=t) one tail		0
t Critical one tail		1.646
P(T<=t) two tail		0
t Critical two tail		1.9617

a r = .2543

b $H_0 : \rho = 0$

$H_1 : \rho \neq 0$

t = 9.65, p-value = 0. There is enough evidence to infer that there is a linear relationship between age and medical expense.

c $H_0 : \rho_S = 0$

$H_1 : \rho_S > 0$

Spearman Rank Correlation		
Age and Expense		
Spearman Rank Correlation		0.1848
z Stat		6.78
P(Z<=z) one tail		0
z Critical one tail		1.6449
P(Z<=z) two tail		0
z Critical two tail		1.96

z = 6.78, p-value = 0. There is enough evidence to infer that older Canadians incur higher medical expenses.

18.71 $H_0 : \rho_S = 0$

$H_1 : \rho_S \neq 0$

Spearman Rank Correlation		
Weight and Price		
Spearman Rank Correlation		0.9656
z Stat		6.62
P(Z<=z) one tail		0
z Critical one tail		1.2816
P(Z<=z) two tail		0
z Critical two tail		1.6449

z = 6.62, p-value = 0; there is enough evidence to infer that the two variables are related.

18.72 $H_0 : \rho_S = 0$

$H_1 : \rho_S \neq 0$

Spearman Rank Correlation		
US Index and Japanese Index		
Spearman Rank Correlation		0.42
z Stat		3.20
P(Z<=z) one tail		0.0007
z Critical one tail		1.6449
P(Z<=z) two tail		0.0014
z Critical two tail		1.96

z = 3.20, p-value = .0014. There is enough evidence to conclude that the returns are related.

18.73 $H_0 : \rho = 0$

$H_1 : \rho \neq 0$

Correlation		
Italian Index and Hong Kong Index		
Pearson Coefficient of Correlation		0.1974
t Stat		1.52
df		57
P(T<=t) one tail		0.0669
t Critical one tail		1.672
P(T<=t) two tail		0.1338
t Critical two tail		2.0025

t = 1.52, p-value = .1338. There is not enough evidence to infer that the returns on the indexes are linearly related.

18.74 $H_0 : \rho_S = 0$

$H_1 : \rho_S \neq 0$

Spearman Rank Correlation	
Italian Index and Hong Kong Index	
Spearman Rank Correlation	0.2485
z Stat	1.89
P(Z<=z) one tail	0.0292
z Critical one tail	1.6449
P(Z<=z) two tail	0.0584
z Critical two tail	1.96

z = 1.89, p-value = .0584. There is not enough evidence to infer that the returns on the indexes are linearly related.

18.75 $H_0 : \rho = 0$

$H_1 : \rho \neq 0$

Correlation			
UK Index and Australian Index			
Pearson Coefficient of Correlation			0.5608
t Stat			5.11
df			57
P(T<=t) one tail			0
t Critical one tail			1.672
P(T<=t) two tail			0
t Critical two tail			2.0025

t = 5.11, p-value = 0. There is enough evidence to infer that the returns on the indexes are linearly related.

18.76

SUMMARY OUTPUT					
Regression Statistics					
Multiple R	0.9714				
R Square	0.9436				
Adjusted R Square	0.9295				
Standard Error	1.27				
Observations	6				
ANOVA					
	df	*SS*	*MS*	*F*	*Significance F*
Regression	1	107.57	107.57	66.8918	0.0012
Residual	4	6.43	1.61		
Total	5	114.00			
	Coefficients	*tandard Err*	*t Stat*	*P-value*	
Intercept	8.24	0.54	15.28	0.0001	
X	-1.07	0.13	-8.18	0.0012	
RESIDUAL OUTPUT					
Observation	*Predicted Y*	*Residuals*	*Standard Residuals*		
1	13.57	1.43	1.26		
2	10.37	-1.37	-1.21		
3	8.24	-1.24	-1.10		
4	5.05	0.95	0.84		
5	3.98	0.02	0.02		
6	0.79	0.21	0.19		

a $\hat{y} = 8.24 - 1.07x$

e There are no outliers.

18.77 a $\hat{y} = 11.25 + 2.62 x$

SUMMARY OUTPUT					
Regression Statistics					
Multiple R	0.6833				
R Square	0.4668				
Adjusted R Square	0.3907				
Standard Error	8.19				
Observations	9				
ANOVA					
	df	*SS*	*MS*	*F*	*Significance F*
Regression	1	410.8	410.82	6.13	0.0425
Residual	7	469.2	67.03		
Total	8	880.0			
	Coefficients	*Standard Error*	*t Stat*	*P-value*	
Intercept	11.25	5.95	1.89	0.1005	
X	2.62	1.06	2.48	0.0425	
RESIDUAL OUTPUT					
Observation	*Predicted Y*	*Residuals*	*Standard Residuals*		
1	13.87	-8.87	-1.16		
2	16.48	11.52	1.50		
3	19.10	-2.10	-0.27		
4	21.72	-7.72	-1.01		
5	24.33	2.67	0.35		
6	26.95	6.05	0.79		
7	29.57	9.43	1.23		
8	32.18	-6.18	-0.81		
9	34.80	-4.80	-0.63		

d There are no outliers.

e

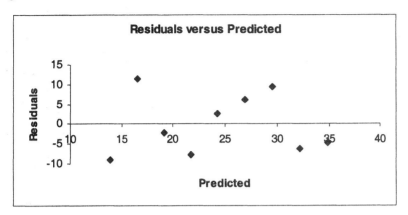

The variance of the error variable appears to be constant.

18.78a

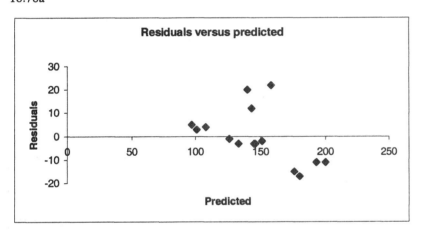

The variance increases as the predicted value of y increases.

b

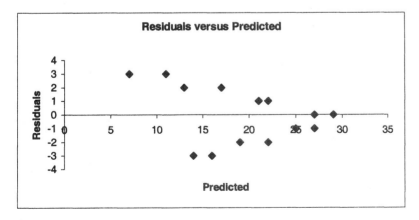

The variance decreases as the predicted value of y increases.

c

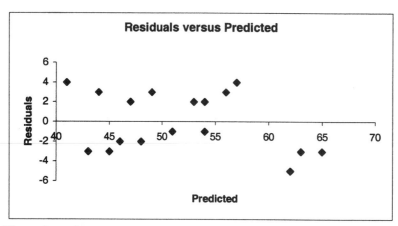

The variance is constant.

18.79b

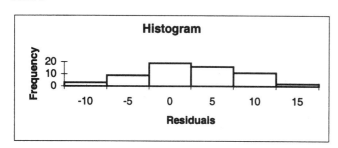

It appears that the errors are normally distributed.

c Observations 18, 25, 53, and 59 have standardized residuals whose absolute values exceed 2.0

d

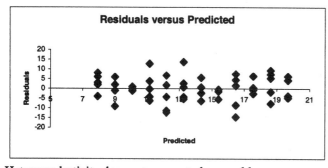

Heteroscedasticity does not appear to be a problem.

18.80a

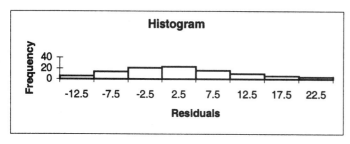

b

The errors appear to be normally distributed and the variance is constant.

18.81

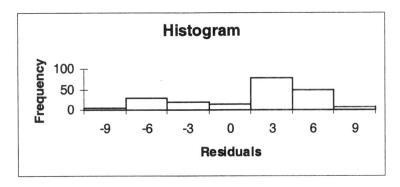

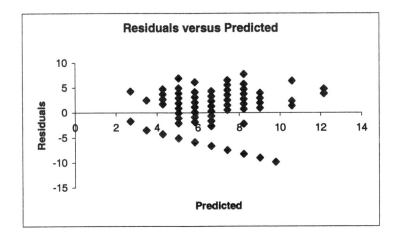

The errors are approximately normal, but the variance is not constant.

18.82b

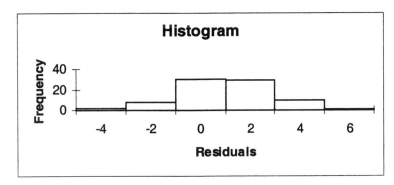

c Observations 1, 15, 21, 31, and 64 have standardized residuals whose absolute values exceed 2.0.

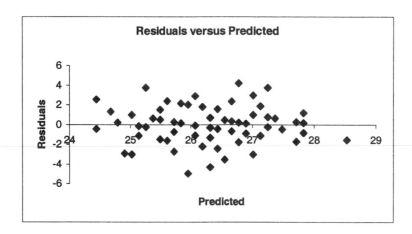

d Heteroscedasticity is not a problem.

18.83

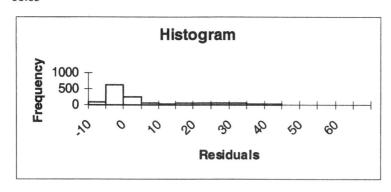

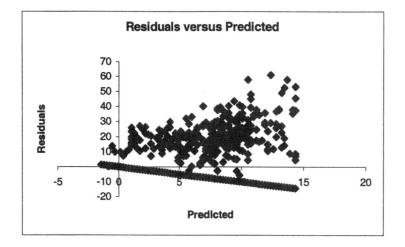

The histogram of the residuals is very positively skewed and the variance of the error variable is not constant.

18.84

SUMMARY OUTPUT					
Regression Statistics					
Multiple R	0.2919				
R Square	0.0852				
Adjusted R Square	0.0471				
Standard Error	132.96				
Observations	26				
ANOVA					
	df	*SS*	*MS*	*F*	*Significance F*
Regression	1	39521	39521	2.24	0.1479
Residual	24	424281	17678		
Total	25	463802			
	Coefficients	*Standard Error*	*t Stat*	*P-value*	
Intercept	296.92	64.31	4.62	0.0001	
Ads	21.36	14.28	1.50	0.1479	

a $\hat{y} = 296.92 + 21.36x$

b On average each ad generates 21.36 customers.

c t = 1.50, p-value = .1479/2 = .0740; there is not enough evidence to infer that the larger the number of ads the larger the number of customers.

d R^2 = .0852; 8.52% of the variation in the number of customers is explained by the variation in the number of ads.

e The poor fit of the model precludes its use for prediction.

18.85

SUMMARY OUTPUT					
Regression Statistics					
Multiple R	0.7522				
R Square	0.5659				
Adjusted R Square	0.5417				
Standard Error	43.32				
Observations	20				
ANOVA					
	df	*SS*	*MS*	*F*	*Significance F*
Regression	1	44024	44024.24	23.46	0.0001
Residual	18	33777	1876.49		
Total	19	77801			
	Coefficients	*Standard Error*	*t Stat*	*P-value*	
Intercept	114.85	58.69	1.96	0.0660	
Age	2.47	0.51	4.84	0.0001	

a $\hat{y} = 114.85 + 2.47x$

b $b_1 = 2.47$; for each additional month of age, repair costs increase on average by \$2.47.

$b_0 = 114.85$ is the y-intercept.

c $R^2 = .5659$; 56.59% of the variation in repair costs is explained by the variation in age.

d $t = 4.84$, p-value = .0001. There is enough evidence to infer that repair costs and age are linearly related.

e

Prediction Interval		Repairs	
Predicted value		411.65	
Prediction Interval			
Lower limit		318.12	
Upper limit		505.18	
Interval Estimate of Expected Value			
Lower limit		390.09	
Upper limit		433.22	

Lower prediction limit = 318.12, upper prediction limit = 505.18

18.86

Spearman Rank Correlation			
Rating and Sugar			
Spearman Rank Correlation			0.7993
z Stat			11.28
P(Z<=z) one tail			0
z Critical one tail			1.6449
P(Z<=z) two tail			0
z Critical two tail			1.96

$z = 11.28$, p-value = 0. There is enough evidence to infer that sugar content and drinkers' ratings of the cola are related.

18.87

SUMMARY OUTPUT					
Regression Statistics					
Multiple R	0.1929				
R Square	0.0372				
Adjusted R Square	0.0028				
Standard Error	27.64				
Observations	30				
ANOVA					
	df	*SS*	*MS*	*F*	*Significance F*
Regression	1	826.35	826.35	1.08	0.3072
Residual	28	21385.59	763.77		
Total	29	22211.94			
	Coefficients	*Standard Error*	*t Stat*	*P-value*	
Intercept	60.50	21.30	2.84	0.0083	
Fertilizer	0.0606	0.0583	1.04	0.3072	

a $\hat{y} = 60.50 + .0606x$. The slope is .0606, which tells us that for each additional unit of fertilizer, corn yield increases on average by .0606. The y-intercept is 60.50, which has no real meaning.

b $t = 1.04$, p-value = .3072. There is not enough evidence to infer a linear relationship between amount of fertilizer and corn yield.

c $R^2 = .0372$; 3.72% of the variation in corn yield is explained by the variation in amount of fertilizer.

d The model is too poor to be used to predict.

18.88

Correlation			
CO and NO3			
Pearson Coefficient of Correlation			0.8913
t Stat			13.62
df			48
P(T<=t) one tail			0
t Critical one tail			1.6772
P(T<=t) two tail			0
t Critical two tail			2.0106

Assuming normality: $t = 13.62$, p-value = 0; there is enough evidence to infer that the belief is correct.

18.89

SUMMARY OUTPUT					
Regression Statistics					
Multiple R	0.4394				
R Square	0.1931				
Adjusted R Square	0.1258				
Standard Error	0.0567				
Observations	14				
ANOVA					
	df	*SS*	*MS*	*F*	*Significance F*
Regression	1	0.0092	0.0092	2.87	0.1160
Residual	12	0.0386	0.0032		
Total	13	0.0478			
	Coefficients	*Standard Error*	*t Stat*	*P-value*	
Intercept	-0.227	0.43	-0.53	0.6069	
Team BA	2.794	1.65	1.69	0.1160	

a $\hat{y} = -.227 + 2.794x$. The slope is 2.794; for each additional point increase in batting average, the team's winning percentage increases on average by 2.794 points.

b $s_\varepsilon = .0567$. This statistic is large relative to the average winning percentage, .500. The model is poor.

c $t = 1.69$, p-value $= .1160/2 = .0580$; there is not enough evidence to infer a positive linear relationship between team batting average and winning percentage.

d $R^2 = .1931$; 19.31% of the variation in winning percentage is explained by the variation in team batting average.

e

Prediction Interval			
		Winning%	
Predicted value		0.542	
Prediction Interval			
Lower limit		0.428	
Upper limit		0.655	
Interval Estimate of Expected Value			
Lower limit		0.490	
Upper limit		0.593	

Lower prediction limit = .428, Upper prediction limit = .655.

18.90

SUMMARY OUTPUT					
Regression Statistics					
Multiple R	0.4930				
R Square	0.2431				
Adjusted R Square	0.1800				
Standard Error	0.0549				
Observations	14				
ANOVA					
	df	*SS*	*MS*	*F*	*Significance F*
Regression	1	0.0116	0.0116	3.85	0.0733
Residual	12	0.0362	0.0030		
Total	13	0.0478			
	Coefficients	*Standard Error*	*t Stat*	*P-value*	
Intercept	0.83	0.17	4.94	0.0003	
Team ERA	-0.080	0.041	-1.96	0.0733	

$\hat{y}$ = .83 - .080x. The slope is -.080; for each additional point increase in ERA, the team's winning percentage decreases on average by .080 points.

b s_ε = .0549. This statistic is large relative to the average winning percentage, .500. The model is poor.

c t = -1.96, p-value = .0733/2 = .0367; there is enough evidence to infer a negative linear relationship between ERA and winning percentage.

d R^2 = .2431; 24.31% of the variation in winning percentage is explained by the variation in ERA.

e

Prediction Interval		
	Winning%	
Predicted value	0.508	
Prediction Interval		
Lower limit	0.406	
Upper limit	0.609	
Interval Estimate of Expected Value		
Lower limit	0.481	
Upper limit	0.535	

Lower prediction limit = .406, upper prediction limit = .609

18.91

Correlation			
Winning times and Temperature			
Pearson Coefficient of Correlation			0.7242
t Stat			4.58
df			19
P(T<=t) one tail			0.0001
t Critical one tail			1.7291
P(T<=t) two tail			0.0002
t Critical two tail			2.093

t = 4.58, p-value = .0002. There is enough evidence of a linearly relation between temperature and winning times.

18.92

Correlation			
Winning times and Temperature			
Pearson Coefficient of Correlation			0.5984
t Stat			3.26
df			19
P(T<=t) one tail			0.0021
t Critical one tail			1.7291
P(T<=t) two tail			0.0042
t Critical two tail			2.093

t = 3.26, p-value = .0042. There is enough evidence of a linearly relation between temperature and winning times.

18.93a

Correlation			
Weight and B/A Level			
Pearson Coefficient of Correlation			0.4177
t Stat			3.19
df			48
P(T<=t) one tail			0.0013
t Critical one tail			1.6772
P(T<=t) two tail			0.0026
t Critical two tail			2.0106

a t = 3.19, p-value = .0026. There is sufficient evidence to infer that weight and blood-alcohol level are related.

b

Spearman Rank Correlation			
Weight and B/A Level			
Spearman Rank Correlation			0.3702
z Stat			2.59
P(Z<=z) one tail			0.0048
z Critical one tail			1.6449
P(Z<=z) two tail			0.0096
z Critical two tail			1.96

b z = 2.59, p-value = .0096. There is sufficient evidence to infer that weight and blood-alcohol level are linearly related.

18.94

SUMMARY OUTPUT					
Regression Statistics					
Multiple R	0.2248				
R Square	0.0505				
Adjusted R Square	0.0467				
Standard Error	8.28				
Observations	250				
ANOVA					
	df	SS	MS	F	Significance F
Regression	1	905.60	905.60	13.20	0.0003
Residual	248	17010.97	68.59		
Total	249	17916.56			
	Coefficients	Standard Error	t Stat	P-value	
Intercept	17.93	11.48	1.56	0.1194	
Height	0.604	0.166	3.63	0.0003	

$\hat{y} = 17.93 + .60x$. The slope is .60; for each additional inch of height, annual income increases on average by .60 thousand dollars ($600).

b t = 3.63, p-value = .0003/2 = .0002. There is enough evidence to infer a positive linear relationship between height and income.

c $R^2 = .0505$; 5.05% of the variation in incomes is explained by the variation in heights.

d The model is too poor to be used to predict or estimate.

413

18.95a

Correlation			
Tar and Nicotine			
Pearson Coefficient of Correlation			0.9766
t Stat			21.78
df			23
P(T<=t) one tail			0
t Critical one tail			1.7139
P(T<=t) two tail			0
t Critical two tail			2.0687

Assuming normality: r = .9766, t = 21.78, p-value = 0. There is sufficient evidence to infer that levels of tar and nicotine are linearly related.

b

Correlation			
Nicotine and CO			
Pearson Coefficient of Correlation			0.9259
t Stat			11.76
df			23
P(T<=t) one tail			0
t Critical one tail			1.7139
P(T<=t) two tail			0
t Critical two tail			2.0687

Assuming normality: r = .9259, t = 11.76, p-value = 0. There is sufficient evidence to infer that levels of nicotine and carbon monoxide are linearly related.

18.96

Correlation			
Debt and Television			
Pearson Coefficient of Correlation			0.554
t Stat			13.77
df			428
P(T<=t) one tail			0
t Critical one tail			1.6484
P(T<=t) two tail			0
t Critical two tail			1.9655

t = 13.77, p-value = 0. There is enough evidence of a positive linear relationship. The theory appears to be valid.

18.97

Correlation			
Test and Nondefective			
Pearson Coefficient of Correlation			0.3984
t Stat			3.01
df			48
P(T<=t) one tail			0.0021
t Critical one tail			1.6772
P(T<=t) two tail			0.0042
t Critical two tail			2.0106

$t = 3.01$, p-value $= .0042$. There is enough evidence to infer that there is a linear relationship between test scores and job performances. The dexterity tests should continue.

Case 18.1

SUMMARY OUTPUT					
Regression Statistics					
Multiple R	0.3079				
R Square	0.0948				
Adjusted R Square	0.0829				
Standard Error	28577				
Observations	78				
ANOVA					
	df	*SS*	*MS*	*F*	*Significance F*
Regression	1	6502546112	6502546112	7.96	0.0061
Residual	76	62067169717	816673286		
Total	77	68569715830			
	Coefficients	*Standard Error*	*t Stat*	*P-value*	
Intercept	18018	7269	2.48	0.0154	
Copies	130.76	46.34	2.82	0.0061	

$t = 2.82$, p-value $= .0061$. There is enough evidence of a linear relationship. However, the coefficient of determination is $R^2 = .0948$, which means that only 9.48% of the variation in revenues is explained by the variation in the number of copies.

Case 18.2

Regression using the best 6 OACs:

SUMMARY OUTPUT					
Regression Statistics					
Multiple R	0.4883				
R Square	0.2385				
Adjusted R Square	0.2363				
Standard Error	0.8295				
Observations	363				
ANOVA					
	df	*SS*	*MS*	*F*	*Significance F*
Regression	1	77.78	77.78	113.04	0.0000
Residual	361	248.39	0.69		
Total	362	326.17			
	Coefficients	*Standard Error*	*t Stat*	*P-value*	
Intercept	-5.35	1.31	-4.08	0.0001	
Best-6	0.155	0.015	10.63	0.0000	

$t = 10.63$, p-value $= 0$. There is evidence of a linear relationship between the average of the best 6

OACs and university GPA. $R^2 = .2385$, $s_\varepsilon = .8295$

Regression using the best 4 OACs plus English and calculus:

SUMMARY OUTPUT					
Regression Statistics					
Multiple R	0.5924				
R Square	0.3509				
Adjusted R Square	0.3491				
Standard Error	0.7658				
Observations	363				
ANOVA					
	df	*SS*	*MS*	*F*	*Significance F*
Regression	1	114.46	114.46	195.17	0.0000
Residual	361	211.71	0.59		
Total	362	326.17			
	Coefficients	*Standard Error*	*t Stat*	*P-value*	
Intercept	-3.32	0.85	-3.89	0.0001	
B4+E+C	0.137	0.010	13.97	0.0000	

$t = 13.97$, p-value $= 0$; there is evidence of a linear relationship between the average of the best 4

OACs plus English and calculus and university GPA. $R^2 = .3509$, $s_\varepsilon = .7658$.

The second model fits better (higher coefficient of determination and lower standard error of estimate) and as such is likely to be a better predictor of university GPA.

Case 18.3 a

SUMMARY OUTPUT					
Regression Statistics					
Multiple R	0.9896				
R Square	0.9794				
Adjusted R Square	0.9787				
Standard Error	356				
Observations	32				
ANOVA					
	df	*SS*	*MS*	*F*	*Significance F*
Regression	1	180066717	180066717	1424	0.0000
Residual	30	3793289	126443		
Total	31	183860006			
	Coefficients	*Standard Error*	*t Stat*	*P-value*	
Intercept	16.23	114.70	0.14	0.8884	
A-Park	0.693	0.018	37.74	0.0000	

The regression equation is $\hat{y} = 16.23 + .693x$. This equation was used to predict museum attendance when it was closed (observations 33 to 179). The sum of the predictions is 785,009.

b

SUMMARY OUTPUT					
Regression Statistics					
Multiple R	0.9909				
R Square	0.9819				
Adjusted R Square	0.9811				
Standard Error	573				
Observations	26				
ANOVA					
	df	*SS*	*MS*	*F*	*Significance F*
Regression	1	426295375	426295375	1299	0.0000
Residual	24	7875875	328161		
Total	25	434171250			
	Coefficients	*Standard Error*	*t Stat*	*P-value*	
Intercept	459.5	295.4	1.56	0.1330	
A-Park	0.970	0.027	36.04	0.0000	

The regression equation is $\hat{y} = 459.5 + .970x$. This equation was used to predict museum attendance when it was closed (observations 33 to 179). The sum of the predictions is 1,162,994.

c The predicted lost revenue should be based on the regression using the first 32 weeks. Multiply 785,009 by the price of tickets and subtract fixed costs to produce the amount the insurance company should pay the museum.

Chapter 19

19.1

SUMMARY OUTPUT					
Regression Statistics					
Multiple R	0.4924				
R Square	0.2425				
Adjusted R Square	0.2019				
Standard Error	40.24				
Observations	60				
ANOVA					
	df	*SS*	*MS*	*F*	*Significance F*
Regression	3	29030	9677	5.97	0.0013
Residual	56	90694	1620		
Total	59	119724			
	Coefficients	*Standard Error*	*t Stat*	*P-value*	
Intercept	51.39	23.517	2.19	0.0331	
Lot size	0.700	0.559	1.25	0.2156	
Trees	0.679	0.229	2.96	0.0045	
Distance	-0.378	0.195	-1.94	0.0577	

a $\hat{y} = 51.39 + .700x_1 + .679x_2 - .378x_3$

b The standard error of estimate is $s_\varepsilon = 40.24$. It is an estimate of the standard deviation of the error variable.

c The coefficient of determination is $R^2 = .2425$; 24.25% of the variation in prices is explained by the model.

d The coefficient of determination adjusted for degrees of freedom is .2019. It differs from

R^2 because it includes an adjustment for the number of independent variables.

e $\qquad H_0 : \beta_1 = \beta_2 = \beta_3 = 0$

$\qquad H_1 :$ At least one β_i is not equal to zero

F = 5.97, p-value = .0013. There is enough evidence to conclude that the model is valid.

f $b_1 = .700$; for each addition thousand square feet the price on average increases by .700 thousand dollars provided that the other variables remain constant.

$b_2 = .679$; for each addition tree the price on average increases by .679 thousand dollars provided that the other variables remain constant.

$b_3 = -.378$; for each addition foot from the lake the price on average decreases by .378 thousand dollars provided that the other variables remain constant.

g $H_0 : \beta_i = 0$

        $H_1 : \beta_i \neq 0$

Lot size: t = 1.25, p-value = .2156

Trees: t = 2.96, p-value = .0045

Distance: t = -1.94, p-value = .0577

Only for the number of trees is there enough evidence to infer a linear relationship with price.

19.2

SUMMARY OUTPUT					
Regression Statistics					
Multiple R	0.8734				
R Square	0.7629				
Adjusted R Square	0.7453				
Standard Error	3.75				
Observations	30				
ANOVA					
	df	*SS*	*MS*	*F*	*Significance F*
Regression	2	1223.18	611.59	43.43	0.0000
Residual	27	380.18	14.08		
Total	29	1603.37			
	Coefficients	*Standard Error*	*t Stat*	*P-value*	
Intercept	13.01	3.528	3.69	0.0010	
Assignment	0.194	0.200	0.97	0.3417	
Midterm	1.112	0.122	9.12	0.0000	

a $\hat{y} = 13.01 + .194x_1 + 1.112x_2$

b The standard error of estimate is $s_\varepsilon = 3.75$. It is an estimate of the standard deviation of the error variable.

c The coefficient of determination is $R^2 = .7629$; 76.29% of the variation in final exam marks is explained by the model.

d The coefficient of determination adjusted for degrees of freedom is .7453. It differs from R^2 because it includes an adjustment for the number of independent variables.

e $H_0 : \beta_1 = \beta_2 = 0$

        H_1 : At least one β_i is not equal to zero

F = 43.43, p-value = 0. There is enough evidence to conclude that the model is valid.

f $b_1 = .194$; for each addition mark on assignments the final exam mark on average increases by .194 provided that the other variable remains constant.

$b_2 = 1.112$; for each addition midterm mark the final exam mark on average increases by 1.112 provided that the other variable remains constant.

g $H_0 : \beta_1 = 0$

   $H_1 : \beta_1 \neq 0$

t = .97, p-value = .3417. There is not enough evidence to infer that assignment marks and final exam marks are linearly related.

h $H_0 : \beta_2 = 0$

   $H_1 : \beta_2 \neq 0$

t = 9.12, p-value = 0. There is sufficient evidence to infer that midterm marks and final exam marks are linearly related.

19.3a

SUMMARY OUTPUT					
Regression Statistics					
Multiple R	0.9453				
R Square	0.8935				
Adjusted R Square	0.8711				
Standard Error	40.13				
Observations	24				
ANOVA					
	df	*SS*	*MS*	*F*	*Significance F*
Regression	4	256793	64198	39.86	0.0000
Residual	19	30602	1611		
Total	23	287395			
	Coefficients	*Standard Error*	*t Stat*	*P-value*	
Intercept	-111.8	134.3	-0.83	0.4155	
Permits	4.76	0.40	12.06	0.0000	
Mortgage	16.99	15.16	1.12	0.2764	
A Vacancy	-10.53	6.39	-1.65	0.1161	
O Vacancy	1.31	2.79	0.47	0.6446	

b The standard error of estimate is $s_\varepsilon = 40.13$. It is an estimate of the standard deviation of the error variable.

c The coefficient of determination is $R^2 = .8935$; 89.35% of the variation in monthly sales of drywall is explained by the model.

d The coefficient of determination adjusted for degrees of freedom is .8711. It differs from R^2 because it includes an adjustment for the number of independent variables.

e $H_0 : \beta_1 = \beta_2 = \beta_3 = \beta_4 = 0$

H_1 : At least one β_i is not equal to zero

$F = 39.86$, p-value = 0. There is enough evidence to conclude that the model is valid.

f $b_1 = 4.76$; for each addition building permit monthly sales on average increase by 4.76 hundred sheets provided that the other variables remain constant.

$b_2 = 16.99$; for each addition one point increase in mortgage rates monthly sales on average increase by 16.99 hundred sheets provided that the other variables remain constant.

$b_3 = -10.53$; for each one percentage point increase in the apartment vacancy rate monthly sales decrease on average by 10.53 hundred sheets provided that the other variables remain constant.

$b_4 = 1.31$; for each one percentage point increase in the office vacancy rate monthly sales increase on average by 1.31 hundred sheets provided that the other variables remain constant.

g $H_0 : \beta_i = 0$

$H_1 : \beta_i \neq 0$

Permits: t = 12.06, p-value = 0

Mortgage: t = 1.12, p-value = .2764

A Vacancy: t = -1.65, p-value = .1161

O Vacancy: t = .47, p-value = .6446

Only the number of building permits is linearly related to monthly sales.

19.4a

SUMMARY OUTPUT					
Regression Statistics					
Multiple R	0.5169				
R Square	0.2672				
Adjusted R Square	0.2635				
Standard Error	3.23				
Observations	400				
ANOVA					
	df	SS	MS	F	Significance F
Regression	2	1507.5	753.7	72.37	0.0000
Residual	397	4134.9	10.4		
Total	399	5642.4			
	Coefficients	Standard Error	t Stat	P-value	
Intercept	37.56	3.20	11.73	0.0000	
Mother	-0.023	0.039	-0.58	0.5615	
Father	0.485	0.041	11.78	0.0000	

b The standard error of estimate is $s_\varepsilon = 3.23$. It is t an estimate of the standard deviation of the error variable.

c The coefficient of determination is $R^2 = .2672$; 26.72% of the variation in heights is explained by the model.

d The coefficient of determination adjusted for degrees of freedom is .2635. It differs from R^2 because it includes an adjustment for the number of independent variables.

e $\qquad H_0 : \beta_1 = \beta_2 = 0$

$\qquad H_1 :$ At least one β_i is not equal to zero

$F = 72.37$, p-value = 0. There is enough evidence to conclude that the model is valid.

f $b_1 = -.023$; for each addition inch of height of mothers the son's height decreases on average by .023 inches provided that the other variable remains constant.

$b_2 = .485$; for each addition inch of height of fathers the son's height increases on average by .485 inches provided that the other variable remains constant.

g $\qquad H_0 : \beta_1 = 0$

$\qquad H_1 : \beta_1 \neq 0$

$t = 11.78$, p-value = 0. There is enough evidence to infer that fathers' and sons' height are linearly related.

h $\qquad H_0 : \beta_2 = 0$

$\qquad H_1 : \beta_2 \neq 0$

$t = -.58$, p-value = .5615. There is no evidence to infer that mothers' and sons' heights are linearly related.

19.5

SUMMARY OUTPUT					
Regression Statistics					
Multiple R	0.8378				
R Square	0.7020				
Adjusted R Square	0.6825				
Standard Error	1.92				
Observations	50				
ANOVA					
	df	*SS*	*MS*	*F*	*Significance F*
Regression	3	399.86	133.29	36.12	0.0000
Residual	46	169.76	3.69		
Total	49	569.62			
	Coefficients	*Standard Error*	*t Stat*	*P-value*	
Intercept	6.06	2.60	2.33	0.0244	
Age	-0.0078	0.0664	-0.12	0.9069	
Years	0.603	0.097	6.25	0.0000	
Pay	-0.070	0.052	-1.34	0.1864	

a The regression equation is $\hat{y} = 6.06 - .0078x_1 + .603x_2 - .070x_3$

$b_1 = -.0078$; for each addition year of age severance pay decreases on average by .0078 provided that the other variables remain constant.

$b_2 = .603$; for each year with the company severance pay increases on average by .603 weeks provided that the other variables remain constant.

$b_3 = -.070$; for each thousand dollar increase in pay severance pay decreases on average by .070 weeks provided that the other variables remain constant.

b $s_\varepsilon = 1.92$, $R^2 = .7020$, F = 36.12, p-value = 0. The model is valid and the fit is reasonably good.

c $\qquad H_0 : \beta_i = 0$

$\qquad H_1 : \beta_i \neq 0$

Age: t = -.12, p-value = .9069

Years: t = 6.25, p-value = 0

Pay: t = -1.34, p-value = .1864

Only the number of years with the company is linearly related to severance pay

d.

Prediction Interval		
	Weeks SP	
Predicted value	9.57	
Prediction Interval		
Lower limit	5.64	
Upper limit	13.50	
Interval Estimate of Expected Value		
Lower limit	8.86	
Upper limit	10.27	

The offer of 5 weeks severance pay falls below the prediction interval and thus Bill is correct.

19.6

SUMMARY OUTPUT					
Regression Statistics					
Multiple R	0.5369				
R Square	0.2882				
Adjusted R Square	0.2660				
Standard Error	2.03				
Observations	100				
ANOVA					
	df	*SS*	*MS*	*F*	*Significance F*
Regression	3	160.24	53.41	12.96	0.0000
Residual	96	395.70	4.12		
Total	99	555.93			
	Coefficients	*Standard Error*	*t Stat*	*P-value*	
Intercept	0.721	1.870	0.39	0.7006	
HS GPA	0.611	0.101	6.06	0.0000	
SAT	0.0027	0.0029	0.94	0.3482	
Activities	0.046	0.064	0.72	0.4720	

b The standard error of estimate is $s_\varepsilon = 2.03$. It is an estimate of the standard deviation of the error variable.

c The coefficient of determination is $R^2 = .2882$; 28.82% of the variation in university GPAs is explained by the model.

d The coefficient of determination adjusted for degrees of freedom is .2660.

e $\quad H_0 : \beta_1 = \beta_2 = \beta_3 = 0$

$\quad H_1$: At least one β_i is not equal to zero

$F = 12.96$, p-value = 0. There is enough evidence to conclude that the model is valid.

f $b_1 = .611$; for each additional point of high school GPA university GPA increases on average by .611 provided that the other variables remain constant.

$b_2 = .0027$; for each additional point of SAT university GPA increases on average by .0027 provided that the other variables remain constant.

$b_3 = .046$; for each additional hour of activities university GPA increases on average by .046 provided that the other variables remain constant.

g $\quad H_0 : \beta_i = 0$

$\quad H_1 : \beta_i \neq 0$

High school GPA: t = 6.06, p-value = 0

SAT: t = .94, p-value = .3482

Activities: t = .72, p-value = .4720

Only high school GPA is linearly related to university GPA.

h

Prediction Interval		Univ GPA	
Predicted value		8.55	
Prediction Interval			
Lower limit		4.45	
Upper limit		12.65	
Interval Estimate of Expected Value			
Lower limit		7.79	
Upper limit		9.31	

We predict that the student's GPA will fall between 4.45 and 12.00 (12 is the maximum).

i

Prediction Interval		Univ GPA	
Predicted value		7.56	
Prediction Interval			
Lower limit		4.13	
Upper limit		11.00	
Interval Estimate of Expected Value			
Lower limit		6.90	
Upper limit		8.22	

The mean GPA is estimated to lie between 6.90 and 8.22.

19.7

SUMMARY OUTPUT					
Regression Statistics					
Multiple R	0.4419				
R Square	0.1953				
Adjusted R Square	0.0803				
Standard Error	2.59				
Observations	25				
ANOVA					
	df	*SS*	*MS*	*F*	*Significance F*
Regression	3	34.10	11.37	1.70	0.1979
Residual	21	140.56	6.69		
Total	24	174.66			
	Coefficients	*Standard Error*	*t Stat*	*P-value*	
Intercept	12.31	4.70	2.62	0.0160	
Direct	0.57	1.72	0.33	0.7437	
Newspaper	3.32	1.54	2.16	0.0427	
Television	0.73	1.96	0.37	0.7123	

a The regression equation is $\hat{y} = 12.31 + .57x_1 + 3.32x_2 + .73x_3$

b The coefficient of determination is $R^2 = .1953$; 19.53% of the variation in sales is explained by the model. The coefficient of determination adjusted for degrees of freedom is .0803. The model fits poorly.

c The standard error of estimate is $s_\varepsilon = 2.59$. It is an estimate of the standard deviation of the error variable.

d $\qquad H_0 : \beta_1 = \beta_2 = \beta_3 = 0$

$\qquad H_1$: At least one β_i is not equal to zero

F = 1.70, p-value = .1979. There is not enough evidence to conclude that the model is valid.

e $\qquad H_0 : \beta_i = 0$

$\qquad H_1 : \beta_i \neq 0$

Direct: t = .33, p-value = .7437

Newspaper: t = 2.16, p-value = .0427

Television: t = .37, p-value = .7123

Only expenditures on newspaper advertising is linearly related to sales.

f & g

Prediction Interval		
	Sales	
Predicted value	18.21	
Prediction Interval		
Lower limit	12.27	
Upper limit	24.15	
Interval Estimate of Expected Value		
Lower limit	15.70	
Upper limit	20.73	

f We predict that sales will fall between $12,270 and $24,150.

g We estimate that mean sales will fall between $15,700 and $20,730.

h The interval in part f predicts one week's gross sales, whereas the interval in part h estimates the mean weekly gross sales.

19.8

SUMMARY OUTPUT					
Regression Statistics					
Multiple R	0.8415				
R Square	0.7081				
Adjusted R Square	0.7021				
Standard Error	213.7				
Observations	100				
ANOVA					
	df	SS	MS	F	Significance F
Regression	2	10744454	5372227	117.64	0.0000
Residual	97	4429664	45667		
Total	99	15174118			
	Coefficients	Standard Error	t Stat	P-value	
Intercept	576.8	514.0	1.12	0.2646	
Space	90.61	6.48	13.99	0.0000	
Water	9.66	2.41	4.00	0.0001	

a The regression equation is $\hat{y} = 576.8 + 90.61x_1 + 9.66x_2$

b The standard error of estimate is $s_\varepsilon = 213.7$. It is an estimate of the standard deviation of the error variable.

c The coefficient of determination is $R^2 = .7081$; 70.81% of the variation in sales is explained by the model. The coefficient of determination adjusted for degrees of freedom is .7021. The model fits reasonably well.

d $\quad H_0 : \beta_1 = \beta_2 = 0$

$\quad\quad H_1$: At least one β_i is not equal to zero

F = 117.64, p-value = 0. There is enough evidence to conclude that the model is valid.

e & f

Prediction Interval		
		Consumption
Predicted value		8175
Prediction Interval		
Lower limit		7748
Upper limit		8601
Interval Estimate of Expected Value		
Lower limit		8127
Upper limit		8222

e We predict that the house will consume between 7748 and 8601 units of electricity.

f We estimate that the average house will consume between 8127 and 8222 units of electricity.

19.9

SUMMARY OUTPUT					
Regression Statistics					
Multiple R	0.7825				
R Square	0.6123				
Adjusted R Square	0.5835				
Standard Error	2.16				
Observations	30				
ANOVA					
	df	SS	MS	F	Significance F
Regression	2	199.65	99.82	21.32	0.0000
Residual	27	126.44	4.68		
Total	29	326.09			
	Coefficients	Standard Error	t Stat	P-value	
Intercept	29.60	2.08	14.22	0.0000	
Vacancy	-0.31	0.07	-4.58	0.0001	
Unemployment	-1.11	0.24	-4.73	0.0001	

a The regression equation is $\hat{y} = 29.60 - .31x_1 - 1.11x_2$

b The coefficient of determination is $R^2 = .6123$; 61.23% of the variation in office rents is explained by the model. The model fits reasonably well.

c $\quad\quad H_0 : \beta_1 = \beta_2 = 0$

$\quad\quad H_1$: At least one β_i is not equal to zero

$F = 21.32$, p-value = 0. There is enough evidence to conclude that the model is valid.

d $\quad\quad H_0 : \beta_i = 0$

$\quad\quad H_1 : \beta_i \neq 0$

Vacancy rate: $t = -4.58$, p-value = .0001

Unemployment rate: $t = -4.73$, p-value = .0001

Both vacancy and unemployment rates are linearly related to rents.

e

Prediction Interval			
		Rent	
Predicted value		18.72	
Prediction Interval			
Lower limit		14.18	
Upper limit		23.27	
Interval Estimate of Expected Value			
Lower limit		17.76	
Upper limit		19.68	

The city's office rent is predicted to lie between $14.18 and $23.27.

19.10

SUMMARY OUTPUT					
Regression Statistics					
Multiple R	0.4455				
R Square	0.1985				
Adjusted R Square	0.1903				
Standard Error	4.19				
Observations	200				
ANOVA					
	df	*SS*	*MS*	*F*	*Significance F*
Regression	2	856.42	428.21	24.39	0.0000
Residual	197	3458.98	17.56		
Total	199	4315.40			
	Coefficients	*Standard Error*	*t Stat*	*P-value*	
Intercept	13.03	2.54	5.12	0.0000	
Age	-0.279	0.045	-6.22	0.0000	
Income	0.094	0.031	3.00	0.0030	

a The regression equation is $\hat{y} = 13.03 - .279x_1 + .094x_2$

b The coefficient of determination is $R^2 = .1985$; 19.85% of the variation in internet use is explained by the model. The model fits poorly.

c $H_0 : \beta_1 = \beta_2 = 0$

H_1 : At least one β_i is not equal to zero

$F = 24.39$, p-value = 0. There is enough evidence to conclude that the model is valid.

d

Prediction Interval		
	Internet	
Predicted value	6.55	
Prediction Interval		
Lower limit	-0.40	
Upper limit	13.50	
Interval Estimate of Expected Value		
Lower limit	5.98	
Upper limit	7.13	

Internet use is predicted to fall between 0 (minimum) and 13.50 hours per week.

e

Prediction Interval		Internet	
Predicted value		7.94	
Prediction Interval			
Lower limit		-0.49	
Upper limit		16.37	
Interval Estimate of Expected Value			
Lower limit		6.27	
Upper limit		9.61	

Mean Internet use is estimated to lie between 6.27 and 9.61 hours per week.

19.11a

Prediction Interval		Price	
Predicted value		103.87	
Prediction Interval			
Lower limit		35.50	
Upper limit		172.24	
Interval Estimate of Expected Value			
Lower limit		91.86	
Upper limit		115.88	

The selling price is predicted to be between $35,500 and $172,240.

b

Prediction Interval		Price	
Predicted value		64.80	
Prediction Interval			
Lower limit		-7.18	
Upper limit		136.78	
Interval Estimate of Expected Value			
Lower limit		39.29	
Upper limit		90.30	

The mean selling price of the lots is estimated to be between $39,290 and $90,300.

19.12a & b

Prediction Interval		
		Final
Predicted value		30.9
Prediction Interval		
Lower limit		23.0
Upper limit		38.8
Interval Estimate of Expected Val		
Lower limit		29.0
Upper limit		32.9

a Pat's final exam mark is predicted to be between 23 and 38.8 (out of 50).

b Lower limit = 12/20 + 14/30 + 23/50 = 49%,

Upper limit = 12/20 + 14/30 + 38.8/50 = 64.8%,

19.13

Prediction Interval		
		Drywall
Predicted value		260.0
Prediction Interval		
Lower limit		167.1
Upper limit		352.9
Interval Estimate of Expected Value		
Lower limit		220.3
Upper limit		299.7

We predict that the company will sell between 16,710 and 35,290 sheets of drywall.

19.14 a The histogram is roughly bell-shaped indicating that the error variable is approximately normal.

b There is no sign of heteroscedasticity. The error variable's variance is constant.

19.15

	Price	Lot size	Trees	Distance
Price	1			
Lot size	0.3035	1		
Trees	0.3891	0.2857	1	
Distance	-0.2326	-0.1895	0.0794	1

The independent variables are only weakly correlated. The conclusions produced from the t-tests ate valid.

19.16

	Final	Assignment	Midterm
Final	1		
Assignment	0.1803	1	
Midterm	0.8687	0.1037	1

The two variables are very weakly correlated. The two t-tests are valid.

19.17 a The histogram is somewhat bell-shaped indicating that the error variable is at least approximately normal.

b There is no sign of heteroscedasticity. The error variable's variance is constant.

19.18

	Father	Son	Mother
Father	1		
Son	0.5163	1	
Mother	0.2511	0.1055	1

a The heights of mothers and fathers are weakly correlated. The amount of correlation however, is not likely a problem.

b The two test results are valid.

19.19

	MBA GPA	UnderGPA	GMAT	Work
MBA GPA	1			
UnderGPA	0.0121	1		
GMAT	0.6365	-0.0457	1	
Work	0.2080	0.0006	-0.0466	1

The independent variables are only weakly correlated. The conclusions produced from the t-tests ate valid.

19.20 a The regression equation is $\hat{y} = -103.1 + 5.82x_1 + 8.56x_2$

b Observations 63, 81, 82, and 97 should be checked

c The histogram is bell-shaped. The error variable is normally distributed.

d The variance of the error variable grows as $\hat{y}$ increases. It appears that the error variable's variance is not constant.

19.21 a The regression equation is $\hat{y} = -12.34 + 3.31x_1 + 1.08x_2$

b Observations 36 and 43 should be checked.

c The histogram is approximately bell-shaped. The errors are normally distributed.

d The variance of the error variable grows as $\hat{y}$ increases. It appears that the error variable's variance is not constant.

19.22 The histogram of the residuals is bell shaped and the variance of the error variable appears to be constant.

19.23 The histogram is positively skewed and the variance of the error variable is not constant.

19.24 The histogram of the residuals is bell shaped and the variance of the error variable appears to be constant.

19.25a

	Weeks SP	Age	Years	Pay
Weeks SP	1			
Age	0.6700	1		
Years	0.8309	0.8080	1	
Pay	0.1130	0.1725	0.2610	1

The correlation between Age and Years is high enough to cause multicollinearity.

c The histogram is bell-shaped. The error variable appears to be normal.

d The variance of the error variable appears to be constant.

e Observation 10 should be checked.

19.26a The histogram is slightly skewed but it does appear that the errors are normally distributed. The error variable's variance appears to be constant.

b

	HS GPA	SAT	Activities
HS GPA	1		
SAT	-0.1019	1	
Activities	0.1310	-0.1653	1

The correlations among the independent variables are small. Multicollinearity is not a problem.

c Observation 91's standardized residual is greater than 2. It should be checked.

19.27a The histogram is bell-shaped indicating that the errors are normally distributed.
The error variable's variance does not appear to be constant.

b

	Sales	Direct	Newspaper	Television
Sales	1			
Direct	-0.0026	1		
Newspaper	0.4320	-0.1376	1	
Television	0.1293	-0.1246	0.1468	1

The correlations among independent variables are small; multicollinearity is not a problem.

19.28a The histogram is bell-shaped; the errors appear to be normally distributed. The error variable's variance appears to be constant.

b

	Consumption	Space	Water
Consumption	1		
Space	0.8123	1	
Water	0.3451	0.1578	1

There is a weak correlation between the two independent variables.

19.29 The histogram is somewhat positively skewed, but not sufficiently to infer that the errors are not normally distributed. The variance of the error variable appears to be constant.

19.30 The histogram is negatively skewed. It appears that the errors are not normally distributed. The variance of the error variable is not constant.

19.31 $d_L = .95$, $d_U = 1.89$, $4 - d_U = 2.11$, $4 - d_L = 3.05$. There is evidence of first-order autocorrelation.

19.32 $d_L = 1.46$, $d_U = 1.63$. There is evidence of positive first-order autocorrelation.

19.33 $d_L = 1.41$, $d_U = 1.64$, $4 - d_U = 2.36$, $4 - d_L = 2.59$. The test is inconclusive

19.34 $4 - d_U = 4 - 1.73 = 2.27$, $4 - d_L = 4 - 1.19 = 2.81$. There is no evidence of negative first-order autocorrelation.

19.35 a The regression equation is $\hat{y} = 303.3 + 14.94\,x_1 + 10.52\,x_2$

c Check observations 8, 15, 34, and 94.

d The histogram is bell-shaped.

e The error variable variance appears to be constant.

f $d = .7749$; $d_L = 1.63$, $d_U = 1.72$, $4 - d_U = 2.28$, $4 - d_L = 2.37$. There is evidence of first-order autocorrelation.

g The model is $y = \beta_0 + \beta_1 x_1 + \beta_2 x_2 + \beta_3 t + \varepsilon$

The regression equation is $\hat{y} = 10.00 + 6.78\,x_1 + 9.37\,x_2 + 9.64t$

h First model: $s_\varepsilon = 348.7$ and $R^2 = .2825$. Second model: $s_\varepsilon = 208.1$ and $R^2 = .7471$

The second model fits better.

19.36 a The regression equation is $\hat{y} = 2260 + .423x$

c Check observation 4.

d The histogram is bell-shaped.

e The error variable variance appears to be constant.

f $d = .7859$; $d_L \approx 1.50$, $d_U \approx 1.59$, $4 - d_U \approx 2.41$, $4 - d_L \approx 2.50$. There is evidence of first-order autocorrelation.

g The model is $y = \beta_0 + \beta_1 x + \beta_2 t + \varepsilon$

The regression equation is $\hat{y} = 446.2 + 1.10x + 38.92t$

h First model: $s_\varepsilon = 709.7$ and $R^2 = .0146$. Second model: $s_\varepsilon = 413.7$ and $R^2 = .6718$.

The second model fits better.

19.37 a $\hat{y} = 3476 - 47.90\,x_1 + 22.54\,x_2 + 1.41\,x_3$

c Observations 72 and 75 should be checked.

d The histogram is bell-shaped.

e The variance of the errors appears to be constant.

f $d = .7009$; $d_L = 1.56$, $d_U = 1.72$, $4 - d_U = 2.28$, $4 - d_L = 2.44$. There is evidence of first-order autocorrelation.

g The model is $y = \beta_0 + \beta_1 x_1 + \beta_2 x_2 + \beta_3 x_3 + \beta_4 t + \varepsilon$

The regression equation is $\hat{y} = 3248 - 52.71\,x_1 + 17.05\,x_2 + 2.14\,x_3 + 10.44t$

h First model: $s_\varepsilon = 305.8$ and $R^2 = .6481$. Second model: $s_\varepsilon = 186.8$ and $R^2 = .8704$. The second model fits better.

19.38 a The errors appear to be normally distributed.

b There does not appear to be a change in spread; there is no sign of heteroscedasticity.

19.39 a The independent variables are uncorrelated.

b There is little multicollinearity; the t-tests of the coefficients are valid.

19.40 $d = 1.755$; $d_L = 1.01$, $d_U = 1.78$, $4 - d_U = 2.22$, $4 - d_L = 2.99$. The test is inconclusive.

19.41 The histogram is bell-shaped; the errors appear to be normally distributed. The variance of the error variable appears to be constant.

$d = 2.2003$; $d_L = 1.30$, $d_U = 1.46$, $4 - d_U = 2.54$, $4 - d_L = 2.70$. There is no evidence of first-order autocorrelation

19.42 The histogram is bell-shaped; apparently the errors are normally distributed.

c Check observations 1, 11, 25, 28, and 46.

d The error variable variance appears to be constant.

e The errors appear to be independent.

f $d = 1.9547$; $d_L = 1.55$, $d_U = 1.62$, $4 - d_U = 2.38$, $4 - d_L = 2.45$. There is no evidence of first-order autocorrelation.

19.43

SUMMARY OUTPUT					
Regression Statistics					
Multiple R	0.6143				
R Square	0.3774				
Adjusted R Square	0.3462				
Standard Error	68.63				
Observations	22				
ANOVA					
	df	*SS*	*MS*	*F*	*Significance F*
Regression	1	57089	57089	12.12	0.0024
Residual	20	94196	4710		
Total	21	151285			
	Coefficients	*Standard Error*	*t Stat*	*P-value*	
Intercept	898.0	35.97	24.97	0.0000	
Snowfall	11.33	3.25	3.48	0.0024	

a The regression equation is $\hat{y} = 898.0 + 11.33x$

b The histogram is bell-shaped. The errors appear to be normally distributed. Heteroscedasticity may exist although the plot is not clear.

$d = 1.0062; d_L = 1.24, d_U = 1.53, 4 - d_U = 2.47, 4 - d_L = 2.76$. There is evidence of first-order autocorrelation.

c The problem is that the errors are not independent. We add a time variable to the model. Thus, the new model is $y = \beta_0 + \beta_1 x + \beta_2 t + \varepsilon$.

SUMMARY OUTPUT					
Regression Statistics					
Multiple R	0.8390				
R Square	0.7040				
Adjusted R Square	0.6728				
Standard Error	48.55				
Observations	22				
ANOVA					
	df	*SS*	*MS*	*F*	*Significance F*
Regression	2	106501	53250	22.59	0.0000
Residual	19	44785	2357		
Total	21	151285			
	Coefficients	*Standard Error*	*t Stat*	*P-value*	
Intercept	960.6	28.88	33.26	0.0000	
Snowfall	13.88	2.37	5.86	0.0000	
t	-7.69	1.68	-4.58	0.0002	

The regression equation is $\hat{y} = 960.6 + 13.88x - 7.69t$

d The standard error of estimate is 48.55 and the coefficient of determination is .7040.

e $b_1 = 13.88$; for each additional inch of snowfall sales on average increase by 13.88 assuming that time stays the same. $b_2 = -7.69$; sales decreases on average by 7.69 per week assuming the snowfall stays the same. The y-intercept is 960.6.

19.44

Prediction Interval		
	MBA GPA	
Predicted value	8.54	
Prediction Interval		
Lower limit	6.87	
Upper limit	10.20	
Interval Estimate of Expected Value		
Lower limit	7.98	
Upper limit	9.10	

Lower prediction limit = 6.87, upper prediction limit = 10.20

19.45

Prediction Interval		
	MBA GPA	
Predicted value	7.66	
Prediction Interval		
Lower limit	6.05	
Upper limit	9.27	
Interval Estimate of Expected Value		
Lower limit	7.31	
Upper limit	8.02	

Lower confidence limit = 7.31, upper confidence limit = 8.02

19.46a

SUMMARY OUTPUT					
Regression Statistics					
Multiple R	0.7023				
R Square	0.4933				
Adjusted R Square	0.4726				
Standard Error	558.7				
Observations	52				
ANOVA					
	df	*SS*	*MS*	*F*	*Significance F*
Regression	2	14887583	7443791	23.85	0.0000
Residual	49	15294148	312125		
Total	51	30181731			
	Coefficients	*Standard Error*	*t Stat*	*P-value*	
Intercept	3719	857.6	4.34	0.0001	
Price A	-46.77	10.83	-4.32	0.0001	
Price B	58.52	10.46	5.59	0.0000	

b $s_\varepsilon = 558.7$ and $R^2 = .4933$; The model's fit is only moderately good.

c $b_1 = -46.77$; for each one cent increase in the price of milk sales decrease on average by 46.77 provided that the competitor's price remains unchanged.

$b_2 = 58.52$; for each one cent increase in the competitor's price of milk sales increase on average by 58.52 provided that the company's price remains unchanged.

d $\qquad H_0 : \beta_i = 0$

$\qquad H_1 : \beta_i \neq 0$

Company's price: t = -4.32, p-value = .0001

Competitor's price: t = 5.59, p-value = 0

Both prices are linearly related to sales.

e $\qquad H_0 : \beta_1 = \beta_2 = 0$

$\qquad H_1$: At least one β_i is not equal to zero

$\qquad$ F = MSR/MSE

F = 23.85, p-value = 0. There is enough evidence to conclude that the model is valid.

f

Prediction Interval		
	Sales	
Predicted value	3312	
Prediction Interval		
Lower limit	2341	
Upper limit	4284	
Interval Estimate of Expected Value		
Lower limit	3055	
Upper limit	3570	

We predict that sales will fall between 2341 and 4284.

19.47a The histogram is not bell-shaped. The errors may not be normal. The variance of the errors appears to be constant. The errors appear to be correlated.

d = .5971; $d_L \approx 1.46$, $d_U \approx 1.63$, $4 - d_U = 2.37$, $4 - d_L = 2.54$. There is evidence of first-order autocorrelation.

b

	Sales	Price A	Price B
Sales	1		
Price A	-0.4121	1	
Price B	0.5481	0.0485	1

There is no multicollinearity.

19.48a

SUMMARY OUTPUT					
Regression Statistics					
Multiple R	0.5926				
R Square	0.3511				
Adjusted R Square	0.3352				
Standard Error	6.99				
Observations	126				
ANOVA					
	df	*SS*	*MS*	*F*	*Significance F*
Regression	3	3227.61	1075.87	22.01	0.0000
Residual	122	5964.52	48.89		
Total	125	9192.13			
	Coefficients	*Standard Error*	*t Stat*	*P-value*	
Intercept	-1.97	9.55	-0.21	0.8369	
Minor HR	0.67	0.09	7.64	0.0000	
Age	0.14	0.52	0.26	0.7961	
Years Pro	1.18	0.67	1.75	0.0819	

b $b_1 = .67$; for each additional minor league home run the number of major league home runs increases on average by .67 provided that the other variables remain constant.

$b_2 = .14$; for each additional year of age the number of major league home runs increases on average by .14 provided that the other variables remain constant.

$b_3 = 1.18$; for each additional year as a professional the number of major league home runs increases on average by 1.18 provided that the other variables remain constant.

c $s_\varepsilon = 6.99$ and $R^2 = .3511$; the model's fit is not very good.

d $\qquad H_0 : \beta_1 = \beta_2 = \beta_3 = 0$

$\qquad H_1$: At least one β_i is not equal to zero

F = 22.01, p-value = 0. There is enough evidence to conclude that the model is valid.

e $\qquad H_0 : \beta_i = 0$

$\qquad H_1 : \beta_i \neq 0$

Minor league home runs: t = 7.64, p-value = 0

Age: t = .26, p-value = .7961

Years professional: t = 1.75, p-value = .0819

At the 5% significance level only the number of minor league home runs is linearly related to the number of major league home runs.

f

Prediction Interval		Major HR	
		Major HR	
Predicted value		24.31	
Prediction Interval			
Lower limit		9.86	
Upper limit		38.76	
Interval Estimate of Expected Value			
Lower limit		20.16	
Upper limit		28.45	

We predict that the player will hit between 9.86 (rounded to 10) and 38.76 (rounded to 39) home runs.

g

Prediction Interval		Major HR	
		Major HR	
Predicted value		19.56	
Prediction Interval			
Lower limit		4.88	
Upper limit		34.25	
Interval Estimate of Expected Value			
Lower limit		14.66	
Upper limit		24.47	

It is estimated that the average player will hit between 14.66 and 24.47 home runs

19.49a The error variable appears to be normal. The variance of the errors may not be constant.

b

	Major HR	Minor HR	Age	Years Pro
Major HR	1			
Minor HR	0.5537	1		
Age	0.1873	0.0354	1	
Years Pro	0.1883	-0.0392	0.7355	1

Age and years professional are highly correlated. This result is logical and we should have used only one of these variables.

19.50

SUMMARY OUTPUT					
Regression Statistics					
Multiple R	0.6447				
R Square	0.4157				
Adjusted R Square	0.3724				
Standard Error	57.29				
Observations	30				
ANOVA					
	df	*SS*	*MS*	*F*	*Significance F*
Regression	2	63043	31521	9.60	0.0007
Residual	27	88626	3282		
Total	29	151669			
	Coefficients	*Standard Error*	*t Stat*	*P-value*	
Intercept	194.84	32.58	5.98	0.0000	
Fetilizer	0.12	0.07	1.66	0.1088	
Water	0.025	0.006	4.06	0.0004	

a $\hat{y} = 194.84 + .12x_1 + .025x_2$

b $H_0 : \beta_1 = 0$

   $H_1 : \beta_1 \neq 0$

t = 1.66, p-value = .1088. There is not enough evidence to infer that the amount of fertilizer and yield are linearly related.

c $H_0 : \beta_2 = 0$

   $H_1 : \beta_2 \neq 0$

t = 4.06, p-value = .0004. There is enough evidence to infer that the amount of water and yield are linearly related.

d $s_\varepsilon = 57.29$ and $R^2 = .4157$; the model's fit is not very good.

e

Prediction Interval		
	Yield	
Predicted value	232.0	
Prediction Interval		
Lower limit	104.7	
Upper limit	359.2	
Interval Estimate of Expected Value		
Lower limit	183.3	
Upper limit	280.6	

The yield is predicted to fall between 104.7 and 359.2.

19.51 The histogram is slightly negatively skewed but not enough to conclude that the error variable is not normal. There appears to be a decrease in the variance as the predicted value increases. A transformation is recommended to remedy the violations of the required conditions.

19.52a

SUMMARY OUTPUT					
Regression Statistics					
Multiple R	0.5975				
R Square	0.3570				
Adjusted R Square	0.3034				
Standard Error	7.72				
Observations	40				
ANOVA					
	df	*SS*	*MS*	*F*	*Significance F*
Regression	3	1192.73	397.58	6.66	0.0011
Residual	36	2148.06	59.67		
Total	39	3340.79			
	Coefficients	*Standard Error*	*t Stat*	*P-value*	
Intercept	35.68	7.28	4.90	0.0000	
Math Degree	0.25	0.07	3.54	0.0011	
Age	0.24	0.19	1.32	0.1945	
Income	0.13	0.15	0.87	0.3889	

a $\hat{y} = 35.68 + .25x_1 + .24x_2 + .13x_3$

b $H_0 : \beta_1 = \beta_2 = \beta_3 = 0$

  H_1 : At least one β_i is not equal to zero

F = 6.66, p-value = .0011. There is enough evidence to conclude that the model is valid.

c The error variable appears to be normal. The variance of the errors appears to be constant.

d

	Test Score	*Math Degree*	*Age*	*Income*
Test Score	1			
Math Degree	0.5066	1		
Age	0.3325	0.0766	1	
Income	0.3120	0.0994	0.5698	1

The correlation between income and age is high enough to distort the t-tests.

e $b_1 = .25$; for each one percentage point increase in the proportion of teachers with mathematics degrees the test score increases on average by .25 provided the other variables are constant.

$b_2 = .24$; for each one year increase in mean age test score increases on average by .24 provided the other variables are constant (which may not be possible because of the multicollinearity).

$b_3 = .13$; for each one thousand dollar increase in salary test score increases on average by .13 provided the other variables are constant (which may not be possible because of the multicollinearity).

$$H_0 : \beta_i = 0$$

$$H_1 : \beta_i \neq 0$$

Proportion of teachers with at least one mathematics degree: t = 3.54, p-value = .0011

Age: t = 1.32, p-value = .1945

Income: t = .87, p-value = .3889.

The proportion of teachers with at least one mathematics degree is linearly related to test scores. The other two variables may be related to test scores but the multicollinarity makes it difficult to discern.

f

Prediction Interval		
	Test Score	
Predicted value	65.02	
Prediction Interval		
Lower limit	49.02	
Upper limit	81.02	
Interval Estimate of Expected Value		
Lower limit	61.75	
Upper limit	68.28	

The school's test score is predicted to fall between 49.02 and 81.02.

19.53a

SUMMARY OUTPUT					
Regression Statistics					
Multiple R	0.8608				
R Square	0.7411				
Adjusted R Square	0.7301				
Standard Error	2.66				
Observations	100				
ANOVA					
	df	*SS*	*MS*	*F*	*Significance F*
Regression	4	1929.5	482.38	67.97	0.0000
Residual	95	674.2	7.10		
Total	99	2603.8			
	Coefficients	*Standard Error*	*t Stat*	*P-value*	
Intercept	3.24	5.42	0.60	0.5512	
Mother	0.45	0.05	8.27	0.0000	
Father	0.41	0.05	8.26	0.0000	
Gmothers	0.017	0.066	0.25	0.8028	
Gfathers	0.087	0.066	1.32	0.1890	

b $H_0 : \beta_1 = \beta_2 = \beta_3 = 0$

H_1 : At least one β_i is not equal to zero

$F = 67.97$, p-value = 0. There is enough evidence to conclude that the model is valid.

c The errors appear to be normally distributed. The variance of the error variable appears to be constant.

d

	Longevity	*Mother*	*Father*	*Gmothers*	*Gfathers*
Longevity	1				
Mother	0.7056	1			
Father	0.6643	0.2766	1		
Gmothers	0.3626	0.4343	0.2409	1	
Gfathers	0.4713	0.3910	0.3752	-0.0077	1

The correlations are likely large enough to produce a problem.

e $b_1 = .45$; for each one year increase in the mother's age the customer's age increases on average by .45 provided the other variables are constant (which may not be possible because of the multicollinearity).

$b_2 = .41$; for each one year increase in the father's age the customer's age increases on average by .41 provided the other variables are constant (which may not be possible because of the multicollinearity).

$b_3 = .017$; for each one year increase in the grandmothers' mean age the customer's age increases on average by .017 provided the other variables are constant (which may not be possible because of the multicollinearity).

$b_4 = .087$; for each one year increase in the grandfathers' mean age the customer's age increases on average by .087 provided the other variables are constant (which may not be possible because of the multicollinearity).

$$H_0 : \beta_i = 0$$

$$H_1 : \beta_i \neq 0$$

Mothers: t = 8.27, p-value = 0

Fathers: t = 8.26, p-value = 0

Grandmothers: t = .25, p-value .8028

Grandfathers: t = 1.32, p-value = .1890

The ages of mothers and fathers are linearly related to the ages of their children. The other two variables may be related to the customers' longevity but the multicollinarity makes it difficult to discern.

f

Prediction Interval		
	Longevity	
Predicted value	71.43	
Prediction Interval		
Lower limit	65.54	
Upper limit	77.31	
Interval Estimate of Expected Value		
Lower limit	68.85	
Upper limit	74.00	

The man is predicted to live to an age between 65.54 and 77.31

g

Prediction Interval		
	Longevity	
Predicted value	71.71	
Prediction Interval		
Lower limit	65.65	
Upper limit	77.77	
Interval Estimate of Expected Value		
Lower limit	68.75	
Upper limit	74.66	

The mean longevity is estimated to fall between 68.75 and 74.66.

19.54

SUMMARY OUTPUT					
Regression Statistics					
Multiple R	0.8491				
R Square	0.7209				
Adjusted R Square	0.7090				
Standard Error	7.01				
Observations	50				
ANOVA					
	df	SS	MS	F	Significance F
Regression	2	5963.2	2981.6	60.70	0.0000
Residual	47	2308.8	49.12		
Total	49	8272.0			
	Coefficients	Standard Error	t Stat	P-value	
Intercept	47.77	7.63	6.26	0.0000	
Evaluation	0.78	1.30	0.60	0.5529	
Articles	1.06	0.13	8.08	0.0000	

Diagnosing violations: The error variable appears to be normal. The error variable's variance appears to be constant. The required conditions are satisfied.

Assessing the Model:

$s_\varepsilon = 7.01$ and $R^2 = .7209$; the model fits well.

Testing the validity of the model:

$$H_0 : \beta_1 = \beta_2 = 0$$

$$H_1 : \text{At least one } \beta_i \text{ is not equal to zero}$$

F = 60.70, p-value = 0. There is enough evidence to conclude that the model is valid.

Drawing inferences about the independent variables:

$$H_0 : \beta_i = 0$$

$$H_1 : \beta_i \neq 0$$

Evaluations: t = .60, p-value = .5529

Articles: t = 8.08, p-value = 0.

The number of articles a professor publishes is linearly related to salary. Teaching evaluations are not.

19.55

SUMMARY OUTPUT					
Regression Statistics					
Multiple R	0.8984				
R Square	0.8072				
Adjusted R Square	0.7990				
Standard Error	7.07				
Observations	50				
ANOVA					
	df	*SS*	*MS*	*F*	*Significance F*
Regression	2	9831.9	4915.9	98.37	0.0000
Residual	47	2348.7	49.97		
Total	49	12180.6			
	Coefficients	*Standard Error*	*t Stat*	*P-value*	
Intercept	-28.43	6.89	-4.13	0.0001	
Boxes	0.60	0.06	10.85	0.0000	
Weight	0.37	0.08	4.42	0.0001	

a $\hat{y} = -28.43 + .60x_1 + .37x_2$

b $s_\varepsilon = 7.07$ and $R^2 = .8072$; the model fits well.

c The error variable appears to be normally distributed. The variance of the errors appears to be constant.

d

	Time	*Boxes*	*Weight*
Time	1		
Boxes	0.8526	1	
Weight	0.5694	0.3577	1

The correlation between boxes and weight is large enough to produce multicollinearity problems.

e $b_1 = .60$; for each one additional box, the amount of time to unload increases on average by .60 minutes provided the weight is constant (which may not be possible because of the multicollinearity).

$b_2 = .37$; for each additional hundred pounds the amount of time to unload increases on average by .37 minutes provided the number of bxes is constant (which may not be possible because of the multicollinearity).

$$H_0 : \beta_i = 0$$

$$H_1 : \beta_i \neq 0$$

Boxes: t = 10.85, p-value = 0

Weight: t = 4.42, p-value = .0001

Both variables are linearly related to time to unload.

f & g

Prediction Interval			
		Time	
Predicted value		50.70	
Prediction Interval			
Lower limit		35.16	
Upper limit		66.24	
Interval Estimate of Expected Value			
Lower limit		44.43	
Upper limit		56.96	

It is predicted that the truck will be unloaded in a time between 35.16 and 66.24 minutes. The mean time to unload the trucks is estimated to lie between 44.43 and 56.96 minutes.

19.56

SUMMARY OUTPUT					
Regression Statistics					
Multiple R	0.6584				
R Square	0.4335				
Adjusted R Square	0.4096				
Standard Error	2.91				
Observations	100				
ANOVA					
	df	*SS*	*MS*	*F*	*Significance F*
Regression	4	615.44	153.86	18.17	0.0000
Residual	95	804.35	8.47		
Total	99	1419.79			
	Coefficients	*Standard Error*	*t Stat*	*P-value*	
Intercept	11.91	1.79	6.67	0.0000	
Education	-0.43	0.13	-3.26	0.0016	
Age	0.029	0.025	1.16	0.2501	
Children	0.093	0.224	0.42	0.6780	
Income	-0.074	0.028	-2.69	0.0085	

b $\qquad H_0 : \beta_1 = \beta_2 = \beta_3 = \beta_4 = 0$

$\qquad H_1 :$ At least one β_i is not equal to zero

$F = 18.17$, p-value $= 0$. There is enough evidence to conclude that the model is valid.

c The errors appear to be normally distributed. The variance of the errors is not constant.

d

	Lottery	*Education*	*Age*	*Children*	*Income*
Lottery	1				
Education	-0.6202	1			
Age	0.1767	-0.1782	1		
Children	-0.0230	0.1073	0.1072	1	
Income	-0.5891	0.7339	-0.0418	0.0801	1

There is a strong correlation between income and education. The t-tests of these two coefficients may be distorted.

e $\qquad H_0 : \beta_i = 0$

$\qquad H_1 : \beta_i < 0$ (for beliefs 1 and 4)

$\qquad H_1 : \beta_i > 0$ for beliefs 2 and 3)

Belief 1: t = -3.26, p-value = .0016/2 = .0008

Belief 2: t = 1.16, p-value = .2501/2 = .1251

Belief 3: t = .42, p-value = .6780/2 = .3390

Belief 4: t = -2.69, p-value = .0085/2 = .0043

Despite multicollinearity, there is enough evidence to support beliefs 1 and 4. There is no evidence to support beliefs 2 and 3.

Case 19.1

SUMMARY OUTPUT					
Regression Statistics					
Multiple R	0.1228				
R Square	0.0151				
Adjusted R Square	0.0131				
Standard Error	8.30				
Observations	2029				
ANOVA					
	df	*SS*	*MS*	*F*	*Significance F*
Regression	4	2137	534.3	7.75	0.0000
Residual	2024	139561	69.0		
Total	2028	141698			
	Coefficients	*Standard Error*	*t Stat*	*P-value*	
Intercept	-1.15	2.20	-0.52	0.6012	
SAT	0.0051	0.0013	3.96	0.0001	
MBA	0.674	0.376	1.79	0.0730	
Age	-0.141	0.042	-3.31	0.0009	
Tenure	0.082	0.176	0.47	0.6412	

The model is valid (F = 7.75, p-value = 0) but the model does not fit well (R^2 = .0151; only 1.51% of the variation in returns is explained by the model).

Interpreting the coefficients in this sample:

For each additional one-point increase in the SAT score, returns increase on average by .0051 provided the other variables remain constant.

The returns of mutual funds managed by MBAs are on average .674 larger than the returns of mutual funds managed by people without an MBA

For each additional one-year increase in age of the manager , returns decrease on average by .141 provided the other variables remain constant.

For each additional one-year increase in the manager's job tenure, returns increase on average by .082 provided the other variables remain constant.

Testing the coefficients:

SAT: t = 3.96, p-value = .0001

MBA: t = 1.79, p-value = .0730

Age: t = -3.31, p-value = .0009

Tenure: t = .47, p-value = .6412

There is overwhelming evidence to infer that SAT scores of the undergraduate university and age of the manager are linearly related to returns. There is weak evidence that MBAs and non-MBAs have different mean returns. There is not enough evidence to conclude that job tenure is linearly related to returns.

Case 19.2

Analysis of Betas

SUMMARY OUTPUT					
Regression Statistics					
Multiple R	0.3597				
R Square	0.1294				
Adjusted R Square	0.1277				
Standard Error	0.2245				
Observations	2029				
ANOVA					
	df	*SS*	*MS*	*F*	*Significance F*
Regression	4	15.15	3.79	75.20	0.0000
Residual	2024	101.97	0.050		
Total	2028	117.12			
	Coefficients	*Standard Error*	*t Stat*	*P-value*	
Intercept	0.152	0.059	2.56	0.0107	
SAT	0.00050	0.000035	14.55	0.0000	
MBA	0.0366	0.0102	3.60	0.0003	
Age	0.0088	0.0011	7.66	0.0000	
Tenure	-0.0352	0.0047	-7.42	0.0000	

The model is valid (F = 75.20, p-value = 0) with $R^2 = .1294$; only 12.94% of the variation in betas is explained by the model.

Interpreting the coefficients in this sample:

For each additional one-point increase in the SAT score, betas increase on average by .00050 provided the other variables remain constant.

455

The betas of mutual funds managed by MBAs are on average .0366 larger than the betas of mutual funds managed by people without an MBA

For each additional one-year increase in age of the manager, betas increase on average by .0088 provided the other variables remain constant.

For each additional one-year increase in the manager's job tenure, betas decrease on average by .0352 provided the other variables remain constant.

Testing the coefficients:

SAT: t = 14.55, p-value = 0

MBA: t = 3.60, p-value = .0003

Age: t = 7.66, p-value = 0

Tenure: t = -7.42, p-value = 0

There is overwhelming evidence to infer that all four independent variables are linearly related to mutual fund betas.

Analysis of MERs

SUMMARY OUTPUT					
Regression Statistics					
Multiple R	0.2697				
R Square	0.0728				
Adjusted R Square	0.0705				
Standard Error	0.6847				
Observations	2029				
ANOVA					
	df	*SS*	*MS*	*F*	*Significance F*
Regression	5	74.42	14.88	31.74	0.0000
Residual	2023	948.48	0.469		
Total	2028	1022.90			
	Coefficients	*Standard Error*	*t Stat*	*P-value*	
Intercept	2.89	0.183	15.73	0.0000	
SAT	-0.00055	0.00011	-5.21	0.0000	
MBA	-0.082	0.031	-2.65	0.0081	
Age	0.013	0.0035	3.80	0.0001	
Tenure	0.0375	0.0145	2.59	0.0097	
Log Assets	-0.209	0.023	-9.13	0.0000	

The model is valid (F = 31.74, p-value = 0) with R^2 = .0728; only 7.28% of the variation in MERs is explained by the model.

Interpreting the coefficients in this sample:

For each additional one-point increase in the SAT score, MERs decrease on average by .00055 provided the other variables remain constant.

The MERs of mutual funds managed by MBAs are on average .082 smaller than the MERs of mutual funds managed by people without an MBA

For each additional one-year increase in age of the manager, MERs increase on average by .013 provided the other variables remain constant.

For each additional one-year increase in the manager's job tenure, MERs increase on average by .0375 provided the other variables remain constant.

For each additional one-point increase in the log of the assets, MERs decrease on average by .209 provided the other variables remain constant.

Testing the coefficients:

SAT: $t = -5.21$, p-value $= 0$

MBA: $t = -2.65$, p-value $= .0081$

Age: $t = 3.80$, p-value $= .0001$

Tenure: $t = 2.59$, p-value $= .0097$

Log Assets: $t = -9.13$, p-value $= 0$

There is overwhelming evidence to infer that all five independent variables are linearly related to mutual fund MERs.

Case 19.3

The 125 ridings are the complete population. However, for the purposes of the analysis that follows we will assume that these ridings are a sample of all referendums that the government will hold in the future.

SUMMARY OUTPUT					
Regression Statistics					
Multiple R	0.3721				
R Square	0.1385				
Adjusted R Square	0.1171				
Standard Error	0.9811				
Observations	125				
ANOVA					
	df	*SS*	*MS*	*F*	*Significance F*
Regression	3	18.72	6.24	6.48	0.0004
Residual	121	116.47	0.96		
Total	124	135.18			
	Coefficients	*Standard Error*	*t Stat*	*P-value*	
Intercept	1.57	0.739	2.12	0.0362	
Pct Yes	0.00026	0.012	0.02	0.9827	
Pct Allo	0.0367	0.0103	3.56	0.0005	
Pct Anglo	-0.0090	0.0130	-0.70	0.4878	

The only independent variable related to the percentage of rejected ballots is the percentage of Allophones. It does indicate that in ridings where there was a large number of Allophones the percentage of rejected ballots was also high.

b Scrutineers tended to reject "No" ballots.

20.1 a

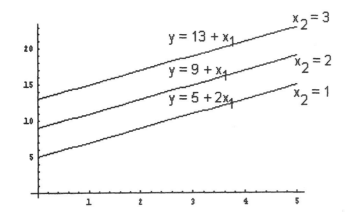

b

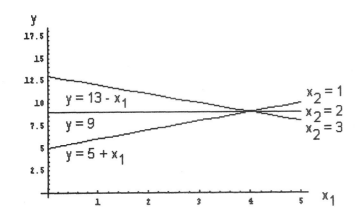

20.2 a

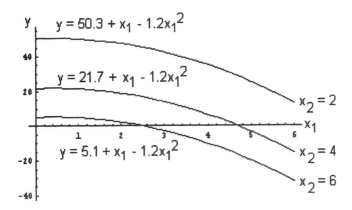

b

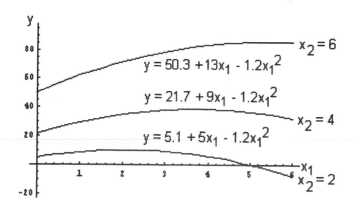

20.3 a Sales $= \beta_0 + \beta_1 \text{Space} + \beta_2 \text{Space}^2 + \varepsilon$

b

SUMMARY OUTPUT					
Regression Statistics					
Multiple R	0.6378				
R Square	0.4068				
Adjusted R Square	0.3528				
Standard Error	41.15				
Observations	25				
ANOVA					
	df	*SS*	*MS*	*F*	*Significance F*
Regression	2	25540	12770	7.54	0.0032
Residual	22	37248	1693		
Total	24	62788			
	Coefficients	*Standard Error*	*t Stat*	*P-value*	
Intercept	-108.99	97.24	-1.12	0.2744	
Space	33.09	8.59	3.85	0.0009	
Space-sq	-0.666	0.177	-3.75	0.0011	

$s_\varepsilon = 41.15$ and $R^2 = .4068$. The model's fit is relatively poor.

$F = 7.54$, p-value $= .0032$. However, there is enough evidence to support the validity of the model.

20.4a   First-order model: a Demand $= \beta_0 + \beta_1 \text{Price} + \varepsilon$

Second-order model: a Demand $= \beta_0 + \beta_1 \text{Price} + \beta_2 \text{Price}^2 + \varepsilon$

First-order model:

SUMMARY OUTPUT					
Regression Statistics					
Multiple R	0.9249				
R Square	0.8553				
Adjusted R Square	0.8473				
Standard Error	13.29				
Observations	20				
ANOVA					
	df	*SS*	*MS*	*F*	*Significance F*
Regression	1	18798	18798.0	106.44	0.0000
Residual	18	3179	176.6		
Total	19	21977			
	Coefficients	*Standard Error*	*t Stat*	*P-value*	
Intercept	453.6	15.18	29.87	0.0000	
Price	-68.91	6.68	-10.32	0.0000	

Second-order model:

SUMMARY OUTPUT					
Regression Statistics					
Multiple R	0.9862				
R Square	0.9726				
Adjusted R Square	0.9693				
Standard Error	5.96				
Observations	20				
ANOVA					
	df	*SS*	*MS*	*F*	*Significance F*
Regression	2	21374	10687	301.15	0.0000
Residual	17	603	35.49		
Total	19	21977			
	Coefficients	*Standard Error*	*t Stat*	*P-value*	
Intercept	766.9	37.40	20.50	0.0000	
Price	-359.1	34.19	-10.50	0.0000	
Price-sq	64.55	7.58	8.52	0.0000	

c The second order model fits better because its standard error of estimate is 5.96, whereas that of the first-order models is 13.29

d $\hat{y} = 766.9 - 359.1(2.95) + 64.55(2.95)^2 = 269.3$

20.5a First-order model: a Time $= \beta_0 + \beta_1 \text{Day} + \varepsilon$

Second-order model: a Time $= \beta_0 + \beta_1 \text{Day} + \beta_2 \text{Day}^2 + \varepsilon$

b First-order model

SUMMARY OUTPUT					
Regression Statistics					
Multiple R	0.9222				
R Square	0.8504				
Adjusted R Square	0.8317				
Standard Error	1.79				
Observations	10				
ANOVA					
	df	*SS*	*MS*	*F*	*Significance F*
Regression	1	145.34	145.34	45.48	0.0001
Residual	8	25.56	3.20		
Total	9	170.90			
	Coefficients	*Standard Error*	*t Stat*	*P-value*	
Intercept	41.40	1.22	33.90	0.0000	
Day	-1.33	0.20	-6.74	0.0001	

F = 45.48, p-value = 0. The model is valid.

Second-order model

SUMMARY OUTPUT					
Regression Statistics					
Multiple R	0.9408				
R Square	0.8852				
Adjusted R Square	0.8524				
Standard Error	1.67				
Observations	10				
ANOVA					
	df	*SS*	*MS*	*F*	*Significance F*
Regression	2	151.28	75.64	26.98	0.0005
Residual	7	19.62	2.80		
Total	9	170.90			
	Coefficients	*Standard Error*	*t Stat*	*P-value*	
Intercept	43.73	1.97	22.21	0.0000	
Day	-2.49	0.82	-3.03	0.0191	
Day-sq	0.106	0.073	1.46	0.1889	

F = 26.98, p-value = .0005. The model is valid.

c The second-order model is only slightly better because its standard error of estimate is smaller.

20.6a MBA GPA= $\beta_0 + \beta_1 \text{UnderGPA} + \beta_2 \text{GMAT} + \beta_3 \text{Work} + \beta_4 \text{UnderGPA} \times \text{GMAT} + \varepsilon$

b

SUMMARY OUTPUT					
Regression Statistics					
Multiple R	0.6836				
R Square	0.4674				
Adjusted R Square	0.4420				
Standard Error	0.790				
Observations	89				
ANOVA					
	df	*SS*	*MS*	*F*	*Significance F*
Regression	4	45.97	11.49	18.43	0.0000
Residual	84	52.40	0.62		
Total	88	98.37			
	Coefficients	*Standard Error*	*t Stat*	*P-value*	
Intercept	-11.11	14.97	-0.74	0.4601	
UnderGPA	1.19	1.46	0.82	0.4159	
GMAT	0.0311	0.0255	1.2182	0.2265	
Work	0.0956	0.0312	3.0618	0.0030	
UGPA-GMAT	-0.0019	0.0025	-0.7773	0.4392	

$s_\varepsilon = .790$ and $R^2 = .4674$. The model's fit is relatively poor.

c MBA example $s_\varepsilon = .788$ and $R^2 = .4635$. There is little difference between the fits of the two models.

20.7a

SUMMARY OUTPUT					
Regression Statistics					
Multiple R	0.9330				
R Square	0.8705				
Adjusted R Square	0.8597				
Standard Error	4745				
Observations	40				
ANOVA					
	df	*SS*	*MS*	*F*	*Significance F*
Regression	3	5446857189	1815619063	80.65	0.0000
Residual	36	810445659	22512379		
Total	39	6257302848			
	Coefficients	*Standard Error*	*t Stat*	*P-value*	
Intercept	-82044	48530	-1.69	0.0996	
Home %	98443	97463	1.01	0.3192	
Visiting %	106779	98313	1.09	0.2846	
Home-Visit	53204	196610	0.27	0.7882	

b $\qquad H_0 : \beta_1 = \beta_2 = \beta_3 = 0$

$\qquad H_1 :$ At least on β_i is not equal to 0

F = 80.65, p-value = 0. There is enough evidence to infer that the model is valid.

c $H_0 : \beta_3 = 0$

   $H_1 : \beta_3 \neq 0$

$t = .27$, p-value $= .7882$. There is not enough evidence to infer that there is an interaction effect between the two teams' winning percentages.

20.8a

SUMMARY OUTPUT					
Regression Statistics					
Multiple R	0.9255				
R Square	0.8566				
Adjusted R Square	0.8362				
Standard Error	5.20				
Observations	25				
ANOVA					
	df	*SS*	*MS*	*F*	*Significance F*
Regression	3	3398.7	1132.9	41.83	0.0000
Residual	21	568.78	27.08		
Total	24	3967.4			
	Coefficients	*Standard Error*	*t Stat*	*P-value*	
Intercept	260.7	162.27	1.61	0.1230	
Temperature	-3.32	2.09	-1.59	0.1270	
Currency	-164.3	667.12	-0.25	0.8078	
Temp Curr	3.64	8.54	0.43	0.6741	

b

SUMMARY OUTPUT					
Regression Statistics					
Multiple R	0.9312				
R Square	0.8671				
Adjusted R Square	0.8322				
Standard Error	5.27				
Observations	25				
ANOVA					
	df	SS	MS	F	Significance F
Regression	5	3440.3	688.07	24.80	0.0000
Residual	19	527.09	27.74		
Total	24	3967.4			
	Coefficients	Standard Error	t Stat	P-value	
Intercept	274.8	283.8	0.97	0.3449	
Temperature	-1.72	6.88	-0.25	0.8053	
Currency	-828.6	888.5	-0.93	0.3627	
Temp-sq	0.00	0.05	-0.05	0.9608	
Curr-sq	2054.0	1718.5	1.20	0.2467	
Temp Curr	-0.87	10.57	-0.08	0.9353	

c Both models fit equally well. The standard errors of estimate and coefficients of determination are quite similar.

20.9a

SUMMARY OUTPUT					
Regression Statistics					
Multiple R	0.3788				
R Square	0.1435				
Adjusted R Square	0.1167				
Standard Error	1.58				
Observations	100				
ANOVA					
	df	SS	MS	F	Significance F
Regression	3	40.38	13.46	5.36	0.0019
Residual	96	241.06	2.51		
Total	99	281.44			
	Coefficients	Standard Error	t Stat	P-value	
Intercept	-4.86	1.83	-2.66	0.0092	
Faceoff	0.121	0.037	3.31	0.0013	
PM-diff	0.135	0.399	0.34	0.7360	
Face PM	-0.0009	0.0080	-0.12	0.9086	

b $\quad H_0 : \beta_1 = \beta_2 = \beta_3 = 0$

H_1 : At least on β_i is not equal to 0

$F = 5.36$, p-value $= .0019$. There is enough evidence to infer that the model is valid.

c $\quad H_0 : \beta_3 = 0$

$H_1 : \beta_3 \neq 0$

$t = -.12$, p-value $= .9086$. There is not enough evidence to infer that there is an interaction effect between face-offs won and penalty minutes differential.

20.10a Yield $= \beta_0 + \beta_1$ Pressure $+ \beta_2$ Temperature $+ \beta_3$ Pressure ^{2}

$+ \beta_4$ Temperature $^2 + \beta_5$ Pressure Temperature $+ \varepsilon$

b

SUMMARY OUTPUT					
Regression Statistics					
Multiple R	0.8290				
R Square	0.6872				
Adjusted R Square	0.6661				
Standard Error	512				
Observations	80				
ANOVA					
	df	*SS*	*MS*	*F*	*Significance F*
Regression	5	42657846	8531569	32.52	0.0000
Residual	74	19413277	262342		
Total	79	62071123			
	Coefficients	*Standard Error*	*t Stat*	*P-value*	
Intercept	74462	7526	9.89	0.0000	
Pressure	14.40	5.92	2.43	0.0174	
Temperature	-613.3	59.95	-10.23	0.0000	
Press-sq	-0.0159	0.0032	-5.04	0.0000	
Temp-sq	1.23	0.12	9.86	0.0000	
Press Temp	0.038	0.017	2.19	0.0316	

c $s_\varepsilon = 512$ and $R^2 = .6872$. The model's fit is good.

20.11

SUMMARY OUTPUT					
Regression Statistics					
Multiple R	0.4341				
R Square	0.1884				
Adjusted R Square	0.1673				
Standard Error	1.82				
Observations	80				
ANOVA					
	df	*SS*	*MS*	*F*	*Significance F*
Regression	2	59.53	29.77	8.94	0.0003
Residual	77	256.42	3.33		
Total	79	315.95			
	Coefficients	*Standard Error*	*t Stat*	*P-value*	
Intercept	30.89	4.03	7.67	0.0000	
Age	-0.13	0.22	-0.60	0.5531	
Age-sq	0.00019	0.00295	0.07	0.9482	

$s_\varepsilon = 1.82$ and $R^2 = .1884$. The model's fit is poor. This model is no better than the first-order model used in Exercise 18.9.

20.12 a $I_1 = 1$ if Catholic, $I_1 = 0$ otherwise

$I_2 = 1$ if Protestant, $I_2 = 0$ otherwise

b $I_1 = 1$ if 8:00 A.M. to 4:00 P.M., $I_1 = 0$ otherwise

$I_2 = 1$ if 4:00 P.M. to midnight, $I_2 = 0$ otherwise

c $I_1 = 1$ if Jack Jones, $I_1 = 0$ otherwise

$I_2 = 1$ if Mary Brown, $I_2 = 0$ otherwise

$I_3 = 1$ if George Fosse, $I_3 = 0$ otherwise

20.13 a Macintosh

b IBM

c other

20.14a

Prediction Interval			
		MBA GPA	
Predicted value		10.11	
Prediction Interval			
Lower limit		8.55	
Upper limit		11.67	
Interval Estimate of Expected Value			
Lower limit		9.53	
Upper limit		10.68	

Prediction: MBA GPA will lie between 8.55 and 11.67

b

Prediction Interval			
		MBA GPA	
Predicted value		9.73	
Prediction Interval			
Lower limit		8.15	
Upper limit		11.31	
Interval Estimate of Expected Value			
Lower limit		9.10	
Upper limit		10.36	

Prediction: MBA GPA will lie between 8.15 and 11.31

20.15a

SUMMARY OUTPUT					
Regression Statistics					
Multiple R	0.8973				
R Square	0.8051				
Adjusted R Square	0.7947				
Standard Error	2.32				
Observations	100				
ANOVA					
	df	*SS*	*MS*	*F*	*Significance F*
Regression	5	2096.3	419.26	77.66	0.0000
Residual	94	507.46	5.40		
Total	99	2603.8			
	Coefficients	*Standard Error*	*t Stat*	*P-value*	
Intercept	23.57	5.98	3.94	0.0002	
Mother	0.31	0.05	5.65	0.0000	
Father	0.30	0.05	6.37	0.0000	
Gmothers	0.032	0.058	0.55	0.5853	
Gfathers	0.078	0.057	1.36	0.1777	
Smoker	-3.72	0.67	-5.56	0.0000	

b Exercise 19.53: $\hat{y} = 3.24 + .451\text{Mother} + .411\text{Father} + .0166\text{Gmothers} + .0869\text{Gfathers}$

There are large differences to all the coefficients.

c $\qquad H_0 : \beta_5 = 0$

$\qquad H_1 : \beta_5 \neq 0$

t = -5.56, p-value = 0. There is enough evidence to infer that smoking affects longevity.

20.16a

SUMMARY OUTPUT					
Regression Statistics					
Multiple R	0.8368				
R Square	0.7002				
Adjusted R Square	0.6659				
Standard Error	811				
Observations	40				
ANOVA					
	df	*SS*	*MS*	*F*	*Significance F*
Regression	4	53729535	13432384	20.43	0.0000
Residual	35	23007438	657355		
Total	39	76736973			
	Coefficients	*Standard Error*	*t Stat*	*P-value*	
Intercept	3490	469.16	7.44	0.0000	
Yest Att	0.37	0.078	4.73	0.0000	
I1	1623	492.55	3.30	0.0023	
I2	733.5	394.37	1.86	0.0713	
I3	-765.5	484.66	-1.58	0.1232	

b $\qquad H_0 : \beta_1 = \beta_2 = \beta_3 = \beta_4 = 0$

$\qquad\qquad H_1$: At least on β_i is not equal to 0

$F = 20.43$, p-value = 0. There is enough evidence to infer that the model is valid.

c $\qquad H_0 : \beta_i = 0$

$\qquad\qquad H_1 : \beta_i \neq 0$

I_2 : t = 1.86, p-value = .0713

I_3 : t = -1.58, p-value = .1232

Weather is not a factor in attendance.

d $\qquad H_0 : \beta_4 = 0$

$\qquad\qquad H_1 : \beta_4 > 0$

t = 3.30, p-value = .0023/2 = .0012. There is sufficient evidence to infer that weekend attendance is larger than weekday attendance.

20.17a

SUMMARY OUTPUT					
Regression Statistics					
Multiple R	0.8582				
R Square	0.7365				
Adjusted R Square	0.7169				
Standard Error	16.40				
Observations	30				
ANOVA					
	df	*SS*	*MS*	*F*	*Significance F*
Regression	2	20303	10151	37.73	0.0000
Residual	27	7265	269.1		
Total	29	27568			
	Coefficients	*Standard Error*	*t Stat*	*P-value*	
Intercept	304.0	13.39	22.70	0.0000	
Batch Size	3.30	0.42	7.79	0.0000	
Product	23.00	5.99	3.84	0.0007	

b Expensive batch: $\hat{y} = 304 + 3.30$Batch Size $+ 23.00(1) = 327 + 3.30$Batch Size. Fixed and variable costs are estimated to be \$327.00 and \$3.30, respectively.

Other batch: $\hat{y} = 304 + 3.30$Batch Size $+ 23.00(0) = 304 + 3.30$Batch Size. Fixed and variable costs are estimated to be \$304 and \$3.30, respectively.

20.18a

SUMMARY OUTPUT					
Regression Statistics					
Multiple R	0.7753				
R Square	0.6011				
Adjusted R Square	0.5754				
Standard Error	24206				
Observations	100				
ANOVA					
	df	*SS*	*MS*	*F*	*Significance F*
Regression	6	82119688412	13686614735	23.36	0.0000
Residual	93	54491075988	585925548		
Total	99	136610764400			
	Coefficients	*Standard Error*	*t Stat*	*P-value*	
Intercept	29217	14589	2.00	0.0481	
Bedrooms	-938	6893	-0.14	0.8921	
H Size	79.9	51.5	1.55	0.1245	
Lot Size	-5.07	16.55	-0.31	0.7601	
I1	20487	6993	2.93	0.0043	
I2	12795	7259	1.76	0.0812	
I3	19512	7965	2.45	0.0162	

b $I_1 = 20,487$; in this sample on average two-story houses sell for \$20,487 more than other houses with the same number of bedrooms, square footage, and lot size.

$I_2 = 12,795$; in this sample on average side-split houses sell for \$12,795 more than other houses with the same number of bedrooms, square footage, and lot size.

$I_3 = 19,512$; in this sample on average back-split sell for \$19,512 more than other houses with the same number of bedrooms, square footage, and lot size.

Note that "other" refers to houses that are not two-story, side-split, or back-split.

$$H_0 : \beta_i = 0$$

$$H_1 : \beta_i \neq 0$$

I_1 : t = 2.93, p-value = .0043

I_2 : t = 1.76, p-value = .0812

I_3 : t = 2.45, p-value = .0162

We can infer that two-story and back-split houses sell for more than other.

471

20.19

SUMMARY OUTPUT					
Regression Statistics					
Multiple R	0.4780				
R Square	0.2284				
Adjusted R Square	0.2084				
Standard Error	1.78				
Observations	80				
ANOVA					
	df	*SS*	*MS*	*F*	*Significance F*
Regression	2	72.17	36.09	11.40	0.0000
Residual	77	243.78	3.17		
Total	79	315.95			
	Coefficients	*Standard Error*	*t Stat*	*P-value*	
Intercept	29.50	1.17	25.17	0.0000	
Age	-0.097	0.029	-3.37	0.0012	
Gender	0.85	0.43	2.00	0.0491	

$$H_0 : \beta_2 = 0$$

$$H_1 : \beta_2 > 0$$

t = 2.00, p-value = .0491/2 = .0246. There is enough evidence to infer that female telemarketers stay at their jobs longer than male telemarketers.

20.20a

SUMMARY OUTPUT					
Regression Statistics					
Multiple R	0.5602				
R Square	0.3138				
Adjusted R Square	0.2897				
Standard Error	5.84				
Observations	60				
ANOVA					
	df	*SS*	*MS*	*F*	*Significance F*
Regression	2	887.90	443.95	13.03	0.0000
Residual	57	1941.70	34.06		
Total	59	2829.60			
	Coefficients	*Standard Error*	*t Stat*	*P-value*	
Intercept	7.02	3.24	2.17	0.0344	
Length	0.250	0.056	4.46	0.0000	
Type	-1.35	0.95	-1.43	0.1589	

b $H_0 : \beta_2 = 0$

$$H_1 : \beta_2 \neq 0$$

t = -1.43, p-value = .1589. There is not enough evidence to infer that the type of commercial affects memory test scores.

c Let

$I_1 = 1$ if humorous

$I_1 = 0$ otherwise

$I_2 = 1$ if musical

$I_2 = 0$ otherwise

SUMMARY OUTPUT					
Regression Statistics					
Multiple R	0.6231				
R Square	0.3882				
Adjusted R Square	0.3554				
Standard Error	5.56				
Observations	60				
ANOVA					
	df	*SS*	*MS*	*F*	*Significance F*
Regression	3	1098.51	366.17	11.85	0.0000
Residual	56	1731.09	30.91		
Total	59	2829.60			
	Coefficients	*Standard Error*	*t Stat*	*P-value*	
Intercept	2.53	2.15	1.18	0.2445	
Length	0.223	0.054	4.10	0.0001	
I-1	2.91	1.81	1.61	0.1130	
I-2	5.50	1.83	3.01	0.0039	

d $H_0 : \beta_i = 0$

      $H_1 : \beta_i \neq 0$

I_1 : t = 1.61, p-value = .1130

I_2 : t = 3.01, p-value = .0039

There is enough evidence to infer that there is a difference in memory test scores between watchers of humorous and serious commercials.

e The variable type of commercial in parts (a) and (b) is nominal. It is usually meaningless to conduct a regression analysis with such variables without converting them to indicator variables.

20.21a

SUMMARY OUTPUT					
Regression Statistics					
Multiple R	0.9233				
R Square	0.8525				
Adjusted R Square	0.8429				
Standard Error	6.25				
Observations	50				
ANOVA					
	df	*SS*	*MS*	*F*	*Significance F*
Regression	3	10384	3461.4	88.64	0.0000
Residual	46	1796	39.05		
Total	49	12181			
	Coefficients	*Standard Error*	*t Stat*	*P-value*	
Intercept	-41.42	7.00	-5.92	0.0000	
Boxes	0.64	0.05	12.79	0.0000	
Weight	0.35	0.08	4.65	0.0000	
Codes	4.54	1.21	3.76	0.0005	

b Let

$I_1 = 1$ if morning

$I_1 = 0$ otherwise

$I_2 = 1$ if early afternoon

$I_2 = 0$ otherwise

SUMMARY OUTPUT					
Regression Statistics					
Multiple R	0.9727				
R Square	0.9461				
Adjusted R Square	0.9414				
Standard Error	3.82				
Observations	50				
ANOVA					
	df	*SS*	*MS*	*F*	*Significance F*
Regression	4	11525	2881	197.66	0.0000
Residual	45	656	14.58		
Total	49	12181			
	Coefficients	*Standard Error*	*t Stat*	*P-value*	
Intercept	-29.72	3.73	-7.97	0.0000	
Boxes	0.62	0.03	19.99	0.0000	
Weight	0.35	0.05	7.54	0.0000	
I-1	-6.76	1.50	-4.51	0.0000	
I-2	6.48	1.45	4.47	0.0001	

c Model 1: $s_\varepsilon = 6.25$ and $R^2 = .8525$.

Model 2: $s_\varepsilon = 3.82$ and $R^2 = .9461$.

The second model fits better.

d $H_0 : \beta_i = 0$

           $H_1 : \beta_i \neq 0$

I_1: t = -4.51, p-value = 0. There is enough evidence to infer that the average time to unload in the morning is different from that in the late afternoon.

I_2: t = 4.47, p-value = .0001. There is enough evidence to infer that the average time to unload in the early afternoon is different from that in the late afternoon.

20.22a Let

      $I_1 = 1$ if no scorecard

      $I_1 = 0$ otherwise

      $I_2 = 1$ if scorecard overturned more than 10% of the time

      $I_2 = 0$ otherwise

b

SUMMARY OUTPUT					
Regression Statistics					
Multiple R	0.7299				
R Square	0.5327				
Adjusted R Square	0.5181				
Standard Error	4.20				
Observations	100				
ANOVA					
	df	*SS*	*MS*	*F*	*Significance F*
Regression	3	1933	644.5	36.48	0.0000
Residual	96	1696	17.67		
Total	99	3629			
	Coefficients	*Standard Error*	*t Stat*	*P-value*	
Intercept	4.65	2.06	2.26	0.0260	
Loan Size	0.00012	0.00015	0.83	0.4084	
I-1	4.08	1.14	3.57	0.0006	
I-2	10.18	1.01	10.08	0.0000	

c $s_\varepsilon = 4.20$ and $R^2 = .5327$. The model's fit is mediocre.

d

	Pct Bad	Loan Size	I-1	I-2
Pct Bad	1			
Loan Size	0.1099	1		
I-1	-0.1653	-0.0346	1	
I-2	0.6835	0.0737	-0.5471	1

There is a high correlation between I_1 and I_2 that may distort the t-tests.

e $b_1 = .00012$; in this sample for each additional dollar lent the default rate increases by .00012 provided the other variables remain the same.

$b_2 = 4.08$; In this sample banks that don't use scorecards on average have default rates 4.08 percentage points higher than banks that overturn their scorecards less than 10% of the time.

$b_3 = 10.18$; In this sample banks that overturn their scorecards more than 10% of the time on average have default rates 10.18 percentage points higher than banks that overturn their scorecards less than 10% of the time.

e

Prediction Interval		
	Pct Bad	
Predicted value	9.94	
Prediction Interval		
Lower limit	1.39	
Upper limit	18.49	
Interval Estimate of Expected Value		
Lower limit	8.08	
Upper limit	11.81	

We predict that the bank's default rate will fall between 1.39 and 18.49%.

20.23 a Let

$I_1 = 1$ if welding machine

$I_1 = 0$ otherwise

$I_2 = 1$ if lathe

$I_2 = 0$ otherwise

SUMMARY OUTPUT					
Regression Statistics					
Multiple R	0.7706				
R Square	0.5938				
Adjusted R Square	0.5720				
Standard Error	48.59				
Observations	60				
ANOVA					
	df	*SS*	*MS*	*F*	*Significance F*
Regression	3	193271	64424	27.29	0.0000
Residual	56	132223	2361		
Total	59	325494			
	Coefficients	*Standard Error*	*t Stat*	*P-value*	
Intercept	119.3	35.00	3.41	0.0012	
Age	2.54	0.40	6.31	0.0000	
I-1	-11.76	19.70	-0.60	0.5531	
I-2	-199.4	30.71	-6.49	0.0000	

b $b_1 = 2.54$; in this sample for each additional month repair costs increase on average by \$2.54 provided that the other variable remains constant.

$b_2 = -11.76$; in this sample welding machines cost on average \$11.76 less to repair than stamping machines for the same age of machine.

$b_3 = -199.4$; in this sample lathes cost on average \$199.40 less to repair than stamping machines for the same age of machine.

c $H_0 : \beta_2 = 0$

$H_1 : \beta_2 < 0$

t = -.60, p-value .5531/2 = .2766. There is no evidence to infer that welding machines cost less to repair than stamping machines.

20.24a

SUMMARY OUTPUT					
Regression Statistics					
Multiple R	0.7296				
R Square	0.5323				
Adjusted R Square	0.5075				
Standard Error	2.36				
Observations	100				
ANOVA					
	df	*SS*	*MS*	*F*	*Significance F*
Regression	5	593.90	118.78	21.40	0.0000
Residual	94	521.72	5.55		
Total	99	1115.62			
	Coefficients	*Standard Error*	*t Stat*	*P-value*	
Intercept	10.26	1.17	8.76	0.0000	
Wage	-0.00020	0.00004	-5.69	0.0000	
Pct PT	-0.11	0.03	-3.62	0.0005	
Pct U	0.060	0.012	4.83	0.0000	
Av Shift	1.56	0.50	3.11	0.0025	
U/M Rel	-2.64	0.49	-5.36	0.0000	

b $H_0 : \beta_4 = 0$

$H_1 : \beta_4 \neq 0$

t = 3.11, p-value = .0025. There is enough evidence to infer that the availability of shiftwork affects absenteeism.

c $H_0 : \beta_5 = 0$

$H_1 : \beta_5 < 0$

t = -5.36, p-value = 0. There is enough evidence to infer that in organizations where the union-management relationship is good absenteeism is lower.

20.25

SUMMARY OUTPUT					
Regression Statistics					
Multiple R	0.9737				
R Square	0.9482				
Adjusted R Square	0.9454				
Standard Error	3015				
Observations	100				
ANOVA					
	df	*SS*	*MS*	*F*	*Significance F*
Regression	5	15636303318	3127260664	344.04	0.0000
Residual	94	854451113	9089905		
Total	99	16490754431			
	Coefficients	*Standard Error*	*t Stat*	*P-value*	
Intercept	-5916	3141	-1.88	0.0627	
Years	1022	48.93	20.88	0.0000	
PhD	725.7	961.5	0.75	0.4523	
Evaluation	3729	619.82	6.02	0.0000	
Articles	439.15	80.69	5.44	0.0000	
Gender	1089.7	632.0	1.72	0.0879	

a $H_0 : \beta_1 = \beta_2 = \beta_3 = \beta_4 = \beta_5 = 0$

H_1 : At least on β_i is not equal to 0

F = 344.04, p-value = 0. There is enough evidence to infer that the model is valid.

b $H_0 : \beta_5 = 0$

$H_1 : \beta_5 > 0$

t = 1.72, p-value = .0879/2 = .0440. There is evidence that male professors are better paid than female professors with the same qualifications.

20.26

SUMMARY OUTPUT					
Regression Statistics					
Multiple R	0.8311				
R Square	0.6907				
Adjusted R Square	0.5670				
Standard Error	1.856229516				
Observations	8				
ANOVA					
	df	*SS*	*MS*	*F*	*Significance F*
Regression	2	38.47	19.24	5.58	0.0532
Residual	5	17.23	3.45		
Total	7	55.70			
	Coefficients	*Standard Error*	*t Stat*	*P-value*	
Intercept	2.01	4.02	0.50	0.6385	
Score	3.25	1.00	3.25	0.0227	
Gender	-0.039	1.353	-0.03	0.9782	

In this case male-dominated jobs are paid on average $.039 (3.9 cents) *less* than female-dominated jobs after adjusting for the value of each job.

20.27 All weights = .2

SUMMARY OUTPUT					
Regression Statistics					
Multiple R	0.7623				
R Square	0.5812				
Adjusted R Square	0.4136				
Standard Error	2.16				
Observations	8				
ANOVA					
	df	SS	MS	F	Significance F
Regression	2	32.37	16.19	3.47	0.1135
Residual	5	23.33	4.67		
Total	7	55.70			
	Coefficients	Standard Error	t Stat	P-value	
Intercept	4.70	4.07	1.15	0.3011	
Score	2.57	1.01	2.55	0.0514	
Gender	0.26	1.56	0.16	0.8761	

In this case male-dominated jobs are paid on average $.26 (26 cents) more than female-dominated jobs after adjusting for the value of each job.

20.28 The strength of this approach lies in regression analysis. This statistical technique allows us to determine whether gender is a factor in determining salaries. However, the conclusion is very much dependent upon the subjective assignment of weights. Change the value of the weights and a totally different conclusion is achieved.

20.29 a

Results of stepwise regression					
Step 1 - Entering variable: Years					
Summary measures					
	Multiple R	0.8309			
	R-Square	0.6903			
	Adj R-Square	0.6839			
	StErr of Est	1.9170			
ANOVA Table					
	Source	df	SS	MS	F	p-value
	Explained	1	393.2178	393.2178	106.9967	0.0000
	Unexplained	48	176.4022	3.6750		
Regression coefficients					
		Coefficient	Std Err	t-value	p-value
	Constant	3.6214	0.6967	5.1979	0.0000
	Years	0.5743	0.0555	10.3439	0.0000

b In this printout only the significant variable number of years of employment was included in the equation.

20.30 a

Results of stepwise regression					
Step 1 - Entering variable: HS_GPA					
Summary measures					
	Multiple R	0.5283			
	R-Square	0.2791			
	Adj R-Square	0.2718			
	StErr of Est	2.0222			
ANOVA Table					
	Source	df	SS	MS	F	p-value
	Explained	1	155.1690	155.1690	37.9438	0.0000
	Unexplained	98	400.7654	4.0894		
Regression coefficients					
		Coefficient	Std Err	t-value	p-value
	Constant	2.4095	0.8168	2.9501	0.0040
	HS_GPA	0.6108	0.0992	6.1599	0.0000

b In this printout only the significant variable high school GPA was included in the equation.

20.31

Results of stepwise regression					
Step 1 - Entering variable: Newspaper					
Summary measures					
	Multiple R	0.4320			
	R-Square	0.1866			
	Adj R-Square	0.1512			
	StErr of Est	2.4853			
ANOVA Table					
	Source	df	SS	MS	F	p-value
	Explained	1	32.5931	32.5931	5.2766	0.0311
	Unexplained	23	142.0701	6.1770		
Regression coefficients					
		Coefficient	Std Err	t-value	p-value
	Constant	14.1559	2.5161	5.6261	0.0000
	Newspaper	3.3344	1.4516	2.2971	0.0311

This result was predictable because in Exercise 19.7 only the variable newspaper advertising expenditures was statistically significant.

20.32

Results of stepwise regression					
Step 1 - Entering variable: Age					
Summary measures					
	Multiple R	0.4022			
	R-Square	0.1617			
	Adj R-Square	0.1575			
	StErr of Est	4.2743			
ANOVA Table					
	Source	df	SS	MS	F	p-value
	Explained	1	697.9702	697.9702	38.2034	0.0000
	Unexplained	198	3617.4248	18.2698		
Regression coefficients					
		Coefficient	Std Err	t-value	p-value
	Constant	18.4099	1.8394	10.0084	0.0000
	Age	-0.2826	0.0457	-6.1809	0.0000
Step 2 - Entering variable: Income					
Summary measures		Change	% Change		
	Multiple R	0.4455	0.0433	%10.8	
	R-Square	0.1985	0.0367	%22.7	
	Adj R-Square	0.1903	0.0328	%20.8	
	StErr of Est	4.1903	-0.0841	-%2.0	
ANOVA Table					
	Source	df	SS	MS	F	p-value
	Explained	2	856.4167	428.2084	24.3879	0.0000
	Unexplained	197	3458.9783	17.5583		
Regression coefficients					
		Coefficient	Std Err	t-value	p-value
	Constant	13.0272	2.5422	5.1245	0.0000
	Age	-0.2791	0.0448	-6.2248	0.0000
	Income	0.0938	0.0312	3.0040	0.0030

Both independent variables were included because both are linearly related to Internet use.

20.33

Results of stepwise regression					
Step 1 - Entering variable: Team_Wlk					
Summary measures					
	Multiple R	0.7694			
	R-Square	0.5920			
	Adj R-Square	0.5580			
	StErr of Est	46.4245			
ANOVA Table					
	Source	df	SS	MS	F	p-value
	Explained	1	37530.6688	37530.6688	17.4138	0.0013
	Unexplained	12	25862.7598	2155.2300		
Regression coefficients					
		Coefficient	Std Err	t-value	p-value
	Constant	323.9143	97.2859	3.3295	0.0060
	Team_Wlk	0.7293	0.1748	4.1730	0.0013
Step 2 - Entering variable: Team_BA					
Summary measures		Change	% Change		
	Multiple R	0.9054	0.1360	%17.7	
	R-Square	0.8198	0.2277	%38.5	
	Adj R-Square	0.7870	0.2290	%41.0	
	StErr of Est	32.2287	-14.1958	-%30.6	
ANOVA Table					
	Source	df	SS	MS	F	p-value
	Explained	2	51967.8817	25983.9408	25.0162	0.0001
	Unexplained	11	11425.5469	1038.6861		
Regression coefficients					
		Coefficient	Std Err	t-value	p-value
	Constant	-621.5870	262.4466	-2.3684	0.0373
	Team_Wlk	0.7832	0.1222	6.4102	0.0001
	Team_BA	3520.0708	944.1736	3.7282	0.0033

Step 3 - Entering variable: Team_Hmr					
Summary measures			Change	% Change	
	Multiple R	0.9439	0.0385	%4.3	
	R-Square	0.8910	0.0713	%8.7	
	Adj R-Square	0.8583	0.0713	%9.1	
	StErr of Est	26.2825	-5.9461	-%18.4	
ANOVA Table					
	Source	df	SS	MS	F	p-value
	Explained	3	56485.7152	18828.5717	27.2573	0.0000
	Unexplained	10	6907.7134	690.7713		
Regression coefficients					
		Coefficient	Std Err	t-value	p-value
	Constant	-703.6769	216.4194	-3.2514	0.0087
	Team_Wlk	0.5491	0.1353	4.0590	0.0023
	Team_BA	3898.0793	784.0344	4.9718	0.0006
	Team_Hmr	0.8099	0.3167	2.5574	0.0285

The number of walks, batting average, and home runs are all linearly related to runs scored.

20.34

Results of stepwise regression					
Step 1 - Entering variable: Erns_Alw					
Summary measures					
	Multiple R	0.9817			
	R-Square	0.9638			
	Adj R-Square	0.9608			
	StErr of Est	12.3977			
ANOVA Table					
	Source	df	SS	MS	F	p-value
	Explained	1	49094.9973	49094.9973	319.4155	0.0000
	Unexplained	12	1844.4313	153.7026		
Regression coefficients					
		Coefficient	Std Err	t-value	p-value
	Constant	45.7408	38.2382	1.1962	0.2547
	Erns_Alw	1.0280	0.0575	17.8722	0.0000

Step 2 - Entering variable: SO					
Summary measures		Change	% Change		
Multiple R	0.9897	0.0079	%0.8		
R-Square	0.9794	0.0157	%1.6		
Adj R-Square	0.9757	0.0149	%1.6		
StErr of Est	9.7554	-2.6423	-%21.3		
ANOVA Table					
Source	df	SS	MS	F	p-value
Explained	2	49892.5864	24946.2932	262.1305	0.0000
Unexplained	11	1046.8422	95.1675		
Regression coefficients					
	Coefficient	Std Err	t-value	p-value	
Constant	-5.8828	34.9758	-0.1682	0.8695	
Erns_Alw	1.0212	0.0453	22.5331	0.0000	
SO	0.4828	0.1668	2.8950	0.0146	

Step 3 - Entering variable: Hits_Alw					
Summary measures		Change	% Change		
Multiple R	0.9942	0.0045	%0.5		
R-Square	0.9884	0.0089	%0.9		
Adj R-Square	0.9849	0.0092	%0.9		
StErr of Est	7.6893	-2.0661	-%21.2		
ANOVA Table					
Source	df	SS	MS	F	p-value
Explained	3	50348.1753	16782.7251	283.8500	0.0000
Unexplained	10	591.2533	59.1253		
Regression coefficients					
	Coefficient	Std Err	t-value	p-value	
Constant	-72.0567	36.4459	-1.9771	0.0762	
Erns_Alw	0.8958	0.0576	15.5495	0.0000	
SO	0.4062	0.1343	3.0237	0.0128	
Hits_Alw	0.1096	0.0395	2.7759	0.0196	

The number of earned runs (no surprise), the number of strikeouts, and the number of hits allowed are all factors in determining the number of runs allowed.

20.35a Mileage $= \beta_0 + \beta_1 \text{Speed} + \beta_2 \text{Speed}^2 + \varepsilon$

b

SUMMARY OUTPUT					
Regression Statistics					
Multiple R	0.8428				
R Square	0.7102				
Adjusted R Square	0.6979				
Standard Error	3.86				
Observations	50				
ANOVA					
	df	*SS*	*MS*	*F*	*Significance F*
Regression	2	1719.87	859.94	57.60	0.0000
Residual	47	701.64	14.93		
Total	49	2421.51			
	Coefficients	*Standard Error*	*t Stat*	*P-value*	
Intercept	9.34	1.71	5.47	0.0000	
Speed	0.80	0.08	10.39	0.0000	
Speed-sq	-0.0079	0.0007	-10.73	0.0000	

c $s_\varepsilon = 3.86$ and $R^2 = .7102$. The model fits moderately well.

20.36a Apply a first-order model with interaction.

b

SUMMARY OUTPUT					
Regression Statistics					
Multiple R	0.8623				
R Square	0.7436				
Adjusted R Square	0.7299				
Standard Error	1.27				
Observations	60				
ANOVA					
	df	*SS*	*MS*	*F*	*Significance F*
Regression	3	260.22	86.74	54.14	0.0000
Residual	56	89.72	1.60		
Total	59	349.93			
	Coefficients	*Standard Error*	*t Stat*	*P-value*	
Intercept	640.8	53.80	11.91	0.0000	
Cars	-64.17	5.27	-12.19	0.0000	
Speed	-10.63	0.90	-11.85	0.0000	
Cars Speed	1.08	0.09	12.26	0.0000	

486

c: $H_0 : \beta_1 = \beta_2 = \beta_3 = 0$

H_1 : At least on β_i is not equal to 0

$F = 54.14$, p-value = 0. There is enough evidence to infer that the model is valid.

20.37a

SUMMARY OUTPUT					
Regression Statistics					
Multiple R	0.8668				
R Square	0.7514				
Adjusted R Square	0.7284				
Standard Error	1.27				
Observations	60				
ANOVA					
	df	*SS*	*MS*	*F*	*Significance F*
Regression	5	262.95	52.59	32.65	0.0000
Residual	54	86.99	1.61		
Total	59	349.93			
	Coefficients	*Standard Error*	*t Stat*	*P-value*	
Intercept	404.5	327.0	1.24	0.2214	
Cars	-66.57	6.54	-10.19	0.0000	
Speed	-2.35	10.54	-0.22	0.8246	
Cars-sq	0.11	0.10	1.10	0.2741	
Speed-sq	-0.070	0.085	-0.82	0.4180	
Cars Speed	1.08	0.10	11.21	0.0000	

b $F = 32.65$, p-value = 0. There is enough evidence to infer that the model is valid.

20.38 a Let

$I_1 = 1$ if ad was in newspaper

$I_1 = 0$ otherwise

$I_2 = 1$ if ad was on radio

$I_2 = 0$ otherwise

b

SUMMARY OUTPUT					
Regression Statistics					
Multiple R	0.6946				
R Square	0.4824				
Adjusted R Square	0.4501				
Standard Error	44.87				
Observations	52				
ANOVA					
	df	*SS*	*MS*	*F*	*Significance F*
Regression	3	90057	30019	14.91	0.0000
Residual	48	96627	2013		
Total	51	186684			
	Coefficients	*Standard Error*	*t Stat*	*P-value*	
Intercept	282.6	17.46	16.19	0.0000	
Ads	25.23	3.98	6.34	0.0000	
I-1	-23.36	15.83	-1.48	0.1467	
I-2	-46.59	16.44	-2.83	0.0067	

b $\quad H_0 : \beta_1 = \beta_2 = \beta_3 = 0$

$\quad H_1$: At least on β_i is not equal to 0

$F = 14.91$, p-value = 0. There is enough evidence to infer that the model is valid.

c $\quad H_0 : \beta_i = 0$

$\quad H_1 : \beta_i \neq 0$

I_1 : t = -1.48, p-value = .1467

I_2 : t = -2.83, p-value = .0067

There is enough evidence to infer that the advertising medium makes a difference.

20.39

SUMMARY OUTPUT					
Regression Statistics					
Multiple R	0.9347				
R Square	0.8736				
Adjusted R Square	0.8654				
Standard Error	0.018				
Observations	50				
ANOVA					
	df	*SS*	*MS*	*F*	*Significance F*
Regression	3	0.107	0.036	106.01	0.0000
Residual	46	0.015	0.00034		
Total	49	0.122			
	Coefficients	*Standard Error*	*t Stat*	*P-value*	
Intercept	0.357	0.059	6.03	0.0000	
BA	-0.401	0.236	-1.70	0.0964	
ERA	0.076	0.005	15.98	0.0000	
Fired	-0.051	0.006	-8.61	0.0000	

b $\qquad H_0 : \beta_3 = 0$

$\qquad H_1 : \beta_3 < 0$

$t = -8.61$, p-value = 0. There is enough evidence to infer that a team that fires its manager within 12 months wins less frequently than other teams.

20.40a Units $= \beta_0 + \beta_1 \, \text{Years} + \beta_2 \, \text{Years}^2 + \varepsilon$

b

SUMMARY OUTPUT					
Regression Statistics					
Multiple R	0.4351				
R Square	0.1893				
Adjusted R Square	0.1726				
Standard Error	87.98				
Observations	100				
ANOVA					
	df	*SS*	*MS*	*F*	*Significance F*
Regression	2	175291	87646	11.32	0.0000
Residual	97	750764	7740		
Total	99	926056			
	Coefficients	*Standard Error*	*t Stat*	*P-value*	
Intercept	331.2	17.55	18.87	0.0000	
Years	21.45	5.50	3.90	0.0002	
Years-sq	-0.85	0.32	-2.61	0.0105	

c $s_{\varepsilon} = 87.98$ and $R^2 = .1893$. The model fits poorly.

20.41a Depletion $= \beta_0 + \beta_1 \text{Temperature} + \beta_2 \text{PH-level} + \beta_3 \text{PH-level}^2 + \beta_4 I_4 + \beta_5 I_5 + \varepsilon$

where

$I_1 = 1$ if mainly cloudy

$I_1 = 0$ otherwise

$I_2 = 1$ if sunny

$I_2 = 0$ otherwise

b

SUMMARY OUTPUT					
Regression Statistics					
Multiple R	0.8085				
R Square	0.6537				
Adjusted R Square	0.6452				
Standard Error	4.14				
Observations	210				
ANOVA					
	df	*SS*	*MS*	*F*	*Significance F*
Regression	5	6596	1319	77.00	0.0000
Residual	204	3495	17.13		
Total	209	10091			
	Coefficients	*Standard Error*	*t Stat*	*P-value*	
Intercept	1003	55.12	18.19	0.0000	
Temperature	0.19	0.03	6.78	0.0000	
PH Level	-265.6	14.75	-18.01	0.0000	
PH-sq	17.76	0.98	18.07	0.0000	
I-1	-1.07	0.70	-1.53	0.1282	
I-2	1.16	0.70	1.65	0.0997	

c $\quad H_0 : \beta_1 = \beta_2 = \beta_3 = \beta_4 = \beta_5 = 0$

H_1 : At least on β_i is not equal to 0

$F = 77.00$, p-value = 0. There is enough evidence to infer that the model is valid.

d $\quad H_0 : \beta_1 = 0$

$H_1 : \beta_1 > 0$

$t = 6.78$, p-value = 0. There is enough evidence to infer that higher temperatures deplete chlorine more quickly.

e $\quad H_0 : \beta_3 = 0$

$H_1 : \beta_3 > 0$

$t = 18.07$, p-value = 0. There is enough evidence to infer that there is a quadratic relationship between chlorine depletion and PH level.

f $\quad H_0 : \beta_i = 0$

$H_1 : \beta_i \neq 0$

$I_1 : t = -1.53$, p-value = .1282. There is not enough evidence to infer that chlorine depletion differs between mainly cloudy days and partly sunny days.

$I_2 : t = 1.65$, p-value = .0997. There is not enough evidence to infer that chlorine depletion differs between sunny days and partly sunny days.

Weather is not a factor in chlorine depletion.

Chapter 21

21.1 Time series	Moving average
48	
41	(48+41+37)/3 = 42.00
37	(41+37+32)/3 = 36.67
32	(37+32+36)/3 = 35.00
36	(32+36+31)/3 = 33.00
31	(36+31+43)/3 = 36.67
43	(31+43+52)/3 = 42.00
52	(43+52+60)/3 = 51.67
60	(52+60+48)/3 = 53.33
48	(60+48+41)/3 = 49.67
41	(48+41+30)/3 = 39.67
30	

21.2 Time series	Moving average
48	
41	
37	(48 +41+37+32+36)/5 = 38.8
32	(41+37+32+36+31)/5 = 35.4
36	(37+32+36+31+43)/5 = 35.8
31	(32+36+31+43+52)/5 = 38.8
43	(36+31+43+52+60)/5 = 44.4
52	(31+43+52+60+48)/5 = 46.8
60	(43+52+60+48+41)/5 = 48.8
48	(52+60+48+41+30)/5 = 46.2
41	
30	

21.3

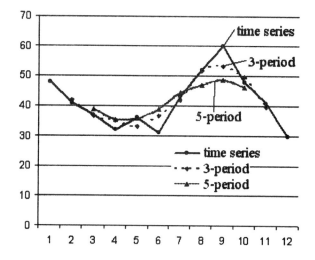

21.4 Time series   Moving average

16
22   (16+22+19)/3 = 19.00
19   (22+19+24)/3 = 21.67
24   (19+24+30)/3 = 24.33
30   (24+30+26)/3 = 26.67
26   (30+26+24)/3 = 26.67
24   (26+24+29)/3 = 26.33
29   (24+29+21)/3 = 24.67
21   (29+21+23)/3 = 24.33
23   (21+23+19)/3 = 21.00
19   (23+19+15)/3 = 19.00
15

21.5 Time series   Moving average

16
22
19   (16+22+19+24+30)/5 = 22.2
24   (22+19+24+30+26)/5 = 24.2
30   (19+24+30+26+24)/5 = 24.6
26   (24+30+26+24+29)/5 = 26.6
24   (30+26+24+29+21)/5 = 26.0
29   (26+24+29+21+23)/5 = 24.6
21   (24+29+21+23+19)/5 = 23.2
23   (29+21+23+19+15)/5 = 21.4
19
15

21.6

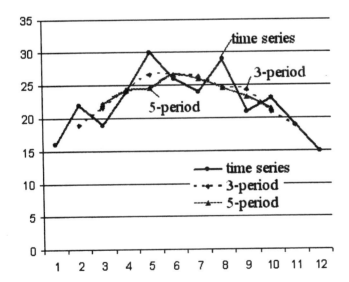

21.7 Time series	Exponentially smoothed time series
12	12
18	.1(18) +. 9(12) = 12.60
16	.1(16) +. 9(12.60) = 12.94
24	.1(24) +. 9(12.94) = 14.05
17	.1(17) +. 9(14.05) = 14.34
16	.1(16) +. 9(14.34) = 14.51
25	.1(25) +. 9(14.51) = 15.56
21	.1(21) +. 9(15.56) = 16.10
23	.1(23) + .9(16.10) = 16.79
14	.1(14) + .9(16.79) = 16.51

21.8 Time series	Exponentially smoothed time series
12	12
18	.8(18) +. 2(12) = 16.80
16	.8(16) +. 2(16.80) = 16.16
24	.8(24) +. 2(16.16) = 22.43
17	.8(17) +. 2(22.43) = 18.09
16	.8(16) +. 2(18.09) = 16.42
25	.8(25) +. 2(16.42) = 23.28
21	.8(21) +. 2(23.28) = 21.46
23	.8(23) + .2(21.46) = 22.69
14	.8(14) + .2(22.69) = 15.74

21.9

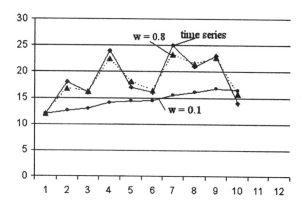

There appears to be a gradual upward trend.

21.10 Time series	Exponentially smoothed time series
38	38
43	.1(43) +. 9(38) = 38.50
42	.1(42) +. 9(38.50) = 38.85
45	.1(45) +. 9(38.85) = 39.47
46	.1(46) +. 9(39.47) = 40.12
48	.1(48) +. 9(40.12) = 40.91
50	.1(50) +. 9(40.91) = 41.82
49	.1(49) +. 9(41.82) = 42.53
46	.1(46) + .9(42.53) = 42.88
45	.1(45) + .9(42.88) = 43.09

20.11 Time series   Exponentially smoothed time series

38	38
43	.8(43) +. 2(38) = 42.00
42	.8(42) +. 2(42.00) = 42.00
45	.8(45) +. 2(42.00) = 44.40
46	.8(46) +. 2(44.40) = 45.68
48	.8(48) +. 2(45.68) = 47.54
50	.8(50) +. 2(47.54) = 49.51
49	.8(49) +. 2(49.51) = 49.10
46	.8(46) + .2(49.10) = 46.62
45	.8(45) + .2(46.62) = 45.32

21.12

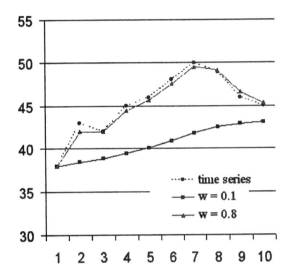

There is a trend component.

21.13 & 21.14

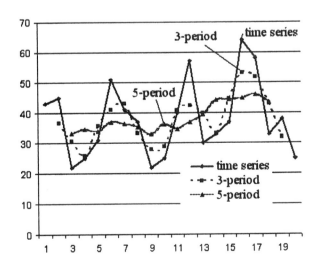

Sales	3-Day moving average	5-Day moving average
43		
45	(43+45+22)/3 = 36.67	
22	(45+22+25)/3 = 30.67	(43+45+22+25+31)/5 = 33.2
25	(22+25+31)/3 = 26.00	(45+22+25+31+51)/5 = 34.8
31	(25+31+51)/3 = 35.67	(22+25+31+51+41)/5 = 34.0
51	(31+51+41)/3 = 41.00	(25+31+51+41+37)/5 = 37.0
41	(51+41+37)/3 = 43.00	(31+51+41+37+22)/5 = 36.4
37	(41+37+22)/3 = 33.33	(51+41+37+22+25)/5 = 35.2
22	(37+22+25)/3 = 28.00	(41+37+22+25+40)/5 = 33.0
25	(22+25+40)/3 = 29.00	(37+22+25+40+57)/5 = 36.2
40	(25+40+57)/3 = 40.67	(22+25+40+57+30)/5 = 34.8
57	(40+57+30)/3 = 42.33	(25+40+57+30+33)/5 = 37.0
30	(57+30+33)/3 = 40.00	(40+57+30+33+37)/5 = 39.4
33	(30+33+37)/3 = 33.33	(57+30+33+37+64)/5 = 44.2
37	(33+37+64)/3 = 44.67	(30+33+37+64+58)/5 = 44.4
64	(37+64+58)/3 = 53.00	(33+37+64+58+33)/5 = 45.0
58	(64+58+33)/3 = 51.67	(37+64+58+33+38)/5 = 46.0
33	(58+33+38)/3 = 43.00	(64+58+33+38+25)/5 = 43.6
38	(33+38+25)/3 = 32.00	
25		

c There appears to be a seasonal (weekly) pattern.

21.15a Sales	4-quarter moving average	Centered moving average
18		
22		
	(18+22+27+31)/4 = 24.50	
27		(24.50+28.25)/2 = 26.375
	(22+27+31+33)/4 = 28.25	
31		(28.25+27.75)/2 = 28.000
	(27+31+33+20)/4 = 27.75	
33		(27.75+30.50)/2 = 29.125
	(31+33+20+38)/4 = 30.50	
20		(30.50+29.25)/2 = 29.875
	(33+20+38+26)/4 = 29.25	
38		(29.25+27.25)/2 = 28.250
	(20+38+26+25)/4 = 27.25	
26		(27.25+31.25)/2 = 29.250
	(38+26+25+36)/4 = 31.25	
25		(31.25+32.75)/2 = 32.000
	(26+25+36+44)/4 = 32.75	
36		(32.75+33.50)/2 = 33.125
	(25+36+44+29)/4 = 33.50	
44		(33.50+37.50)/2 = 35.500
	(36+44+29+41)/4 = 37.50	
29		(37.50+36.75)/2 = 37.125
	(44+29+41+33)/4 = 36.75	
41		(36.75+38.75)/2 = 37.750
	(29+41+33+52)/4 = 38.75	
33		(38.75+42.75)/2 = 40.750
	(41+33+52+25)/4 = 42.75	
52		
45		

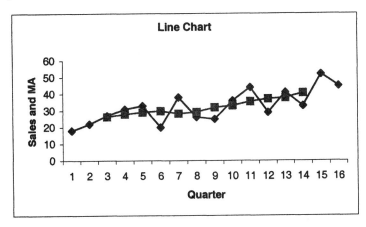

c There appears to be a gradual trend of increasing sales.

21.16 & 21.17

Sales	Exponentially smoothed w = .4	Exponentially smoothed w = .8
18	18	18
22	.4(22)+.6(18) = 19.60	.8(22)+.2(18) = 21.20
27	.4(27)+.6(19.6) = 22.56	.8(27)+.2(21.2) = 25.84
31	.4(31)+.6(22.56) = 25.94	.8(31)+.2(25.84) = 29.97
33	.4(33)+.6(25.94) = 28.76	.8(33)+.2(29.97) = 32.39
20	.4(20)+.6(28.76) = 25.26	.8(20)+.2(32.39) = 22.48
38	.4(38)+.6(25.26) = 30.35	.8(38)+.2(22.48) = 34.90
26	.4(26)+.6(30.35) = 28.61	.8(26)+.2(34.90) = 27.78
25	.4(25)+.6(28.61) = 27.17	.8(25)+.2(27.78) = 25.56
36	.4(36)+.6(27.17) = 30.70	.8(36)+.2(25.56) = 33.91
44	.4(44)+.6(30.70) = 36.02	.8(44)+.2(33.91) = 41.98
29	.4(29)+.6(36.02) = 33.21	.8(29)+.2(41.98) = 31.60
41	.4(41)+.6(33.21) = 36.33	.8(41)+.2(31.60) = 39.12
33	.4(33)+.6(36.33) = 35.00	.8(33)+.2(39.12) = 34.22
52	.4(52)+.6(35.00) = 41.80	.8(52)+.2(34.22) = 48.44
45	.4(45)+.6(41.80) = 43.08	.8(45)+.2(48.44) = 45.69

21.16 b

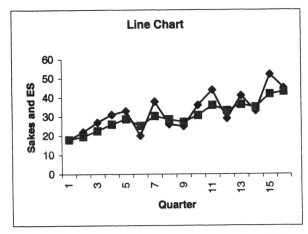

21.17 b

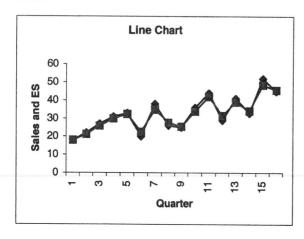

21.18

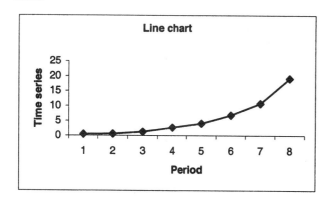

The quadratic model would appear to be the best model.

21.19

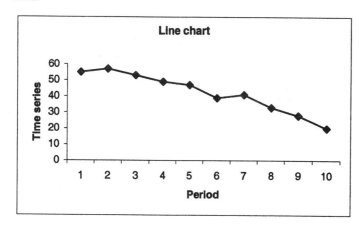

The linear trend model appears to be best.

21.20

$$\hat{y} = -4.96 + 2.38t \qquad (R^2 = .81)$$
$$\hat{y} = 3.14 - 2.48t + .54t^2 \qquad (R^2 = .98)$$

The quadratic trend line fits better.

21.21

$$\hat{y} = 63.87 - 3.94t \qquad (R^2 = .94)$$
$$\hat{y} = 57.2 - .61t + .30t^2 \qquad (R^2 = .98)$$

The quadratic trend line fits slightly better.

21.22

Week	Day	Period t	y	$\hat{y}$	$y/\hat{y}$
1	1	1	12	17.2	0.699
	2	2	18	17.5	1.027
	3	3	16	17.9	0.894
	4	4	25	18.3	1.369
	5	5	31	18.6	1.664
2	1	6	11	19.0	0.579
	2	7	17	19.4	0.878
	3	8	19	19.7	0.963
	4	9	24	20.1	1.194
	5	10	27	20.5	1.320
3	1	11	14	20.8	0.672
	2	12	16	21.2	0.755
	3	13	16	21.6	0.742
	4	14	28	21.9	1.277
	5	15	25	22.3	1.122
4	1	16	17	22.7	0.750
	2	17	21	23.0	0.912
	3	18	20	23.4	0.855
	4	19	24	23.8	1.010
	5	20	32	24.1	1.327

	Day					
Week	Monday	Tuesday	Wednesday	Thursday	Friday	Total
1	.699	1.027	.894	1.369	1.664	
2	.579	.878	.963	1.194	1.320	
3	.672	.755	.742	1.277	1.122	
4	.750	.912	.855	1.010	1.327	
Average	.675	.893	.864	1.213	1.358	5.003
Seasonal Index	.675	.892	.864	1.212	1.357	5.000

21.23

Year	Quarter	y	$\hat{y}$	$y / \hat{y}$
1	1	55	46.6	1.179
	2	44	45.6	0.965
	3	46	44.5	1.033
	4	39	43.5	0.897
2	1	41	42.4	0.967
	2	38	41.3	0.919
	3	37	40.3	0.919
	4	30	39.2	0.765
3	1	43	38.2	1.127
	2	39	37.1	1.051
	3	39	36.0	1.082
	4	35	35.0	1.001
4	1	36	33.9	1.061
	2	32	32.9	0.974
	3	30	31.8	0.943
	4	25	30.7	0.813
5	1	50	29.7	1.685
	2	25	28.6	0.874
	3	24	27.6	0.871
	4	22	26.5	0.830

		Quarter				
Year	1	2	3	4	Total
1	1.179	0.965	1.033	0.897	
2	0.967	0.919	0.919	0.765	
3	1.127	1.051	1.082	1.001	
4	1.061	0.974	0.943	0.813	
5	1.685	0.874	0.871	0.830	
Average	1.204	0.957	0.970	0.861	3.991
Seasonal Index	1.207	0.959	0.972	0.863	4.000

21.24

Year	Quarter	Period t	y	$\hat{y}$	$y/\hat{y}$
1997	1	1	52	62.9	0.827
	2	2	67	64.1	1.046
	3	3	85	65.2	1.303
	4	4	54	66.4	0.813
1998	1	5	57	67.6	0.843
	2	6	75	68.8	1.090
	3	7	90	70.0	1.286
	4	8	61	71.1	0.857
1999	1	9	60	72.3	0.830
	2	10	77	73.5	1.048
	3	11	94	74.7	1.259
	4	12	63	75.9	0.830
2000	1	13	66	77.0	0.857
	2	14	82	78.2	1.048
	3	15	98	79.4	1.234
	4	16	67	80.6	0.831

Year	Quarter 1	Quarter 2	Quarter 3	Quarter 4	Total
1997	.827	1.046	1.303	.813	
1998	.843	1.090	1.286	.857	
1999	.830	1.048	1.259	.830	
2000	.857	1.048	1.234	.831	
Average	.839	1.058	1.271	.833	4.001
Seasonal Index	.839	1.058	1.270	.833	4.000

21.25a

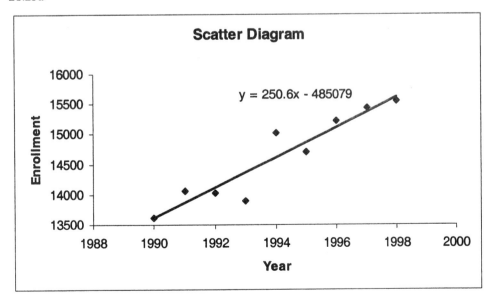

Scatter Diagram

y = 250.6x - 485079

b $\hat{y} = -485,079 + 250\text{Year}$

501

21.26a

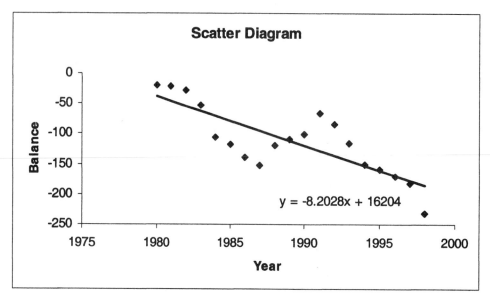

b $\hat{y} = 16{,}204 - 8.21\text{Year}$

21.27

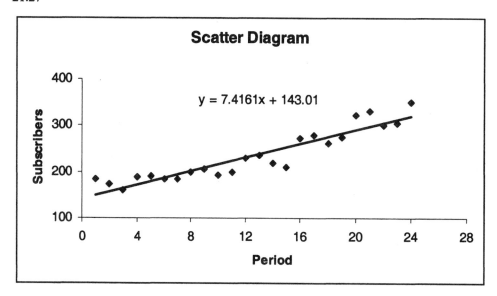

$\hat{y} = 143 + 7.42\,t$

Year	Quarter	Period t	y	$\hat{y} = 143 + 7.42t$	$y / \hat{y}$
1996	1	1	184	150.42	1.223
	2	2	173	157.84	1.096
	3	3	160	165.26	0.968
	4	4	189	172.68	1.095
1997	1	5	191	180.1	1.061
	2	6	185	187.52	0.987
	3	7	184	194.94	0.944
	4	8	200	202.36	0.988
1998	1	9	205	209.78	0.977
	2	10	192	217.2	0.884
	3	11	200	224.62	0.890
	4	12	229	232.04	0.987
1999	1	13	236	239.46	0.986
	2	14	219	246.88	0.887
	3	15	211	254.3	0.830
	4	16	272	261.72	1.039
2000	1	17	280	269.14	1.040
	2	18	261	276.56	0.944
	3	19	275	283.98	0.968
	4	20	322	291.4	1.105
2001	1	21	331	298.82	1.108
	2	22	301	306.24	0.983
	3	23	306	313.66	0.976
	4	24	351	321.08	1.093

| | Quarter | | | | |
Year	1	2	3	4	Total
1996	1.223	1.096	.968	1.095	
1997	1.060	.987	.944	.988	
1998	.977	.884	.890	.987	
1999	.986	.887	.830	1.039	
2000	1.040	.944	.968	1.105	
2001	1.108	.983	.976	1.093	
Average	1.066	.964	.929	1.051	4.010
Seasonal Index	1.063	.962	.927	1.048	4.000

21.28 Regression line: $\hat{y} = 145 + 1.66\,t$

Week	Day	Period t	y	$\hat{y} = 145 + 1.66t$	$y / \hat{y}$
1	1	1	240	146.66	1.636
	2	2	85	148.32	0.573
	3	3	93	149.98	0.620
	4	4	106	151.64	0.699
	5	5	125	153.3	0.815
	6	6	188	154.96	1.213
	7	7	314	156.62	2.005
2	1	8	221	158.28	1.396
	2	9	80	159.94	0.500
	3	10	75	161.6	0.464
	4	11	121	163.26	0.741
	5	12	110	164.92	0.667
	6	13	202	166.58	1.213
	7	14	386	168.24	2.294
3	1	15	235	169.9	1.383
	2	16	86	171.56	0.501
	3	17	74	173.22	0.427
	4	18	100	174.88	0.572
	5	19	117	176.54	0.663
	6	20	205	178.2	1.150
	7	21	402	179.86	2.235
4	1	22	219	181.52	1.206
	2	23	91	183.18	0.497
	3	24	102	184.84	0.552
	4	25	89	186.5	0.477
	5	26	105	188.16	0.558
	6	27	192	189.82	1.011
	7	28	377	191.48	1.969

Week	Sunday	Monday	Tuesday	Wednesday	Thursday	Friday	Saturday	Total
1	1.636	.573	.620	.699	.815	1.213	2.005	
2	1.396	.500	.464	.741	.667	1.213	2.294	
3	1.383	.501	.427	.572	.663	1.150	2.235	
4	1.206	.497	.552	.477	.558	1.011	1.969	
Average	1.405	.518	.516	.657	.676	1.187	2.126	7.085
Seasonal Index	1.404	.517	.515	.621	.675	1.145	2.123	7.000

21.29 Regression line: $\hat{y} = 90.4 + 2.02\,t$

Year	Quarter	t	y	$\hat{y} = 90.4 + 2.02t$	$y/\hat{y}$
1996	1	1	106	92.42	1.147
	2	2	92	94.44	0.974
	3	3	65	96.46	0.674
	4	4	121	98.48	1.229
1997	1	5	115	100.5	1.144
	2	6	100	102.52	0.975
	3	7	73	104.54	0.698
	4	8	135	106.56	1.267
1998	1	9	114	108.58	1.050
	2	10	105	110.6	0.949
	3	11	79	112.62	0.701
	4	12	140	114.64	1.221
1999	1	13	121	116.66	1.037
	2	14	111	118.68	0.935
	3	15	82	120.7	0.679
	4	16	163	122.72	1.328

Year	Quarter 1	2	3	4	Total
1996	1.147	.974	.674	1.229	
1997	1.144	.975	.698	1.267	
1998	1.050	.949	.701	1.221	
1999	1.037	.935	.679	1.328	
Average	1.095	.959	.688	1.261	4.003
Seasonal Index	1.094	.958	.688	1.260	4.000

21.30

$$MAD = \frac{|166 - 173| + |179 - 186| + |195 - 192| + |214 - 211| + |220 - 223|}{5}$$

$$= \frac{7 + 7 + 3 + 3 + 3}{5} = \frac{23}{5} = 4.60$$

$$= (166 - 173)^2 + (179 - 186)^2 + (195 - 192)^2 + (214 - 211)^2 + (220 - 223)^2$$

$$= 49 + 49 + 9 + 9 + 9 = 125$$

21.31 Model 1:

$$MAD = \frac{|6.0 - 7.5| + |6.6 - 6.3| + |7.3 - 5.4| + |9.4 - 8.2|}{4}$$

$$= \frac{1.5 + .3 + 1.9 + 1.2}{4}$$

$$= \frac{4.9}{4} = 1.225$$

Model 2:

$$\text{MAD} = \frac{|6.0 - 6.3| + |6.6 - 6.7| + |7.3 - 7.1| + |9.4 - 7.5|}{4}$$

$$= \frac{.3 + .1 + .2 + 1.9}{4} = \frac{2.5}{4} = .625$$

Model 2 is more accurate.

Model 1: $\text{SSE} = (6.0 - 7.5)^2 + (66.6 - 6.3)^2 + (7.3 - 5.4)^2 + (9.4 - 8.2)^2$

$$= 2.25 + .09 + 3.61 + 1.44 = 7.39$$

Model 2: $\text{SSE} = (6.0 - 6.3)^2 + (6.6 - 6.7)^2 + 7.3 - 7.1)^2 + (9.4 - 7.5)^2$

$$= .09 + .01 + .04 + 3.61 = 3.75$$

Model 2 is more accurate.

21.32

$$MAD = \frac{|57 - 63| + |60 - 72| + |70 - 86| + |75 - 71| + |70 - 60|}{5}$$

$$= \frac{6 + 12 + 16 + 4 + 10}{5} = \frac{48}{5} = 9.6$$

$$\text{SSE} = (57 - 63)^2 + (60 - 72)^2 + (70 - 86)^2 + (75 - 71)^2 + (70-60)^2$$

$$= 36 + 144 + 256 + 16 + 100 = 552$$

21.33   Technique 1:

$$\text{MAD} = \frac{|19 - 21| + |24 - 27| + |28 - 29| + |32 - 31| + |38 - 35|}{5}$$

$$= \frac{2 + 3 + 1 + 1 + 3}{5} = \frac{10}{5} = 2.0$$

$$\text{SSE} = (19 - 22)^2 + (24 - 27)^2 + (32 - 31)^2 + (38 - 35)^2$$

$$= 4 + 9 + 1 + 1 + 9 = 24$$

Technique 2:

$$\text{MAD} = \frac{|19 - 22| + |24 - 24| + |28 - 26| + |32 - 28| + |38 - 30|}{5}$$

$$= \frac{3 + 0 + 2 + 4 + 8}{5} = \frac{15}{5} = 3.0$$

$$\text{SSE} = (19 - 22)^2 + (24 - 24)^2 + (28 - 26)^2 + (32 - 28)^{2+} (28 - 30)^2$$

$$= 9 + 0 + 4 + 16 + 64 = 93$$

Technique 3:

$$\text{MAD} = \frac{|19-17|+|24-20|+|28-25|+|32-31|+|38-39|}{5}$$

$$= \frac{2+4+3+1+1}{5} = \frac{11}{5} = 2.2$$

$$\text{SSE} = (19 - 17)^2 + (24 - 20)^2 + (28 - 25)^2 + (32 - 31)^2 + (38 - 39)^2$$

$$= 4 + 16 + 9 + 1 + 1 = 31$$

By both measures, technique 1 is the most accurate.

21.34

Quarter	t	$\hat{y} = 150 + 3t$	SI	Forecast
1	41	273	.7	191.1
2	42	276	1.2	331.2
3	43	279	1.5	418.5
4	44	282	.6	169.2

21.35

Day	t	$\hat{y} = 120 + 2.3t$	SI	Forecast
Sunday	29	186.7	1.5	280.1
Monday	30	189.0	.4	75.6
Tuesday	31	191.3	.5	95.7
Wednesday	32	193.6	.6	116.2
Thursday	33	195.9	.7	137.1
Friday	34	198.2	1.4	277.5
Saturday	35	200.5	1.9	381.0

21.36 $\hat{y}_t = 625 - 1.3y_{t-1} = 625 - 1.3(65) = 540.5$

21.37 $\hat{y}_t = 155 + 21y_{t-1} = 155 + 21(11) = 386$ `

21.38 $F_{17} = F_{18} = F_{19} = F_{20} = S_{16} = 43.08$

21.39

Day	t	$\hat{y} = 16.8 + .366t$	SI	Forecast
1	21	24.49	.675	16.53
2	22	24.85	.892	22.17
3	23	25.22	.864	21.79
4	24	25.58	1.212	31.01
5	25	25.95	1.357	35.21

21.40

Quarter	t	$\hat{y} = 47.7 - 1.06t$	SI	Forecast
1	21	25.44	1.207	30.71
2	22	24.38	.959	23.38
3	23	23.32	.972	22.67
4	24	22.26	.863	19.21

21.41

Quarter	t	$\hat{y} = 61.75 + 1.18t$	SI	Forecast
1	17	81.81	0.839	68.64
2	18	82.99	1.058	87.80
3	19	84.17	1.270	106.90
4	20	85.35	0.833	71.10
1	21	86.53	0.839	72.60
2	22	87.71	1.058	92.80
3	23	88.89	1.270	112.89
4	24	90.07	0.833	75.03

21.42a $\hat{y}_{1999} = 3717 + .760 y_{1998} = 3717 + .760(15,546) = 15,532$

b $F_{1999} = S_{1998} = 15,359$

21.43 a $\hat{y}_{1999} = -16.08 + .959 y_{1998} = -16.08 + .959(-231.1) = -237.7$

$F_{1999} = S_{1998} = -214.7$

21.44

Quarter	t	$\hat{y} = 143 + 7.42t$	SI	Forecast
1	25	328.50	1.063	349.20
2	26	335.92	.962	323.16
3	27	343.34	.927	318.28
4	28	350.76	1.048	367.60

21.45

Day	t	$\hat{y} = 145 + 1.66t$	SI	Forecast
1	29	193.14	1.404	271.17
2	30	194.80	0.517	100.71
3	31	196.46	0.515	101.18
4	32	198.12	0.621	123.03
5	33	199.78	0.675	134.85
6	34	201.44	1.145	230.65
7	35	203.10	2.123	431.18

21.46

Day	t	$\hat{y} = 90.4 + 2.02t$	SI	Forecast
1	17	124.74	1.094	136.47
2	18	126.76	0.958	121.44
3	19	128.78	0.688	88.60
4	20	130.80	1.260	164.81

21.47

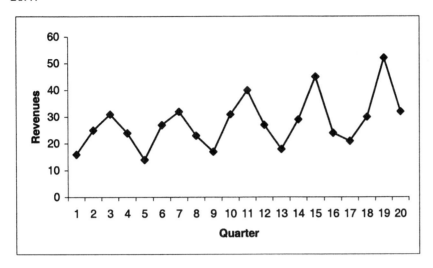

21.48 The only component appears to be seasonality.

21.49 $\hat{y} = 20.21 + .732t$

21.50

Seasonal Indexes	
Season	**Index**
1	0.6464
2	1.0450
3	1.4050
4	0.9037

21.51

Quarter	t	$\hat{y} = 20.21 + .732t$	SI	Forecast
1	21	35.58	0.646	23.00
2	22	36.31	1.045	37.95
3	23	37.05	1.405	52.05
4	24	37.78	0.904	34.14

Chapter 22

22.1 Chance variation is caused by a number of randomly occurring events that are part of the production process and that in general cannot be eliminated without changing the process.

22.3 Special variation is caused by specific events or factors that are frequently temporary and that can usually be identified and eliminated

2.4a Chance variation represents the variation in student achievement caused by differences in preparation, motivation, and ability.

b Special variation represents variation due to unprepared instructors and poor facilities.

22.5 $\alpha = P(|z| > 2.5) = 2(.5 - .4938) = .0124$

22.6 $ARL = \dfrac{1}{.0124} = 81$

22.7 $\alpha = P(|z| > 2.0) = 2(.5 - .4772) = .0456$

22.8 $ARL = \dfrac{1}{.0456} = 22$

22.9 $ARL = \dfrac{1}{.0026} = 385$

Number of units = Production $\times$ ARL = 100(385) = 38,500

22.10a From Beta-mean spreadsheet, $\beta = .6604$

b Probability = $.6604^8 = .0362$

22.11 $P = 1 - \beta = 1 - .6604 = .3396$; $ARL = \dfrac{1}{P} = \dfrac{1}{.3396} = 2.94$

2.12 Number of units = Production $\times$ ARL = 50(385) = 19,250

2.13a From Beta-mean spreadsheet, $\beta = .8133$

b Probability = $.8133^8 = .1914$

22.14 $P = 1 - \beta = 1 - .8133 = .1867$; $ARL = \dfrac{1}{P} = \dfrac{1}{.1867} = 5.36$

22.15 Sampling 3 units per hour means that on average we will produce 38,500 units before erroneously concluding that the process is out of control when it isn't. Sampling 2 units per half hour reduces this figure by 50%. Sampling 4 units per hour means that when the process goes out of control, the probability of not detecting a shift of 1.5 standard deviations is .6604 and we will produce on average $2.94 \times 100 = 294$ units until the chart indicates a problem. Sampling 2 units per half hour increases the probability of not detecting the shift to .8133 and decreases the average number of units produced when the process is out of control to $50 \times 5.36 = 268$.

22.16 Number of units = Production $\times$ ARL = 2000(385) = 770,000

22.17a From Beta-mean spreadsheet, $\beta = .7389$

b Probability = $.7389^4 = .2981$

22.18 $P = 1 - \beta = 1 - .7389 = .2611$; $ARL = \dfrac{1}{P} = \dfrac{1}{.2611} = 3.83$

22.19 Number of units = Production $\times$ ARL = 4000(385) = 1,540,000

22.20a From Beta-mean spreadsheet, $\beta = .3660$

b Probability = $.3660^4 = .0179$

22.21 $P = 1 - \beta = 1 - .3660 = .6340$; $ARL = \dfrac{1}{P} = \dfrac{1}{.6340} = 1.58$

22.22 Sampling 10 units per half hour means that on average we will produce 770,000 units before erroneously concluding that the process is out of control when it isn't. Sampling 20 units per hour doubles this figure. Sampling 10 units per half hour means that when the process goes out of control, the probability of not detecting a shift of .75 standard deviations is .7389 and we will produce on average $3.83 \times 2000 = 7660$ units until the chart indicates a problem. Sampling 20 units per hour decreases the probability of not detecting the shift to .3660 and decreases the average number of units produced when the process is out of control to $4000 \times 1.58 = 6320$.

22.23 Centerline = $\bar{\bar{x}} = 453.6$

Lower control limit = $\bar{\bar{x}} - \dfrac{3S}{\sqrt{n}} = 453.6 - 3\left(\dfrac{12.5}{\sqrt{4}}\right) = 434.85$

Upper control limit = $\bar{\bar{x}} + \dfrac{3S}{\sqrt{n}} = 453.6 + 3\left(\dfrac{12.5}{\sqrt{4}}\right) = 472.35$

22.24 Centerline = $\bar{\bar{x}} = 181.1$

Lower control limit = $\bar{\bar{x}} - \dfrac{3S}{\sqrt{n}} = 181.1 - 3\left(\dfrac{11.0}{\sqrt{9}}\right) = 170.1$

Upper control limit = $\bar{\bar{x}} + \dfrac{3S}{\sqrt{n}} = 181.1 + 3\left(\dfrac{11.0}{\sqrt{9}}\right) = 192.1$

Zone boundaries: 170.10, 173.77, 177.73, 181.10, 184.77, 188.43, 192.10

22.25 a Centerline = $\bar{\bar{x}} = 13.3$

Lower control limit = $\bar{\bar{x}} - \dfrac{3S}{\sqrt{n}} = 13.3 - 3\left(\dfrac{3.8}{\sqrt{4}}\right) = 7.6$

Upper control limit = $\bar{\bar{x}} + \dfrac{3S}{\sqrt{n}} = 13.3 + 3\left(\dfrac{3.8}{\sqrt{4}}\right) = 19.0$

c The process is out of control at points 8, 9, 21, 22, and 25.

22.26a

Statistical Process Control								
		Data						
Upper control limit		10.0885						
Centerline		4.452						
Lower control limit		0						

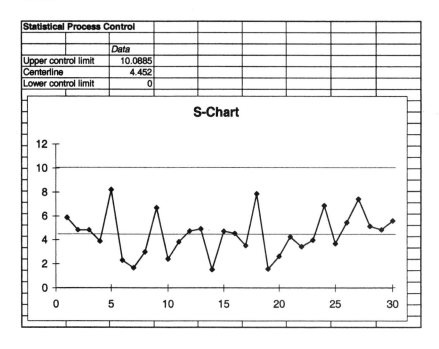

Upper control limit	19.9668						
Centerline	12.7386						
Lower control limit	5.5103						
Pattern Test #2 Failed at Points: 29							
Pattern Test #6 Failed at Points: 29, 30							

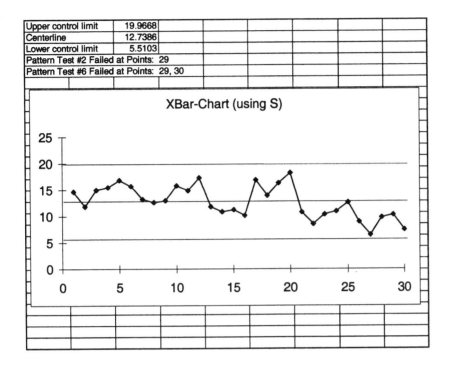

c The process is out of control at samples 29 and 30.

d A level shift occurred.

22.27a

Statistical Process Control							
		2by4 lumber					
Upper control limit		0.1851					
Centerline		0.0721					
Lower control limit		0					

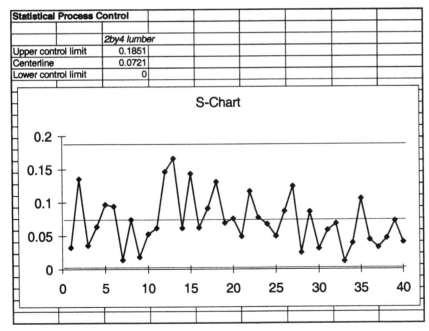

Statistical Process Control								
		2by4 lumber						
Upper control limit		96.0635						
Centerline		95.9231						
Lower control limit		95.7827						
Pattern Test #1 Failed at Points:	1, 4, 5, 28, 35, 36, 37, 39, 40							
Pattern Test #5 Failed at Points:	3, 4, 5, 6, 9, 10, 35, 36, 37, 38, 39, 40							
Pattern Test #6 Failed at Points:	5, 6, 7, 8, 9, 35, 36, 37, 38, 39, 40							

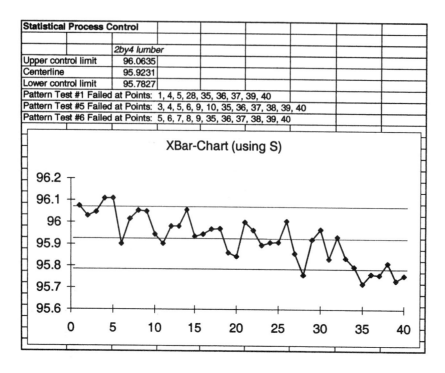

b The process is out of control at the first sample.

c Clean out the sawdust more frequently.

22.28

Statistical Process Control								
		AEU						
Upper control limit		0.0031						
Centerline		0.0015						
Lower control limit		0						

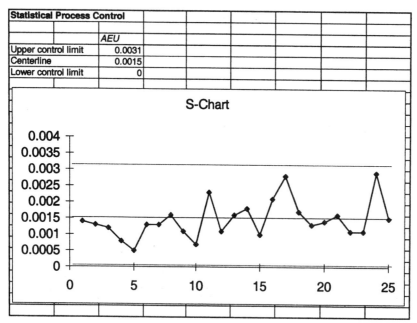

Statistical Process Control							
		AEU					
Upper control limit		0.4408					
Centerline		0.4387					
Lower control limit		0.4366					

XBar-Chart (using S)

The process is under control.

$$22.29 \ S = \frac{Upper\ control\ limit - Centerline}{3} = \frac{.4408 - .4387}{3} = .0007$$

$$CPL = \frac{\bar{\bar{x}} - LSL}{3S} = \frac{.4387 - .4370}{3(.0007)} = .81$$

$$CPU = \frac{USL - \bar{\bar{x}}}{3S} = \frac{4400 - .4387}{3(.0007)} = .62$$

$$C_{pk} = Min(CPL, CPU) = .62$$

22.30

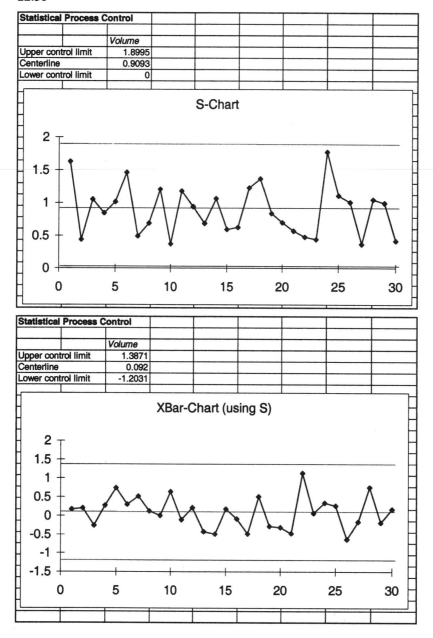

Statistical Process Control

		Volume						
Upper control limit		1.8995						
Centerline		0.9093						
Lower control limit		0						

Statistical Process Control

		Volume						
Upper control limit		1.3871						
Centerline		0.092						
Lower control limit		-1.2031						

The process is under control.

22.31 $S = \dfrac{Upper\ control\ limit - Centerline}{3} = \dfrac{1001.3871 - 1000.092}{3} = .4317$

$CPL = \dfrac{\overline{\overline{x}} - LSL}{3S} = \dfrac{1000.092 - 998}{3(.4317)} = 1.62$

$CPU = \dfrac{USL - \overline{\overline{x}}}{3S} = \dfrac{1002 - 1000.092}{3(.4317)} = 1.47$

$C_{pk} = Min(CPL, CPU) = 1.47$

22.32

Statistical Process Control							
		Headrest					
Upper control limit		2.3313					
Centerline		0.9078					
Lower control limit		0					

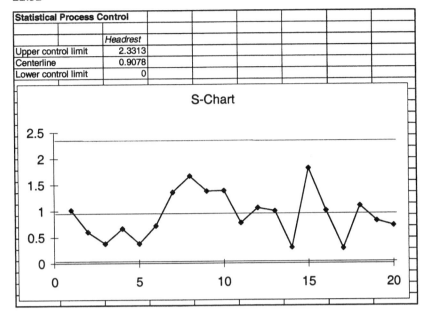

Statistical Process Control							
		Headrest					
Upper control limit		241.3248					
Centerline		239.5617					
Lower control limit		237.7986					
Pattern Test #1 Failed at Points:	19, 20						
Pattern Test #5 Failed at Points:	20						

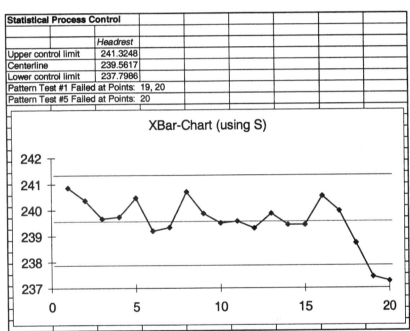

a The process is out of control.

b The process is out of control at sample 19.

c The width became too small.

22.33

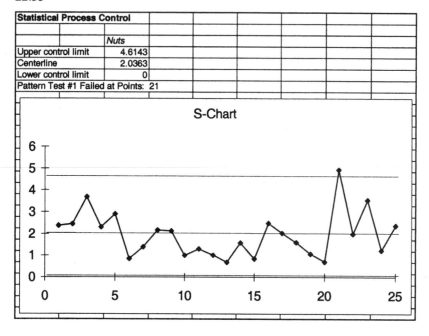

Statistical Process Control									
		Nuts							
Upper control limit		4.6143							
Centerline		2.0363							
Lower control limit		0							
Pattern Test #1 Failed at Points: 21									

The process is out of control at sample 21. It is not necessary to draw the $\bar{x}$ chart.

22.34

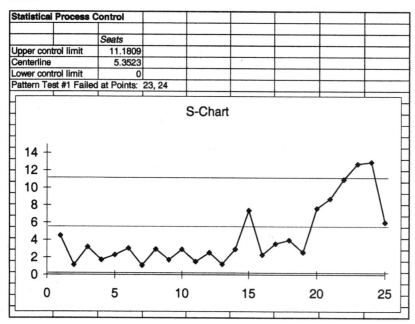

Statistical Process Control									
		Seats							
Upper control limit		11.1809							
Centerline		5.3523							
Lower control limit		0							
Pattern Test #1 Failed at Points: 23, 24									

The process is out of control at sample 23. It is not necessary to draw the $\bar{x}$ chart.

518

22.35

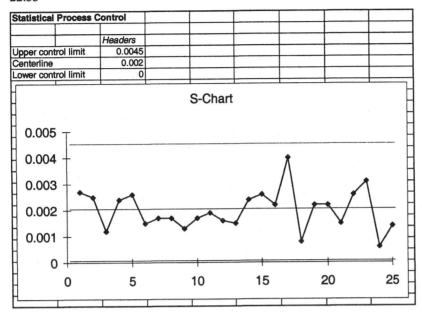

Statistical Process Control								
		Headers						
Upper control limit		0.0045						
Centerline		0.002						
Lower control limit		0						

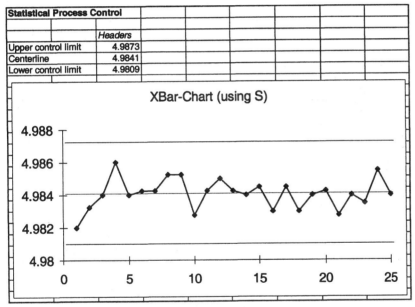

Statistical Process Control								
		Headers						
Upper control limit		4.9873						
Centerline		4.9841						
Lower control limit		4.9809						

The process is under control.

$$22.36 \quad S = \frac{Upper\ control\ limit - Centerline}{3} = \frac{4.9873 - 4.9841}{3} = .00107$$

$$CPL = \frac{\overline{\overline{x}} - LSL}{3S} = \frac{4.9841 - 4.981}{3(.00107)} = .97$$

$$CPU = \frac{USL - \overline{\overline{x}}}{3S} = \frac{4.987 - 4.9841}{3(.00107)} = .90$$

$$C_{pk} = Min(CPL, CPU) = .90$$

519

22.37

Statistical Process Control									
		Bolts							
Upper control limit		1.2895							
Centerline		0.5021							
Lower control limit		0							

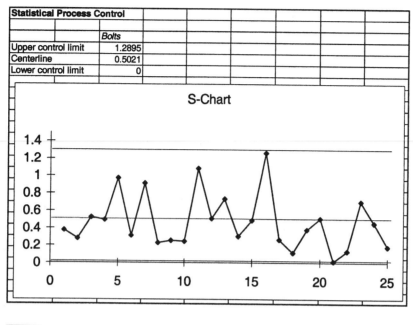

Statistical Process Control									
		Bolts							
Upper control limit		7.7864							
Centerline		6.81							
Lower control limit		5.8336							
Pattern Test #5 Failed at Points:		25							
Pattern Test #6 Failed at Points:		23, 24, 25							

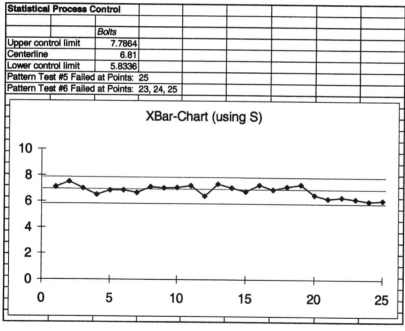

The process went out of control at sample 23.

22.38

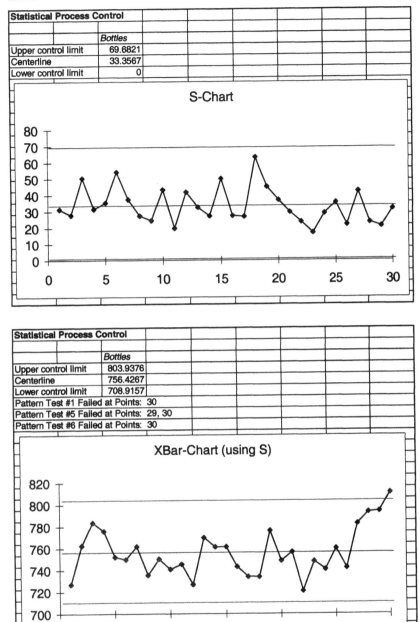

Statistical Process Control									
		Bottles							
Upper control limit		69.6821							
Centerline		33.3567							
Lower control limit		0							

Statistical Process Control									
		Bottles							
Upper control limit		803.9376							
Centerline		756.4267							
Lower control limit		708.9157							
Pattern Test #1 Failed at Points:	30								
Pattern Test #5 Failed at Points:	29, 30								
Pattern Test #6 Failed at Points:	30								

The process went out of control at sample 29.

521

22.39a

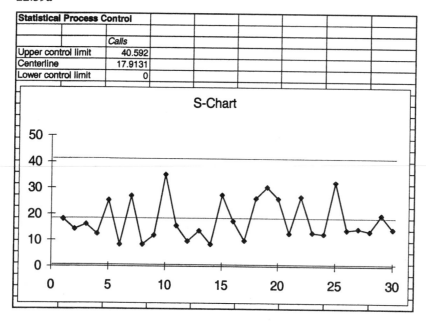

Statistical Process Control							
		Calls					
Upper control limit		40.592					
Centerline		17.9131					
Lower control limit		0					

S-Chart

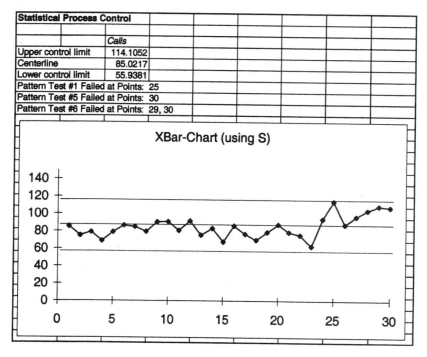

Statistical Process Control							
		Calls					
Upper control limit		114.1052					
Centerline		85.0217					
Lower control limit		55.9381					
Pattern Test #1 Failed at Points:		25					
Pattern Test #5 Failed at Points:		30					
Pattern Test #6 Failed at Points:		29, 30					

XBar-Chart (using S)

b The process went out of control at sample 25

522

22.40

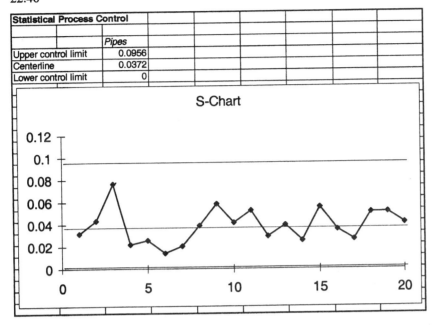

Statistical Process Control							
	Pipes						
Upper control limit	0.0956						
Centerline	0.0372						
Lower control limit	0						

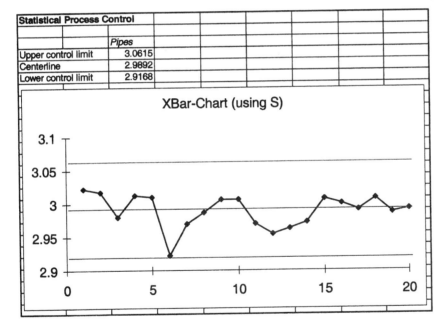

Statistical Process Control							
	Pipes						
Upper control limit	3.0615						
Centerline	2.9892						
Lower control limit	2.9168						

The process is under control.

22.41 $S = \dfrac{Upper\ control\ limit - Centerline}{3} = \dfrac{3.0615 - 2.9892}{3} = .0241$

$CPL = \dfrac{\bar{\bar{x}} - LSL}{3S} = \dfrac{2.9892 - 2.9}{3(.0241)} = 1.23$

$$CPU = \frac{USL - \overline{\overline{x}}}{3S} = \frac{3.1 - 2.9892}{3(.0241)} = 1.53$$

$$C_{pk} = Min(CPL, CPU) = 1.23$$

22.42 $S = \dfrac{Upper\ control\ limit - Centerline}{3} = \dfrac{1504.572 - 1496.952}{3} = 2.54$

$$CPL = \frac{\overline{\overline{x}} - LSL}{3S} = \frac{1496.952 - 1494.5}{3(2.54)} = .32$$

$$CPU = \frac{USL - \overline{\overline{x}}}{3S} = \frac{1497.5 - 1496.952}{3(2.54)} = .07$$

$$C_{pk} = Min(CPL, CPU) = .07$$

The value of the index is low because the statistics used to calculate the control limits and centerline were taken when the process was out of control.

22.43 Centerline = $\overline{p} = .035$

Lower control limit = $\overline{p} - 3\sqrt{\dfrac{\overline{p}(1 - \overline{p})}{n}} = .035 - 3\sqrt{\dfrac{(.035)(1 - .035)}{1000}} = .0176$

Upper control limit = $\overline{p} + 3\sqrt{\dfrac{\overline{p}(1 - \overline{p})}{n}} = .035 + 3\sqrt{\dfrac{(.035)(1 - .035)}{1000}} = .0524$

22.44 Centerline = $\overline{p} = .0324$

Lower control limit = $\overline{p} - 3\sqrt{\dfrac{\overline{p}(1 - \overline{p})}{n}} = .0324 - 3\sqrt{\dfrac{(.0324)(1 - .0324)}{200}} = -.00516\ (= 0)$

Upper control limit = $\overline{p} + 3\sqrt{\dfrac{\overline{p}(1 - \overline{p})}{n}} = .0324 + 3\sqrt{\dfrac{(.0324)(1 - .0324)}{200}} = .06996$

Statistical Process Control								
	Copiers							
Upper control limit	0.07							
Centerline	0.0324							
Lower control limit	0							
Pattern Test #1 Failed at Points: 25								

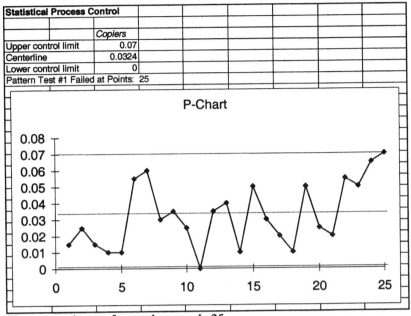

The process is out of control at sample 25.

22.45 Centerline = $\bar{p}$ = .00352

Lower control limit = $\bar{p} - 3\sqrt{\dfrac{\bar{p}(1-\bar{p})}{n}}$ = .00352 - $3\sqrt{\dfrac{(.00352)(1-.00352)}{500}}$ = -.00443 (=0)

Upper control limit = $\bar{p} + 3\sqrt{\dfrac{\bar{p}(1-\bar{p})}{n}}$ = .00352 + $3\sqrt{\dfrac{(.00352)(1-.00352)}{500}}$ = .01147

Statistical Process Control								
	PCBs							
Upper control limit	0.0115							
Centerline	0.0035							
Lower control limit	0							

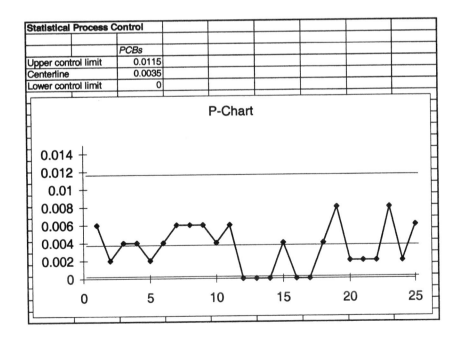

The process is under control.

22.46 Centerline = $\bar{p}$ = . 0383

Lower control limit = $\bar{p} - 3\sqrt{\dfrac{\bar{p}(1-\bar{p})}{n}}$ = .0383 - $3\sqrt{\dfrac{(.0383)(1-.0383)}{100}}$ = -.0193 (= 0)

Upper control limit = $\bar{p} + 3\sqrt{\dfrac{\bar{p}(1-\bar{p})}{n}}$ = .0383 + $3\sqrt{\dfrac{(.0383)(1-.0383)}{100}}$ = .0959

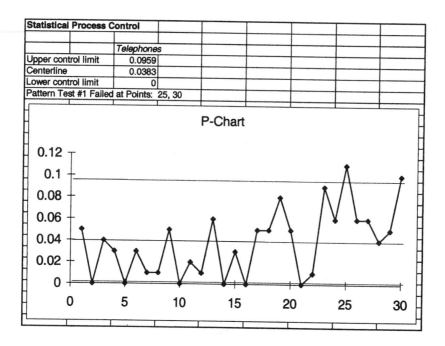

Statistical Process Control							
	Telephones						
Upper control limit	0.0959						
Centerline	0.0383						
Lower control limit	0						
Pattern Test #1 Failed at Points: 25, 30							

The process is out of control at samples 25 and 30.

22.47 Centerline = $\bar{p}$ = .0169

Lower control limit = $\bar{p} - 3\sqrt{\dfrac{\bar{p}(1-\bar{p})}{n}}$ = .0169 - $3\sqrt{\dfrac{(.0169)(1-.0169)}{1000}}$ = .0047

Upper control limit = $\bar{p} + 3\sqrt{\dfrac{\bar{p}(1-\bar{p})}{n}}$ = .0169 + $3\sqrt{\dfrac{(.0169)(1-.0169)}{1000}}$ = .0291

Statistical Process Control								
		Pages						
Upper control limit		0.0291						
Centerline		0.0169						
Lower control limit		0.0047						
Pattern Test #2 Failed at Points: 37								

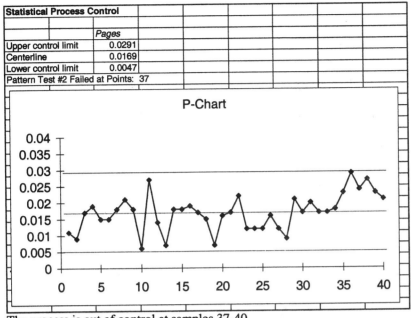

The process is out of control at samples 37-40.

22.48

Statistical Process Control								
		Batteries						
Upper control limit		0.047						
Centerline		0.0257						
Lower control limit		0.0045						
Pattern Test #1 Failed at Points: 28, 29, 30								

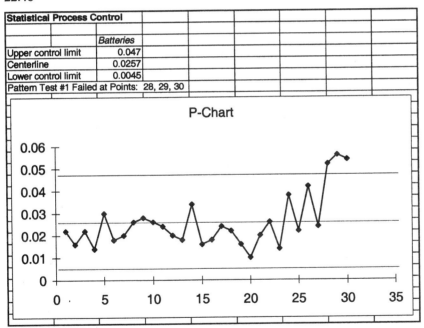

The process is out of control at sample 28.

22.49

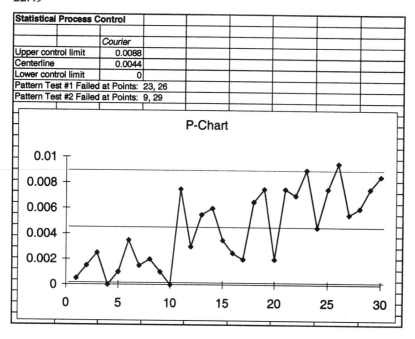

Statistical Process Control								
	Courier							
Upper control limit	0.0088							
Centerline	0.0044							
Lower control limit	0							
Pattern Test #1 Failed at Points: 23, 26								
Pattern Test #2 Failed at Points: 9, 29								

The process went out of control at sample 9.

22.50

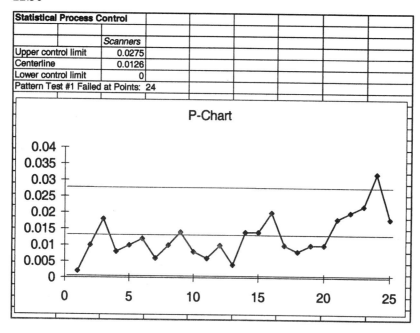

Statistical Process Control								
	Scanners							
Upper control limit	0.0275							
Centerline	0.0126							
Lower control limit	0							
Pattern Test #1 Failed at Points: 24								

The process is out of control at sample 24.

Chapter 23

23.1

	a_1	a_2
s_1	0	29
s_2	0	5
s_3	14	0
s_4	36	0

23.2

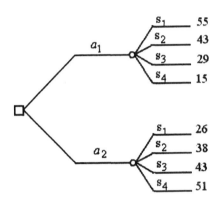

23.3 $EMV(a_1) = .4(55) + .1(43) + .3(29) + .2(15) = 38.0$

$EMV(a_2) = .4(26) + .1(38) + .3(43) + .2(51) = 37.3$

23.4

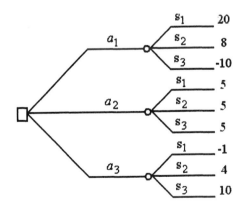

23.5	a_1	a_2	a_3
s_1	0	15	21
s_2	0	3	4
s_3	20	5	0

23.6 $EOL(a_1) = .2(0) + .6(0) + .2(20) = 4.0$

$EOL(a_2) = .2(15) + .6(3) + .2(5) = 5.8$

$EOL(a_3) = .2(21) + .6(4) + .2(0) = 6.6$

The EOL decision is a_1.

23.7a

Demand	a_0	a_1	Produce a_2	a_3
s_0	0	-3.00	-6.00	-9.00
s_1	0	5.00	2.00	-1.00
s_2	0	5.00	10.00	7.00
s_3	0	5.00	10.00	15.00

b

Demand	a_0	a_1	Produce a_2	a_3
s_0	0	3.00	6.00	9.00
s_1	5.00	0	3.00	6.00
s_2	10.00	5.00	0	3.00
s_3	15.00	10.00	5.00	0

c

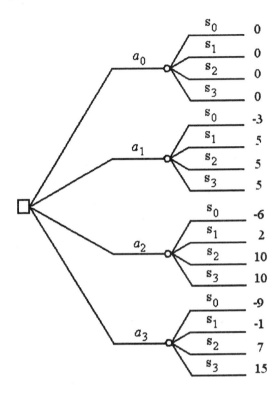

23.8a EMV(a_0) = 0

EMV(a_1) = .25(-3.00) + .25(5.00) + .25(5.00) + .25(5.00) = 3.00

EMV(a_2) = . 25(-6.00) + .25(2.00) + .25(10.00) + .25(10.00) = 4.00

EMV(a_3) = . 25(-9.00) + .25(-1.00) + .25(7.00) + .25(15.00) = 3.00

EMV decision is a_2 (bake 2 cakes)

b EOL(a_0) = .25(0) + .25(5.00) + .25(10.00) + .25(15.00) = 7.50

EOL(a_1) = .25(3.00) + .25(0) + .25(5.00) + .25(10.00) = 4.50

EOL(a_2) = . 25(6.00) + .25(3.00) + .25(0) + .25(5.00) = 3.50

EOL(a_2) = . 25(9.00) + .25(6.00) + .25(3.00) + .25(0) = 4.50

EOL decision is a_2 (bake 2 cakes)

23.9

	a_1 (flat fee)	a_2 Pay per snowfall
s_0	-40,000	0
s_1	-40,000	-18,000
s_2	-40,000	-36,000
s_3	-40,000	-54,000
s_4	-40,000	-72,000

23.10 $EMV(a_1) = -40,000$

$EMV(a_2) = .05(0) + .15(-18,000) + .30(-36,000) + .40(-54,000) + .10(-72,000) = -42,300$

EMV decision is a_1

23.11a   Payoff Table

	a_{100}	a_{200}	a_{300}
s_{100}	$12(100)-10(100)$ $= 200$	$12(100)-9(200)+6(100)$ $= 0$	$12(100)-8.50(300)+6(200)$ $= -150$
s_{150}	$12(100)-10(100)$ $= 200$	$12(150)-9(200)+6(50)$ $= 300$	$12(150)-8.50(300)+6(150)$ $= 150$
s_{200}	$12(100)-10(100)$ $= 200$	$12(200)-9(200)$ $= 600$	$12(200)-8.50(300)+6(100)$ $= 450$
s_{250}	$12(100)-10(100)$ $= 200$	$12(200)-9(200)$ $= 600$	$12(250)-8.50(300)+6(50)$ $= 750$

b   Opportunity Loss Table

	a_{100}	a_{200}	a_{300}
s_{100}	0	200	350
s_{150}	100	0	150
s_{200}	400	0	150
s_{250}	550	150	0

c

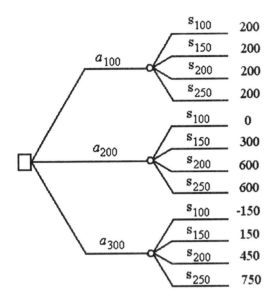

	s_{100}	200
a_{100}	s_{150}	200
	s_{200}	200
	s_{250}	200
	s_{100}	0
a_{200}	s_{150}	300
	s_{200}	600
	s_{250}	600
	s_{100}	-150
a_{300}	s_{150}	150
	s_{200}	450
	s_{250}	750

23.12

$EMV(a_{100}) = 200$

$EMV(a_{200}) = .20(0) + .25(300) + .40(600) + .15(600) = 405$

$EMV(a_{300}) = .20(-150) + .25(150) + .40(450) + .15(750) = 300$

EMV decision is order 200 shirts.

23.13 $P(s_0) = .607, P(s_1) = .303, P(s_2) = .076, P(s_3) = .012, P(s_4) = .002$

Payoff Table

	a_0	a_1	a_2	a_3
s_0	0	-6,000	-12,000	-18,000
s_1	0	7,000	1,000	-5,000
s_2	0	7,000	14,000	8,000
s_3	0	7,000	14,000	21,000

Opportunity Loss Table

	a_0	a_1	a_2	a_3
s_0	0	6,000	12,000	18,000
s_1	7,000	0	6,000	12,000
s_2	14,000	7,000	0	6,000
s_3	21,000	14,000	7,000	0

533

23.14a EMV(Small) = .15(-220) + .55(-330) + .30(-440) = -346.5

EMV(Medium) = .15(-300) + .55(-320) + .30(-390) = -338.0

EMV(Large) = .15(-350) + .55(-350) + .30(-350) =-350.0

EMV decision: build a medium size plant; EMV*= -338.0

b   Opportunity Loss Table

	Small	Medium	Large
Low	0	80	130
Moderate	10	0	30
High	90	40	0

c EOL(Small) = .15(0) + .55(10) + .30(90) = 32.5

EOL(Medium) = .15(80) + .55(0) + .30(40) = 24.0

EOL(Large) = .15(130) + .55(30) + .30(0) = 36.0

EOL decision: build a medium size plant

23.15a $P(s_{10}) = 9/90 = .10$, $P(s_{11}) = 18/90 = .20$, $P(s_{12}) = 36/90 = .40$, $P(s_{13}) = 27/90 = .30$

Payoff Table

	a_{10}	a_{11}	a_{12}	a_{13}
s_{10}	30	10(5)- 11(2)+2 = 30	10(5)-12(2)+3.50 = 29.50	10(5)-13(2)+4.50 = 28.50
s_{11}	30	11(5)-11(2) = 33	11(5)-12(2)+2 = 33	11(5)-13(2)+3.50 = 32.50
s_{12}	30	11(5)-11(2) = 33	12(5)-12(2) = 36	12(5)- 13(2)+2 = 36
s_{13}	30	11(5)-11(2) = 33	12(5)-12(2) = 36	13(5)-13(2) = 39

b EMV(a_{10}) = 30

EMV(a_{11}) = .10(30) + .20(33) + .40(33) + .30(33) = 32.70

EMV(a_{12}) = .10(29.50) + .20(33) + .40(36) + .30(36) = 34.75

EMV(a_{13}) = .10(28.50) + .20(32.50) + .40(36) + .30(39) = 35.45

EMV decision: buy 13 bushels

23.16   Payoff Table

                                   Decision

                         Produce   Don't produce

Market share

5%   -28 million   0

10%   2 million   0

15%   8 million   0

EMV(produce) = .15(-28 million) + .45(2 million) + .40 (8 million) = -.1 million

EMV (don't produce) = 0

EMV decision: don't produce

23.17 EPPI = .10(110) + .25(150) + .50(220) + .15(250) = 196

$EMV(a_1)$ = .10(60) + .25(40) + .50(220) + .15(250) = 163.5

$EMV(a_2)$ = .10(110) + .25(110) + .50(120) + .15(120) = 116.5

$EMV(a_3)$ = .10(75) + .25(150) + .50(85) + .15(130) = 107

EVPI = EPPI – EMV* = 196 – 163.5 = 32.5

23.18   Opportunity Loss Table

          a_1 a_2 a_3

s_1 50   0   35

s_2 110   40   0

s_3 0   100   135

s_4 0   130   120

$EOL(a_1)$ = .10(50) + .25(110) + .50(0) + .15(0) = 32.5

$EOL(a_2)$ = .10(0) + .25(40) + .50(100) + .15(130) = 79.5

$EOL(a_3)$ = .10(35) + .25(0) + .50(135) + .15(120) = 89

EOL* = 32.5

23.19 EPPI = .5(65) + .5(110) = 87.5

$EMV(a_1)$ = .5(65) + .5(70) = 67.5

$EMV(a_2)$ = .5(20) + .5(110) = 65.0

$EMV(a_3)$ = .5(45) + .5(80) = 62.5

$EMV(a_4)$ = .5(30) + .5(95) = 62.5

EVPI = EPPI – EMV* = 87.5 – 67.5 = 20

23.20 a EPPI = .75(65) + .25(110) = 76.25

$EMV(a_1) = .75(65) + .25(70) = 66.25$

$EMV(a_2) = .75(20) + .25(110) = 42.5$

$EMV(a_3) = .75(45) + .25(80) = 53.75$

$EMV(a_4) = .75(30) + .25(95) = 46.25$

EVPI = EPPI − EMV* = 76.25 − 66.25 = 10

b EPPI = .95(65) + .05(110) = 67.25

$EMV(a_1) = .95(65) + .05(70) = 65.25$

$EMV(a_2) = .95(20) + .05(110) = 24.5$

$EMV(a_3) = .95(45) + .05(80) = 46.75$

$EMV(a_4) = .95(30) + .05(95) = 33.25$

EVPI = EPPI − EMV* = 67.25 − 65.25 = 2

23.21 As the difference between the two prior probabilities increases EVPI decreases.

23.22 Posterior Probabilities for I_1

s_j	$P(s_j)$	$P(I_1|s_j)$	$P(s_j \text{ and } I_1)$	$P(s_j | I_1)$
s_1	.25	.40	(.25)(.40) = .10	.12/.20 = .500
s_2	.40	.25	(.40)(.25) = .10	.10/.20 = .500
s_3	.35	0	(.35)(0) = .0	0/.20 = 0
			$P(I_1) = .20$	

Posterior Probabilities for I_2

s_j	$P(s_j)$	$P(I_2|s_j)$	$P(s_j \text{ and } I_2)$	$P(s_j | I_2)$
s_1	.25	.30	(.25)(.30) = .075	.075/.28 = .268
s_2	.40	.25	(.40)(.25) = .10	.10/.28 = .357
s_3	.35	30	(.35)(.30) = .105	.105/.28 = .375
			$P(I_2) = .28$	

536

Posterior Probabilities for I_3

s_j	$P(s_j)$	$P(I_3 \mid s_j)$	$P(s_j \text{ and } I_3)$	$P(s_j \mid I_3)$
s_1	.25	.20	$(.25)(.20) = .05$	$.05/.29 = .172$
s_2	.40	.25	$(.40)(.25) = .10$	$.10/.29 = .345$
s_3	.35	.40	$\underline{(.35)(.40) = .14}$	$.14/.29 = .483$
			$P(I_3) = .29$	

Posterior Probabilities for I_4

s_j	$P(s_j)$	$P(I_4 \mid s_j)$	$P(s_j \text{ and } I_4)$	$P(s_j \mid I_4)$
s_1	.25	.10	$(.25)(.10) = .025$	$.025/.23 = .109$
s_2	.40	.25	$(.40)(.25) = .10$	$.10/.23 = .435$
s_3	.35	.30	$\underline{(.35)(.30) = .105}$	$.105/.23 = .456$
			$P(I_4) = .23$	

23.23 Posterior Probabilities for I_1

s_j	$P(s_j)$	$P(I_1 \mid s_j)$	$P(s_j \text{ and } I_1)$	$P(s_j \mid I_1)$
s_1	.5	.98	$(.5)(.98) = .49$	$.49/.515 = .951$
s_2	.5	.05	$\underline{(.5)(.05) = .025}$	$.025/.515 = .049$
			$P(I_1) = .515$	

Posterior Probabilities for I_2

s_j	$P(s_j)$	$P(I_2 \mid s_j)$	$P(s_j \text{ and } I_2)$	$P(s_j \mid I_2)$
s_1	.5	.02	$(.5)(.02) = .01$	$.01/.485 = .021$
s_2	.5	.95	$\underline{(.5)(.95) = .475}$	$.475/.485 = .979$
			$P(I_2) = .485$	

23.24a Prior probabilities: $EMV(a_1) = .5(10) + .5(22) = 16$

$EMV(a_2) = .5(18) + .5(19) = 18.5$

$EMV(a_3) = .5(23) + .5(15) = 19$

$EMV^* = 19$

I_1: $EMV(a_1) = .951(10) + .049(22) = 10.588$

$EMV(a_2) = .951(18) + .049(19) = 18.049$

$EMV(a_3) = .951(23) + .049(15) = 22.608$

Optimal act: a_3

I_2: $EMV(a_1) = .021(10) + .979(22) = 21.748$

$EMV(a_2) = .021(18) + .979(19) = 18.979$

$EMV(a_3) = .021(23) + .979(15) = 15.168$

Optimal act: a_1

b $EMV^ = .515(22.608) + .485(21.748) = 22.191$

$EVSI = EMV^ - EMV* = 22.191 - 19 = 3.191$

23.25 Prior probabilities: $EMV(a_1) = .333(60) + .333(90) + .333(150) = 100$

$EMV(a_2) = 90$

$EMV* = 100$

Posterior Probabilities for I_1

s_j	$P(s_j)$	$P(I_1 \vert s_j)$	$P(s_j \text{ and } I_1)$	$P(s_j \vert I_1)$
s_1	.333	.7	$(.333)(.7) = .233$	$.233/.467 = .499$
s_2	.333	.5	$(.333)(.5) = .167$	$.167/.467 = .358$
s_3	.333	.2	$(.333)(.2) = .067$	$.067/.467 = .143$
			$P(I_1) = .467$	

Posterior Probabilities for I_2

s_j	$P(s_j)$	$P(I_2 \vert s_j)$	$P(s_j \text{ and } I_2)$	$P(s_j \vert I_2)$
s_1	.333	.3	$(.333)(.3) = .100$	$.100/.534 = .187$
s_2	.333	.5	$(.333)(.5) = .167$	$.167/.534 = .313$
s_3	.333	.8	$(.333)(.8) = .267$	$.267/.534 = .500$
			$P(I_2) = .534$	

I_1: $EMV(a_1) = .499(60) + .358(90) + .143(150) = 83.61$

$EMV(a_2) = 90$

I_2: $EMV(a_1) = .187(60) + .313(90) + .500(150) = 114.39$

$EMV(a_2) = 90$

$EMV^ = .467(90) + .534(114.39) = 103.11$

$EVSI = EMV^ - EMV* = 103.11 - 100 = 3.11$

23.26 Prior probabilities: $EMV(a_1) = .5(60) + .4(90) + .1(150) = 81$

$EMV(a_2) = 90$

$EMV* = 90$

Posterior Probabilities for I_1

s_j	$P(s_j)$	$P(I_1|s_j)$	$P(s_j$ and $I_1)$	$P(s_j|I_1)$
s_1	.5	.7	$(.5)(.7) = .35$	$.35/.57 = .614$
s_2	.4	.5	$(.4)(.5) = .20$	$.20/.57 = .351$
s_3	.1	.2	$(.1)(.2) = .02$	$.02/.57 = .035$
			$P(I_1) = .57$	

Posterior Probabilities for I_2

s_j	$P(s_j)$	$P(I_2|s_j)$	$P(s_j$ and $I_2)$	$P(s_j|I_2)$
s_1	.5	.3	$(.5)(.3) = .15$	$.15/.43 = .349$
s_2	.4	.5	$(.4)(.5) = .20$	$.20/.43 = .465$
s_3	.1	.8	$(.1)(.8) = .08$	$.08/.43 = .186$
			$P(I_1) = .43$	

I_1: $EMV(a_1) = .614(60) + .351(90) + .035(150) = 73.68$

$EMV(a_2) = 90$

I_1: $EMV(a_1) = .349(60) + .465(90) + .186(150) = 90.69$

$EMV(a_2) = 90$

$EMV` = .57(90) + .43(90.69) = 90.30$

$EVSI = EMV` - EMV^* = 90.30 - 90 = .30$

23.27 Prior probabilities: $EMV(a_1) = .90(60) + .05(90) + .05(150) = 66$

$EMV(a_2) = 90$

$EMV^* = 90$

Posterior Probabilities for I_1

s_j	$P(s_j)$	$P(I_1|s_j)$	$P(s_j$ and $I_1)$	$P(s_j|I_1)$
s_1	.90	.7	$(.90)(.7) = .63$	$.63/.665 = .947$
s_2	.05	.5	$(.05)(.5) = .025$	$.025/.665 = .038$
s_3	.05	.2	$(.05)(.2) = .01$	$.01/.665 = .015$
			$P(I_1) = .665$	

Posterior Probabilities for I_2

s_j	$P(s_j)$	$P(I_2\|s_j)$	$P(s_j \text{ and } I_2)$	$P(s_j\|I_2)$
s_1	.90	.3	$(.90)(.3) = .27$	$.27/.335 = .806$
s_2	.05	.5	$(.05)(.5) = .025$	$.025/.335 = .075$
s_3	.05	.8	$(.05)(.8) = .04$	$.04/.335 = .119$
			$P(I_1) = .335$	

I_1: $EMV(a_1) = .947(60) + .038(90) + .015(150) = 62.49$

$EMV(a_2) = 90$

I_2: $EMV(a_1) = .806(60) + .075(90) + .119(150) = 72.96$

$EMV(a_2) = 90$

$EMV` = .665(90) + .335(90) = 90$

$EVSI = EMV` - EMV* = 90 - 90 = 0$

23.28 As the prior probabilities become more diverse EVSI decreases.

23.29

Payoff Table

Demand	Purchase lot	Don't purchase lot
10,000	$10,000(5)-125,000 = -75,000$	0
30,000	$30,000(5) - 125,000 = 25,000$	0
50,000	$50,000(5)-125,000 = 125,000$	0

$EMV(\text{purchase}) = .2(-75,000) + .5(25,000) + .3(125,000) = 35,000$

$EMV(\text{don't purchase}) = 0$

$EPPI = .2(0) + .5(25,000) + .3(125,000) = 50,000$

$EVPI = EPPI - EMV* = 50,000 - 35,000 = 15,000$

23.30 $EMV* = 0$

$EPPI = .15(0) + .45(2 \text{ million}) + .40(8 \text{ million}) = 4.1 \text{ million}$

$EVPI = EPPI - EMV* = 4.1 \text{ million} - 0 = 4.1 \text{ million}$

23.31 Likelihood probabilities (binomial probabilities)

$P(I \mid s_1) = P(x = 3, n = 25 \mid p = .05) = .0930$

$P(I \mid s_2) = P(x = 3, n = 25 \mid p = .10) = .2265$

$P(I \mid s_3) = P(x = 3, n = 25 \mid p = .15) = .2174$

Posterior Probabilities

s_j	$P(s_j)$	$P(I \mid s_j)$	$P(s_j \text{ and } I)$	$P(s_j \mid I)$
s_1	.15	.0930	$(.15)(.0930) = .0140$	$.0140/.2029 = .0690$
s_2	.45	.2265	$(.45)(.2265) = .1019$	$.1019/.2029 = .5022$
s_3	.40	.2174	$(.40)(.2174) = .0870$	$.0870/.2029 = .4288$
			$P(I) = .2029$	

EMV(produce) = .0690(-28 million) + .5022(2 million) + .4288(8 million) = 2.503 million

EMV (don't produce) = 0

EMV decision: produce

23.32a   Payoff Table

Market share	Switch	Don't switch
5%	$5(100,000) - 700,000 = -200,000$	285,000
10%	$10(100,000) - 700,000 = 300,000$	285,000
20%	$20(100,000) - 700,000 = 1,300,000$	285,000

b EMV(switch) = .4(-200,000) + .4(300,000) + .2(1,300,000) = 300,000

EMV(don't switch) = 285,000

Optimal act: switch (EMV* = 300,000)

c EPPI = .4(285,000) + .4(300,000) + .2(1,300,000) = 494,000

EVPI = EPPI – EMV* = 494,000 – 300,000= 194,000

23.33   Payoff Table

Participating Households	Proceed	Don't proceed
50,000	$50(500) - 55,000 = -30,000$	0
100,000	$100(500) - 55,000 = -5,000$	0
200,000	$200(500) - 55,000 = 45,000$	0
300,000	$300(500) - 55,000 = 95,000$	0

Likelihood probabilities (binomial probabilities)

$P(I \mid s_1) = P(x = 3, n = 25 \mid p = .05) = .0930$

$P(I \mid s_2) = P(x = 3, n = 25 \mid p = .10) = .2265$

$P(I \mid s_3) = P(x = 3, n = 25 \mid p = .20) = .1358$

$P(I \mid s_4) = P(x = 3, n = 25 \mid p = .30) = .0243$

Posterior Probabilities

s_j	$P(s_j)$	$P(I \mid s_j)$	$P(s_j$ and $I)$	$P(s_j \mid I)$
s_1	.5	.0930	$(.5)(.0930) = .0465$	$.0465/.1305 = .3563$
s_2	.3	.2265	$(.3)(.2265) = .0680$	$.0680/.1305 = .5211$
s_3	.1	.1358	$(.1)(.1358) = .0136$	$.0136/.1305 = .1042$
s_4	.1	.0243	$\underline{(.1)(.0243) = .0024}$	$.0024/.1305 = .0184$
			$P(I) = .1305$	

EMV(proceed) = .3563(-30,000) + .5211(-5,000) + .1042(45,000) + .0184(95,000) = -6,858

EMV (don't proceed = 0

EMV decision: don't proceed

23.34 Likelihood probabilities (binomial probabilities)

$P(I \mid s_1) = P(x = 12, n = 100 \mid p = .05) = .0028$

$P(I \mid s_2) = P(x = 12, n = 100 \mid p = .10) = .0988$

$P(I \mid s_3) = P(x = 12, n = 100 \mid p = .20) = .0128$

$P(I \mid s_4) = P(x = 12, n = 100 \mid p = .30) = .000013$

Posterior Probabilities

s_j	$P(s_j)$	$P(I \mid s_j)$	$P(s_j$ and $I)$	$P(s_j \mid I)$
s_1	.5	.0028	$(.5)(.0028) = .0014$	$.0014/.0323 = .0433$
s_2	.3	.0988	$(.3)(.0988) = .0296$	$.0296/.0323 = .9164$
s_3	.1	.0128	$(.1)(.0128) = .0013$	$.0013/.0323 = .0402$
s_4	.1	.000013	$\underline{(.1)(.000013) = .000001}$	$.000001/.0323 = .000031$
			$P(I) = .0323$	

EMV(proceed) = .0433(-30,000) + .9164(-5,000) + .0402(45,000) + .000031(95,000) = -4,069

EMV (don't proceed = 0

EMV decision: don't proceed

23.35 Posterior Probabilities for I_1

s_j	$P(s_j)$	$P(I_1 \mid s_j)$	$P(s_j$ and $I_1)$	$P(s_j \mid I_1)$
s_1	.15	.5	$(.15)(.5) = .075$	$.075/.30 = .25$
s_2	.55	.3	$(.55)(.3) = .165$	$.165/.30 = .55$
s_3	.30	.2	$\underline{(.30)(.2) = .06}$	$.06/.30 = .20$
			$P(I_1) = .30$	

Posterior Probabilities for I_2

s_j	$P(s_j)$	$P(I_2|s_j)$	$P(s_j \text{ and } I_2)$	$P(s_j|I_2)$
s_1	.15	.3	$(.15)(.3) = .045$	$.045/.435 = .103$
s_2	.55	.6	$(.55)(.6) = .33$	$.33/.435 = .759$
s_3	.30	.2	$\underline{(.30)(.2) = .06}$	$.06/.435 = .138$
			$P(I_2) = .435$	

Posterior Probabilities for I_3

s_j	$P(s_j)$	$P(I_3|s_j)$	$P(s_j \text{ and } I_3)$	$P(s_j|I_3)$
s_1	.15	.2	$(.15)(.2) = .03$	$.03/.265 = .113$
s_2	.55	.1	$(.55)(.1) = .055$	$.055/.265 = .208$
s_3	.30	.6	$\underline{(.30)(.6) = .18}$	$.18/.265 = .679$
			$P(I_3) = .265$	

I_1: $\text{EMV}(a_1) = .25(-220) + .55(-330) + .20(-440) = -324.5$

$\text{EMV}(a_2) = .25(-300) + .55(-320) + .20(-390) = -329.0$

$\text{EMV}(a_3) = .251(-350) + .55(-350) + .20(-350) = -350$

Optimal act: a_1

I_2: $\text{EMV}(a_1) = .103(-220) + .759(-330) + .138(-440) = -333.85$

$\text{EMV}(a_2) = .103(-300) + .759(-320) + .138(-390) = -327.59$

$\text{EMV}(a_3) = .103(-350) + .759(-350) + .138(-350) = -350$

Optimal act: a_2

I_3: $\text{EMV}(a_1) = .113(-220) + .208(-330) + .679(-440) = -392.26$

$\text{EMV}(a_2) = .113(-300) + .208(-320) + .679(-390) = -365.28$

$\text{EMV}(a_3) = .113(-350) + .208(-350) + .679(-350) = -350$

Optimal act: a_3

$\text{EMV`} = .30(-324.5) + .435(-327.59) + .265(-350) = -332.60$

$\text{EVSI} = \text{EMV`} - \text{EMV*} = -332.60 - (-338) = 5.40$

23.36

I_0 = neither person supports format change

I_1 = one person supports format change

I_2 = both people support format change

Likelihood probabilities $P(I_i \mid s_j)$

	I_0	I_1	I_2
5%	.9025	.0950	.0025
10%	.81	.18	.01
20%	.64	.32	.04

Posterior Probabilities for I_0

s_j	$P(s_j)$	$P(I_0 \mid s_j)$	$P(s_j \text{ and } I_0)$	$P(s_j \mid I_0)$
s_1	.4	.9025	(.4)(.9025) = .361	.361/.813 = .444
s_2	.4	.81	(.4)(.81) = .324	.324/.813 = .399
s_3	.2	.64	(.2)(.64) = .128	.128/.813 = .157
			$P(I_0) = .813$	

Posterior Probabilities for I_1

s_j	$P(s_j)$	$P(I_1 \mid s_j)$	$P(s_j \text{ and } I_1)$	$P(s_j \mid I_1)$
s_1	.4	.0950	(.4)(.0950) = .038	.038/.174 = .218
s_2	.4	.18	(.4)(.18) = .072	.072/.174 = .414
s_3	.2	.32	(.2)(.32) = .064	.064/.174 = .368
			$P(I_1) = .174$	

Posterior Probabilities for I_3

s_j	$P(s_j)$	$P(I_2 \mid s_j)$	$P(s_j \text{ and } I_2)$	$P(s_j \mid I_2)$
s_1	.4	.0025	(.4)(.0025) = .001	.001/.013 = .077
s_2	.4	.01	(.4)(.01) = .004	.004/.013 = .308
s_3	.2	.04	(.2)(.04) = .008	.008/.013 = .615
			$P(I_2) = .013$	

I_1: EMV(switch) = .444(-200,000) + .399(300,000) + .157(1,300,000) = 235,000

EMV(don't switch) = 285,000

Optimal act: don't switch

I_2: EMV(switch) = .218(-200,000) + .414(300,000) + .368(1,300,000) = 559,000

EMV(don't switch) = 285,000

Optimal act: switch

I_3: EMV(switch) = .077(-200,000) + .308(300,000) + .615(1,300,000) = 876,500

EMV(don't switch) = 285,000

Optimal act: switch

EMV` = .813(285,000) + .174(546,000) + .013(876,500) = 338,104

EVSI = EMV` - EMV* = 338,104 – 300,000 = 38,104

23.37

Likelihood probabilities (binomial probabilities)

$P(I \mid s_1) = P(x = 2, n = 25 \mid p = .05) = .2305$

$P(I \mid s_2) = P(x = 2, n = 25 \mid p = .10) = .2659$

$P(I \mid s_3) = P(x = 2, n = 25 \mid p = .20) = .0708$

Posterior Probabilities for I

s_j	$P(s_j)$	$P(I \mid s_j)$	$P(s_j \text{ and } I)$	$P(s_j \mid I)$
s_1	.4	.2305	(.4)(.2305) = .0922	.0922/.2127 = .4334
s_2	.4	.2659	(.4)(.2659) = .1064	.1064/.2127 = .5000
s_3	.2	.0708	(.2)(.0708) = .0142	.0142/.2127 = .0667
			$P(I) = .2127$	

EMV(switch) = .4334(-200,000) + .5000(300,000) + .0667(1,300,000) = 149,873

EMV(don't switch) = 285,000

Optimal act: don't switch

23.38a

Payoff Table

Demand	Battery 1	Battery 2	Battery 3
50,000	20(50,000)-900,000 = 100,000	23(50,000)-1,150,000 0	25(50,000)-1,400,000 -150,000
100,000	20(100,000)-900,000 =1,100,000	23(100,000)-1,150,000 1,150,000	25(100,000)-1,400,000 1,100,000
150,000	20(150,000)-900,000 =2,100,000	23(150,000)-1,150,000 2,300,000	25(150,000)-1,400,000 2,350,000

b   Opportunity Loss table

Demand	Battery 1	Battery 2	Batter3
50,000	0	100,000	250,000
100,000	50,000	0	50,000
150,000	250,000	50,000	9

c EMV(Battery 1) = .3(100,000) + .3(1,100,000) + .4(2,100,000) = 1,200,000

EMV(Battery 2) = .3(0) + .3(1,150,000) + .4(2,300,000) = 1,265,000

EMV(Battery 3) = .3(-150,000) + .3(1,100,000) + .4(2,350,000) = 1,225,000

EMV decision: Battery 2

d EOL(Battery 2) = .3(100,000) + .3(0) + .4(50,000) = 50,000

EVPI = EOL* = 50,000

23.39   Payoff Table

Percentage change	Change ad	Don't change
-2	-258,000	0
-1	-158,000	0
0	-58,000	0
1	42,000	0
2	142,000	0

EMV(Change ad) = -1(-258,000) + .1(-158,000) + .2(-58,000) + .3(42,000) + .3(142,000) = 2,000

EMV (don't change) = 0.

Optimal decision: change ad

23.40

I_0 = person does not believe the ad

I_1 = person believes the ad

Likelihood probabilities $P(I_i \mid s_j)$

	I_0	I_1
30%	.70	.30
31%	.69	.31
32%	.68	.32
33%	.67	.33
34%	.66	.34

Posterior Probabilities for I_0

s_j	$P(s_j)$	$P(I_0 \mid s_j)$	$P(s_j \text{ and } I_0)$	$P(s_j \mid I_0)$
s_1	.1	.70	(.1)(.70) = .070	.070/.674 = .104
s_2	.1	.69	(.1)(.69) = .069	.069/.674 = .102
s_3	.2	.68	(.2)(.68) = .136	.136/.674 = .202
s_4	.3	.67	(.3)(.67) = .201	.201/.674 = .298
s_5	.3	.66	(.3)(.66) = .198	.198/.674 = .294
			$P(I_0) = .674$	

Posterior Probabilities for I_1

s_j	$P(s_j)$	$P(I_1|s_j)$	$P(s_j \text{ and } I_1)$	$P(s_j|I_1)$
s_1	.1	.30	$(.1)(.30) = .030$	$.030/.326 = .092$
s_2	.1	.31	$(.1)(.31) = .031$	$.031/.326 = .095$
s_3	.2	.32	$(.2)(.32) = .064$	$.064/.326 = .196$
s_4	.3	.33	$(.3)(.33) = .099$	$.099/.326 = .304$
s_5	.3	.34	$\underline{(.3)(.34) = .102}$	$.102/.326 = .313$
			$P(I_1) = .326$	

I_0: EMV(Change ad) = $.104(-258,000) + .102(-158,000) + .202(-58,000) + .298(42,000) +$

$.294(142,000) = -400$

EMV (don't change) = 0.

Optimal decision: don't change ad

I_1: EMV(Change ad) = $.092(-258,000) + .095(-158,000) + .196(-58,000) + .304(42,000) +$

$.313(142,000) = 7,100$

EMV (don't change) = 0.

Optimal decision: change ad

EMV` = $.674(0) + .326(7,100) = 2,315$

EVSI = EMV` - EMV* = $2,315 - 2,000 = 315$

23.41

Likelihood probabilities (binomial probabilities)

$P(I \mid s_1) = P(x = 1, n = 5 \mid p = .30) = .3602$

$P(I \mid s_2) = P(x = 1, n = 5 \mid p = .31) = .3513$

$P(I \mid s_3) = P(x = 1, n = 2 \mid p = .32) = .3421$

$P(I \mid s_4) = P(x = 1, n = 2 \mid p = .33) = .3325$

$P(I \mid s_5) = P(x = 1, n = 2 \mid p = .34) = .3226$

Posterior Probabilities for I

s_j	$P(s_j)$	$P(I|s_j)$	$P(s_j \text{ and } I)$	$P(s_j | I)$
s_1	.1	.3602	$(.1)(.3602) = .0360$	$.0360/.3361 = .1072$
s_2	.1	.3513	$(.1)(.3513) = .0351$	$.0351/.3361 = .1045$
s_3	.2	.3421	$(.2)(.3421) = .0684$	$.0684/.3361 = .2036$
s_4	.3	.3325	$(.3)(.3325) = .0997$	$.0997/.3361 = .2968$
s_5	.3	.3226	$\underline{(.3)(.3226) = .0968}$	$.0968/.3361 = .2879$
			$P(I) = .3361$	

EMV(Change ad) = .1072(-258,000) + .1045(-158,000) + .2036(-58,000) + .2968(42,000)

       + .2879(142,000) = -2,620

EMV (don't change) = 0.

Optimal decision: don't change ad

23.42

EMV(25 telephones) = 50,000

EMV(50 telephones) = .50(30,000) + .25(60,000) + .25(60,000) = 45,000

EMV(100 telephones) = .50(20,000) + .25(40,000) + .25(80,000) = 40,000

Optimal decision: 25 telephones (EMV* = 50,000)

I_1 = small number of calls

I_2 = medium number of calls

I_3 = large number of calls

Likelihood probabilities (Poisson distribution)

	I_1	I_2	I_3
$\mu = 5$	$P(X < 8 \mid \mu = 5)$ $= .8667$	$P(8 \le X < 17 \mid \mu = 5)$ $= .1334$	$P(X \ge 17 \mid \mu = 5)$ $= 0$
$\mu = 10$	$P(X < 8 \mid \mu = 10)$ $= .2202$	$P(8 \le X < 17 \mid \mu = 10)$ $= .7527$	$P(X \ge 17 \mid \mu = 10)$ $= .0270$
$\mu = 15$	$P(X < 8 \mid \mu = 15)$ $= .0180$	$P(8 \le X < 17 \mid \mu = 15)$ $= .6461$	$P(X \ge 17 \mid \mu = 15)$ $= .3359$

Posterior Probabilities for I_1

s_j	$P(s_j)$	$P(I_1 \vert s_j)$	$P(s_j \text{ and } I_1)$	$P(s_j \vert I_1)$
s_1	.50	.8667	$(.50)(.8667) = .4333$	$.4333/.4929 = .8792$
s_2	.25	.2202	$(.25)(.2202) = .0551$	$.0551/.4929 = .1117$
s_3	.25	.0180	$(.25)(.0180) = .0045$	$.0045/.4929 = .0091$
			$P(I_1) = .4929$	

Posterior Probabilities for I_2

s_j	$P(s_j)$	$P(I_2 \vert s_j)$	$P(s_j \text{ and } I_2)$	$P(s_j \vert I_2)$
s_1	.50	.1334	$(.50)(.1334) = .0667$	$.0667/.4164 = .1601$
s_2	.25	.7527	$(.25)(.7527) = .1882$	$.1882/.4164 = .4519$
s_3	.25	.6461	$(.25)(.6461) = .1615$	$.1615/.4164 = .3879$
			$P(I_2) = .4164$	

Posterior Probabilities for I_3

s_j	$P(s_j)$	$P(I_3 \vert s_j)$	$P(s_j \text{ and } I_3)$	$P(s_j \vert I_3)$
s_1	.50	.0	$(.50)(0) = 0$	$0/.0907 = 0$
s_2	.25	.0270	$(.25)(.0270) = .0068$	$.0068/.0907 = .0745$
s_3	.25	.3359	$(.25)(.3359) = .0840$	$.0840/.0907 = .9254$
			$P(I_3) = .0907$	

I_1: EMV(25 telephones) = 50,000

EMV(50 telephones) = .8792(30,000) + .1117(60,000) + .0091(60,000) = 33,624

EMV(100 telephones) = .8792(20,000) + .1117(40,000) + .0091(80,000) = 22,780

Optimal act: 25 telephones

I_2: EMV(25 telephones) = 50,000

EMV(50 telephones) = .1601(30,000) + .4519(60,000) + .3879(60,000) = 55,191

EMV(100 telephones) = .1601(20,000) + .4519(40,000) + .38791(80,000) = 52,310

Optimal act: 50 telephones

I_3: EMV(25 telephones) = 50,000

EMV(50 telephones) = 0(30,000) + .0745(60,000) + .9254(60,000) = 60,000

EMV(100 telephones) = 0(20,000) + .0745(40,000) + .9254(80,000) = 77,012

Optimal act: 100 telephones

EMV` = .4929(50,000) + .4164(55,191) + .0907(77,012) = 54,612

EVSI = EMV` - EMV* = 54,612 – 50,000 = 4,612

Because the value is greater than the cost ($4,000) Max should not sample. If he sees a small number of calls install 25 telephones. If there is a medium number install 50 telephones. If there is a large number of calls, install 100 telephones.

23.43a EMV(Model 101) = .2(20 million) + .4(100 million) + .4(210 million) = 128 million

EMV (Model 202) = .1(70 million) + .4(100 million) + .5(150 million) = 122 million

Optimal decision: Model 101

b Likelihood probabilities (binomial distribution) for Model 101

$P(X =1, n = 10| p = .05) = .3151$

$P(X =1, n = 10| p = .10) = .3874$

$P(X =1, n = 10| p = .15) = .3474$

Posterior Probabilities for Model 101

s_j	$P(s_j)$	$P(I|s_j)$	$P(s_j$ and $I)$	$P(s_j | I)$
s_1	.2	.3151	(.2)(.3151) = .0630	.0630/.3570 = .1766
s_2	.4	.3874	(.4)(.3874) = .1550	.1550/.3570 = .4341
s_3	.4	.3474	(.4)(.3474) = .1390	.1390/.3570 = .3893
			P(I) = .3570	

EMV(Model 101) = .1766(20 million) + .4341(100 million) + .3893(210 million) = 128.7 million

Likelihood probabilities (binomial distribution) for Model 202

$P(X =9, n = 20| p = .30) = .0654$

$P(X =9, n = 20| p = .40) = .1597$

$P(X =9, n = 20| p = .50) = .1602$

Posterior Probabilities for Model 202

s_j	$P(s_j)$	$P(I|s_j)$	$P(s_j$ and $I)$	$P(s_j | I)$
s_1	.1	.0654	(.1)(.0654) = .0065	.0065/.1505 = .0434
s_2	.4	.1597	(.4)(.1597) = .0639	.0639/.1505 = .4245
s_3	.5	.1602	(.5)(.1602) = .0801	.0801/.1505 = .5321
			P(I) = .1505	

EMV(Model 101) = .0434(70 million) + .4245(100 million) + .5321(150 million) = 125.3 million

Optimal decision: Model 101

23.44 EMV(Release in North America) = .5(33 million) + .3(12 million) + .2(-15 million) = 17.1 million

EMV(European distributor) = 12 million

Optimal decision: Release in North America

Posterior Probabilities for I_1 (Rave review)

s_j	$P(s_j)$	$P(I_1 \mid s_j)$	$P(s_j \text{ and } I_1)$	$P(s_j \mid I_1)$
s_1	.5	.8	(.5)(.8) = .40	.40/.63 = .635
s_2	.3	.5	(.3)(.5) = .15	.15/.63 = .238
s_3	.2	.4	(.2)(.4) = .08	.08/.63 = .127
			$P(I_1) = .63$	

EMV(Release in North America) = .635(33 million) + .238(12 million) + .127(-15 million) =21.9 million

EMV(European distributor) = 12 million

Optimal decision: Release in North America

Posterior Probabilities for I_2 (lukewarm response)

s_j	$P(s_j)$	$P(I_2 \mid s_j)$	$P(s_j \text{ and } I_2)$	$P(s_j \mid I_2)$
s_1	.5	.1	(.5)(.1) = .05	.05/.20 = .25
s_2	.3	.3	(.3)(.3) = .09	.09/.20 = .45
s_3	.2	.3	(.2)(.3) = .06	.06/.20 = .30
			$P(I_2) = .20$	

EMV(Release in North America) = .25(33 million) + .45(12 million) + .30(-15 million) = 9.2 million

EMV(European distributor) = 12 million

Optimal decision: Sell to European distributor

Posterior Probabilities for I_3 (poor response)

s_j	$P(s_j)$	$P(I_3 \mid s_j)$	$P(s_j \text{ and } I_3)$	$P(s_j \mid I_3)$
s_1	.5	.1	(.5)(.1) = .05	.05/.17 = .294
s_2	.3	.2	(.3)(.2) = .06	.06/.17 = .353
s_3	.2	.3	(.2)(.3) = .06	.06/.17 = .353
			$(I_3) = .17$	

EMV(Release in North America) = .294(33 million) + .353(12 million) + .353(-15 million) = 8.6 million

EMV(European distributor) = 12 million

Optimal decision: Sell to European distributor.

EMV` = .63(21.9 million) + .20(12 million) + .17(12 million) = 18.2 million

EVSI = EMV` - EMV* = 18.2 million – 17.1 million = 1.1 million

Because EVSI is greater than the sampling cost (100,000) the studio executives should show the movie to a random sample of North Americans. If the response is a rave review release the movie in North America. If not sell it to Europe.

Chapter 24

24.1 t-test of ρ or β_1

$$H_0 : \rho = 0 \text{ or } H_0 : \beta_1 = 0$$

$$H_1 : \rho > 0 \text{ or } H_1 : \beta_1 > 0$$

$$t = r\sqrt{\frac{n-2}{1-r^2}} \text{ or } t = \frac{b_1 - \beta_1}{s_{b_1}}$$

Correlation			
Fund and Gold			
Pearson Coefficient of Correlation			0.7929
t Stat			6.63
df			26
P(T<=t) one tail			0
t Critical one tail			1.7056
P(T<=t) two tail			0
t Critical two tail			2.0555

t = 6.63, p-value = 0. There is overwhelming evidence that there is a positive linear relationship between the value of the fund and the price of gold.

24.2 z-test of *p*

$$H_0 : p = .5$$

$$H_1 : p \neq .5$$

$$z = \frac{\hat{p} - p}{\sqrt{\dfrac{p(1-p)}{n}}}$$

z-Test of a Proportion			
Sample proportion	0.88	z Stat	3.15
Sample size	17	P(Z<=z) one-tail	0.0008
Hypothesized proportion	0.5	z Critical one-tail	1.6449
Alpha	0.05	P(Z<=z) two-tail	0.0016
		z Critical two-tail	1.9600

z = 3.15, p-value = .0016. There is overwhelming evidence to conclude that the new technology affects the sex of the baby.

24.3 Analysis of variance, single-factor, independent samples design

$$H_0 : \mu_1 = \mu_2 = \mu_3$$

H_1 : At least two means differ

$F = MST/MSE$

ANOVA						
Source of Variation	SS	df	MS	F	P-value	F crit
Between Groups	126.03	2	63.02	3.30	0.0439	3.1588
Within Groups	1087.30	57	19.08			
Total	1213.33	59				

F = 3.30, p-value = .0439. There is evidence to infer that at least one rust-proofing method is different from the others.

24.4 t-test of μ_D

$$H_0 : \mu_D = 0$$

$$H_1 : \mu_D < 0$$

$$t = \frac{\bar{x}_D - \mu_D}{s_D / \sqrt{n_D}}$$

t-Test: Paired Two Sample for Means		
	Prior	After
Mean	24.91	26.24
Variance	48.65	87.88
Observations	100	100
Pearson Correlation	0.7859	
Hypothesized Mean Difference	0	
df	99	
t Stat	-2.29	
P(T<=t) one-tail	0.0121	
t Critical one-tail	1.6604	
P(T<=t) two-tail	0.0242	
t Critical two-tail	1.9842	

t = -2.29, p-value = .0121. There is enough evidence to conclude that company should proceed to stage 2.

24.5a Ch-squared goodness-of-fit test (the percentages must be converted to actual and expected values and we must include those who did not have cancer)

$$H_0 : p_1 = 143/420,000, \; p_2 = 9/420,000, \; p_3 = 80/420,000, \; p_4 = 52/420,000,$$
$$p_5 = 57/420,000, \; p_6 = 12/420,000, \; p_7 = 13/420,000, \; p_8 = 419.634/420,000$$

H_1 : At least one p_i is not equal to its specified value.

$$\chi^2 = \sum_{i=1}^{8} \frac{(f_i - e_i)^2}{e_i}$$

Actual	Expected		
135	143		
7	9		
77	80		
32	52		
42	57		
8	12		
13	13		
419686	419634	p-value =	0.0515

p-value = .0515. There is not enough evidence to conclude that there is a relationship between cell phone use and cancer.

b The data are observational. Even if we regard the statistical result as significant we cannot automatically infer that cell phone use causes cancer. Additionally, an examination of the actual and expected values reveals that in all 7 types of cancers the actual values are *less than or equal* to the expected values, indicating that (if anything) cell phone use prevents cancer.

24.6 a t-estimator of μ

t-Estimate: Mean			
			Overdue
Mean			7.0875
Standard Deviation			6.9682
LCL			6.4026
UCL			7.7724

b LCL = 50,000($.25)(6.4026) = $80,033

UCL = 50,000($.25)(7.7724) = $97,155

It does appear that not all fines are collected.

24.7 z-test of p

$$H_0 : p = .5$$

$$H_1 : p > .5$$

$$z = \frac{\hat{p} - p}{\sqrt{\dfrac{p(1-p)}{n}}}$$

z-Test: Proportion			
			Correct
Sample Proportion			0.4393
Observations			280
Hypothesized Proportion			0.5
z Stat			-2.03
P(Z<=z) one-tail			0.0211
z Critical one-tail			1.6449
P(Z<=z) two-tail			0.0422
z Critical two-tail			1.96

$z = -2.03$, p-value = 1- .0211 = .9789. There is no evidence to infer that the therapist can identify the correct hand. In fact, there is evidence to the contrary.

24.8 Chi-squared test of a contingency table

H_0 : The two variables are independent

H_1 : The two variables are dependent

$$\chi^2 = \sum_{i=1}^{6} \frac{(f_i - e_i)^2}{e_i}$$

Contingency Table				
	Age Category			
Alcohol		1	2	TOTAL
	1	87	325	412
	2	44	297	341
	3	87	214	301
	TOTAL	218	836	1054
	chi-squared Stat			25.0273
	df			2
	p-value			0
	chi-squared Critical			5.9915

$\chi^2 = 25.0273$, p-value = 0. There is overwhelming evidence to infer that differences exist among the age categories with respect to alcohol use.

24.9 a Equal-variances t-test of $\mu_1 - \mu_2$

$H_0 : (\mu_1 - \mu_2) = 0$

$H_1 : (\mu_1 - \mu_2) > 0$

$$t = \frac{(\bar{x}_1 - \bar{x}_2) - (\mu_1 - \mu_2)}{\sqrt{s_p^2\left(\dfrac{1}{n_1} + \dfrac{1}{n_2}\right)}}$$

t-Test: Two-Sample Assuming Equal Variances		
	Female	Male
Mean	9.87	8.48
Variance	4.04	3.68
Observations	151	161
Pooled Variance	3.85	
Hypothesized Mean Difference	0	
df	310	
t Stat	6.27	
P(T<=t) one-tail	0.0000	
t Critical one-tail	1.6498	
P(T<=t) two-tail	0.0000	
t Critical two-tail	1.9676	

$t = 6.27$, p-value = 0. There is overwhelming evidence to indicate that teenage girls do more housework than teenage boys.

b Equal-variances t-test of $\mu_1 - \mu_2$

$$H_0 : (\mu_1 - \mu_2) = 0$$

$$H_1 : (\mu_1 - \mu_2) < 0$$

$$t = \frac{(\bar{x}_1 - \bar{x}_2) - (\mu_1 - \mu_2)}{\sqrt{s_p^2\left(\dfrac{1}{n_1} + \dfrac{1}{n_2}\right)}}$$

t-Test: Two-Sample Assuming Equal Variances		
	Inside	Outside
Mean	8.34	9.72
Variance	3.84	3.91
Observations	128	184
Pooled Variance	3.88	
Hypothesized Mean Difference	0	
df	310	
t Stat	-6.05	
P(T<=t) one-tail	0.0000	
t Critical one-tail	1.6498	
P(T<=t) two-tail	0.0000	
t Critical two-tail	1.9676	

$t = -6.05$, p-value = 0. There is overwhelming evidence to conclude that children whose mother works outside the home do more housework than children whose mother works in the home.

24.10 z-test of $p_1 - p_2$ (case 2)

$$H_0 : p_1 - p_2 = -.15$$

$$H_1 : p_1 - p_2 < -.15$$

$$z = \frac{(\hat{p}_1 - \hat{p}_2) - (p_1 - p_2)}{\sqrt{\dfrac{\hat{p}_1(1 - \hat{p}_1)}{n_1} + \dfrac{\hat{p}_2(1 - \hat{p}_2)}{n_2}}}$$

z-Test: Two Proportions			
		Comm 1	Comm 2
Sample Proportions		0.268	0.486
Observations		500	500
Hypothesized Difference		-0.15	
z Stat		-2.28	
P(Z<=z) one tail		0.0114	
z Critical one-tail		1.6449	
P(Z<=z) two-tail		0.0228	
z Critical two-tail		1.96	

z = -2.28, p-value = .0114. There is evidence to indicate that the second commercial is viable.

24.11 Equal-variances t-test of $\mu_1 - \mu_2$

$$H_0 : (\mu_1 - \mu_2) = 0$$

$$H_1 : (\mu_1 - \mu_2) > 0$$

$$t = \frac{(\bar{x}_1 - \bar{x}_2) - (\mu_1 - \mu_2)}{\sqrt{s_p^2 \left(\dfrac{1}{n_1} + \dfrac{1}{n_2} \right)}}$$

t-Test: Two-Sample Assuming Equal Variances			
		Lunch	No Lunch
Mean		69.38	60.98
Variance		175.34	144.92
Observations		50	50
Pooled Variance		160.13	
Hypothesized Mean Difference		0	
df		98	
t Stat		3.32	
P(T<=t) one-tail		0.0006	
t Critical one-tail		1.6606	
P(T<=t) two-tail		0.0013	
t Critical two-tail		1.9845	

t = 3.32, p-value = .0006. There is overwhelming evidence to conclude that eating lunch before an exam improves the grade.

24.12 One-way analysis of variance

$$H_0 : \mu_1 = \mu_2 = \mu_3 = \mu_4$$

$$H_1 : \text{At least two means differ}$$

$$F = MST/MSE$$

ANOVA						
Source of Variation	SS	df	MS	F	P-value	F crit
Between Groups	717.3	3	239.1	1.37	0.2543	2.6507
Within Groups	34294.5	196	175.0			
Total	35011.8	199				

F = 1.37, p-value = .2543. There is no evidence to infer that the type of meal affects test scores.

24.13 t-tests of μ_D

$$H_0 : \mu_D = 0$$

$$H_1 : \mu_D \neq 0$$

$$t = \frac{\bar{x}_D - \mu_D}{s_D / \sqrt{n_D}}$$

Points per game

t-Test: Paired Two Sample for Means		
	PPG93/94	PPG92/93
Mean	0.43	0.48
Variance	0.11	0.12
Observations	50	50
Pearson Correlation	0.85	
Hypothesized Mean Difference	0	
df	49	
t Stat	-2.09	
P(T<=t) one-tail	0.0208	
t Critical one-tail	1.6766	
P(T<=t) two-tail	0.0416	
t Critical two-tail	2.0096	

t = -2.09, p-value = .0416. There is enough evidence to conclude that with respect to points per game players are inconsistent.

Plus/minus:

t-Test: Paired Two Sample for Means		
	+/- 93/94	+/- 92/93
Mean	0.26	3.16
Variance	192.2	223.6
Observations	50	50
Pearson Correlation	0.21	
Hypothesized Mean Difference	0	
df	49	
t Stat	-1.13	
P(T<=t) one-tail	0.1314	
t Critical one-tail	1.6766	
P(T<=t) two-tail	0.2627	
t Critical two-tail	2.0096	

$t = -1.13$, p-value = .2627. There is no evidence to infer that with respects to plus/minus players are inconsistent.

24.14 Multiple regression, test of coefficients

$$t = \frac{b_i - \beta_i}{s_{b_i}}$$

The ordinary multiple regression model fit quite well. The coefficient of determination is .7042 and the p-value of the F-test is 0. However, no independent variable is linearly related to salary. This is a clear sign of multicollinearity. Stepwise regression was used with the outcome shown below.

The only independent variables that are linearly related to salary are assists in 1992-93 and goals in 1992-93. It appears that players' salaries are most strongly related to the number of goals and the number of assists in the previous season.

Results of stepwise regression					
Step 1 - Entering variable: Ast92_93					
Summary measures					
	Multiple R	0.7725			
	R-Square	0.5967			
	Adj R-Square	0.5883			
	StErr of Est	380046			
ANOVA Table					
	Source	df	SS	MS	F	p-value
	Explained	1	10258242603399	10258242603399	71.0232	0.0000
	Unexplained	48	6932882522112	144435052544		
Regression coefficients					
		Coefficient	Std Err	t-value	p-value
	Constant	38326	82113	0.4667	0.6428
	Ast92_93	25747	3055	8.4275	0.0000
Step 2 - Entering variable: Goal92_93					
Summary measures		Change	% Change		
	Multiple R	0.8086	0.0361	%4.7	
	R-Square	0.6538	0.0571	%9.6	
	Adj R-Square	0.6390	0.0507	%8.6	
	StErr of Est	355860	-24186	-%6.4	
ANOVA Table					
	Source	df	SS	MS	F	p-value
	Explained	2	11239219530119	5619609765060	44.3760	0.0000
	Unexplained	47	5951905595392	126636289264		
Regression coefficients					
		Coefficient	Std Err	t-value	p-value
	Constant	65924	77524	0.8504	0.3994
	Ast92_93	14124	5062	2.7904	0.0076
	Goal92_93	18523	6655	2.7832	0.0077

24.15 Wilcoxon rank sum tests

H_0 : The two population locations are the same.

H_1 : The location of population 1 is to the left of the location of population 2.

$$z = \frac{T - E(T)}{\sigma_T}$$

a

Wilcoxon Rank Sum Test			
		Rank Sum	Observations
Days flu shot		20461	150
Days placebo		24689	150
z Stat		-2.81	
P(Z<=z) one-tail		0.0024	
z Critical one-tail		1.6449	
P(Z<=z) two-tail		0.0048	
z Critical two-tail		1.96	

z = -2.81, p-value = .0024. There is overwhelming evidence to indicate that the number of sick days is less for those who take the flu shots.

b

Wilcoxon Rank Sum Test			
		Rank Sum	Observations
Visits flu shot		19152	150
Visits placebo		25998	150
z Stat		-4.56	
P(Z<=z) one-tail		0	
z Critical one-tail		1.6449	
P(Z<=z) two-tail		0	
z Critical two-tail		1.96	

z = -4.56, p-value = 0. There is overwhelming evidence to indicate that those who take the flu shots visit their doctors less frequently.

24.16 Analysis of variance, single-factor independent samples design

$H_0 : \mu_1 = \mu_2 = \mu_3$

$H_1 :$ At least two means differ

F = MST/MSE

ANOVA						
Source of Variation	SS	df	MS	F	P-value	F crit
Between Groups	91.43	2	45.72	1.09	0.3441	3.1588
Within Groups	2397.50	57	42.06			
Total	2488.93	59				

F = 1.09, p-value = .3441. There is no evidence to infer that sales of cigarettes differ according to placement.

24.17 z-test of $p_1 - p_2$ (case 1) Code 3 results were omitted.

$H_0 : (p_1 - p_2) = 0$

$H_1 : (p_1 - p_2) < 0$

$$z = \frac{(\hat{p}_1 - \hat{p}_2)}{\sqrt{\hat{p}(1-\hat{p})\left(\frac{1}{n_1} + \frac{1}{n_2}\right)}}$$

z-Test: Two Proportions			
		Folic acid	Placebo
Sample Proportions		0.0101	0.0343
Observations		597	612
Hypothesized Difference		0	
z Stat		-2.85	
P(Z<=z) one tail		0.0022	
z Critical one-tail		1.6449	
P(Z<=z) two-tail		0.0044	
z Critical two-tail		1.96	

z = -2.85, p-value = .0022. There is overwhelming evidence to conclude that folic acid reduces the incidence of spina bifida.

24.18 t-test of μ

$$H_0 : \mu = 480$$

$$H_1 : \mu < 480$$

$$t = \frac{\bar{x} - \mu}{s / \sqrt{n}}$$

t-Test: Mean			
			Complaints
Mean			460.53
Standard Deviation			81.10
Hypothesized Mean			480
df			29
t Stat			-1.31
P(T<=t) one-tail			0.0994
t Critical one-tail			1.6991
P(T<=t) two-tail			0.1988
t Critical two-tail			2.0452

t = -1.31, p-value = .0994. There is little evidence to conclude that the seminars should be instituted.

24.19 a One way analysis of variance

ANOVA						
Source of Variation	SS	df	MS	F	P-value	F crit
Between Groups	25113	3	8371	85.98	0.0000	2.6332
Within Groups	30766	316	97.4			
Total	55880	319				

Two factor analysis of variance

ANOVA						
Source of Variation	*SS*	*df*	*MS*	*F*	*P-value*	*F crit*
Sample	17024	1	17024	174.85	0.0000	3.8711
Columns	7411	1	7411	76.12	0.0000	3.8711
Interaction	679	1	679	6.97	0.0087	3.8711
Within	30766	316	97.4			
Total	55880	319				

There is enough evidence to infer that differences are caused by weight, gender, and interaction.

24.20 t-tests of μ_D

a $\qquad H_0 : \mu_D = 40$

$\qquad H_1 : \mu_D > 40$

$$t = \frac{\bar{x}_D - \mu_D}{s_D / \sqrt{n_D}}$$

t-Test: Paired Two Sample for Means		
	SAT after	*SAT before*
Mean	1235	1162
Variance	37970	28844
Observations	40	40
Pearson Correlation	0.9366	
Hypothesized Mean Difference	40	
df	39	
t Stat	2.98	
P(T<=t) one-tail	0.0024	
t Critical one-tail	1.6849	
P(T<=t) two-tail	0.0049	
t Critical two-tail	2.0227	

t = 2.98, p-value = .0024. There is enough evidence to conclude that the ETS claim is false.

b $\qquad H_0 : \mu_D = 110$

$\qquad H_1 : \mu_D < 110$

$$t = \frac{\bar{x}_D - \mu_D}{s_D / \sqrt{n_D}}$$

t-Test: Paired Two Sample for Means		
	SAT after	*SAT before*
Mean	1235	1162
Variance	37970	28844
Observations	40	40
Pearson Correlation	0.9366	
Hypothesized Mean Difference	110	
df	39	
t Stat	-3.39	
P(T<=t) one-tail	0.0008	
t Critical one-tail	1.6849	
P(T<=t) two-tail	0.0016	
t Critical two-tail	2.0227	

t = -3.39, p-value = .0008. There is enough evidence to conclude that the Kaplan claim is also false.

24.21 Equal-variances t-test of $\mu_1 - \mu_2$

$$H_0 : (\mu_1 - \mu_2) = 0$$

$$H_1 : (\mu_1 - \mu_2) < 0$$

$$t = \frac{(\bar{x}_1 - \bar{x}_2) - (\mu_1 - \mu_2)}{\sqrt{s_p^2 \left(\frac{1}{n_1} + \frac{1}{n_2} \right)}}$$

t-Test: Two-Sample Assuming Equal Variances		
	Fixed	*Commission*
Mean	60245	63563
Variance	110372125	115677016
Observations	90	90
Pooled Variance	113024571	
Hypothesized Mean Difference	0	
df	178	
t Stat	-2.09	
P(T<=t) one-tail	0.0189	
t Critical one-tail	1.6535	
P(T<=t) two-tail	0.0377	
t Critical two-tail	1.9734	

t = -2.09, p-value .0189. There is enough evidence to conclude that commission salespeople outperform fixed-salary salespersons.

24.22 a t-test of μ

$$H_0 : \mu = 0$$

$$H_1 : \mu > 0$$

$$t = \frac{\bar{x} - \mu}{s / \sqrt{n}}$$

t-Test: Mean			
			Decrease
Mean			24.73
Standard Deviation			17.92
Hypothesized Mean			0
df			222
t Stat			20.61
P(T<=t) one-tail			0
t Critical one-tail			1.6517
P(T<=t) two-tail			0
t Critical two-tail			1.9707

t = 20.61, p-value = 0. There is overwhelming evidence to infer that there is a decreases in metabolism when children watch television.

b Wilcoxon rank sum test

H_0 : The two population locations are the same.

H_1 : The location of population 1 is to the right of the location of population 2.

$$z = \frac{T - E(T)}{\sigma_T}$$

Wilcoxon Rank Sum Test			
		Rank Sum	Observations
Obese		5750	41
Nonobese		19226	182
z Stat		3.10	
P(Z<=z) one-tail		0.001	
z Critical one-tail		1.6449	
P(Z<=z) two-tail		0.002	
z Critical two-tail		1.96	

z = 3.10, p-value = .0010. There is enough evidence to conclude that the decrease in metabolism is greater among obese children.

24.23 a z-test of p (success = mathematics major wins)

$H_0 : p = .5$

$H_1 : p > .5$

$$z = \frac{\hat{p} - p}{\sqrt{\frac{p(1 - p)}{n}}}$$

z-Test: Proportion			
			Math win
Sample Proportion			0.558
Observations			500
Hypothesized Proportion			0.5
z Stat			2.59
P(Z<=z) one-tail			0.0047
z Critical one-tail			1.6449
P(Z<=z) two-tail			0.0094
z Critical two-tail			1.96

$z = 2.59$, p-value = .0047. There is enough evidence to infer that mathematics majors win more frequently than English majors.

b Wilcoxon signed rank sum test

H_0 : The two population locations are the same.

H_1 : The location of population 1 is to the right of the location of population 2.

$$z = \frac{T - E(T)}{\sigma_T}$$

Wilcoxon Signed Rank Sum Test		
Difference		*English - Math*
T+		67513.5
T-		57736.5
Observations (for test)		500
z Stat		1.51
P(Z<=z) one-tail		0.0652
z Critical one-tail		1.6449
P(Z<=z) two-tail		0.1304
z Critical two-tail		1.96

$z = 1.51$, p-value = .0652. There is weak evidence to infer that English majors outscore mathematics majors.

c Part (a) ignores the magnitude of the paired differences.

24.24 Two-factor analysis of variance

F = MS(AB)/MSE

F = MS(A)/MSE

F = MS(B)/MSE

ANOVA						
Source of Variation	SS	df	MS	F	P-value	F crit
Sample	427.61	2	213.81	39.97	0.0000	3.0589
Columns	20.17	1	20.17	3.77	0.0541	3.9068
Interaction	17.77	2	8.89	1.66	0.1935	3.0589
Within	770.32	144	5.35			
Total	1235.87	149				

Test for gender: F = 3.77, p-value = .0541. There is not enough evidence of a difference between men and women.

Test for fitness: F = 39.97, p-value = 0. There is overwhelming evidence of differences among the three levels of fitness.

Test for interaction: F = 1.66, p-value = .1935. There is no evidence of interaction.

24.25 i Chi-squared goodness-of-fit test

$$H_0 : p_1 = 1/3, \ p_2 = 1/3, \ p_3 = 1/3$$

H_1 : At least one p_i is not equal to its specified value

$$\chi^2 = \sum \frac{(f_i - e_i)^2}{e_i}$$

Actual	Expected
43	50
45	50
62	50
p-value	0.1130

p- value = .1130. There is no evidence to infer that the proportions of each personality type are different.

ii Kruskal Wallis test

H_0 : The locations of all 3 populations are the same

H_1 : At least two population locations differ

$$H = \left[\frac{12}{n(n+1)} \sum \frac{T_j^2}{n_j} \right] - 3(n+1)$$

Kruskal-Wallis Test		
Group	Rank Sum	Observations
Type A	2579	43
Type B	3773	45
Type C	4973	62
H Stat		7.8783
df		2
p-value		0.0195
chi-squared Critical		5.9915

H = 7.8783, p-value = .0195. There is enough evidence to indicate that satisfaction levels differ among the three personality types.

iii One-way analysis of variance

$$H_0 : \mu_1 = \mu_2 = \mu_3$$

$$H_1 : \text{At least two means differ}$$

$$F = MST/MSE$$

ANOVA						
Source of Variation	*SS*	*df*	*MS*	*F*	*P-value*	*F crit*
Between Groups	70.20	2	35.10	3.51	0.0325	3.0576
Within Groups	1471.38	147	10.01			
Total	1541.58	149				

F = 3.51, p-value = .0325. There is enough evidence to conclude that life insurance sales differ among the three personality types.

24.26 Multiple regression t-tests of the coefficients

$$H_0 : \beta_i = 0$$

$$H_1 : \beta_i \neq 0$$

$$t = \frac{b_i - \beta_i}{s_{b_i}}$$

	Coefficients	*Standard Error*	*t Stat*	*P-value*
Intercept	1.01	1.39	0.72	0.4704
Dexterity	-0.059	0.150	-0.39	0.6953
Detail	-0.177	0.159	-1.11	0.2708
Teamwork	0.182	0.157	1.16	0.2485
Math	0.065	0.162	0.40	0.6874
ProbSolve	1.00	0.160	6.27	0.0000
Tech	1.78	0.159	11.24	0.0000

Only problem-solving skill (p-value = 0) and technical knowledge (p-value = 0) are linearly related to quality.

24.27 Spearman rank correlation coefficient test

a $\qquad H_0 : \rho_S = 0$

$\qquad H_1 : \rho_S \neq 0$

$\qquad z = r_S \sqrt{n-1}$

Spearman Rank Correlation			
Satisfied and Severity			
Spearman Rank Correlation			-0.2604
z Stat			-3.90
P(Z<=z) one tail			0
z Critical one tail			1.6449
P(Z<=z) two tail			0
z Critical two tail			1.96

z = -3.90, p-value = .0001. There is overwhelming evidence to conclude that satisfaction level is affected by severity of illness.

b $\qquad H_0 : \rho_S = 0$

$\qquad H_1 : \rho_S < 0$

Spearman Rank Correlation			
Satisfied and Days			
Spearman Rank Correlation			-0.3846
z Stat			-5.76
P(Z<=z) one tail			0
z Critical one tail			1.6449
P(Z<=z) two tail			0
z Critical two tail			1.96

z = -5.76, p-value = 0. There is overwhelming evidence to conclude that satisfaction level is higher for patients who stay for shorter periods of time.

24.28 a Equal-variances t-test of $\mu_1 - \mu_2$

$\qquad H_0 : (\mu_1 - \mu_2) = 0$

$\qquad H_1 : (\mu_1 - \mu_2) < 0$

$\qquad t = \dfrac{(\bar{x}_1 - \bar{x}_2) - (\mu_1 - \mu_2)}{\sqrt{s_p^2 \left(\dfrac{1}{n_1} + \dfrac{1}{n_2} \right)}}$

t-Test: Two-Sample Assuming Equal Variances		
	Four or more	Less
Mean	6.00	7.40
Variance	5.62	8.61
Observations	100	100
Pooled Variance	7.11	
Hypothesized Mean Difference	0	
df	198	
t Stat	-3.71	
P(T<=t) one-tail	0.0001	
t Critical one-tail	1.6526	
P(T<=t) two-tail	0.0003	
t Critical two-tail	1.9720	

t = -3.71, p-value = .0001. There is enough evidence to infer that children who wash their hands four or more times per day have less sick days due to cold and flu.

b Wilcoxon rank sum test

H_0 : The two population locations are the same.

H_1 : The location of population 1 is to the left of the location of population 2.

$$z = \frac{T - E(T)}{\sigma_T}$$

Wilcoxon Rank Sum Test			
		Rank Sum	Observations
Four or more		7584	100
Less		12516	100
z Stat		-6.03	
P(Z<=z) one-tail		0	
z Critical one-tail		1.6449	
P(Z<=z) two-tail		0	
z Critical two-tail		1.96	

z = -6.03, p-value = 0. There is enough evidence to infer that children who wash their hands four or more times per day have less sick days due to stomach illness.

24.29 t-test of μ_D

$$H_0 : \mu_D = 0$$

$$H_1 : \mu_D < 0$$

$$t = \frac{\bar{x}_D - \mu_D}{s_D / \sqrt{n_D}}$$

t-Test: Paired Two Sample for Means		
	First Sat	Second SAT
Mean	1175	1190
Variance	28422	35392
Observations	40	40
Pearson Correlation	0.91	
Hypothesized Mean Difference	0	
df	39	
t Stat	-1.20	
P(T<=t) one-tail	0.1182	
t Critical one-tail	1.6849	
P(T<=t) two-tail	0.2365	
t Critical two-tail	2.0227	

$t = -1.20$, p-value = .1182. There is no evidence to indicate that repeating the SAT produces higher exam scores.

24.30 Multiple regression t-tests of the coefficients

$$H_0 : \beta_i = 0$$

$$H_1 : \beta_i \neq 0$$

$$t = \frac{b_i - \beta_i}{s_{b_i}}$$

	Coefficients	Standard Error	t Stat	P-value
Intercept	-778.7	1290.2	-0.60	0.5483
P Evap	2.70	1.98	1.36	0.1772
Precip	0.30	0.31	0.98	0.3295

Neither variable appears to be related to flow.

24.31 Chi-squared test of a contingency table

$$H_0 : \text{The two variables are independent}$$

$$H_1 : \text{The two variables are dependent}$$

$$\chi^2 = \sum_{i=1}^{12} \frac{(f_i - e_i)^2}{e_i}$$

Contingency Table					
	Favored				
Result		1	2	3	TOTAL
	1	31	25	17	73
	2	46	16	19	81
	3	27	7	15	49
	4	16	2	3	21
	TOTAL	120	50	54	224
	chi-squared Stat			13.4477	
	df			6	
	p-value			0.0365	
	chi-squared Critical			12.5916	

$\chi^2 = 13.4477$, p-value = .0365. There is enough evidence to infer that Pro-Line's forecasts are related to outcomes and thus, can be useful to bettors.

22.32 Wilcoxon rank sum tests

H_0 : The two population locations are the same.

H_1 : The location of population 1 is to the left of the location of population 2.

$$z = \frac{T - E(T)}{\sigma_T}$$

Question 1

Wilcoxon Rank Sum Test			
		Rank Sum	Observations
No		875.5	26
Yes		8169.5	108
z Stat		-4.95	
P(Z<=z) one-tail		0	
z Critical one-tail		1.6449	
P(Z<=z) two-tail		0	
z Critical two-tail		1.96	

z = -4.95, p-value = 0. There is overwhelming evidence to infer that customers who say they will return assess quality of work higher than customers who do not plan to return.

Question 2

Wilcoxon Rank Sum Test			
		Rank Sum	Observations
No		1477	26
Yes		7568	108
z Stat		-1.56	
P(Z<=z) one-tail		0.0589	
z Critical one-tail		1.6449	
P(Z<=z) two-tail		0.1178	
z Critical two-tail		1.96	

z = = -1.56, p-value = .0589. There is not enough evidence to infer that customers who say they will return assess fairness of price higher than customers who do not plan to return.

Question 3

Wilcoxon Rank Sum Test			
		Rank Sum	Observations
No		1656	26
Yes		7389	108
z Stat		-0.56	
P(Z<=z) one-tail		0.2888	
z Critical one-tail		1.6449	
P(Z<=z) two-tail		0.5776	
z Critical two-tail		1.96	

z = -.56, p-value = .2888. There is no evidence to infer that customers who say they will return assess explanation of work and guarantee higher than customers who do not plan to return.

Question 4

Wilcoxon Rank Sum Test			
		Rank Sum	Observations
No		1461	26
Yes		7584	108
z Stat		-1.65	
P(Z<=z) one-tail		0.049	
z Critical one-tail		1.6449	
P(Z<=z) two-tail		0.098	
z Critical two-tail		1.96	

z = -1.65, p-value = .0490. There is evidence to infer that customers who say they will return assess the checkout process higher than customers who do not plan to return.

24.33 Kruskal Wallis tests

H_0 : The location of all 3 populations is the same

H_1 : At least two population locations differ

$$H = \left[\frac{12}{n(n+1)} \sum \frac{T_j^2}{n_j} \right] - 3(n+1)$$

Question 1

Kruskal-Wallis Test		
Group	Rank Sum	Observations
Positive	2495.5	33
Negative	1018	21
No	5531.5	80
H Stat		6.6286
df		2
p-value		0.0364
chi-squared Critical		5.9915

H = 6.6286, p-value = .0364. There is evidence to conclude that customers who make positive, negative, and no comment differ in their assessment of quality of work performed.

Question 2

Kruskal-Wallis Test		
Group	Rank Sum	Observations
Positive	2381.5	33
Negative	1143.5	21
No	5520	80
H Stat		2.9676
df		2
p-value		0.2268
chi-squared Critical		5.9915

H = 2.9676, p-value = .2268. There is no evidence to conclude that customers who make positive, negative, and no comment differ in their assessment of fairness of price

Question 3

Kruskal-Wallis Test		
Group	Rank Sum	Observations
Positive	2291	33
Negative	1335	21
No	5419	80
H Stat		0.299
df		2
p-value		0.8611
chi-squared Critical		5.9915

H = .299, p-value = .8611. There is no evidence to conclude that customers who make positive, negative, and no comment differ in their assessment of explanation of work and guarantee.

Question 4

Kruskal-Wallis Test		
Group	Rank Sum	Observations
Positive	1933.5	33
Negative	1200	21
No	5911.5	80
H Stat		5.4012
df		2
p-value		0.0672
chi-squared Critical		5.9915

H = 5.4012, p-value = .0672. There is not enough evidence to conclude that customers who make positive, negative, and no comment differ in their assessment of the checkout process.

24.34 Questions 1 to 4: Kruskal Wallis tests

H_0 : The location of all 3 populations is the same

H_1 : At least two population locations differ

$$H = \left[\frac{12}{n(n+1)} \sum \frac{T_j^2}{n_j} \right] - 3(n+1)$$

Question 1

Kruskal-Wallis Test		
Group	Rank Sum	Observations
Store 1	15555	100
Store 2	15692	100
Store 3	13903	100
H Stat		2.6349
df		2
p-value		0.2678
chi-squared Critical		5.9915

H = 2.6349, p-value = .2678. There is no evidence to conclude that there are differences in the assessment of quality of work performed among the three stores.

Question 2

Kruskal-Wallis Test		
Group	Rank Sum	Observations
Store 1	16613	100
Store 2	14648	100
Store 3	13889	100
H Stat		5.2525
df		2
p-value		0.0723
chi-squared Critical		5.9915

H = 5.2525, p-value = .0723. There is no evidence to conclude that there are differences in the assessment of fairness of price among the three stores

Question 3

Kruskal-Wallis Test		
Group	Rank Sum	Observations
Store 1	14996	100
Store 2	15448	100
Store 3	14706	100
H Stat		0.3716
df		2
p-value		0.8304
chi-squared Critical		5.9915

H = .3716, p-value = .8304. There is no evidence to conclude that there are differences in the assessment of explanation of work and guarantee among the three stores

Question 4

Kruskal-Wallis Test		
Group	Rank Sum	Observations
Store 1	15270	100
Store 2	15600	100
Store 3	14280	100
H Stat		1.2542
df		2
p-value		0.5341
chi-squared Critical		5.9915

H = 1.2542, p-value = .5341. There is no evidence to conclude that there are differences in the assessment of the checkout process among the three stores

Question 5 and comments: Chi-squared test of a contingency table

H_0 : The two variables are independent

H_1 : The two variables are dependent

$$\chi^2 = \sum \frac{(f_i - e_i)^2}{e_i}$$

Question 5

Contingency Table					
	Return				
Store		1	2	3	TOTAL
	1	28	24	34	86
	2	72	76	66	214
	TOTAL	100	100	100	300
	chi-squared Stat			2.4777	
	df			2	
	p-value			0.2897	
	chi-squared Critical			5.9915	

$\chi^2 = 2.4777$, p-value = .2897. There is no evidence to conclude that differences exist among the three stores with respect to whether the customer will return in the future.

Comments

Contingency Table					
	Comment				
Store		1	2	3	TOTAL
	1	34	20	34	88
	2	12	7	28	47
	3	54	73	38	165
	TOTAL	100	100	100	300
	chi-squared Stat			30.9799	
	df			4	
	p-value			0	
	chi-squared Critical			9.4877	

$\chi^2 = 30.9799$, p-value = 0. There is overwhelming evidence to conclude that differences exist among the three stores with respect to customer comments.

24.35a Equal-variances t-test of $\mu_1 - \mu_2$

$$H_0 : (\mu_1 - \mu_2) = 0$$

$$H_1 : (\mu_1 - \mu_2) > 0$$

$$t = \frac{(\bar{x}_1 - \bar{x}_2) - (\mu_1 - \mu_2)}{\sqrt{s_p^2 \left(\frac{1}{n_1} + \frac{1}{n_2} \right)}}$$

t-Test: Two-Sample Assuming Equal Variances		
	Home	Outside
Mean	59.21	54.91
Variance	102.03	88.28
Observations	196	152
Pooled Variance	96.03	
Hypothesized Mean Difference	0	
df	346	
t Stat	4.06	
P(T<=t) one-tail	0.0000	
t Critical one-tail	1.6493	
P(T<=t) two-tail	0.0001	
t Critical two-tail	1.9668	

t = 4.06, p-value = 0. There is enough evidence to infer that men whose wives stay at home earn more than men whose wives work outside the home.

b It may be that men whose wives stay at home work harder, and thus earn more.

22.36a Chi-squared goodness-of-fit test

$H_0 : p_2 = 1/36, \ p_3 = 2/36, \ldots, \ p_{12} = 1/36$

H_1 : At least one p_i is not equal to its specified value

$$\chi^2 = \sum \frac{(f_i - e_i)^2}{e_i}$$

Total	Actual	Probability	Expected
2	37	0.028	27.78
3	59	0.056	55.56
4	77	0.083	83.33
5	120	0.111	111.11
6	134	0.139	138.89
7	161	0.167	166.67
8	144	0.139	138.89
9	117	0.111	111.11
10	67	0.083	83.33
11	52	0.056	55.56
12	32	0.028	27.78
		p-value	0.4943

p-value = .4943. There is no evidence to indicate that the dice are not fairly balanced.

b z-test of p

$H_0 : p = 1/6$

$H_1 : p < 1/6$

$$z = \frac{\hat{p} - p}{\sqrt{\dfrac{p(1-p)}{n}}}$$

z-Test: Proportion		
		2 Dice
Sample Proportion		0.161
Observations		1000
Hypothesized Proportion		0.1667
z Stat		-0.48
P(Z<=z) one-tail		0.3143
z Critical one-tail		1.2816
P(Z<=z) two-tail		0.6286
z Critical two-tail		1.6449

z = -.48, p-value = .3143. There is no evidence to infer that the dice are set up so that the probability of 7 is less than 6/36.

24.37 Two-way analysis of variance

$H_0 : \mu_1 = \mu_2 = \mu_3$

$H_1 :$ At least two means differ

$F = MST/MSE$

ANOVA						
Source of Variation	*SS*	*df*	*MS*	*F*	*P-value*	*F crit*
Rows	91250.3	25	3650	386.41	0.0000	1.7273
Columns	168.8	2	84.38	8.93	0.0005	3.1826
Error	472.3	50	9.45			
Total	91891.3	77				

F = 8.93, p-value = .0005. There is enough evidence to conclude that the backup times differ among the three systems.

24.38 Question 1: Equal-variances t-test of $\mu_1 - \mu_2$

$H_0 : (\mu_1 - \mu_2) = 0$

$H_1 : (\mu_1 - \mu_2) < 0$

$$t = \frac{(\bar{x}_1 - \bar{x}_2) - (\mu_1 - \mu_2)}{\sqrt{s_p^2 \left(\dfrac{1}{n_1} + \dfrac{1}{n_2} \right)}}$$

t-Test: Two-Sample Assuming Equal Variances		
	U.S.	*Canada*
Mean	26.98	29.44
Variance	55.90	56.82
Observations	300	300
Pooled Variance	56.36	
Hypothesized Mean Difference	0	
df	598	
t Stat	-4.00	
P(T<=t) one-tail	0.0000	
t Critical one-tail	1.6474	
P(T<=t) two-tail	0.0001	
t Critical two-tail	1.9639	

t = -4.00, p-value = 0. There is enough evidence to indicate that recovery is faster in the United States.

Question 2: z-tests of $p_1 - p_2$ (case 1)

$H_0 : (p_1 - p_2) = 0$

$H_1 : (p_1 - p_2) < 0$

$$z = \frac{(\hat{p}_1 - \hat{p}_2)}{\sqrt{\hat{p}(1-\hat{p})\left(\dfrac{1}{n_1}+\dfrac{1}{n_2}\right)}}$$

z-Test: Two Proportions			
		U.S.	Canada
Sample Proportions		0.6267	0.6867
Observations		300	300
Hypothesized Difference		0	
z Stat		-1.55	
P(Z<=z) one tail		0.0609	
z Critical one-tail		1.6449	
P(Z<=z) two-tail		0.1218	
z Critical two-tail		1.96	

z = -1.55, p-value = .0609. There is not enough evidence to infer that recovery is faster in the United States.

6 months after heart attack:

z-Test: Two Proportions			
		U.S.	Canada
Sample Proportions		0.1867	0.1733
Observations		300	300
Hypothesized Difference		0	
z Stat		0.43	
P(Z<=z) one tail		0.3354	
z Critical one-tail		1.6449	
P(Z<=z) two-tail		0.6708	
z Critical two-tail		1.96	

z = .43, p-value = 1 - .3354 = .6646. There is no evidence to infer that recovery is faster in the United States.

12 months after heart attack

z-Test: Two Proportions			
		U.S.	Canada
Sample Proportions		0.1167	0.11
Observations		300	300
Hypothesized Difference		0	
z Stat		0.26	
P(Z<=z) one tail		0.3984	
z Critical one-tail		1.6449	
P(Z<=z) two-tail		0.7968	
z Critical two-tail		1.96	

$z = .26$, p-value = $1 - .3984 = .6016$. There is no evidence to infer that recovery is faster in the United States.

24.39 t-test of μ_D

$$H_0 : \mu_D = 0$$

$$H_1 : \mu_D < 0$$

$$t = \frac{\bar{x}_D - \mu_D}{s_D / \sqrt{n_D}}$$

t-Test: Paired Two Sample for Means		
	No-Slide	Slide
Mean	3.73	3.78
Variance	0.0653	0.0727
Observations	25	25
Pearson Correlation	0.96	
Hypothesized Mean Difference	0	
df	24	
t Stat	-3.04	
P(T<=t) one-tail	0.0028	
t Critical one-tail	1.7109	
P(T<=t) two-tail	0.0057	
t Critical two-tail	2.0639	

$t = -3.04$, p-value = $.0028$. There is overwhelming evidence to indicate that sliding is slower.

24.40 b Two-factor analysis of variance

F=MS(AB)/MSE

F = MS(A)/MSE

F = MS(B)/MSE

Product C

ANOVA						
Source of Variation	*SS*	*df*	*MS*	*F*	*P-value*	*F crit*
Sample	425.07	1	425.07	14.06	0.0004	4.0195
Columns	223.05	2	111.53	3.69	0.0315	3.1682
Interaction	62.48	2	31.24	1.03	0.3628	3.1682
Within	1632.93	54	30.24			
Total	2343.54	59				

Test for flow: F = 3.69, p-value = .0315. There is evidence to infer that there are differences in yield among the three flows.

Test for temperature: F = 14.06, p-value = .0004. There is evidence to infer that there are differences in yield between the two temperatures

Test for interaction: F = 1.03, p-value = .3628. There is no evidence of interaction.

Product Y

ANOVA						
Source of Variation	*SS*	*df*	*MS*	*F*	*P-value*	*F crit*
Sample	405.08	1	405.08	32.05	0.0000	4.0195
Columns	1714.94	2	857.47	67.85	0.0000	3.1682
Interaction	354.63	2	177.32	14.03	0.0000	3.1682
Within	682.48	54	12.64			
Total	3157.14	59				

Test for flow: F = 67.85, p-value = 0. There is evidence to infer that there are differences in yield among the three flows.

Test for temperature: F = 32.05, p-value = 0. There is evidence to infer that there are differences in yield between the two temperatures

Test for interaction: F = 14.03, p-value = 0. There is enough evidence to conclude that temperature and flow interact to affect product yield.

24.41 z-test of $p_1 - p_2$ (case 1) (The data were unstacked prior to applying the z-test.)

$$H_0 : (p_1 - p_2) = 0$$

$$H_1 : (p_1 - p_2) > 0$$

$$z = \frac{(\hat{p}_1 - \hat{p}_2)}{\sqrt{\hat{p}(1-\hat{p})\left(\frac{1}{n_1} + \frac{1}{n_2}\right)}}$$

z-Test: Two Proportions			
		Optimist	Pessimist
Sample Proportions		0.9499	0.8797
Observations		1478	241
Hypothesized Difference		0	
z Stat		4.26	
P(Z<=z) one tail		0	
z Critical one-tail		1.6449	
P(Z<=z) two-tail		0	
z Critical two-tail		1.96	

$z = 4.26$, p-value = 0. There is sufficient evidence that pessimists are less likely to survive than optimists.

24.42 One-way analysis of variance

$$H_0 : \mu_1 = \mu_2 = \mu_3$$

$$H_1 : \text{At least two means differ}$$

F = MST/MSE

ANOVA						
Source of Variation	SS	df	MS	F	P-value	F crit
Between Groups	595.6	2	297.81	34.35	0.0000	3.0648
Within Groups	1144.5	132	8.67			
Total	1740.1	134				

$F = 34.35$, p-value = 0. There is enough evidence to conclude that the type of music affects test results.

24.43 One-way analysis of variance

$$H_0 : \mu_1 = \mu_2 = \mu_3$$

$$H_1 : \text{At least two means differ}$$

F = MST/MSE

ANOVA						
Source of Variation	SS	df	MS	F	P-value	F crit
Between Groups	16.5	2	8.27	0.86	0.4273	3.0648
Within Groups	1275.1	132	9.66			
Total	1291.6	134				

$F = .86$, p-value = .4273. There is no evidence to infer a difference in test results among the three types of music. The effects of the music wear off after 10 minutes.

24.44 The data are observational. There may be a link between arthritis and Alzheimer's disease that explains the statistical result.

24.45 a Wilcoxon rank sum test

H_0 : The two population locations are the same.

H_1 : The location of population 1 is different from the location of population 2.

$$z = \frac{T - E(T)}{\sigma_T}$$

Wilcoxon Rank Sum Test			
		Rank Sum	Observations
Adults		4248	60
Students		3012	60
z Stat		3.24	
P(Z<=z) one-tail		0.0006	
z Critical one-tail		1.6449	
P(Z<=z) two-tail		0.0012	
z Critical two-tail		1.96	

$z = 3.24$, p-value = .0012. There is overwhelming evidence of a difference between the two groups.

b Students are poor surrogates for adults in marketing studies.

24.46 a One-way analysis of variance

$$H_0 : \mu_1 = \mu_2 = \mu_3 = \mu_4 = \mu_5 = \mu_6$$

H_1 : At least two means differ

F = MST/MSE

ANOVA						
Source of Variation	SS	df	MS	F	P-value	F crit
Between Groups	527465	5	105493	4.43	0.0015	2.35
Within Groups	1571667	66	23813			
Total	2099132	71				

$F = 4.43$, p-value = .0015. There is overwhelming evidence that the six groups differ.

b Two-factor analysis of variance

F=MS(AB)/MSE

F = MS(A)/MSE

F = MS(B)/MSE

ANOVA						
Source of Variation	SS	df	MS	F	P-value	F crit
Sample	303247	2	151623	6.37	0.0030	3.1359
Columns	190139	1	190139	7.98	0.0062	3.9863
Interaction	34080	2	17040	0.72	0.4927	3.1359
Within	1571667	66	23813			
Total	2099132	71				

Test for age: F = 6.37, p-value = .0030. There is enough evidence to conclude that age affects offers.

Test for gender: F = 7.98, p-value = .0062. There is enough evidence to conclude that gender affects offers.

Test for interaction: F = .72, p-value = .4927. There is no evidence of interaction.

24.47 Case 24.1: Wilcoxon rank sum test

H_0 : The two population locations are the same.

H_1 : The location of population 1 is to the left of the location of population 2.

$$z = \frac{T - E(T)}{\sigma_T}$$

Wilcoxon Rank Sum Test			
		Rank Sum	Observations
W Rate		64365.5	101
M Rate		490565.5	952
z Stat		3.83	
P(Z<=z) one-tail		0.0001	
z Critical one-tail		1.6449	
P(Z<=z) two-tail		0.0002	
z Critical two-tail		1.96	

z = 3.83, p-value = .0001. There is enough evidence to conclude that women pay higher rates of interest than men.

Case 24.2 Relationship between interest rates and sales: Spearman rank correlation coefficient test

$H_0 : \rho_S = 0$

$H_1 : \rho_S \neq 0$

$z = r_S \sqrt{n-1}$

Spearman Rank Correlation			
Rates and Sales			
Spearman Rank Correlation			-0.2629
z Stat			-8.5265
P(Z<=z) one tail			0
z Critical one tail			1.64
P(Z<=z) two tail			0
z Critical two tail			1.96

z = -8.5265, p-value = 0. There is overwhelming evidence to infer that interest rates and sales are linearly related.

Relationship between interest rates and ages: Spearman rank correlation coefficient test

$$H_0 : \rho_S = 0$$

$$H_1 : \rho_S \neq 0$$

$$z = r_S \sqrt{n-2}$$

Spearman Rank Correlation			
Rates and Age			
Spearman Rank Correlation			-0.1853
z Stat			-6.01
P(Z<=z) one tail			0
z Critical one tail			1.6449
P(Z<=z) two tail			0
z Critical two tail			1.96

z = -6.01, p-value = 0. There is overwhelming evidence to infer that interest rates and age of business are linearly related.

Difference between sales: Wilcoxon rank sum test

H_0 : The two population locations are the same.

H_1 : The location of population 1 is to the left of the location of population 2.

$$z = \frac{T - E(T)}{\sigma_T}$$

Wilcoxon Rank Sum Test			
		Rank Sum	Observations
W Sales		12285	101
M Sales		542646	952
z Stat		-14.09	
P(Z<=z) one-tail		0	
z Critical one-tail		1.6449	
P(Z<=z) two-tail		0	
z Critical two-tail		1.96	

z = -14.09, p-value = 0. There is sufficient evidence to conclude that businesses owned by women have lower sales than businesses owned by men.

Difference between ages: Wilcoxon rank sum test

H_0: The two population locations are the same.

H_1: The location of population 1 is to the left of the location of population 2.

$$z = \frac{T - E(T)}{\sigma_T}$$

Wilcoxon Rank Sum Test			
		Rank Sum	Observations
W Age		35034.5	101
M Age		519896.5	952
z Stat		-6.26	
P(Z<=z) one-tail		0	
z Critical one-tail		1.6449	
P(Z<=z) two-tail		0	
z Critical two-tail		1.96	

z = -6.26, p-value = 0. There is sufficient evidence to conclude that businesses owned by men are older than businesses owned by women.

Interest rates among the 3 types of businesses: Kruskal Wallis test

H_0: The locations of all 3 populations are the same

H_1: At least two population locations differ

$$H = \left[\frac{12}{n(n+1)} \sum \frac{T_j^2}{n_j} \right] - 3(n+1)$$

Kruskal-Wallis Test		
Group	Rank Sum	Observations
Bus 1	111554	193
Bus 2	42305.5	86
Bus 3	401071.5	774
H Stat		7.2226
df		2
p-value		0.027
chi-squared Critical		5.9915

H = 7.2226, p-value = .0270. There is enough evidence to conclude that there are differences in interest rates among the three types of business.

Case 24.3 Arrival times t-tests of μ_D

$$H_0 : \mu_D = 1$$

$$H_1 : \mu_D > 1$$

$$t = \frac{\bar{x}_D - \mu_D}{s_D / \sqrt{n_D}}$$

Cambridge:

t-Test: Paired Two Sample for Means		
	C Ambulance	C Fire
Mean	12.86	10.64
Variance	9.71	3.39
Observations	280	280
Pearson Correlation	0.2826	
Hypothesized Mean Difference	1	
df	279	
t Stat	6.50	
P(T<=t) one-tail	0.0000	
t Critical one-tail	1.6503	
P(T<=t) two-tail	0.0000	
t Critical two-tail	1.9685	

t = 6.50, p-value = 0. There is sufficient evidence to infer that in Cambridge fire trucks arrive at the scene more than one minute sooner than ambulances.

Kitchener:

t-Test: Paired Two Sample for Means		
	K Ambulance	K Fire
Mean	9.79	8.55
Variance	10.73	3.26
Observations	506	506
Pearson Correlation	0.5524	
Hypothesized Mean Difference	1	
df	505	
t Stat	1.98	
P(T<=t) one-tail	0.0243	
t Critical one-tail	1.6479	
P(T<=t) two-tail	0.0487	
t Critical two-tail	1.9647	

t = 1.98, p-value = .0243. There is sufficient evidence to infer that in Kitchener fire trucks arrive at the scene more than one minute sooner than ambulances.

Waterloo

t-Test: Paired Two Sample for Means		
	W Ambulance	W Fire
Mean	12.86	12.17
Variance	11.01	19.00
Observations	150	150
Pearson Correlation	0.8037	
Hypothesized Mean Difference	1	
df	149	
t Stat	-1.46	
P(T<=t) one-tail	0.0733	
t Critical one-tail	1.6551	
P(T<=t) two-tail	0.1466	
t Critical two-tail	1.9760	

t = -1.46, p-value = 1- .0733 = .9267. There is no evidence to infer that in Waterloo fire trucks arrive at the scene more than one minute sooner than ambulances.

Frequency of arrivals in less than 8 minutes: z-tests of $p_1 - p_2$ (case 1) (Data were recoded so that 2 = yes, 1 = no)

$$H_0 : (p_1 - p_2) = 0$$

$$H_1 : (p_1 - p_2) < 0$$

591

$$z = \frac{(\hat{p}_1 - \hat{p}_2)}{\sqrt{\hat{p}(1 - \hat{p})\left(\dfrac{1}{n_1} + \dfrac{1}{n_2}\right)}}$$

Cambridge

z-Test: Two Proportions		C Ambulance	C Fire
		C Ambulance	C Fire
Sample Proportions		0.0536	0.0857
Observations		280	280
Hypothesized Difference		0	
z Stat		-1.49	
P(Z<=z) one tail		0.0676	
z Critical one-tail		1.6449	
P(Z<=z) two-tail		0.1352	
z Critical two-tail		1.96	

z = -1.49, p-value = .0676. There is not enough evidence to infer that in Cambridge fire trucks arrive at the scene in less than 8 minutes more frequently than do ambulances.

Kitchener

z-Test: Two Proportions		K Ambulance	K Fire
		K Ambulance	K Fire
Sample Proportions		0.2866	0.3992
Observations		506	506
Hypothesized Difference		0	
z Stat		-3.77	
P(Z<=z) one tail		0.0001	
z Critical one-tail		1.6449	
P(Z<=z) two-tail		0.0002	
z Critical two-tail		1.96	

z = -3.77, p-value = .0001. There is enough evidence to infer that in Kitchener fire trucks arrive at the scene in less than 8 minutes more frequently than do ambulances.

Waterloo

z-Test: Two Proportions		W Ambulance	W Fire
		W Ambulance	W Fire
Sample Proportions		0.1	0.1667
Observations		150	150
Hypothesized Difference		0	
z Stat		-1.70	
P(Z<=z) one tail		0.0447	
z Critical one-tail		1.6449	
P(Z<=z) two-tail		0.0894	
z Critical two-tail		1.96	

$z = -1.70$, p-value = .0447. There is enough evidence to infer that in Waterloo fire trucks arrive at the scene in less than 8 minutes more frequently than ambulances.

Case 24.4 t-tests of μ

Positive underpricing:

$$H_0 : \mu = 0$$

$$H_1 : \mu > 0$$

$$t = \frac{\bar{x} - \mu}{s / \sqrt{n}}$$

U_1

t-Test: Mean		
		U1
Mean		9.3337
Standard Deviation		25.9108
Hypothesized Mean		0
df		99
t Stat		3.60
P(T<=t) one-tail		0.0002
t Critical one-tail		1.6604
P(T<=t) two-tail		0.0004
t Critical two-tail		1.9842

$z = 3.60$, p-value = .0002. There is enough evidence to infer underpricing at $t = 1$.

U_2

t-Test: Mean		
		U2
Mean		9.2374
Standard Deviation		26.8588
Hypothesized Mean		0
df		99
t Stat		3.44
P(T<=t) one-tail		0.0004
t Critical one-tail		1.6604
P(T<=t) two-tail		0.0008
t Critical two-tail		1.9842

$z = 3.44$, p-value = .0004. There is enough evidence to infer underpricing at $t = 2$.

U_3

t-Test: Mean			
			U3
Mean			9.3761
Standard Deviation			27.1463
Hypothesized Mean			0
df			99
t Stat			3.45
P(T<=t) one-tail			0.0004
t Critical one-tail			1.6604
P(T<=t) two-tail			0.0008
t Critical two-tail			1.9842

z = 3.45, p-value = .0004. There is enough evidence to infer underpricing at t = 3.

Percentage exceeds 5%:

$$H_0 : \mu = 5$$

$$H_1 : \mu > 5$$

$$t = \frac{\bar{x} - \mu}{s / \sqrt{n}}$$

U_1

t-Test: Mean			
			U1
Mean			9.3337
Standard Deviation			25.9108
Hypothesized Mean			5
df			99
t Stat			1.67
P(T<=t) one-tail			0.0488
t Critical one-tail			1.6604
P(T<=t) two-tail			0.0976
t Critical two-tail			1.9842

z = 1.67, p-value = .0488. There is enough evidence to infer that the underpricing exceeds 5% at t = 1.

U_2

t-Test: Mean			
			U2
Mean			9.2374
Standard Deviation			26.8588
Hypothesized Mean			5
df			99
t Stat			1.58
P(T<=t) one-tail			0.0589
t Critical one-tail			1.6604
P(T<=t) two-tail			0.1178
t Critical two-tail			1.9842

z = 1.58, p-value = .0589. There is not enough evidence to infer that the underpricing exceeds 5% at t = 2.

U_3

t-Test: Mean			
			U3
Mean			9.3761
Standard Deviation			27.1463
Hypothesized Mean			5
df			99
t Stat			1.61
P(T<=t) one-tail			0.0551
t Critical one-tail			1.6604
P(T<=t) two-tail			0.1102
t Critical two-tail			1.9842

z = 1.61, p-value = .0551. There is not enough evidence to infer that the underpricing exceeds 5% at t = 3.

Case 24.5 Question 1: One-way analysis of variance

$H_0 : \mu_1 = \mu_2 = \mu_3 = \mu_4 = \mu_5$

$H_1 :$ At least two means differ

F = MST/MSE

ANOVA						
Source of Variation	SS	df	MS	F	P-value	F crit
Between Groups	95797	4	23949	36.09	0.0000	2.39
Within Groups	375611	566	664			
Total	471408	570				

F = 36.09, p-value = 0. There is enough evidence to conclude that differences in the time to reach a technician exist among the 5 companies.

Question 2: One way analysis of variance

$H_0 : \mu_1 = \mu_2 = \mu_3 = \mu_4 = \mu_5$

$H_1 :$ At least two means differ

F = MST/MSE

ANOVA						
Source of Variation	SS	df	MS	F	P-value	F crit
Between Groups	1249.47	4	312.37	164.60	0.0000	2.39
Within Groups	1074.13	566	1.90			
Total	2323.60	570				

F = 164.60, p-value = 0. There is enough evidence to conclude that differences in the time to solve the problem exist among the 5 companies.

Question 3: Kruskal Wallis test

H_0 : The locations of all 5 populations are the same

H_1 : At least two population locations differ

$$H = \left[\frac{12}{n(n+1)} \sum \frac{T_j^2}{n_j} \right] - 3(n+1)$$

Kruskal-Wallis Test		
Group	Rank Sum	Observations
Apple	27796	110
Compaq	20128.5	75
Dell	14621	62
IBM	82132	243
P-B	18628.5	81
H Stat		44.55
df		4
p-value		0
chi-squared Critical		9.4877

H = 44.55, p-value = 0. There is enough evidence to conclude that differences in the quality of the technical support exist among the 5 companies.

Question 4: Chi-squared test of a contingency table

H_0 : The two variables are independent

H_1 : The two variables are dependent

$$\chi^2 = \sum_{i=1}^{10} \frac{(f_i - e_i)^2}{e_i}$$

Contingency Table							
	Recommnd						
Brand		1	2	3	4	5	TOTAL
	1	29	20	12	25	20	106
	2	81	55	50	218	61	465
	TOTAL	110	75	62	243	81	571
	chi-squared Stat			20.73			
	df			4			
	p-value			0.0004			
	chi-squared Critical			9.4877			

$\chi^2 = 20.73$, p-value = .0004. There is enough evidence to conclude that there are differences among the 5 companies with respect to whether customers would recommend them to a friend.

Case 24.6 a Chi-squared test of a contingency table

H_0 : The two variables are independent

H_1 : The two variables are dependent

$$\chi^2 = \sum_{i=1}^{20} \frac{(f_i - e_i)^2}{e_i}$$

Contingency Table						
	Degree					
Status		1	2	3	4	TOTAL
	1	75	66	5	5	151
	2	17	130	2	1	150
	3	3	43	3	1	50
	4	4	5	0	0	9
	5	11	53	4	2	70
	TOTAL	110	297	14	9	430
	chi-squared Stat			88.48		
	df			12		
	p-value			0		
	chi-squared Critical			21.0261		

$\chi^2 = 88.48$, p-value = 0. There is overwhelming evidence to conclude that there are differences in employment status among the 5 degrees.

b One-way analysis of variance

$$H_0 : \mu_1 = \mu_2 = \mu_3 = \mu_4 = \mu_5$$

$$H_1 : \text{At least two means differ}$$

F = MST/MSE

ANOVA						
Source of Variation	SS	df	MS	F	P-value	F crit
Between Groups	6808229843	4	1702057461	155.16	0.0000	2.40
Within Groups	3203248849	292	10970030			
Total	10011478692	296				

F =155.16, p-value = 0. There is enough evidence to conclude that there are differences in income among the 5 degrees.

c Equal-variances t-test of $\mu_1 - \mu_2$

$$H_0 : (\mu_1 - \mu_2) = 0$$

$$H_1 : (\mu_1 - \mu_2) \neq 0$$

$$t = \frac{(\bar{x}_1 - \bar{x}_2) - (\mu_1 - \mu_2)}{\sqrt{s_p^2 \left(\frac{1}{n_1} + \frac{1}{n_2} \right)}}$$

t-Test: Two-Sample Assuming Equal Variances		
	$ Non Accounting	$ Accounting
Mean	31003	28300
Variance	8060296	5115138
Observations	130	43
Pooled Variance	7336924	
Hypothesized Mean Difference	0	
df	171	
t Stat	5.67	
P(T<=t) one-tail	0.0000	
t Critical one-tail	1.6538	
P(T<=t) two-tail	0.0000	
t Critical two-tail	1.9739	

t = 5.67, p-value = 0. There is enough evidence to infer that accountants and nonaccountant business graduates earn different incomes.

Case 24.7 a Sign test

H_0: The two population locations are the same.

H_1: The location of population 1 is to the left of the location of population 2.

$$z = \frac{x - .5n}{.5\sqrt{n}}$$

Sign Test			
Difference			Fem 7 Days - Fem 14 Days
Positive Differences			15
Negative Differences			32
Zero Differences			19
z Stat			-2.48
P(Z<=z) one-tail			0.0066
z Critical one-tail			1.6449
P(Z<=z) two-tail			0.0132
z Critical two-tail			1.96

z = -2.48, p-value = .0066. There is enough evidence to infer that there is an improvement among female patients.

b Sign test

H_0: The two population locations are the same.

H_1: The location of population 1 is to the left of the location of population 2.

$$z = \frac{x - .5n}{.5\sqrt{n}}$$

Sign Test			
Difference			Male 7 Days - Male 14 Days
Positive Differences			13
Negative Differences			16
Zero Differences			20
z Stat			-0.56
P(Z<=z) one-tail			0.2887
z Critical one-tail			1.6449
P(Z<=z) two-tail			0.5774
z Critical two-tail			1.96

z = -.56, p-value = .2887. There is no evidence to infer that there is an improvement among male patients.

c z-test of $p_1 - p_2$ (case 1)

$$H_0 : (p_1 - p_2) = 0$$

$$H_1 : (p_1 - p_2) \neq 0$$

$$z = \frac{(\hat{p}_1 - \hat{p}_2)}{\sqrt{\hat{p}(1-\hat{p})\left(\dfrac{1}{n_1} + \dfrac{1}{n_2}\right)}}$$

z-Test: Two Proportions			
		Fem Head	Male Head
Sample Proportions		0.1667	0.102
Observations		66	49
Hypothesized Difference		0	
z Stat		0.99	
P(Z<=z) one tail		0.161	
z Critical one-tail		1.6449	
P(Z<=z) two-tail		0.322	
z Critical two-tail		1.96	

z = .99, p-value = .3220. There is not enough evidence of a difference in frequency of headaches between female and male patients.

Case 24.8 a t-tests of μ_D

$$H_0 : \mu_D = 0$$

$$H_1 : \mu_D > 0$$

$$t = \frac{\bar{x}_D - \mu_D}{s_D / \sqrt{n_D}}$$

Weight

t-Test: Paired Two Sample for Means		
	Weight 1	Weight 2
Mean	79.89	78.62
Variance	255.54	251.09
Observations	33	33
Pearson Correlation	0.99	
Hypothesized Mean Difference	0	
df	32	
t Stat	2.90	
P(T<=t) one-tail	0.0034	
t Critical one-tail	1.6939	
P(T<=t) two-tail	0.0067	
t Critical two-tail	2.0369	

t = 2.90, p-value = .0034. There is enough evidence to infer that the program is a success in terms of weight level.

Cholesterol

t-Test: Paired Two Sample for Means		
	Choles 1	Choles 2
Mean	6.87	6.27
Variance	0.58	0.62
Observations	33	33
Pearson Correlation	0.57	
Hypothesized Mean Difference	0	
df	32	
t Stat	4.83	
P(T<=t) one-tail	0.0000	
t Critical one-tail	1.6939	
P(T<=t) two-tail	0.0000	
t Critical two-tail	2.0369	

t = 4.83, p-value = 0. There is enough evidence to infer that the program is a success in terms of cholesterol level.

Fat intake

t-Test: Paired Two Sample for Means		
	TotFat 1	TotFat 2
Mean	66.56	46.72
Variance	967.59	533.91
Observations	33	33
Pearson Correlation	0.63	
Hypothesized Mean Difference	0	
df	32	
t Stat	4.70	
P(T<=t) one-tail	0.0000	
t Critical one-tail	1.6939	
P(T<=t) two-tail	0.0000	
t Critical two-tail	2.0369	

t = 4.70, p-value = 0. There is enough evidence to infer that the program is a success in terms of fat intake.

Cholesterol intake

t-Test: Paired Two Sample for Means		
	DietC 1	DietC 2
Mean	242.42	177.12
Variance	30617.76	13032.42
Observations	33	33
Pearson Correlation	0.42	
Hypothesized Mean Difference	0	
df	32	
t Stat	2.29	
P(T<=t) one-tail	0.0144	
t Critical one-tail	1.6939	
P(T<=t) two-tail	0.0288	
t Critical two-tail	2.0369	

$t = 2.29$, p-value = .0144. There is enough evidence to infer that the program is a success in terms of cholesterol intake.

Calories from fat

t-Test: Paired Two Sample for Means		
	PDCF 1	PDCF 2
Mean	36.54	30.82
Variance	56.72	49.71
Observations	33	33
Pearson Correlation	0.75	
Hypothesized Mean Difference	0	
df	32	
t Stat	6.29	
P(T<=t) one-tail	0.0000	
t Critical one-tail	1.6939	
P(T<=t) two-tail	0.0000	
t Critical two-tail	2.0369	

$t = 6.29$, p-value = 0. There is enough evidence to infer that the program is a success in terms of daily calories from fat.

b Equal-variances t-test of $\mu_1 - \mu_2$

$$H_0 : (\mu_1 - \mu_2) = 0$$

$$H_1 : (\mu_1 - \mu_2) \neq 0$$

$$t = \frac{(\bar{x}_1 - \bar{x}_2) - (\mu_1 - \mu_2)}{\sqrt{s_p^2 \left(\frac{1}{n_1} + \frac{1}{n_2} \right)}}$$

Weight reduction

t-Test: Two-Sample Assuming Equal Variances		
	Variable 1	Variable 2
Mean	0.19	2.28
Variance	6.15	4.60
Observations	16	17
Pooled Variance	5.35	
Hypothesized Mean Difference	0	
df	31	
t Stat	-2.60	
P(T<=t) one-tail	0.0071	
t Critical one-tail	1.6955	
P(T<=t) two-tail	0.0141	
t Critical two-tail	2.0395	

t = -2.60, p-value = .0141. There is enough evidence to infer that gender is a factor in weight reduction.

Cholesterol reduction

t-Test: Two-Sample Assuming Equal Variances		
	Variable 1	Variable 2
Mean	0.44	0.76
Variance	0.40	0.60
Observations	16	17
Pooled Variance	0.50	
Hypothesized Mean Difference	0	
df	31	
t Stat	-1.30	
P(T<=t) one-tail	0.1018	
t Critical one-tail	1.6955	
P(T<=t) two-tail	0.2036	
t Critical two-tail	2.0395	

t = -1.30, p-value = .2036. There is not enough evidence to infer that gender is a factor in cholesterol reduction.

Fat intake reduction

t-Test: Two-Sample Assuming Equal Variances		
	Variable 1	Variable 2
Mean	14.83	24.57
Variance	165.76	973.45
Observations	16	17
Pooled Variance	582.63	
Hypothesized Mean Difference	0	
df	31	
t Stat	-1.16	
P(T<=t) one-tail	0.1276	
t Critical one-tail	1.6955	
P(T<=t) two-tail	0.2552	
t Critical two-tail	2.0395	

t = -1.16, p-value = .2552. There is not enough evidence to infer that gender is a factor in fat intake reduction.

Cholesterol intake reduction

t-Test: Two-Sample Assuming Equal Variances		
	Variable 1	Variable 2
Mean	11.14	116.26
Variance	11576	37165
Observations	16	17
Pooled Variance	24783	
Hypothesized Mean Difference	0	
df	31	
t Stat	-1.92	
P(T<=t) one-tail	0.0322	
t Critical one-tail	1.6955	
P(T<=t) two-tail	0.0645	
t Critical two-tail	2.0395	

t = -1.92, p-value = .0645. There is not enough evidence to infer that gender is a factor in cholesterol intake reduction.

Calories from fat reduction

t-Test: Two-Sample Assuming Equal Variances		
	Variable 1	Variable 2
Mean	4.74	6.63
Variance	23.34	30.71
Observations	16	17
Pooled Variance	27.14	
Hypothesized Mean Difference	0	
df	31	
t Stat	-1.04	
P(T<=t) one-tail	0.1534	
t Critical one-tail	1.6955	
P(T<=t) two-tail	0.3068	
t Critical two-tail	2.0395	

t = -1.04, p-value = .3068. There is not enough evidence to infer that gender is a factor in calories from fat reduction.

c t-test of ρ or β_1

$$H_0 : \rho = 0 \text{ or } H_0 : \beta_1 = 0$$

$$H_1 : \rho \neq 0 \text{ or } H_1 : \beta_1 \neq 0$$

$$t = r\sqrt{\frac{n-2}{1-r^2}} \text{ or } t = \frac{b_1 - \beta_1}{s_{b_1}}$$

Age and weight reduction

Correlation			
Age and Weight Reduc			
Pearson Coefficient of Correlation			-0.098
t Stat			-0.55
df			31
P(T<=t) one tail			0.2937
t Critical one tail			1.6955
P(T<=t) two tail			0.5874
t Critical two tail			2.0395

t = -.55, p-value = .5874. There is not enough evidence that age is a factor in weight reduction.

Age and cholesterol reduction

Correlation			
Age and Choles Reduc			
Pearson Coefficient of Correlation			0.3959
t Stat			2.40
df			31
P(T<=t) one tail			0.0113
t Critical one tail			1.6955
P(T<=t) two tail			0.0226
t Critical two tail			2.0395

t = 2.40, p-value = .0226. There is enough evidence to infer that age is a factor in cholesterol reduction.

Age and Fat intake reduction

Correlation			
Age and TotFat Reduc			
Pearson Coefficient of Correlation			-0.1492
t Stat			-0.84
df			31
P(T<=t) one tail			0.2037
t Critical one tail			1.6955
P(T<=t) two tail			0.4074
t Critical two tail			2.0395

t = -.84, p-value = .4074. There is not enough evidence that age is a factor in fat intake reduction.

Age and Cholesterol intake reduction

Correlation			
Age and DietC Reduc			
Pearson Coefficient of Correlation			-0.1258
t Stat			-0.71
df			31
P(T<=t) one tail			0.2427
t Critical one tail			1.6955
P(T<=t) two tail			0.4854
t Critical two tail			2.0395

$t = -.71$, p-value $= .4854$. There is not enough evidence that age is a factor in cholesterol intake reduction.

Age and Calories from fat reduction

Correlation			
Age and PDCF Reduc			
Pearson Coefficient of Correlation			-0.3628
t Stat			-2.17
df			31
P(T<=t) one tail			0.019
t Critical one tail			1.6955
P(T<=t) two tail			0.038
t Critical two tail			2.0395

$t = -2.17$, p-value $= .0380$. There is enough evidence to infer that age is a factor in calories from fat reduction.

Case 24.9 t-test of μ_D

$$H_0 : \mu_D = 0$$

$$H_1 : \mu_D > 0$$

$$t = \frac{\bar{x}_D - \mu_D}{s_D / \sqrt{n_D}}$$

t-Test: Paired Two Sample for Means		
	W Rate	M Rate
Mean	1.44	1.40
Variance	0.32	0.38
Observations	53	53
Pearson Correlation	0.47	
Hypothesized Mean Difference	0	
df	52	
t Stat	0.48	
P(T<=t) one-tail	0.3158	
t Critical one-tail	1.6747	
P(T<=t) two-tail	0.6315	
t Critical two-tail	2.0066	

$t = .48$, p-value $= .3158$. There is not enough evidence to infer that female business owners pay higher rates of interest than male business owners.

Because this experiment controls for all other relevant factors besides gender we can be confident that this statistical conclusion is definitive.